THEORY OF STRUCTURES

THEORY OF STRUCTURES

Second Edition

S. P. TIMOSHENKO

Emeritus Professor of Engineering Mechanics
Stanford University

D. H. YOUNG

Silas H. Palmer Professor of
Civil Engineering
Stanford University

McGraw-Hill Book Company

New York   St. Louis   San Francisco   Toronto   London   Sydney

THEORY OF STRUCTURES

Preface

This second edition of "Theory of Structures," like the first, is intended primarily as a textbook for undergraduate and first-year graduate courses in structural analysis for civil engineers. To serve this purpose, every effort has been made to maintain a close connection between the methods that are developed for the analysis of various types of structures and the fundamental principles of mechanics on which they are based. It is only through a sound understanding of these principles that the engineer can successfully adapt his methods of analysis to the ever-changing problems that will confront him in this modern era.

The book may be roughly divided into two parts: the first part dealing with statically determinate structures, and the second part dealing with statically indeterminate structures. On this plan, the first four chapters deal successively with a review of statics (primarily graphic statics), statically determinate plane trusses, influence lines for beams and trusses, and statically determinate space trusses. Following this, Chapters 5 and 6 treat the fundamental theorems relating to elastic systems and their applications to the calculation of deflections of beams and trusses. In turn, there are chapters dealing with the analysis of statically indeterminate trusses, arches, and frames. The final chapters are devoted to an introduction to matrix methods in structural analysis, the analysis of stiffened suspension bridges, and an introduction to the dynamics of structures.

The first seven chapters in this second edition of "Theory of Structures" remain essentially the same as in the first edition. Chapters 8 and 9, dealing with arches and frames, have been completely rewritten. The present treatment of arches has been simplified by basing it on the theorem of least work and using the concept of elastic center. Several articles on the analysis of portal-type frames, using the elastic-center concept, have also been added. In rewriting the chapter on the uses of slope-deflection equations in the analysis of continuous beams and frames, we have extended the treatment to include systems with nonprismatic members and have included many examples of this kind.

Since the first appearance of this book (1945), two new aspects of structural analysis have become very important, namely, the use of matrix methods of formulating problems and the analysis of structures under dynamic loading. These are both very extensive subjects, and a number of complete books on each are now available. Chapters 10 and 12 here are intended only as introductions to these topics, but we hope that they will encourage the reader to continue his studies in these directions.

In the preparation of the first edition of this book, the senior author's Russian book "Theory of Structures" (Leningrad, 1926) was extensively used. Acknowledgment is also due to Otto Mohr's "Abhandlugen aus dem Gebiete der technischen Mechanik" and to H. Müller-Breslau's "Die graphische Statik der Baukonstruktionen." The authors also wish to give special thanks to Mr. P. Rabcevich of New York City for the use of a number of examples and problems appearing in Chapters 8 and 9 and to Miss Rose Marie Stampfel and Miss Martha Lee Young for their careful typing of the new portions of the manuscript.

S. P. Timoshenko

D. H. Young

Contents

Chapter 1

Elements of plane statics

1.1 CONCURRENT FORCES IN A PLANE

The *theory of structures* is based to a large extent upon the principles of statics with which the reader is assumed to be familiar. However, we shall review here some parts of statics that are most useful in the analysis of engineering structures. We begin with the principle of the parallelogram of forces as follows: *Two forces P_1 and P_2, as represented by the vectors $\overline{OA}$ and $\overline{OB}$ in Fig. 1.1a, are equivalent in action to a single resultant force R obtained as the diagonal $\overline{OC}$ of the parallelogram formed on the given vectors as shown.* The same resultant force can be obtained also from the *triangle of forces* shown in Fig. 1.1b. This follows from the fact that the triangle ABC in Fig. 1.1b is identical with the triangle OAC in Fig. 1.1a.

If several forces in a plane act at a single point O (Fig. 1.2a), they can always be reduced to one resultant force which also acts through that point. This resultant force can be found by successive applications of the parallelogram of

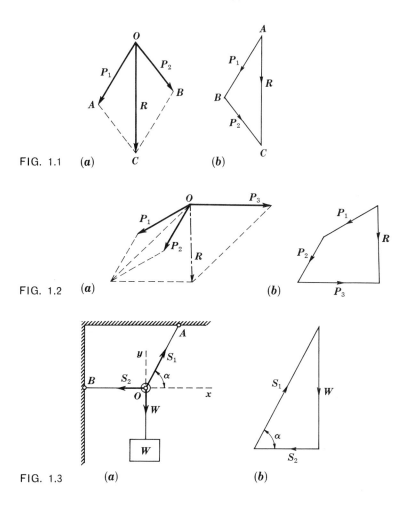

FIG. 1.1   (*a*)   (*b*)

FIG. 1.2   (*a*)   (*b*)

FIG. 1.3   (*a*)   (*b*)

forces as illustrated in Fig. 1.2*a* or as the closing side of the *polygon of forces* constructed as shown in Fig. 1.2*b*.

If the polygon of forces is closed, the resultant force vanishes and the given forces are in *equilibrium*. Thus, if several concurrent forces in a plane are known to be in equilibrium, their free vectors must build a *closed polygon of forces*.

The above graphical condition of equilibrium is very useful in the analysis of structures. Let us consider, for example, the very simple case of a weight *W* supported by strings as shown in Fig. 1.3*a*. Isolating the ring *O* as a *free body*, we conclude that it is in equilibrium under the action of three forces *W*, S_1, and S_2, the lines of action of which coincide with the strings and the magnitudes of which represent the *axial forces*, or *tensions*, in these strings. If the magnitude of the weight W is known, the magnitudes of the tensions S_1 and S_2 are found from the closed triangle of forces as shown in Fig. 1.3b, from which we obtain $S_1 = W \csc \alpha$ and $S_2 = W \cot \alpha$.

From the fact that several concurrent, coplanar forces in equilibrium build a closed polygon, it follows that the algebraic sums of *projections* of the forces on any system of orthogonal axes x and y in their plane of action must be zero. Thus we arrive at the familiar *equations of equilibrium*

$$\Sigma X_i = 0 \qquad \Sigma Y_i = 0 \tag{1.1}$$

where X_i and Y_i denote, respectively, the projections of any force P_i on the axes x and y, and the summations are understood to include all forces in the system. These analytical conditions of equilibrium are equivalent to the graphical condition of a closed polygon of forces, but they are sometimes more convenient to use. Applying the equations of equilibrium to the system shown in Fig. 1.3a, for example, we obtain

$$S_1 \cos \alpha - S_2 = 0$$

$$S_1 \sin \alpha - W = 0$$

from which we find, as before, $S_1 = W \csc \alpha$ and $S_2 = W \cot \alpha$.

The foregoing graphical and analytical conditions of equilibrium are particularly useful in the analysis of pin-connected trusses. Consider, for example, the truss loaded as shown in Fig. 1.4a. The analysis of such a truss entails finding the axial forces induced in the various bars by the action of the external load P. The work can be greatly simplified in this case by noting that some of the bars are *inactive*, i.e., unstressed. For instance, if we isolate the hinge A as a free body (Fig. 1.4b), we see at once that the bars 1 and 2 of the truss are inactive, since two forces can be in equilibrium only if they are collinear in action, and the axes of these two bars are not collinear. Having concluded that the bar 2 is inactive, we consider the equilibrium of the hinge B (Fig. 1.4c), where we find the possibility of three forces in equilibrium, two of which are collinear in action. Then from the first of Eqs. (1.1) it follows

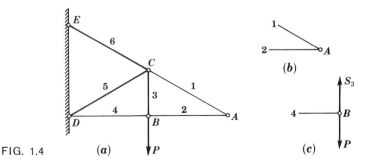

FIG. 1.4   (*a*)   (*b*)   (*c*)

that the force in bar 4 must be zero, and we conclude that this bar also is inactive. Finally, then, only the bars shown in the figure by heavy lines carry axial forces different from zero. Considering, further, the equilibrium of hinge B and using the second of Eqs. (1.1), we conclude that the bar 3 carries a tension equal to the load P. The axial forces in the bars 5 and 6 can be found by considering the conditions of equilibrium for the hinge C, and this completes the analysis of the truss.

PROBLEMS

1 Find the tensile force S_1 in the member AC and the compressive force S_2 in the member AB of the simple truss shown in Fig. 1.5.
    Ans. $S_1 = P \csc \alpha$, $S_2 = P \cot \alpha$.
2 To produce biaxial compression of a concrete cube M, the system of hinged bars shown in Fig. 1.6 is used. Find the compressive forces exerted on the faces of the cube if the frame has the form of a square and the inclined bars lie along its diagonals.
    Ans. $S = \sqrt{2}\, P$.
3 Identify, by inspection, the inactive members of the truss shown in Fig. 1.7, (*a*) when there is a vertical load P at F, (*b*) when the same load is at D.
4 How is the action of the simple truss shown in Fig. 1.8 affected by changing the direction of the diagonal from AD as shown to BC?

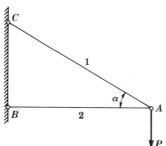

FIG. 1.5

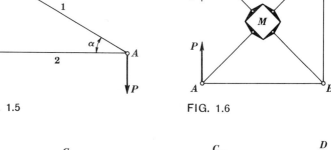

FIG. 1.6

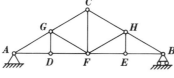

FIG. 1.7

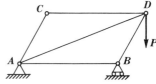

FIG. 1.8

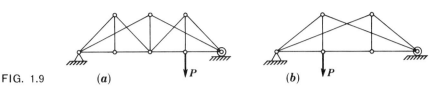

FIG. 1.9   **(a)** $\downarrow P$ **(b)** $\downarrow P$

5   Distinguish by heavy lines the active members of the two trusses supported and loaded as shown in Fig. 1.9.

1.2   THREE FORCES IN EQUILIBRIUM

Three nonparallel forces in a plane can be in equilibrium only if their lines of action meet in one point. To prove this statement, we refer to Fig. 1.10, where P and Q are any two forces that intersect at a point O. Then a third force S can hold these two forces in equilibrium only if it is equal, opposite, and collinear with their resultant R, which, of course, acts through point O. Hence, the force S also must act through point O as shown.

     The foregoing *theorem of three forces* is very useful in the determination of the *reactions* induced at the points of support of a body or structure under the action of given forces. Consider, for example, the crane shown in Fig. 1.11, the mast of which is supported in *bearings* at A and B so that the crane can be rotated around the vertical axis. Under the action of a vertical load P, the crane exerts pressures on its bearings at A and B, and these *actions* of the crane on its supports induce equal and opposite *reactions* on the crane as shown. Thus the vertical force P together with the reactions R_a and R_b are three forces in equilibrium. Neglecting friction in the bearing at B, the reaction R_b must be a horizontal force, and hence the known lines of action of two of the forces (P and R_b) determine the point of concurrence O of the system. The third force R_a, then, must also pass through point O; and so, by the theorem of three forces, its line of action AO is established. Knowing the magnitude of the force P, the mag-

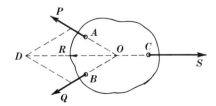

FIG. 1.10

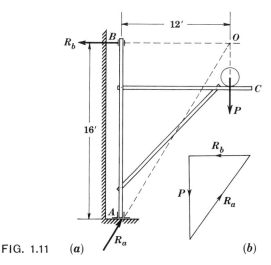

FIG. 1.11   (*a*)   (*b*)

nitudes of the reactions R_a and R_b are found from the closed triangle of forces shown in Fig. 1.11*b*. Since this triangle is similar to triangle *BAO* in Fig. 1.11*a*, we obtain $R_a = \frac{5}{4}P$ and $R_b = \frac{3}{4}\mathrm{P}$.

As a second example of the application of the theorem of three forces in calculating reactions, let us find the axial forces induced in the hinged bars 1, 2, 3, which support a horizontal beam *AB* under the action of an applied force *P*, as shown in Fig. 1.12*a*. Replacing the supporting bars by the reactions S_1, S_2, S_3, which they exert on the beam by virtue of the axial forces induced in them, we find ourselves with a system of four forces (*P*, S_1, S_2, S_3) in a plane that are in equilibrium. To reduce this system to the case of three forces in equilibrium, we imagine that S_1 and S_2 are replaced temporarily by their

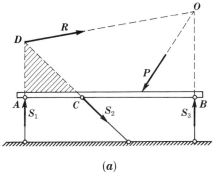

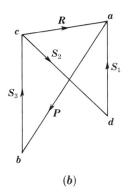

(*a*)   (*b*)

FIG. 1.12

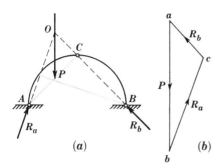

FIG. 1.13

resultant R, as yet unknown in direction but evidently acting through point D obtained as the intersection of the known lines of action of S_1 and S_2. Now, instead of four forces, we have the three forces (P, S_3, and R) that are in equilibrium. The point of concurrence of this system of three forces is evidently point O, obtained as the intersection of the known lines of action of P and S_3. Thus, the line of action DO of the third force R is established as shown, and the closed triangle of forces abc (Fig. 1.12b) can be constructed. From this construction, the magnitudes of S_3 and R are determined. Finally, knowing the force R, as represented by the vector $\overline{ca}$, we find the magnitudes of S_2 and S_1 by resolving R into the two components $\overline{cd}$ and $\overline{da}$ having the known directions of S_2 and S_1, respectively; and, if all constructions have been made to scale, the three reactions are determined. From the directions of the arrows on the vectors in Fig. 1.12b, we conclude that the bars 1 and 3 are under compression while the bar 2 carries tension.

A common type of engineering structure is the *three-hinged arch* shown in Fig. 1.13a. The reactions at the points of support A and B of such a structure under the action of a load P acting as shown can be found by using the theorem of three forces. By virtue of the hinge at the *crown C*, we conclude that the reaction R_b must act along the line BC, which intersects the known line of action of the force P at point O. Thus O is the point of concurrence of the system, and the line of action AO of R_a is established. The magnitudes of the reactions are now found from the closed triangle of forces shown in Fig. 1.13b.

If, in addition to the load P, there is a load Q on the rib CB, the same procedure can be used. We find first the reactions at A and B due to the load P alone, as above. Then repeating the same procedure, we find the reactions due to the load Q alone. Thus, we shall have two reactions at A and two at B. The resultants of these two forces at each point of support are the desired reactions due to the simultaneous action of P and Q.*

As a last example, let us consider the *compound beam* consisting of two

* A more expedient method of handling several forces on the arch is discussed on page 27.

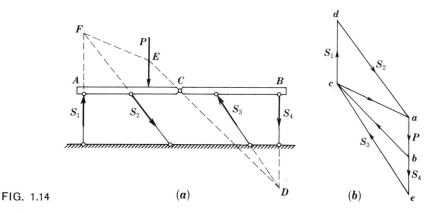

FIG. 1.14   (a)   (b)

portions AC and BC hinged together at C and supported by four hinged bars as shown in Fig. 1.14a. To find the axial forces S_1, S_2, S_3, and S_4 induced in the four supporting bars by the action of a load P, we begin with a consideration of the equilibrium of the beam CB, which is acted upon by only three forces. These forces are the two reactions S_3 and S_4 together with a force at the hinge C that represents the action of the beam AC on the beam CB. The known lines of action of S_3 and S_4 determine the point of concurrence D of these three forces and hence the line of action CD of the force on the hinge C. The equal and opposite reaction exerted by the beam CB on the beam AC has the same line of action. Hence, the beam AC is in the same condition as if it had, in addition to the supporting bars 1 and 2, a third supporting bar along the line CD. With this conclusion in mind, we see that, in considering the equilibrium of the beam AC, we may proceed in exactly the same manner as we did for the beam in Fig. 1.12. Thus, the line of action FE of the resultant of S_1 and S_2 is established, and the closed triangle of forces abc in Fig. 1.14b can be constructed. The remainder of the solution reduces simply to the resolution of the vectors $\overline{ca}$ and $\overline{bc}$ into their respective components S_1, S_2 and S_4, S_3, as shown in Fig. 1.14b. Bars 1 and 3 are in compression while 2 and 4 are in tension.

PROBLEMS

1   Using the theorem of three forces, find the reactions induced at the points of support A and B of the simple beam supported and loaded as shown in Fig. 1.15.
        Ans. $R_a = 0.882P$, $R_b = 0.667P$.

2   Find, graphically, the reactions at A and B for the beam shown in Fig. 1.16.
        Ans. $R_a = 2.24P$, $R_b = 2.82P$.

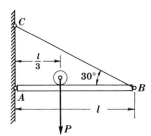

FIG. 1.15

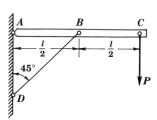

FIG. 1.16

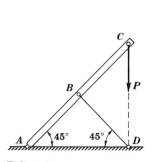

FIG. 1.17

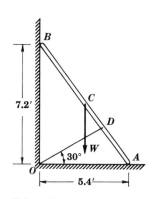

FIG. 1.18

3   Find, graphically, the reactions at A and B for the beam shown in Fig. 1.17.
       Ans. $R_a = P$, $R_b = 1.41P$.

4   A prismatic bar AB of weight W rests on a horizontal floor at A and against a
    vertical wall at B and is kept from falling by a string OD, as shown in Fig. 1.18.
    Neglecting friction at the points of support, find, graphically, the reactions at A
    and B and the tension in the string OD.

5   Find, graphically, the reactions R_a and R_b induced at the points of support of the
    compound structure loaded as shown in Fig. 1.19.
       Hint   The reaction at B must be a horizontal force.

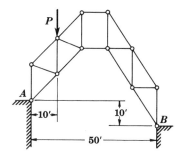

FIG. 1.19

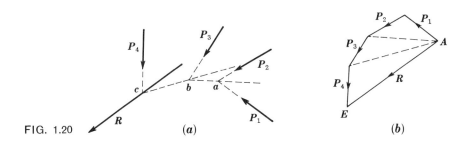

FIG. 1.20   (a)   (b)

1.3 EQUATIONS OF EQUILIBRIUM

In general, a system of coplanar forces, the lines of action of which do not intersect in one point, may reduce to (1) *a resultant force*, (2) *a resultant couple*, or (3) *a state of equilibrium*.

If the given forces P_1, P_2, P_3, P_4 are such that their free vectors build an *unclosed polygon* as shown in Fig. 1.20*b*, the system will always reduce to a resultant force.   The magnitude and direction of this resultant are given by the *closing side* $\overline{AE}$ of the polygon of forces, and its line of action is found by the construction illustrated in Fig. 1.20*a*.

If the given forces are such that their free vectors build a *closed polygon* (Fig. 1.21*b*), the resultant force vanishes, but there is still the possibility of a

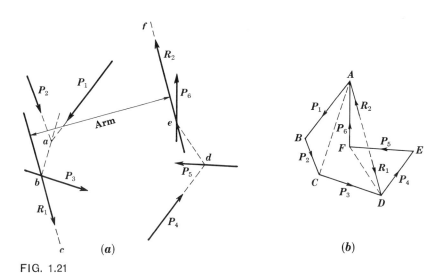

(a)   (b)

FIG. 1.21

resultant couple.   In this case, we arbitrarily divide the forces into two groups P_1, P_2, P_3 and P_4, P_5, P_6, having equal and opposite resultants R_1 and R_2 as represented by the vectors $\overline{AD}$ and $\overline{DA}$ in Fig. 1.21b.   Then, proceeding with each of these groups in the same manner as in the preceding case, we find the lines of action bc and ef of their resultants as shown in Fig. 1.21a, and these two equal and opposite forces represent a resultant couple.

In the particular case, where the lines of action of the forces R_1 and R_2 in Fig. 1.21a are found to coincide, the resultant couple vanishes, and the system of forces is in equilibrium.   Thus, the conditions of equilibrium for any system of forces in a plane are a closed polygon of forces and a vanishing resultant couple.   From the condition of a closed polygon of forces, we conclude that the algebraic sums of projections of the given forces on any pair of orthogonal axes must be zero.   From the condition of a vanishing resultant couple, we conclude, with the help of Varignon's theorem,[1] that the algebraic sum of moments of the given forces with respect to any center in their plane must be zero.   These conditions are expressed analytically by the following *equations of equilibrium:*

$$\Sigma X_i = 0 \qquad \Sigma Y_i = 0 \qquad \Sigma M_i = 0 \qquad\qquad (1.2a)$$

where X_i and Y_i are orthogonal projections of any force P_i, and M_i is the moment of the same force with respect to a chosen center.   The summations are understood to include all forces of the system.

It can easily be shown that the above conditions of equilibrium can also be expressed by the three moment equations[2]

$$\Sigma M_A = 0 \qquad \Sigma M_B = 0 \qquad \Sigma M_C = 0 \qquad\qquad (1.2b)$$

in which A, B, and C are three arbitrary centers that form a triangle in the plane of action of the forces.

Equations (1.2) find a wide application in the theory of structures, particularly in the determination of reactions and in the analysis of trusses.   As a first example, let us consider the determination of the reactions induced at the points of support of the simple crane ABC loaded as shown in Fig. 1.22. If we neglect friction in the guide at B, the supports of the crane can be replaced by reactions R_b, X_a, and Y_a, as shown, where X_a and Y_a are horizontal and vertical components of the unknown reaction at A.   The system of forces as shown is in equilibrium; and, if point A is used as a moment center, Eqs. (1.2a)

---

[1] The moment of the resultant with respect to any center in the plane of action of the forces is equal to the algebraic sum of the moments of the given forces with respect to the same center. See S. Timoshenko and D. H. Young, "Engineering Mechanics," 4th ed., p. 41, McGraw-Hill Book Company, New York, 1956.
[2] See *ibid.*, p. 109.

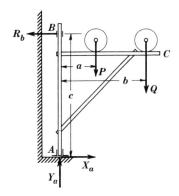

FIG. 1.22

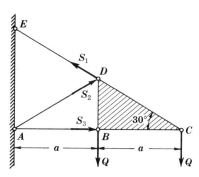

FIG. 1.23

become

$$X_a - R_b = 0$$

$$Y_a - P - Q = 0$$

$$R_b c - Pa - Qb = 0$$

From these equations, we find $X_a = R_b = Pa/c + Qb/c$ and

$$Y_a = P + Q$$

As a second example, let us consider the determination of the axial forces induced in the bars 1, 2, and 3 of the simple truss loaded and supported as shown in Fig. 1.23. Considering only the shaded portion BCD of the truss and replacing the bars 1, 2, and 3 by the reactions that they exert upon this portion, we obtain the free-body diagram as shown. Here we have five forces in equilibrium, and the algebraic sum of their moments with respect to any center in the plane of the truss must be zero. Upon choosing, successively, the points A, D, and C as moment centers, Eqs. (1.2b) become

$$S_1 a - Qa - 2Qa = 0$$

$$\frac{S_3 a}{\sqrt{3}} - Qa = 0$$

$$Qa - S_2 a = 0$$

and we find $S_1 = 3Q$ (tension), $S_3 = \sqrt{3}\, Q$ (compression), and $S_2 = Q$ (compression). It should be noted that the moment centers are chosen so as to give us only one unknown in each equation.

PROBLEMS

1 A prismatic bar AE of negligible weight is hinged to a vertical wall at A and supported by a strut BD, as shown in Fig. 1.24. Find the reactions induced at A and
   B through the action of a sphere of weight Q tied by a string CF that is parallel to
   AE. The radius of the sphere is such that the points B and C are at the same level.
                    Ans. $R_a = 0.65Q$, $R_b = 1.52Q$.
2 Find the axial forces induced in the supporting bars 1, 2, and 3 of the simple truss
   shown in Fig. 1.25.
                    Ans. $S_1 = +5.33P$, $S_2 = +2.01P$, $S_3 = -7.12P$.
3 Evaluate the horizontal and vertical components of the reactions induced at the
   supports A and B of the compound structure shown in Fig. 1.26.
                    Ans. $X_a = 0.167P$, $X_b = 0.833P$, $Y_a = 0.125P$, $Y_b = 1.125P$.
4 Determine the tension induced in the tie bar AB of the plane structure supported
   and loaded as shown in Fig. 1.27.
                    Ans. $S = P/2$.
5 In Fig. 1.24, how will the reactions at A and B be changed if the inclined string
   CF is replaced by a horizontal string CB?

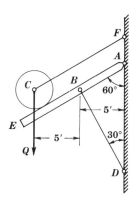

FIG. 1.24

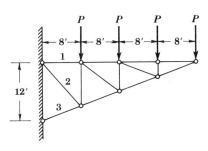

FIG. 1.25

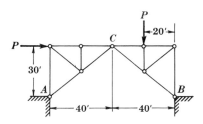

FIG. 1.26

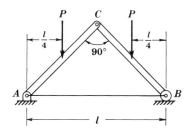

FIG. 1.27

1.4 INTERNAL FORCES

In previous articles, we have discussed the determination of external reactions induced at the supports of a rigid body constrained and loaded in one plane. We shall now consider the internal forces, or *stresses*, that are set up in such a constrained body under the action of applied external forces. Consider, for example, the rigid body supported and loaded in one plane as shown in Fig. 1.28a. Under the action of the applied loads, reactions R_a and R_b are induced at the supports, and these reactive forces are evaluated in the usual manner by considering the conditions of equilibrium of the entire body. Thus, the system of forces external to the body as a whole is completely defined. Now imagine that an arbitrary plane section *mn* divides the body into two parts *J* and *K* as shown. It is evident that forces of internal constraint must exist between these two parts of the body to hold them together. Such internal forces, of course, always occur in pairs of equal and opposite forces at each point of the body and do not enter into our consideration of the equilibrium of the body as a whole. To bring them under consideration, we isolate one portion *K* as a free body (Fig. 1.28b). Then the action of the removed portion *J* is represented by the forces that its various particles exert on those of the free body *K*, and in this way the required internal forces are brought under consideration.

Although the actual distribution of these forces over the section may be complicated, it is evident that they must be statically equivalent to the system of forces acting externally on part *J* and can always be represented by a resultant force *R* applied at the centroid of the cross section together with a couple of moment *M*. The force *R* in turn can be resolved into rectangular components *N* and *V* as shown in Fig. 1.28c. The three quantities *N*, *V*, and *M* on the section *mn* are called the *normal force*, the *shearing force*, and the *bending moment*, respectively. They are usually considered positive when

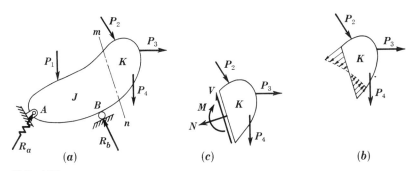

FIG. 1.28

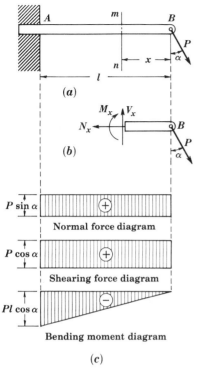

FIG. 1.29

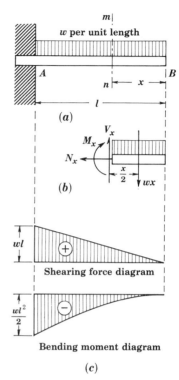

FIG. 1.30

directed as shown in the figure. In general, their magnitudes will depend on the position and orientation of the chosen section, but in any case they can be evaluated by the three equations of equilibrium applicable to the free body K.

The simplest and most important class of structures for which we shall wish to investigate the internal forces on various sections are *beams* submitted to transverse loads. Such beams are usually prismatic in form and are constrained and loaded in a plane of symmetry. Under these conditions, we can best define the general state of stress in terms of the internal forces on cross sections that are normal to the axis of the beam. Consider, for example, the cantilever beam AB, loaded as shown in Fig. 1.29a. Let mn be any normal section defined by its distance x from the free end. Then considering the equilibrium of the free body to the right of this section (Fig. 1.29b) and using Eqs. (1.2a), we find

$$N_x = +P \sin \alpha$$
$$V_x = +P \cos \alpha$$
$$M_x = -Px \cos \alpha$$

From these expressions, we see that the normal force N_x and the shearing force V_x are independent of the position of the section along the beam, while the bending moment M_x is proportional to the distance x. The variations in normal force, shearing force, and bending moment along the beam can be represented graphically by the diagrams shown in Fig. 1.29c, which accordingly are called *normal-force*, *shearing-force*, and *bending-moment diagrams*.

As a second example, consider the same cantilever beam uniformly loaded along its length as shown in Fig. 1.30a. In this case the expressions for normal force, shearing force, and bending moment on any cross section, defined by its distance x from the free end of the beam, become

$$N_x = 0 \qquad V_x = +wx \qquad M_x = -\frac{wx^2}{2}$$

The corresponding diagrams are shown in Fig. 1.30c.

In the case of curved beams, we may find it convenient to proceed in a slightly different manner. Consider, for example, the cantilever beam that has a circular axis of radius R and is loaded as shown in Fig. 1.31a. In this case we can most easily define the position of an arbitrary normal cross section by the angular coordinate ϕ measured as shown in the figure. Then, applying Eqs. (1.2a) to the free body in Fig. 1.31b, we find

$$N_\varphi = -P \sin \phi \qquad V_\varphi = +P \cos \phi \qquad M_\varphi = -PR \sin \phi$$

As a last example, let us consider the simply supported beam with overhang as shown in Fig. 1.32a. Under the action of a load uniformly distributed over the span l, the reaction at A is $wl/2$, and the bending moment at any section distance x to the right of this support is

$$M_x = \frac{wl}{2} x - wx \frac{x}{2} = \frac{wx}{2} (l - x)$$

Thus the bending-moment diagram is a parabola with maximum ordinate $wl^2/8$ at mid-span as shown. The free overhang is without internal forces if we neglect the weight of the beam itself.

If the same beam carries a concentrated load P at the free end as shown in Fig. 1.32b, the reaction at A is Pa/l, and the bending moment at any section

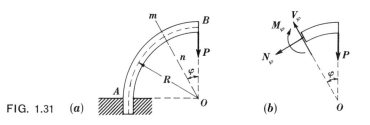

FIG. 1.31   (a)   (b)

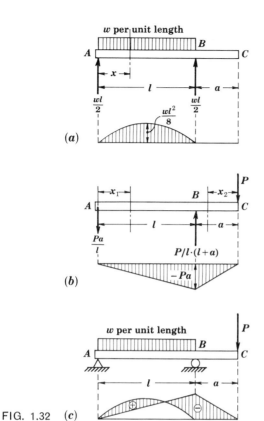

FIG. 1.32

between A and B is

$$M_x = -\frac{Pa}{l} x_1$$

where x_1 defines the location of the section as shown. Likewise, for any section distance x_2 to the left of the free end C of the beam, the bending moment is

$$M_x = -Px_2$$

Thus, in this case, the bending-moment diagram is made up of two straight lines having the common maximum ordinate $-Pa$ at the support B as shown.

If the beam carries both the distributed load and the concentrated load simultaneously, we obtain the corresponding bending-moment diagram, as shown in Fig. 1.32c, simply by superposing the diagrams of Fig. 1.32a and 1.32b. The same procedure can be used in the construction of shearing-force and normal-force diagrams.

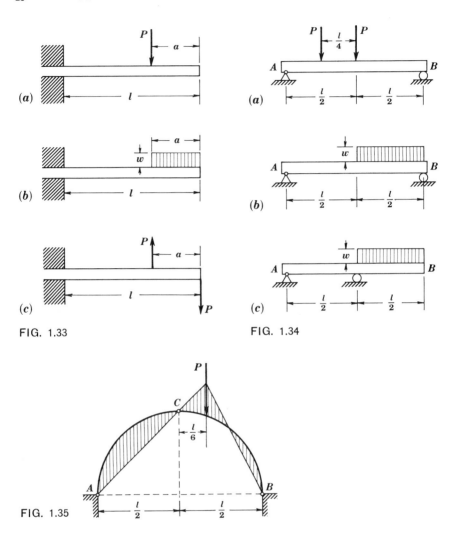

FIG. 1.33

FIG. 1.34

FIG. 1.35

PROBLEMS

1 Construct shearing-force and bending-moment diagrams for each of the cantilever beams shown in Fig. 1.33.

2 Construct normal-force, shearing-force, and bending-moment diagrams for each of the beams shown in Figs. 1.15 to 1.17.

3 Construct shearing-force and bending-moment diagrams for each of the simply supported beams shown in Fig. 1.34.

4 Construct normal-force, shearing-force, and bending-moment diagrams for the bar BC of the structure shown in Fig. 1.27.

5 Prove that the vertical ordinates in Fig. 1.35 represent the bending moments for corresponding points on the semicircular axis of the three-hinged arch loaded as shown. Evaluate the factor by which each ordinate must be multiplied in order to give the corresponding bending moment.

   Ans. $P/3$.

1.5 FUNICULAR POLYGON

We shall now develop a general graphical treatment for coplanar forces that has some practical advantages over the analytical treatment discussed in Art. 1.3. We begin with the very simple case of two forces P and Q as shown in Fig. 1.36a. As we already know, the closing side $\overline{AC}$ of the polygon of forces (Fig. 1.36b) gives both the magnitude and the direction of the resultant R, but the position of its line of action remains to be determined. In general, this can be accomplished as follows: In Fig. 1.36b, we take the arbitrary point O, called a *pole*, and join it by lines 1, 2, and 3 with the apices of the polygon of forces. These lines are called *rays* and, like the other lines in this figure, may be regarded as free force vectors. Taking, for example, the directions as indicated by the arrows inside the triangle AOB, we may consider the force P as the resultant of the forces 1 and 2. In the same manner, the force Q can be considered as the resultant of the forces 2 and 3, the directions of which are indicated by the arrows inside the triangle BOC. Referring now to Fig. 1.36a, it is evident that the action of the forces P and Q will not be changed if each of them is replaced by its two components indicated in Fig. 1.36b. These replacements will be made in the following manner: Beginning at any point a in the plane of action of the forces, we draw the line ab parallel to the ray AO. From the point of intersection b of this line with the line of action of the force P, we draw the line bc parallel to the ray BO; and, from the point of intersection c of this line with the line of action of the force Q, we draw

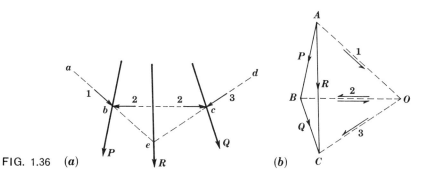

FIG. 1.36 (*a*)   (*b*)

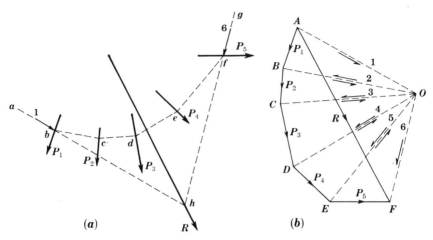

FIG. 1.37

the line *cd* parallel to the ray *CO*. The polygon *abcd*, obtained in this way, is called a *funicular polygon* for the forces *P* and *Q*. The apices of this polygon are on the lines of action of the given forces, and its sides are parallel to the rays of the polygon of forces. We assume now that at point *b* the forces 1 and 2, replacing the force *P*, and at point *c* the forces 2 and 3, replacing the force *Q*, are applied as shown in Fig. 1.36*a*. Thus, the given system of forces *P* and *Q* is replaced by a system of four forces applied at points *b* and *c*. Since the pair of forces 2 acting along the line *bc* are equal and opposite, they may be removed from the system and there remain only the forces 1 and 3, which are equivalent in action to the given forces *P* and *Q*. The magnitude and direction of the resultant of these forces are given by the vector $\overline{AC}$ in Fig. 1.36*b*, and a point on its line of action is given by the point of intersection *e* of the forces 1 and 3 acting along the first and last sides of the funicular polygon in Fig. 1.36*a*.

If we imagine a weightless string going along the sides *ab*, *bc*, and *cd* of the funicular polygon with its ends fixed at *a* and *d*, this string will be in equilibrium under the action of the forces *P* and *Q*. The tensile forces in the portions *ab* and *bc* of the string will be numerically equal to the forces 1 and 2, and their actions on the knot at *b* will balance the force *P*. In the same way the tensile forces in the portions *bc* and *cd* of the string balance the force *Q*. This relation between the constructed polygon *abcd* and the configuration of equilibrium of a string submitted to the action of the given forces explains the origin of the name *funicular polygon*, i.e., string polygon.

The graphical constructions discussed above are perfectly general and can be used also in the case of several coplanar forces $P_1, \ldots, P_5$ acting as shown in Fig. 1.37*a*. Again, we begin with the construction of the polygon of forces

ABCDEF (Fig. 1.37*b*). Choosing an arbitrary pole *O*, drawing the rays 1, 2, 3, 4, 5, 6, and constructing, in the plane of action of the forces, the lines *ab*, *bc*, . . . , *fg*, parallel to these rays, we obtain the funicular polygon *abcdefg* as shown. At the apices of this polygon, each of the given forces P_1, . . . , P_5 is replaced by its two components as represented by rays in Fig. 1.37*b*. The forces acting along the sides *bc*, *cd*, *de*, and *ef* are pairs of equal and opposite forces in equilibrium and may be removed from the system. There remain only the forces 1 and 6 acting at points *b* and *f*, which are equivalent to the given forces P_1, . . . , P_5. The magnitude and direction of the resultant of these forces are given by the closing side $\overline{AF}$ of the polygon of forces (Fig. 1.37*b*), and a point on its line of action by the intersection *h* of the first and last sides of the funicular polygon (Fig. 1.37*a*).

If the polygon of forces is closed, the possibility of a resultant force vanishes. In such a case the first and last rays coincide; hence the first and last sides of the funicular polygon become parallel or coincide. In the first case, the two equal and opposite forces acting along these sides represent a resultant couple. In the second case, they balance each other, and the given system of forces is in equilibrium. These two cases are illustrated in Fig. 1.38. Three given forces P_1, P_2, and P_3 have such magnitudes and directions that their free vectors build a closed polygon (Fig. 1.38*c*). Hence, the rays 1 and 4, directed to the beginning of the first vector $\overline{AB}$ and to the end of the last vector $\overline{CA}$, coincide in one ray *OA*.

If the given forces have the lines of action shown in Fig. 1.38*a*, the first side *ab* and the last side *de* of the funicular polygon are parallel but do not coincide. Hence, the unbalanced forces 1 and 4 acting along these sides represent a couple that is the resultant of the given system of forces.

If the given forces P_1, . . . , P_3 have the lines of action shown in Fig. 1.38*b*, the first and last sides of the funicular polygon coincide, and the equal but opposite forces 1 and 4 acting along these coincident sides balance each other. Hence, in this case, the given system of forces is in equilibrium.

We see that, by using the polygon of forces together with the funicular

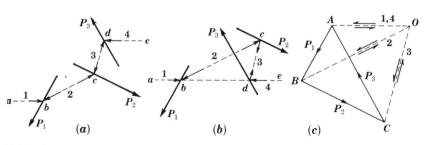

(a)   (b)   (c)

FIG. 1.38

polygon, the three possibilities for a system of forces in a plane (see page 10) can be investigated entirely by graphical methods. If the polygon of forces is unclosed, the given system reduces to a resultant force. If the polygon of forces is closed but the first and last sides of the funicular polygon, which are parallel, do not coincide, the system reduces to a resultant couple. If the polygon of forces is closed and the first and last sides of the funicular polygon coincide, i.e., the funicular polygon is also closed, the system of forces is in equilibrium. Thus, the graphical conditions of equilibrium are a closed polygon of forces and a closed funicular polygon.

As an example, let us determine graphically the reactions at the supports A and B of the beam AC loaded as shown in Fig. 1.39a. Beginning with the load P as represented by the free vector $\overline{AB}$ in Fig. 1.39b and selecting a pole O, we construct the rays 1 and 2, after which the corresponding sides ab and bc of the funicular polygon can be drawn as shown in Fig. 1.39a. Then the closing side ac of this polygon determines the direction of the corresponding ray 3 in Fig. 1.39b, and the reactions R_b and R_a are graphically determined by the vectors $\overline{BC}$ and $\overline{CA}$, respectively. As would be expected, the reaction R_a is directed downward.

As a second example, we take the case of a roof truss ABC supported and loaded as shown in Fig. 1.40a. Here again, to find the reactions at the supports A and B, we begin with the polygon of forces $ABCDEF$, select a pole O, and draw the rays 1 to 6 as shown in Fig. 1.40b. Now, in this case, when we come to construct the funicular polygon in Fig. 1.40a, we note that the hinge A is the only known point on the line of action of R_a. Hence, we must start the funicular polygon at this point. Then, since the load P also acts through point A, that side of the funicular polygon corresponding to the ray 1 vanishes. Otherwise, the funicular polygon is constructed in the usual manner, and we obtain the closing side Ab as shown. After this, we return to Fig. 1.40b, where we obtain the apex G of the polygon of forces by the intersection of the ray 7 (parallel to the closing side of the funicular polygon)

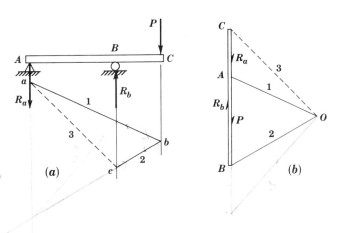

FIG. 1.39

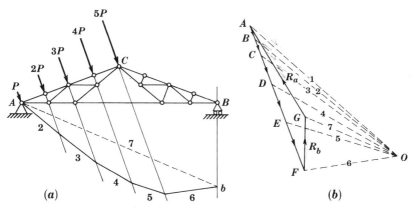

FIG. 1.40

and the known vertical direction of R_b. The required reactions are now completely determined by the vectors $\overline{FG}$ and $\overline{GA}$ as shown.

PROBLEMS

1 Determine graphically the magnitudes of the reactions R_a and R_b of the simply supported beam loaded as shown in Fig. 1.34a.

   Ans. $R_a = 1.25P, R_b = 0.75P$.

2 Using the funicular polygon, determine the magnitudes of the reactions at the supports A and B of the structure shown in Fig. 1.27.

   Ans. $R_a = R_b = P$.

3 Using the funicular polygon, determine the axial forces in the bars 1, 2, and 3 of the simple truss loaded as shown in Fig. 1.25.

4 Determine graphically the reactions at the supports A and B of the simple truss shown in Fig. 1.40a if the hinge A is on rollers while the hinge B is fixed. Assume $AB = 40$ ft, $\angle CAB = \angle CBA = 15°$, $P = 1,000$ lb.

   Ans. $R_a = 9,315$ lb, $R_b = 6,465$ lb.

5 Determine graphically the axial forces in the bars 1, 2, and 3 which support the beam AB loaded as shown in Fig. 1.41. Assume $P = 1,000$ lb.

   Ans. $S_1 = -1,538$ lb, $S_2 = +1,414$ lb, $S_3 = -1,392$ lb.

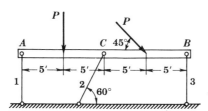

FIG. 1.41

1.6 APPLICATIONS OF THE FUNICULAR POLYGON

In the preceding article, we used the funicular polygon simply as a tool in the graphical composition of forces in a plane and in the evaluation of reactions. We have seen, however, that it possesses a certain physical significance in itself, namely: the configuration of equilibrium of a string under the action of a given system of forces.   This concept can be generalized to the extent that we imagine a string capable of sustaining compression as well as tension.   Thus, for example, the funicular polygon *abcdef* shown in Fig. 1.42*a* may be regarded as a system of hinged bars supported at *a* and *f* so as to form an arch that is in equilibrium under the action of the applied forces.   Sometimes we need to construct such a funicular polygon to satisfy certain specified conditions, such as passing through two or three given points, for example.   This general problem can be greatly simplified by using the following theorem:

> THEOREM   *If, for a given system of forces in a plane, any two funicular polygons are drawn for two different poles O and O', corresponding sides of these polygons will meet in points that lie on a straight line parallel to the line OO' joining the two poles.*

This theorem can be proved as follows: Let F_1, F_2, F_3, . . . (Fig. 1.43*a*) be any system of forces in a plane, and let *ABCDE* . . . (Fig. 1.43*b*) be the corresponding polygon of forces, with *O* and *O'* any two arbitrary poles and 1, 2, 3, 4, . . . and 1', 2', 3', 4', . . . the corresponding rays.   Then, beginning at any two points *a* and *a'* in the plane of action of the forces, two funicular polygons *abcde* . . . and *a'b'c'd'e'* . . . corresponding to the poles *O* and *O'* can be constructed in the usual manner.   Now it follows from the discussion of Art. 1.5 that at point *b*, in Fig. 1.43*a*, we can replace the force F_1 by its components 1 and 2 as represented by the vectors $\overline{AO}$ and $\overline{OB}$ in Fig. 1.43*b*.   In the same way, the forces 2' and 1', represented by the vectors $\overline{BO'}$ and $\overline{O'A}$ (Fig. 1.43*b*), when applied at point *b'* (Fig. 1.43*a*), are equivalent to the *equilibrant* of the force F_1.   Hence, the forces 1, 2, 1', and 2', directed as

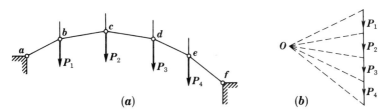

(*a*)   (*b*)

FIG. 1.42

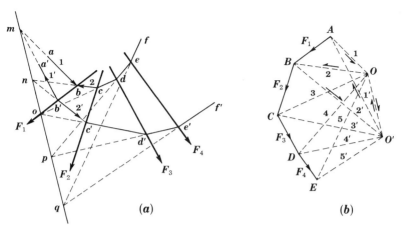

FIG. 1.43

shown in Fig. 1.43*a*, are four forces in equilibrium. From this we conclude that if at point *m* in the plane of action of the forces we replace the forces 1′ and 1 by their resultant as represented by the vector $\overline{O'O}$ (Fig. 1.43*b*) and at point *n* we replace the forces 2 and 2′ by their resultant as represented by the vector $\overline{OO'}$ (Fig. 1.43*b*), these two equal and opposite forces are in equilibrium and consequently must be collinear in action. That is, the points of intersection *m* and *n* of the corresponding first and second sides of the two funicular polygons lie on a straight line parallel to the line *OO′* joining the two poles. Applying the same reasoning in connection with the force F_2, we conclude that the intersections *n* and *o* of the corresponding second and third sides of the two funicular polygons also lie on a straight line parallel to *OO′*, etc. Hence the points *m*, *n*, *o*, *p*, *q*, . . . all lie on one straight line parallel to *OO′*, and the theorem is proved.

FUNICULAR POLYGON THROUGH THREE POINTS By the aid of the foregoing theorem, it is possible to construct, for any system of forces in a plane, a funicular polygon three sides of which will pass through three given points in the plane of action of the forces. We begin with the case of two coplanar forces *P* and *Q* as shown in Fig. 1.44*a* and for which we wish to construct a funicular polygon the three sides of which will pass, respectively, through the given points *m*, *n*, and *p*. We first construct the polygon of forces *ABC* as shown in Fig. 1.44*b*. Then, instead of choosing an arbitrary pole, we first construct two sides *ab* and *bc* of a funicular polygon so that these sides do pass through the given points *m* and *n*, respectively, as shown in Fig. 1.44*a*. The position of the pole *O* corresponding to the funicular polygon that we have thus started and that we shall call the *trial funicular polygon* can now be found

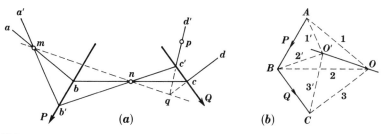

FIG. 1.44

as the intersection of the rays 1 and 2 (Fig. 1.44*b*) drawn through the apices *A* and *B* parallel, respectively, to the sides *ab* and *bc* of the trial funicular polygon. Having the pole *O*, we can draw the ray 3, and then the corresponding side *cd* of the trial funicular polygon can be constructed parallel to this ray as shown in Fig. 1.44*a*. In general, this last side of the trial funicular polygon will not pass through the given point *p*. However, from the trial funicular polygon together with the above theorem, we can easily determine a funicular polygon for the given forces *P* and *Q*, the three sides of which will pass through the given points *m*, *n*, and *p*, respectively, and which we shall accordingly refer to as the *true funicular polygon*. To accomplish this, we note that the first two sides of the trial funicular polygon pass through the given points *m* and *n*, respectively, and that the first two sides of the true funicular polygon must also pass through these points. Hence, the straight line *mn* (Fig. 1.44*a*) is the line on which the intersections of corresponding sides of the trial and true funicular polygons must all lie. Prolonging the third side *cd* of the trial funicular polygon to its intersection *q* with the line *mn*, we obtain a point through which the third side of the true funicular polygon must pass. Remembering that the third side of the true funicular polygon must also pass through point *p*, we have the position of this side *c′d′* as shown in Fig. 1.44*a*. Now through the apex *C* of the polygon of forces we draw the ray 3′ parallel to *c′d′*, and through point *O* we draw a line parallel to the straight line *mnq*. The intersection of these two lines determines the pole *O′* for the true funicular polygon. The rays 1′ and 2′ can now be drawn and the funicular polygon *a′b′c′d′* constructed as shown in Fig. 1.44*a*. The three sides of this funicular polygon pass, respectively, through the three given points *m*, *n*, and *p*, as desired.

If there are several forces in a plane for which we wish to construct a funicular polygon passing through three given points *m*, *n*, and *p*, we first replace the forces between *m* and *n* by their resultant *P* and the forces between *n* and *p* by their resultant *Q* and then proceed as illustrated in Fig. 1.44.

The funicular polygon through three given points is of practical value in connection with the determination of the reactions at the supports of a three-

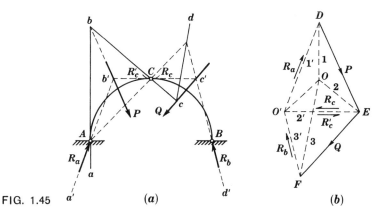

FIG. 1.45   (a)   (b)

hinged arch as shown in Fig. 1.45a.   We first construct, for the applied forces *P* and *Q*, a funicular polygon $a'b'c'd'$, the three sides of which pass, respectively, through the centers of the hinges *A*, *C*, and *B*.   This construction is carried out as explained above and is completely illustrated in Fig. 1.45.   Obviously, the rays $1'$, $2'$, and $3'$, when considered as vectors acting as shown in Fig. 1.45b, represent the reactions R_a, $R_c = R_c'$, and R_b, since, when applied at points *A*, *C*, and *B*, respectively, they fulfill all conditions of equilibrium for the arch as a whole as well as for either portion of it.

PROBLEMS

1   A string *ACB* of length *l* hangs between two vertical walls as shown in Fig. 1.46. Along this string a small pulley *C*, from which is suspended a load *P*, can roll without friction.   In the particular case where $l = 2a = 4b$, what configuration of equilibrium will the system assume?   Make the solution entirely by graphical constructions.

   Ans. $x = 0.355a$.

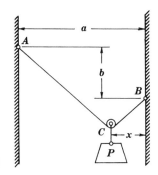

FIG. 1.46

2   The hoisting cable of a crane is carried over a series of pulleys *a*, *b*, *c*, *d*, and *e*, as shown in Fig. 1.47*a*. Using the cable as a funicular polygon for the system of forces that the pulleys exert on the joints of the crane, show that these forces are completely defined by the polygon *ABCDEF* in Fig. 1.47*b*.

3   Determine the proper shape of the top chord *abcdefgh* of the plane truss shown in Fig. 1.48 so that, for the given system of loads *P*, all the diagonal web members will be inactive. What are the corresponding forces in the chord members if $l = 70$ ft and $k = 18$ ft?

4   Construct a funicular polygon through the three points *A*, *C*, *B* to determine the reactions at the supports of the three-hinged arch with semicircular rib as shown in Fig. 1.49.

   Ans. $R_a = 6{,}880$ lb, $R_b = 8{,}220$ lb.

5   A flexible weightless string is fastened at *A*, passes over a pulley at *D*, and carries a load *P* at its free end, as shown in Fig. 1.50. A stiff bar *BC* with small rollers at its ends carries weights *P* and *Q* as shown and can roll freely along the string. Neglecting friction, determine the configuration of equilibrium of the system. Numerical data are given as follows: $a = 18$ ft, $b = 4$ ft, $c = 8$ ft, $P = 2Q$. What compressive force *S* is induced in the bar *BC*? Make the solution entirely by graphical constructions.

   Ans. $S = 0.6Q$.

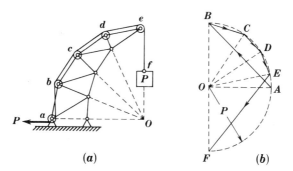

FIG. 1.47   **(a)**   **(b)**

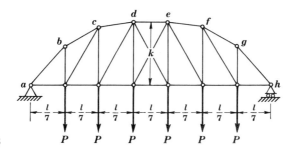

FIG. 1.48

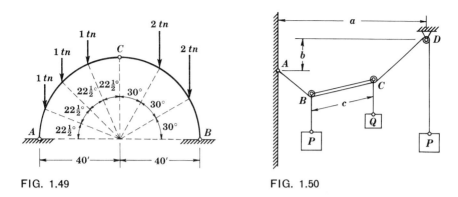

FIG. 1.49   FIG. 1.50

1.7 FUNICULAR CURVES FOR DISTRIBUTED FORCE

In previous discussions, we have dealt entirely with concentrated forces. Sometimes we need to consider the equilibrium of structures under the action of *distributed force*. Consider, for example, the prismatic beam *AB* (Fig. 1.51*a*), the weight of which is uniformly distributed along its length. Such a distribution of force is completely defined by its *intensity q*, that is, the weight per unit length of the beam. It is represented graphically by the rectangle *AabB*, which is called a *load diagram*. In a more general case, we may have nonuniformly distributed load along the beam. Here also the distribution of force can be completely defined by a load diagram like that shown in Fig. 1.51*b*, where the intensity of load at each point is indicated by the corresponding ordinate.

Any given load diagram can always be approximated by a series of trapezoidal elements as shown in Fig. 1.51*b*. Then, if *q* is the average intensity over the length Δx, the corresponding element must represent a force $\Delta P = q \times \Delta x$ that acts through the centroid of that element. In this way, we

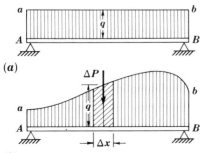

FIG. 1.51   (*b*)

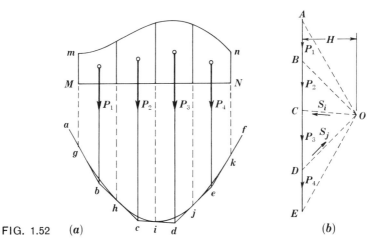

FIG. 1.52   (*a*)   (*b*)

obtain a series of parallel forces the magnitudes of which are represented by
the areas of the corresponding trapezoids and the moments of which, with
respect to any point, are identical with the corresponding statical moments of
those trapezoids.   From this it follows that the resultant force is represented
by the total area of the load diagram and acts through its centroid.

We have already seen that any funicular polygon for a system of coplanar
forces may be interpreted as a possible configuration of equilibrium of a string
fixed at its ends and submitted to the action of the given forces.   In the case of
continuously distributed force in a plane, as discussed above, the corresponding
configuration of equilibrium of a string becomes a smooth curve called a
funicular curve.   Physically, we see the manifestation of such a curve in the
case of a heavy flexible chain that is fixed at its two ends and otherwise
unsupported in the gravity field.   This particular curve is called a *catenary*.

Let *MmnN* (Fig. 1.52*a*) be the load diagram for a given distribution of
vertical force in a plane.   To construct a corresponding funicular curve, we
begin by dividing the load diagram into several parts, each small enough so
that, without serious error, it may be considered as a trapezoid.   Then it
follows that each trapezoid represents a vertical force equal in magnitude to
the area of that trapezoid and acting through its centroid.   We may, therefore,
replace the continuous distribution of force by several vertical forces P_1,
P_2, . . . as shown and construct a funicular polygon *abcdef* for these forces
in the usual manner.   This done, we inscribe a smooth curve tangent to the
sides of the funicular polygon at the points *g*, *h*, *i*, *j*, and *k*, and this is the
required funicular curve.

From the foregoing discussion it follows that between any funicular curve
(Fig. 1.52*a*) and the corresponding diagram of forces (Fig. 1.52*b*) from which
it is derived there exist the following relationships: (1) For every tangent

to the string, there is a corresponding parallel ray in the diagram of forces, the length of which represents the tensile force in the string at the point of tangency. (2) The shortest ray, called the *pole distance H*, represents the tension at the vertex of the funicular curve and, likewise, the horizontal projection of the tension at any other point. (3) For any two points on the funicular curve, rays parallel to the corresponding tangents cut from the *load line* $\overline{AE}$ that portion of the total load which acts between these two points.

As an example of application of the foregoing discussion, let us consider the case of a symmetrical two-hinged arch rib *ACB* subjected to the action of an earth-fill load as shown in Fig. 1.53*a*. In such a case, it will be desirable to make the axis of the rib a funicular curve for the load diagram *AA'B'B* so that the rib will be subjected to pure compression without bending.[1] However, since the load diagram depends upon the shape of the axis of the rib, whereas the proper shape of this axis, in turn, depends upon the load diagram, it is evident that a graphical solution of the problem must be made by trial and error.

We begin by noting that because of symmetry, the left portion *AC* of the arch must have the same shape as the right portion *BC*. Hence, only one-half of the arch need be considered. If the arch were to carry a load uniformly distributed over the span, the proper shape of its axis would be a parabola. It is, therefore, convenient to begin with *AA'C'C* (Fig. 1.53*b*) as a trail load diagram where the points *A*, *D*, *E*, *F*, and *C* lie on a parabola with vertical axis and vertex at *C*.

Assuming earth fill to weigh 100 lb/ft³ and considering a strip of the arch of unit width in the direction normal to the plane of the figure, we find that the loads represented by the four trapezoidal portions of the load diagram will be proportional to the areas of these trapezoids. The actual numerical values are shown at the top of each trapezoid. These loads P_1, . . . , P_4 act through the centroids of the areas of the trapezoids by which they are represented. Constructing the polygon of forces (Fig. 1.53*g*) for these loads and choosing an arbitrary pole *O*, we may construct a funicular polygon *abcdef* (Fig. 1.53*c*) in the usual manner, and we note that the line of action of the resultant of the forces P_1, . . . , P_4 is determined by the point of intersection *g* of the first and last sides of this funicular polygon. Now it is evident that the first and last sides of any other funicular polygon for these same forces must also intersect on the line of action of their resultant. Since we are seeking a funicular curve which passes through point *C* with a horizontal tangent and which passes through point *A*, we may now draw the first and last sides *ag* and *gf* (Fig. 1.53*d*) of the corresponding funicular polygon and thus determine the pole O_1 (Fig. 1.53*g*). Having this pole, we may draw the remaining sides *bc*, *cd*, and *de* of the funicular polygon. The inscribed curve (not shown) tangent to the sides of this funicular polygon at points *A*, *D*, *E*, *F*, and *C*

[1] Shortening of the rib due to axial compression is neglected in this discussion.

represents the first approximation to the desired funicular curve. Comparing this, as shown by the dashed curve *abcdef* in Fig. 1.53*b*, with the assumed parabola *ADEFC*, we find considerable discrepancy, which indicates that a second approximation must be made.

To do this, we now use the diagram *AA'C'C* of Fig. 1.53*d* as a load diagram

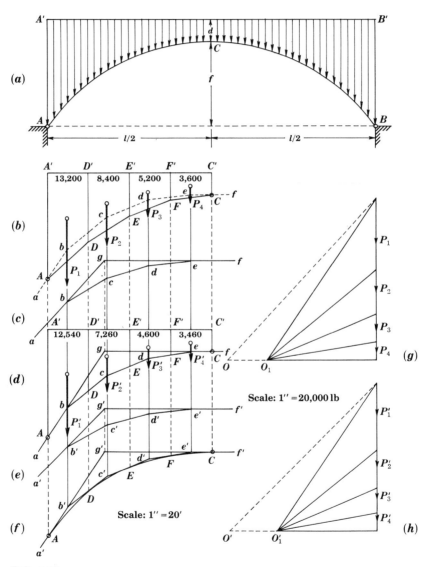

FIG. 1.53

and, as before, find the forces $P'_1, \ldots, P'_4$ as indicated. The magnitude of each load, proportional to the area of the trapezoid by which it is represented, is shown at the top of that trapezoid. The polygon of forces (Fig. 1.53h) for these loads is now constructed, an arbitrary pole O' chosen, and the funicular polygon $a'b'c'd'e'f'$ (Fig. 1.53e) drawn. The intersection g' of the first and last sides of this funicular polygon determines the line of action of the resultant of the loads $P'_1, \ldots, P'_4$. Then, as before, we determine the pole O'_1 (Fig. 1.53h) corresponding to the funicular polygon which passes through point A and horizontally through point C. This funicular polygon $a'b'c'd'e'f'$ (Fig. 1.53f) agrees so closely with $abcdef$ of Fig. 1.53d that we may consider the inscribed curve $ADEFC$ (Fig. 1.53f) as the desired funicular curve. It is interesting to note that in this particular case the obtained curve is not greatly different from the arc of a circle.

1.8 FLEXIBLE SUSPENSION CABLES

In engineering structures, we sometimes encounter flexible cables or chains suspended between supports at the ends and subjected to some kind of distributed vertical load. The equilibrium shape assumed by such a cable is, of course, a funicular curve for the loading to which the cable is subjected. In dealing with this problem, it is desirable to develop the equilibrium shape of the cable analytically rather than graphically.

To do this, we refer to Fig. 1.54a, where $MmnN$ represents a given distribution of vertical load and $abcd$ a funicular curve corresponding to the pole O, as shown in Fig. 1.54b. On this funicular curve, we choose two adjacent points b and c as defined by the coordinates x and $x + dx$. The corresponding slopes can be represented by the expressions

$$\frac{dy}{dx} \quad \text{and} \quad \frac{dy}{dx} + \frac{d}{dx}\left(\frac{dy}{dx}\right) dx$$

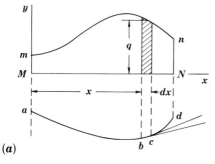

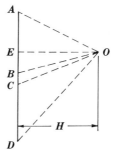

(a)   **(b)**

FIG. 1.54

respectively. Then, from the relationships discussed in the preceding article, we have

$$\frac{dy}{dx} = \tan BOE = \frac{BE}{OE} \tag{a}$$

$$\frac{dy}{dx} + \frac{d^2y}{dx^2}\, dx = \tan COE = \frac{CE}{OE} \tag{b}$$

Subtracting (a) from (b), we obtain

$$\frac{d^2y}{dx^2}\, dx = \frac{BC}{OE} = \frac{q\,dx}{H}$$

which reduces to

$$H\frac{d^2y}{dx^2} = q \tag{1.3}$$

This is the differential equation of a family of funicular curves corresponding to the arbitrary *pole distance H*. For any particular distribution of load as defined by the function q, the corresponding family of curves can be found by integration of this differential equation. Two particular cases of load distribution will now be considered in further detail.

LOAD UNIFORMLY DISTRIBUTED ALONG THE SPAN Referring to Fig. 1.55a, let ACB be a flexible cable supported at A and B and acted upon by a vertical load (not shown) of uniform intensity q_0 with respect to the horizontal span l. With the lowest point C on the curve as origin, let rectangular coordinate axes x and y be taken as shown. Let f_1 and f_2 be the y coordinates of the points of support A and B, and a and b the x coordinates of these points. Then with $q = q_0 = $ const, the solution of Eq. (1.3) becomes

$$y = \frac{q_0 x^2}{2H} \tag{1.4}$$

and we see that the curve of equilibrium assumed by the cable is a *parabola* with vertical axis.

From the equilibrium conditions of any portion CD of the cable, we have, for the tension S at point D,

$$S = \sqrt{H^2 + (q_0 x)^2} \tag{c}$$

This shows that the tension in the cable is a minimum at the lowest point C, where it is equal to H, and that it increases toward the ends, being a maximum at the highest support.

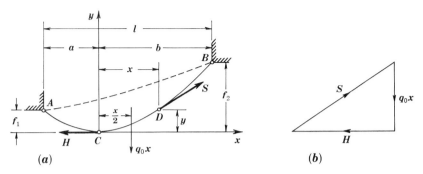

FIG. 1.55

For the tensions at the ends A and B of the cable, respectively, we have from Eq. (c)

$$S_a = \sqrt{H^2 + q_0{}^2a^2} \qquad S_b = \sqrt{H^2 + q_0{}^2b^2} \qquad (d)$$

To determine the distances a and b, locating the low point C with reference to the supports A and B, we use Eq. (1.4) successively for the portions AC and BC and note that when $x = -a$, $y = f_1$, while when $x = b$, $y = f_2$. Thus, we obtain

$$f_1 = \frac{q_0a^2}{2H} \qquad f_2 = \frac{q_0b^2}{2H} \qquad (e)$$

Subtracting the first of these expressions from the second and using the notation $f_2 - f_1 = h$, we obtain

$$2hH = q_0(b^2 - a^2)$$

Then, since $a + b = l$, we have

$$a = \frac{l}{2} - \frac{hH}{q_0l} \qquad b = \frac{l}{2} + \frac{hH}{q_0l} \qquad (f)$$

It will be noted that when $h = 0$, that is, when the supports are on the same level, we obtain $a = b = l/2$.

Substituting the above expression for b into the second of Eqs. (e), we obtain the following equation for calculating H:

$$H = \frac{q_0l^2}{h^2}\left(f_2 - \frac{h}{2} \pm \sqrt{f_1f_2}\right) \qquad (g)$$

In Eq. (g), the minus sign should be used for all cases where the vertex of the parabola lies between the supports, whereas the plus sign should be used when the vertex lies to the same side of both supports, as represented by the dashed curve AB in Fig. 1.55. In the particular case where the supports are on the same level, $f_1 = f_2 = f$, $a = b = l/2$, and proceeding as before, we obtain

$$H = \frac{q_0 l^2}{8f} \qquad (g')$$

In most practical problems the span l, the sags f_1 and f_2, and the intensity q_0 of the uniformly distributed load will be given so that from Eq. (g) or (g') the minimum tension H in the cable may be found, after which any of the quantities previously defined in terms of H can be calculated without difficulty.

The length of the portion CB of the cable is

$$L = \int_C^B ds = \int_0^b \sqrt{1 + \left(\frac{dy}{dx}\right)^2}\, dx$$

Noting from Fig. 1.55b that $dy/dx = q_0 x/H$ and substituting this into the expression for L, we obtain

$$L = \int_0^b \sqrt{1 + \left(\frac{q_0 x}{H}\right)^2}\, dx$$

which, after integration, becomes

$$L = \frac{b}{2} \sqrt{1 + \left(\frac{q_0 b}{H}\right)^2} + \frac{H}{2q_0} \sinh^{-1} \frac{q_0 b}{H} \qquad (h)$$

This can also be used for calculating the length of the portion AC if the distance b is replaced by a.

LOAD UNIFORMLY DISTRIBUTED ALONG THE CABLE   In Fig. 1.56a, let ACB represent the configuration of equilibrium of a flexible cable or chain hanging freely under the action of its own weight uniformly distributed along the length of the curve itself.   As before, let the lowest point C on the curve be taken as the origin of coordinate axes x and y, and let q_0 denote now the weight per unit length of the cable.   Also, let s be the distance from C to D measured along the curve.   Then, the intensity of load q with respect to x becomes $q = q_0\, ds/dx$, and Eq. (1.3) takes the form

$$H \frac{d^2 y}{dx^2} = q_0 \sqrt{1 + \left(\frac{dy}{dx}\right)^2}$$

the solution of which is

$$y = \frac{H}{q_0}\left(\cosh \frac{q_0 x}{H} - 1\right) \qquad (1.5)$$

This is the equation of a *catenary* which can be constructed by using numerical tables for $\cosh (q_0 x/H)$.

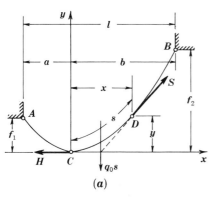
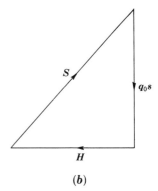

(a)   (b)

FIG. 1.56

The length s of the portion CD of the curve may be determined by integrating the differential relationship

$$ds = \sqrt{dx^2 + dy^2} = \sqrt{1 + \left(\frac{dy}{dx}\right)^2}\, dx \qquad (i)$$

where, from the equilibrium conditions of the portion CD of the cable (Fig. 1.56b), we have

$$\frac{dy}{dx} = \frac{q_0 s}{H} \qquad (j)$$

Substitution of (j) into (i) and subsequent integration give

$$s = \frac{H}{q_0} \sinh \frac{q_0 x}{H} \qquad (k)$$

Also, from the conditions of equilibrium of the segment CD of the cable (Fig. 1.56b), we have

$$S = \sqrt{H^2 + (q_0 s)^2} \qquad (l)$$

Substitution of expression (k) into expression (l) gives

$$S = H \cosh \frac{q_0 x}{H}$$

which, with the use of Eq. (1.5), finally becomes

$$S = H + q_0 y \qquad (m)$$

Again, we see that the tension S in the cable is a minimum at the lowest point C, where it is equal to H, and that it increases toward the ends, being a maximum at the highest support.

For the tensions at the ends A and B, respectively, we have, from Eq. (m),

$$S_a = H + q_0 f_1 \qquad S_b = H + q_0 f_2 \qquad (n)$$

To determine the value of H, we use Eq. (1.5) successively for the portions AC and BC of the cable, obtaining

$$f_1 = \frac{H}{q_0}\left(\cosh\frac{q_0 a}{H} - 1\right) \qquad f_2 = \frac{H}{q_0}\left(\cosh\frac{q_0 b}{H} - 1\right) \qquad (o)$$

which may also be written

$$a = \frac{H}{q_0}\cosh^{-1}\left(\frac{q_0 f_1}{H} + 1\right) \qquad b = \frac{H}{q_0}\cosh^{-1}\left(\frac{q_0 f_2}{H} + 1\right) \qquad (p)$$

Adding these last two equations and remembering that $a + b = l$, we obtain

$$\frac{q_0 l}{H} = \cosh^{-1}\left(\frac{q_0 f_1}{H} + 1\right) + \cosh^{-1}\left(\frac{q_0 f_2}{H} + 1\right) \qquad (q)$$

In most practical problems the span l, the sags f_1 and f_2, and the weight q_0 per unit length of cable will be given so that from Eq. (q) the minimum tension H in the cable can be found, after which any of the quantities, previously defined in terms of H, may be calculated without difficulty.

PROBLEMS

1   The cable shown in Fig. 1.57 carries a total vertical load $Q = 100,000$ lb, uniformly distributed with respect to the horizontal span l. Determine the maximum tensile force in the cable if $l = 100$ ft, $f_1 = 12$ ft, $h = 10$ ft.
     Ans. $S_{max} = 94,700$ lb.
2   The cable shown in Fig. 1.57 carries a total vertical load $Q = 100,000$ lb, uniformly distributed with respect to the horizontal span l. If the maximum allowable tension for the cable is 120,000 lb, what length L of cable should be used? The following numerical data are given: $l = 100$ ft, $h = 10$ ft.
     Ans. $L = 104$ ft.

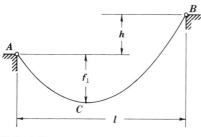

FIG. 1.57

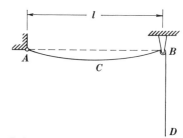

FIG. 1.58

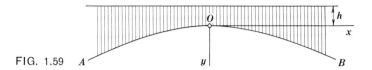

FIG. 1.59

3 A flexible chain 100 ft long and weighing 5 lb per foot of length is freely suspended at its ends from two supports 50 ft apart and having the same elevation. Find the sag f at the middle of the span.
    Ans. $f = 39.8$ ft.

4 The flexible cable shown in Fig. 1.57 hangs freely under its own weight, and the following numerical data are given: $l = 50$ ft, $f_1 = 10$ ft, $h = 20$ ft, and $q_0 = 10$ lb per foot of cable. Find the maximum tension.
    Ans. $S_b = 496$ lb.

5 Determine the shortest overall length L of a flexible chain of uniform weight per unit length that can hang in equilibrium as shown in Fig. 1.58. Neglect friction, and assume that the radius of the pulley at B is very small.
    Ans. $L_{min} = 1.14l + 0.80l = 1.94l$.

6 With reference to the coordinate axes shown in Fig. 1.59, develop the equation of the curve AOB that will be a funicular curve for the load diagram defined by itself and the line $y = -h$. Let wh be the intensity of load at O.
    Ans. $y = h(\cosh \sqrt{w/H}\, x - 1)$.

1.9 GRAPHICAL CONSTRUCTION OF BENDING-MOMENT DIAGRAMS

In previous articles, we have seen that the funicular polygon for a system of forces in a plane has a variety of practical applications. As a further application, we shall now show how it can be used in the construction of bending-moment diagrams for transversely loaded beams.

Referring to Fig. 1.60, let P be a given force for which ab and bc are two

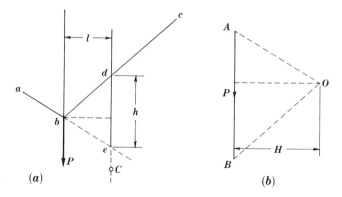

FIG. 1.60   *(a)*   *(b)*

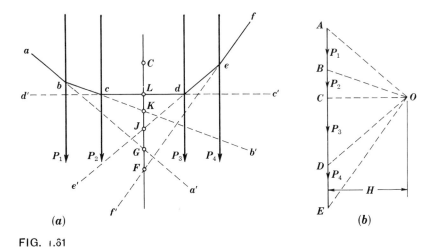

(a)   (b)

FIG. 1.61

adjacent sides of a funicular polygon corresponding to the pole O. Now through any point C (Fig. 1.60a) let a line be drawn parallel to P so that it intersects the two sides of the funicular polygon in points d and e as shown. Then the *intercept h* of this line between the two adjacent sides of the funicular polygon, when multiplied by the *pole distance H* (Fig. 1.60b), represents the moment of the force P with respect to point C. That is,

$$Hh = Pl' \tag{a}$$

where H and P are measured to the scale of force (Fig. 1.60b) and h and l to the scale of length (Fig. 1.60a). This follows at once from the fact that triangle bde is similar to triangle OAB, and hence we may write

$$l:h = H:P$$

which is equivalent to expression (a).

The above conclusion can be used also in the more general case of several parallel forces P_1, P_2, . . . in one plane as shown in Fig. 1.61. Assume, for example, that corresponding to the pole O the funicular polygon $abcdef$ has been constructed in the usual manner. Now through any arbitrary moment center C we draw a line parallel to the lines of action of the given forces. Then the intercept of this line between any two sides of the funicular polygon, when multiplied by the pole distance H, represents the algebraic sum of moments, with respect to point C, of those forces included between the same two sides of the funicular polygon. Thus, for example, to obtain the algebraic sum of moments of all the forces with respect to point C, we take the product of the intercept $\overline{FG}$ and the pole distance H. Again, to obtain the algebraic sum of moments of the forces P_1 and P_2 with respect to point C, we take the intercept $\overline{GL}$ multiplied by H; for the moment of P_4, we take the intercept

$\overline{FJ} \times H$, etc.   The moment is positive or negative accordingly as the intercept is to the right or to the left of the intersection of the two lines that determine it. All this follows directly from Eq. (*a*) since the intersection of any two sides of the funicular polygon determines the line of action of the resultant of those forces included between these two sides and since the moment of the resultant is always equal to the algebraic sum of the moments of its components.

Now, referring to Fig. 1.62, let us again consider a system of parallel forces P_1, P_2, P_3, and P_4, for which *abcdef* is a funicular polygon corresponding to the pole *O*.   If, parallel to the lines of action of the forces, we construct all intercepts between the first side *aa'* and the remainder of the funicular polygon as shown, we obtain a *moment diagram*.   Any ordinate of this diagram, when multiplied by the pole distance *H*, represents the algebraic sum of moments of those forces to the left of that ordinate with respect to a point anywhere on the ordinate.   This statement follows directly from the discussion in reference to Fig. 1.61.   Now, in the case of a transversely loaded beam, we know that this idea of the sum of moments of all forces to one side of a point is of particular value because it defines the *bending moment* in the beam at that point.   Thus, the diagram shown in Fig. 1.62 can be considered as a bending-moment diagram for a cantilever beam *AB* built in at *B* and submitted to the action of the forces $P_1, \ldots, P_4$ as shown.

As a second example, let us consider the simply supported beam loaded transversely as shown in Fig. 1.63*a*.   In this case, the closed funicular polygon *abcde*, which has been constructed in the usual manner for the purpose of determining the reactions R_a and R_b, may be used directly as a bending-moment diagram for the beam.   It is necessary only to multiply each ordinate of the diagram by the pole distance *H* to have the corresponding bending moment.   This follows from the fact that any ordinate of the diagram is simply the intercept between those two sides of the funicular polygon which intersect on the line of action of the resultant of all forces to one side of the intercept.

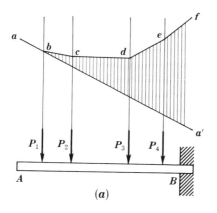

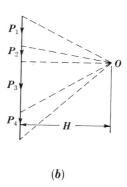

FIG. 1.62   (*a*)   (*b*)

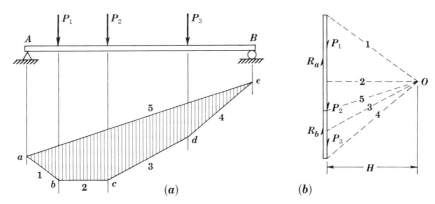

FIG. 1.63

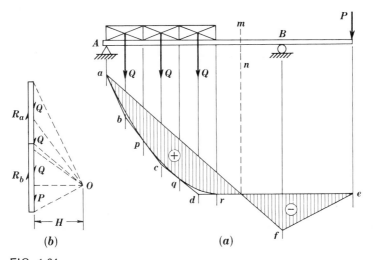

FIG. 1.64

In the case of a beam under distributed load, we divide the load diagram into several finite portions, as shown in Fig. 1.64, and then construct the closed funicular polygon *abcdef* and determine the reactions R_a and R_b in the usual manner. Then, to have a bending-moment diagram for the beam, it is necessary only to inscribe the smooth curve *apqr* corresponding to the distributed load and take the ordinates as shown. We see that in this case there will be a change in the sign of bending moment as we cross the section *mn*. As in the previous cases, the ordinates in Fig. 1.64*a* must be measured to the scale of length and then multiplied by the pole distance *H*, measured to the scale of force, before we obtain the true bending moment.

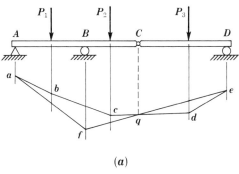

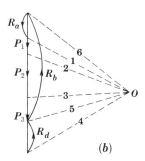

(a)

(b)

FIG. 1.65

In the preceding examples, we have seen that a funicular polygon constructed for the purpose of determining the reactions at the supports of a beam can also be used as a bending-moment diagram. Sometimes the situation can be reversed and the fact that such a funicular polygon is a bending-moment diagram can help us in the determination of reactions. Consider, for example, the compound beam shown in Fig. 1.65a, for which it is desired to determine graphically the reactions at the supports A, B, and D. We begin by constructing in the usual manner the funicular polygon $abcde$ for the given loads P_1, P_2, and P_3 as shown. At this stage of the construction the rays 5 and 6 and the corresponding sides ef and fa of the closed funicular polygon for the entire system are missing, but the fact that there can be no bending moment in the beam at the hinge C enables us to find them. For, by this condition, we conclude that that side of the closed funicular polygon which is common to R_d and R_b must intersect the established side cd on the vertical through the hinge C, that is, at point q. Thus the side ef can be drawn, and thence the closing side fa. The corresponding rays 5 and 6 determine the reactions as shown.

PROBLEMS

1   For the beam shown in Fig. 1.66, construct a closed funicular polygon such that the ordinates of the diagram for bending moment thus obtained will be to the scale 1 in. = 1,000 ft-lb.

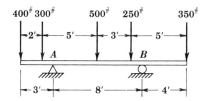

FIG. 1.66

2   Prove that the shaded portion of the funicular diagram shown in Fig. 1.67 represents the bending-moment diagram for the beam AB, while the unshaded portion is the bending-moment diagram for CD.

3   Construct the bending-moment diagram for the girder AB shown in Fig. 1.68. The magnitudes of the loads are in kips (1 kip = 1,000 lb).

4   Determine, by means of a funicular polygon, the reactions at the supports A, B, E, and F of the compound beam loaded as shown in Fig. 1.69.

5   Referring to the three-hinged arch loaded as shown in Fig. 1.70, assume that a pole O has been so chosen that the corresponding funicular polygon $abcde$ passes

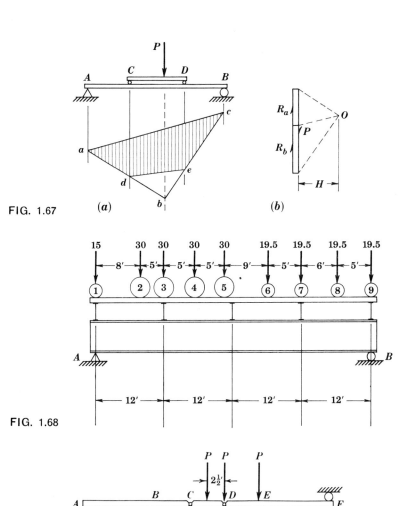

FIG. 1.67   (a)   (b)

FIG. 1.68

FIG. 1.69

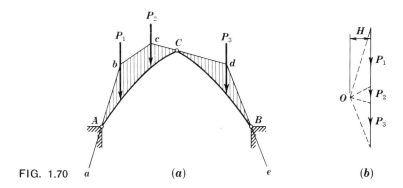

FIG. 1.70 *a*   **(a)**   *e*   **(b)**

through the hinges, A, C, and B of the arch as shown. Then prove that any ordinate of the shaded diagram, when multiplied by the pole distance H, represents the corresponding bending moment in the arch rib.

1.10 PRINCIPLE OF VIRTUAL DISPLACEMENTS

The various analytical and graphical methods of solving problems of statics so far considered have been based on the principle of the *parallelogram of forces*. We shall now consider another general principle of statics called the principle of *virtual displacements*. In certain cases, methods of solution based on the latter principle have a decided advantage over any of those previously considered. The principle is perfectly general, but here we shall limit our discussion of its development and application to coplanar systems.

We begin with the case of a single *particle P* under the action of a system of concurrent forces F_1, F_2, . . . , F_n in one plane as shown in Fig. 1.71. Imagine now that this particle is given a small arbitrary displacement ds as shown. Then any force F_i of the system is said to produce *work* on this displacement. This work is defined as the product of the displacement and the projection of the force on the direction of the displacement, i.e., by the

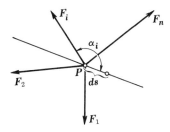

FIG. 1.71

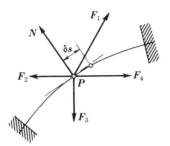

FIG. 1.72

expression

$$ds\ F_i \cos \alpha_i \tag{a}$$

We see, by this definition, that the work will be positive or negative accordingly as the sign of the projection of the force agrees or disagrees with that of the displacement. The *net work* of all the forces, i.e., the algebraic sum of expressions (a), may be written as follows:

$$\sum_{i=1}^{i=n} (ds\ F_i \cos \alpha_i) = ds \sum_{i=1}^{i=n} F_i \cos \alpha_i = ds\ R \cos \alpha \tag{b}$$

where $R \cos \alpha$ is the projection of the resultant R on the direction of the displacement. From expression (b), we conclude that the net work of the system of forces on any displacement ds of the particle is equal to the work of their resultant on the same displacement. Thus, if the net work of the forces on each of two orthogonal projections dx and dy of the displacement ds is zero, we conclude that the resultant force vanishes and the system is in equilibrium. Conversely, *if a particle is known to be in equilibrium, the algebraic sum of the works of all forces acting upon it must be zero for any arbitrary small displacement of the particle.* This is the principle of *virtual displacements*, or *virtual work* as it is sometimes called.

Now let us consider the case of a partially constrained particle, for example, a small bead that can slide along a smooth wire, as shown in Fig. 1.72. In such a case, we distinguish between two kinds of forces acting on the particle: *active forces*, such as F_1, F_2, . . . , F_n, and *reactive forces*, such as N, exerted on the bead by the wire. As a condition of equilibrium, we conclude that the algebraic sum of the work of all forces (both active and reactive) on any small displacement of the particle must be zero. Suppose, however, that we agree to restrict such a displacement to one that is consistent with the constraint, i.e., in the direction of the tangent to the wire at P.* Such an imaginary small displacement of the particle is called a *virtual displacement*, i.e., a possible displacement, and it will be denoted by the symbol δs. If the wire is without

---

* Since the displacement is infinitesimal, an element of the axis of the wire of length ds may be considered as coincident with the tangent at P.

friction (an *ideal constraint*), the reactive force N is normal to this virtual displacement δs and does not produce work. Thus, the work of all the forces is identical with the work of the active forces alone, and we conclude that, *for any virtual displacement of an ideally constrained particle, the algebraic sum of the works of the active forces alone must be zero.* Reactive forces need not be considered at all.

We come finally to the general case of a system of particles. It is in application to such systems that the principle of virtual displacements is of special value. As a specific example of a system of particles, let us consider two blocks A and B that rest on inclined planes and are connected by a flexible but inextensible string overrunning a pulley, as shown in Fig. 1.73. Neglecting friction in the pulley and on the inclined planes, we call this an *ideal system.* Here again we distinguish between active forces such as the weights P and Q and reactive forces such as N_a, N_b, and S. Further, we note that the reactive forces are of two kinds, those external to the system as a whole, like N_a and N_b, and those internal to the system, like the tensile forces S exerted on the particles by the string. A virtual displacement of the system, i.e., a small change in position consistent with the constraints (both external and internal), will be obtained by giving to each particle an imaginary displacement δx along its supporting plane as shown. By virtue of the inextensibility of the string, these displacements must be equal. Then, if the system is in equilibrium, each particle is in equilibrium, and the algebraic sum of the works of all forces on such a displacement of the system as a whole must vanish. However, the forces N_a and N_b, being normal to the inclined planes along which the particles move, do not produce work and need not be considered. Further, the forces S, being equal in magnitude, produce works of opposite sign, which cancel, and they also can be disregarded. Thus again, *for any virtual displacement of an ideal system of particles in equilibrium, the algebraic sum of the works of the active forces alone must be zero.* Applying this conclusion to the case in hand, we write

$$-P \sin \alpha \, \delta x + Q \sin \beta \, \delta x = 0$$

which gives, as a condition of equilibrium of the system,

$$\frac{P}{Q} = \frac{\sin \beta}{\sin \alpha} \tag{c}$$

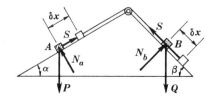

FIG. 1.73

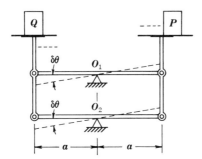

FIG. 1.74

To get the above result by the usual equations of equilibrium, we consider each particle separately and write

$$-P \sin \alpha + S = 0$$

$$Q \sin \beta - S = 0$$

Then, upon eliminating S between these two equations, we obtain condition (c). For a more complicated system of several particles, this latter method will require the writing of a number of simultaneous equations of equilibrium, the solution of which can become very complicated. In such cases, the method based on the principle of virtual displacements often proves to be more practicable.

The principle can be applied also to any ideally connected system of rigid bodies. Consider, for example, the system of levers arranged as shown in Fig. 1.74. To find the relation between P and Q for equilibrium, we note that a virtual displacement of the system can be defined by a small angle of rotation $\delta\theta$ of the horizontal bars. The corresponding displacements of the gravity centers of the weights P and Q are independent of the positions of these bodies on the pans and are always equal. Hence, by the principle of virtual displacements, the weights P and Q must be equal for equilibrium.

Sometimes the principle of virtual displacements can be used to advantage in finding reactions. Consider, for example, the system of connected beams supported and loaded as shown in Fig. 1.75a. To find the reaction at B, we imagine that the constraint there is replaced by a vertical force R_b as shown in Fig. 1.75b. In this way we obtain a nonrigid system for which we have the problem of finding the relation between the forces P and R_b for equilibrium. A virtual displacement of the system can be completely defined by a small vertical displacement δx of the hinge C as indicated in the figure. The corresponding equation of virtual work becomes

$$P \frac{x}{a} \delta x - R_b \frac{a}{a+b} \delta x = 0$$

and we find $R_b = Px(a + b)/a^2$. The reactions at the other supports can be found in a similar manner. The advantage of the present method lies in the fact that only one reaction need be considered at a time and no consideration need be given to the internal forces of the system. That is, we do not have to take the system apart and consider separate free-body diagrams for each of the beams AC, CD, and DF.

As another example, consider the simple frame structure shown in Fig. 1.76a. To find the horizontal component of the reaction at B, we remove the

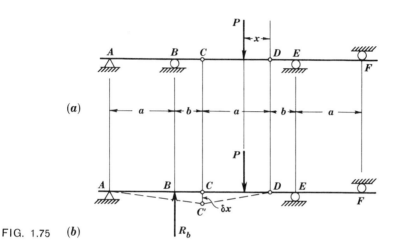

(a)

(b)

FIG. 1.75

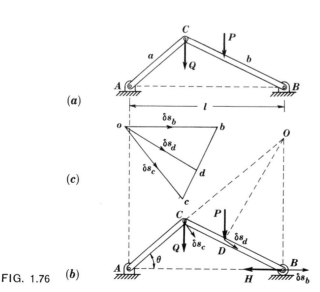

(a)

(c)

FIG. 1.76   (b)

corresponding constraint at this support and replace it by a force H as shown in Fig. 1.76b. The system is now movable, and its configuration can be defined by one coordinate θ. A virtual displacement of the system will be represented by a small change $\delta\theta$ in this angle. As a result of such rotation of the bar AC, point C moves perpendicularly to AC, and point B moves horizontally in compliance with the remaining constraints of the system. This means that the bar CB rotates about its *instantaneous center* O, obtained as the intersection of a vertical line through B and the prolongation of AC. Owing to such rotation of CB, the point D moves in the direction perpendicular to OD, and the virtual displacements of points C, B, and D become

$$\delta s_c = a\,\delta\theta$$

$$\delta s_b = \frac{OB}{OC}\,a\,\delta\theta \qquad\qquad (d)$$

$$\delta s_d = \frac{OD}{OC}\,a\,\delta\theta$$

Thus, the equation of virtual work is

$$-H\frac{OB}{OC}\,a\,\delta\theta + P\cos\,(P,\,\delta s_d)\,\frac{OD}{OC}\,a\,\delta\theta + Q\cos\theta\,a\,\delta\theta = 0$$

and we find

$$H = \frac{OC}{OB}\,Q\cos\theta + \frac{OD}{OB}\,P\cos\,(P,\,\delta s_d) \qquad\qquad (e)$$

The ratios OC/OB and OD/OB and the angle $(P,\,\delta s_d)$ between the direction of the force P and the direction of the displacement δs_d can be found from the figure if it is drawn to scale.

If from a pole o (Fig. 1.76c) we construct vectors $\overline{ob}$, $\overline{od}$, and $\overline{oc}$, representing to a chosen scale the displacements δs_b, δs_d, and δs_c, respectively, we find that the figure $obdc$, so obtained, is geometrically similar to the figure $OBDC$, since corresponding sides are mutually perpendicular and their lengths are in a constant ratio. This relationship between the two figures holds in all cases of displacement of a body in a plane, and such a figure as $obdc$ is called a *displacement diagram*. With the aid of such diagrams, a set of compatible virtual displacements for various points of a system with one degree of freedom can readily be found, after which the equation of virtual work can be written without difficulty.

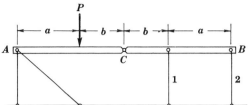

FIG. 1.77

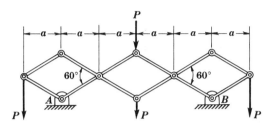

FIG. 1.78

PROBLEMS

1   Referring to the beam in Fig. 1.41 and using the method of virtual displacements, find the tensile force S_2 in the inclined bar due to the loads P acting as shown.

    Ans. $S_2 = 1.41P$, tension.

2   A compound beam ACB is supported and loaded as shown in Fig. 1.77. Using the principle of virtual displacements, find the axial forces induced in the vertical bars 1 and 2.

    Ans. $S_1 = -P$, $S_2 = +Pb/(a + b)$.

3   Calculate the reaction at the support E of the compound beam shown in Fig. 1.69 by the method of virtual work.

    Ans. $R_e = 13P/4$.

4   Using the principle of virtual displacements, find the horizontal and vertical components of the reactions induced at the supports A and B of the pin-connected frame loaded as shown in Fig. 1.78.

    Ans. $X_a = -X_b = \sqrt{3}\,P$, $Y_a = Y_b = 2P$.

5   For the semicircular three-hinged arch shown in Fig. 1.35, construct a displacement diagram and find the horizontal thrust H due to the load P acting as shown.

    Ans. $H = P/3$.

Chapter 2

Statically determinate plane trusses

2.1 SIMPLE TRUSSES

The plane truss is one of the most important of all structural forms. In general, it may be defined as a system of bars all lying in one plane and joined together at their ends so as to form a rigid framework. Consider, for example, the two simple frames shown in Fig. 2.1. The rectangular frame, consisting of four bars pinned together at their ends as shown in Fig. 2.1a, obviously is not rigid but can be collapsed as indicated by dashed lines. The same conclusion holds for any other frame composed of more than four bars that are pinned together in the form of a polygon. On the other hand, three bars pinned together at their ends in the form of a *triangle* (Fig. 2.1b) constitute a rigid frame that cannot be collapsed. That is, neglecting possible small changes in the lengths of the bars, the relative positions of the pins A, B, and C cannot be changed. Thus, the triangular frame alone behaves like a rigid body and may be considered as the simplest form of truss.

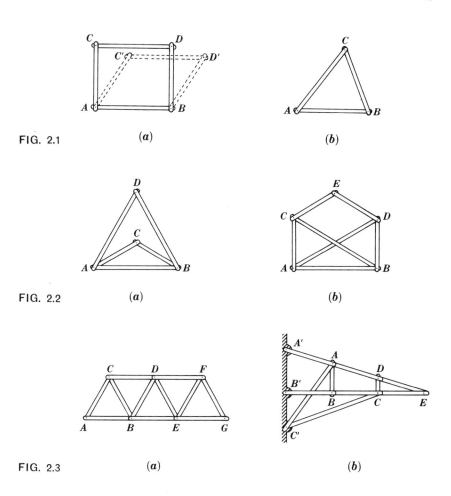

FIG. 2.1   *(a)*   *(b)*

FIG. 2.2   *(a)*   *(b)*

FIG. 2.3   *(a)*   *(b)*

Beginning with a rigid triangle ABC (Fig. 2.2*a*) and attaching to this the bars AD and BD, which are pinned together at D, we obtain the rigid frame $ABCD$. This follows directly from the fact that the rigid triangle ABC together with the bars AD and BD are arranged in triangular form. In the same way, the rigid truss $ABCDE$ shown in Fig. 2.2*b* is obtained by adding to the rigid portion $ABCD$ the two bars DE and CE, which are pinned together at E.

Since the procedure above may be continued indefinitely, we conclude that *a rigid plane truss can always be formed by beginning with three bars pinned together at their ends in the form of a triangle and then adding thereto two new bars for each new pin.* Any system of bars assembled in accordance with this rule is called a *simple truss.* Figure 2.3*a*, for example, shows a truss of this kind.

The triangle *ABC* has been taken as a rigid starting unit and the remainder of the joints *D*, *E*, *F*, and *G* established in alphabetical order, each by the addition of two bars to the existing system.

In Fig. 2.3*b*, we have a simple truss formed in accordance with a slight variation of the foregoing rule. In this case, instead of starting with a triangle, we begin directly with a rigid foundation (say a vertical wall) and establish the joints of the truss in alphabetical order, each by the addition of two bars to the existing system. This simple truss in Fig. 2.3*b* differs from that in Fig. 2.3*a* simply by the fact that it must be considered an integral part of its foundation, whereas the rigidity of the truss in Fig. 2.3*a* is quite independent of its attachment to any foundation.

It can easily be shown that, for each of the two variations of a simple truss as shown in Fig. 2.3, there must exist a definite relationship between the number of bars, or *members*, *m* and the number of pins, or *joints*, *j*. In the case of the truss in Fig. 2.3*a*, we note that, exclusive of the starting triangle *ABC*, which contains three bars and three joints, there are two bars for each joint. Hence, we may write

$$m - 3 = 2(j - 3)$$

from which

$$m = 2j - 3 \qquad (2.1a)$$

In the second case (Fig. 2.3*b*) the question of the starting triangle is eliminated, and we have simply

$$m = 2j \qquad (2.1b)$$

In this latter case the points of attachment to the foundation are not to be counted as joints.

In arranging the bars of a truss, the actual form in any situation will depend largely on the structural and architectural functions that are to be served. There are many standardized forms of trusses for various types of structures, and several examples typical of roof and bridge construction are shown in Fig. 2.4. For each of these examples, the reader should verify the fact that Eq. (2.1*a*) regarding the relationship between number of bars *m* and number of joints *j* is satisfied. At those intersections where no connections are shown it is understood that the bars pass each other freely; such intersections should not be counted as joints. Welded or riveted joints as shown in (*a*) and (*b*) are the most common forms of connection in modern steel structures, although pinned joints as shown in (*c*) and (*d*) are still to be found.

Essentially the function of every truss is simply that of a large beam to carry loads across an open span. In Fig. 2.5 we see a very simple low-truss bridge, which will serve to illustrate this fundamental structural action of a truss.

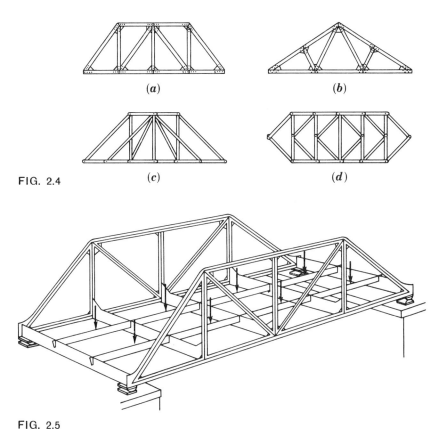

(a) (b)

(c) (d)

FIG. 2.4

FIG. 2.5

Here we have two identical parallel trusses supported at their ends on piers and carrying between them a floor system to which active loads can be applied. This floor system consists of *crossbeams*, supported between corresponding joints of the trusses, and *stringers*, which in turn are supported on the cross-beams. It is evident from such construction that all loads applied to the floor of the bridge will be transmitted to the two trusses only at their joints.

Loads applied to the floor of the bridge as well as the weight of the bridge itself produce bending of the trusses principally in their own planes. Such plane bending of a truss is illustrated in Fig. 2.6*b*. The distortion of the truss as a whole results from slight changes in the lengths of the various members, and in each there is induced a corresponding tension or compression, i.e., an *axial force*. The stress (force per unit area) corresponding to this axial force in any bar is called the *primary stress* in that bar.

In the case of a truss with riveted or welded connections (Fig. 2.6*c*), bending of the truss as a whole also induces some bending of the individual members

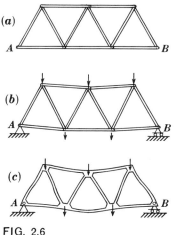

(a)

A   B

(b)

A   B

(c)

A   B

FIG. 2.6

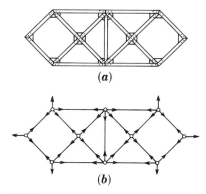

(a)

(b)

FIG. 2.7

because of the rigidity of the joints. Such bending of the bars of a truss superimposes additional bending stresses, which are called *secondary stresses;* these must be investigated as a separate problem. However, if the bars are carefully arranged so that their center lines meet in one point at each joint, we shall find that the presence of secondary stresses due to the rigidity of the joints usually does not greatly affect the magnitudes of primary stresses. Thus, in calculating the latter, the rigidity of the joints can be ignored and *pinned joints assumed.* In this way we dispose temporarily of the necessity to distinguish between trusses with riveted joints and those with pinned joints.

Even in the case of a truss that actually does have pinned joints, there will, of course, be some bending of the bars due to their own weights. This bending, however, is usually slight. It is common practice to ignore it and to replace the distributed weight of each bar by two equal concentrated forces on the joints at its ends; i.e., the weight of the truss is assumed to be concentrated in its joints.

Finally, then, for purposes of analysis, we replace an actual physical truss (Fig. 2.7a) by a corresponding idealized truss (Fig. 2.7b) consisting of a system of weightless bars all lying in one plane and joined together at their ends by frictionless hinges to which external forces acting only in the plane of the truss can be applied. Under such idealized conditions, each bar is under simple tension or compression without bending, and consequently the two equal but opposite forces that it exerts on the pins at its ends are collinear with the axis of the bar. Thus, at each joint of the truss, we have in equilibrium a system of concurrent coplanar forces with known lines of action, and a determination of the magnitudes of these internal forces constitutes the analysis of the truss. However, before we can consider general methods of analysis of plane trusses, we must first consider the question of support of a truss in its plane and the related problem of determination of reactions induced at such supports.

2.2 REACTIONS

Any simple truss of the kind shown in Fig. 2.3*b*, being formed as an integral part of the foundation, is, of course, completely constrained in its own plane and can hold in equilibrium any system of external loads applied at its joints. However, to complete the constraint in one plane of a simple truss like that in Fig. 2.3*a*, we have yet to attach it to a foundation, either by additional bars or by other suitable supports. The most common procedure will be to anchor one point *A* to the foundation by means of a fixed hinge as shown in Fig. 2.6*c*. Such a constraint eliminates all possibility of translation of the truss; there remains only the possibility of rotation around point *A*. During such rotation, another point *B* could move only in a direction normal to the line *AB*. Hence, to complete the constraint of the truss in its own plane it is necessary not to fix the hinge *B* completely but only to support it on rollers that can move freely in one direction. If this one degree of freedom of the hinge *B* is incompatible with rotation about *A*, it follows that such rollers[1] complete the constraint of the truss in its plane.

Practical means of attaining desired degrees of constraint in the support of actual trusses are shown in Fig. 2.8. Such details depend very largely on the size, weight, and span of the truss; the sketches shown here are intended to give only a general idea of their design.

Another general method of supporting a truss in its own plane is to attach it to the foundation by means of additional bars like its own members. The simple truss *ABC* shown in Fig. 2.9, for example, can be attached to the

[1] We assume that these rollers are on a special track that prevents upward as well as downward motion.

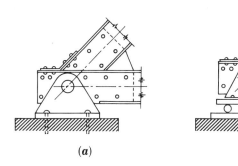

FIG. 2.8   *(a)*   *(b)*

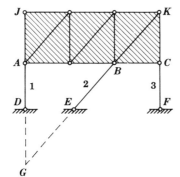

FIG. 2.9   *G*

foundation in this manner by the three bars 1, 2, 3. In general, complete constraint of a truss in one plane can always be attained with three bars so arranged that their axes neither are parallel nor intersect in one point. This may be proved as follows: Imagine first that the truss in Fig. 2.9 is attached to the foundation by two bars *AD* and *BE* that are not parallel.   Then points *A* and *B* of the truss can move, respectively, in directions normal to the axes of these bars.   The result will be equivalent to a rotation of the truss around point *G*, where the axes of the bars *AD* and *BE* intersect.   A third bar *CF*, which constrains point *C* to move in only one direction not compatible with rotation around point *G* (which means simply that the axis of the bar *CF* must not pass through point *G*), obviously completes the constraint of the truss in its own plane.

In the special case where the truss is supported by three parallel bars (Fig. 2.10*a*), it is self-evident that there is freedom for lateral movement and the truss is not completely constrained.   In the same way, a truss supported by three bars the axes of which intersect in one point (Fig. 2.10*b*) is somewhat free to rotate about this point and is incompletely constrained.   Thus, in general, three bars, the axes of which neither are parallel nor intersect in one point,

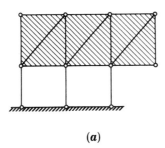

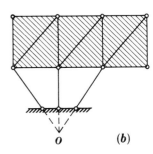

FIG. 2.10   *(a)*   *O*   *(b)*

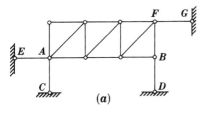
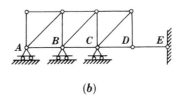

FIG. 2.11

are both necessary and sufficient for the complete constraint of a rigid truss in one plane.

Any supports of a rigid plane truss in excess of those both necessary and sufficient for complete constraint in its own plane are called *redundant supports*. For example, the truss supported by four hinged bars as shown in Fig. 2.11*a* is, of course, amply constrained in its plane; but since any one of these bars may be removed without destroying the complete constraint of the truss, any one of them may be considered as a redundant support. Similarly, it is evident that any one of the rollers by which the truss in Fig. 2.11*b* is supported may be considered as a redundant support; but not so with the bar *DE*, since without this the truss will be free to move horizontally.

When a simple truss, completely constrained in its own plane, is submitted to the action of a system of forces also in this plane, reactions are developed at the points of support, and active forces together with reactive forces constitute a coplanar system of forces in equilibrium. For such a system of forces, we have three conditions of equilibrium as represented by Eqs. (1.2) (page 11), and hence we can determine not more than three unknown elements pertaining to the system of reactions. This, however, happens to be exactly the number of degrees of constraint required for completely fixing the truss in its plane. Thus, in the case of a simple truss supported in a manner both necessary and sufficient for complete constraint, we conclude that the reactions induced at the supports by any system of applied forces can be completely determined by equations of statics. For this reason, such a system of supports is said to be *statically determinate*. Methods of determining such reactions have already been discussed in Arts. 1.2, 1.3, and 1.5.

If the system of supports of a rigid plane truss involves more than three degrees of constraint, i.e., if there are redundant supports as in Fig. 2.11, the three equations of statics will be insufficient for determining the unknowns, and the system is said to be *statically indeterminate*. In such a case, the way in which the loads transmitted through the bars of the truss are divided among the several supports depends on the elastic properties of the bars, and the reactions can be determined only by considering these properties.[1]

[1] This problem is completely discussed in Chap. 7.

In special cases like those shown in Fig. 2.10, a system of supports in one plane, although involving only three degrees of constraint, will also prove to be statically indeterminate.   Take, for example, the case shown in Fig. 2.10*b*, and suppose that the resultant of all active forces applied to the truss is a force which passes through the point *O*.   Since the three reactions induced in the supporting bars must also intersect in this point, we have a system of concurrent forces in a plane for which there are only two independent conditions of equilibrium [Eqs. (1.1), page 3].   Thus, the problem is statically indeterminate.   On the other hand, if the resultant of all active forces applied to the truss is a couple, or a force that does not pass through point *O*, the situation will be quite different.   In this case, if we decide to take point *O* as a moment center, we see at once that it will be necessary to have infinite forces developed in some of the supporting bars since, with zero-moment arms, the reactions exerted on the truss by these bars can in no other way develop a finite moment with respect to point *O* by which to balance the resultant moment of the applied forces.   In such a case, what actually happens is that the supporting bars deform (elongate or contract) sufficiently to allow the truss to rotate into a new position such that the axes of the three supporting bars no longer intersect in one point.   Thus, the final configuration of equilibrium of the system and the corresponding forces developed in the three supporting bars depend on the elastic properties of the system, and we have again a statically indeterminate problem.

PROBLEMS

1   Find the reactions at *A* and *B* for each of the trusses supported and loaded as shown in Fig. 2.12.
   Ans.   (*a*) $R_a = 5P$, $X_b = 2.5 \sqrt{3} P$, $Y_b = 1.5P$.
2   Find the reactions at *A* and *B* for each of the trusses supported and loaded as shown in Fig. 2.13.
   Ans.   (*a*) $R_b = 5P/\sqrt{3}$, $X_a = 2P$, $Y_a = P/\sqrt{3}$.

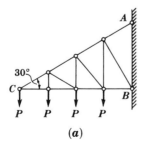

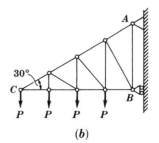

FIG. 2.12   (*a*)   (*b*)

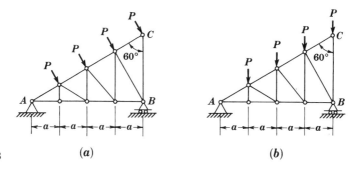

FIG. 2.13   (a)   (b)

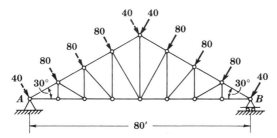

FIG. 2.14

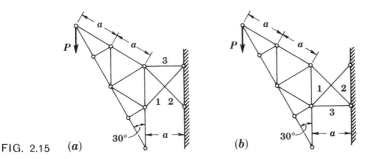

FIG. 2.15   (a)   (b)

3   Find the reactions at A and B of the simple roof truss shown in Fig. 2.14, (a) when the truss is loaded as shown by the solid vectors and (b) when loaded similarly as shown by dashed vectors. The loads are given in kips.

   Ans. (a) $R_b = 184.7$ kips, $X_a = 160$ kips, $Y_a = 92.4$ kips.

4   Find the axial force induced in each of the supporting bars 1, 2, 3 of the truss shown in Fig. 2.15, (a) when arranged as shown in Fig. 2.15a and (b) when arranged as shown in Fig. 2.15b.

   Ans. (a) $S_1 = -2.45P$, $S_2 = -3.87P$, $S_3 = +4.46P$.

5   What axial forces will be induced in the supporting bars of the truss in Fig. 2.9 by the action of a horizontal force P applied at joint K? Assume $AJ = AD = 12$ ft, $BC = 10$ ft.

   Ans. $S_1 = 0$, $S_2 = 1.56P$, $S_3 = -1.20P$.

2.3 METHOD OF JOINTS

We shall now consider in detail the analysis of a simple truss ABC supported and loaded as shown in Fig. 2.16a. Owing to the applied loads P, vertical reactions each equal to $\frac{3}{2}P$ are induced at the supports A and B, and the truss as a whole is in equilibrium under the action of the balanced system of vertical forces shown. As was pointed out in Art. 2.1, these external loads induce axial forces in the various bars of the truss, and each bar in turn exerts on the hinges at its ends two equal but oppositely directed forces having for their common line of action the axis of the bar. The magnitude of either of these forces represents the axial force in the bar; and whether it is directed away from the hinge or toward it determines, accordingly, whether the bar is in tension or in compression. To avoid confusion in dealing with these internal forces, we shall number each bar of the truss as shown and then denote by S_i the magnitude of axial force in any bar i.

We begin the analysis of the truss in this case by consideration of the equilibrium of the hinge A. Taking this hinge as a free body as indicated by the circle around joint A, we find acting upon it the external reaction $\frac{3}{2}P$, together with the internal reactions S_1 and S_2 exerted, respectively, by the bars 1 and 2. We shall not know at once whether these last two forces should be directed away from the hinge or toward it, but only that their lines of action are represented by the axes of the bars exerting them. From this fact, however, a closed triangle of forces (Fig. 2.16b) can be constructed and the

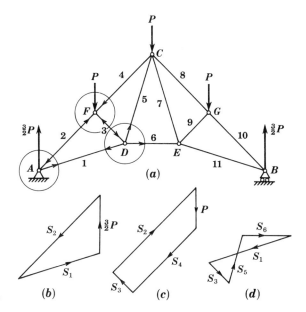

FIG. 2.16

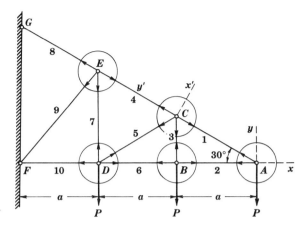

FIG. 2.17

magnitudes of the forces S_1 and S_2 scaled or calculated from this.   Also, from the directions of the arrows, which must follow tail to head around the closed triangle of forces, we see that the bar 1 is in tension while the bar 2 is in compression.   Arrows indicating such action can now be placed at A as shown.

We are now in a position to consider the equilibrium of the hinge F.   We first replace the bar 2 by its known reaction S_2 directed toward the hinge F. There remain then but two unknown forces at F representing the reactions on this hinge of the bars 3 and 4.   Again, we do not know which way these last two forces should be directed; but, knowing their lines of action, we can construct the polygon of forces as shown in Fig. 2.16c.   From this closed polygon, the magnitudes of axial force in the bars 3 and 4 can be found as before.   In this case, we see from the arrows on the polygon of forces that both bars are in compression, and arrows indicating such action can now be inserted in Fig. 2.16a.

Proceeding next to a consideration of the hinge D, the reactions exerted on this hinge by the bars 1 and 3 are already known, and again there remain only two bars (5 and 6) for which the axial forces are unknown.   The closed polygon of forces for this hinge, from which S_5 and S_6 can be found, is shown in Fig. 2.16d.   This completes the analysis of the truss in this particular case, for, owing to symmetry, it is evident that each bar on the right will carry the same axial force as the corresponding bar on the left.

If desired, the two equations of equilibrium [Eqs. (1.1), page 3] can be applied successively to the joints of a simple truss instead of constructing the various polygons of forces as was done above.   This alternative will usually be preferable in cases where the angles between the bars of the truss are such that the projections of the forces are readily calculated.   By way of illustrating this procedure, let us consider the simple truss supported and loaded as shown in Fig. 2.17.   In applying equations of equilibrium instead of the graphical procedure above, it is convenient to assume at the outset that all bars are in tension as indicated by the reactions directed away from the hinges in the figure. Then, automatically, results with the plus sign will indicate tension, whereas those with the minus sign will indicate compression. For example, we imagine the hinge A as an isolated free body acted upon by the three forces P, S_1, and S_2 directed as shown. Then, equating to zero the algebraic sums of projections of these forces on the orthogonal axes x and y, we obtain

$$-\frac{\sqrt{3}}{2} S_1 - S_2 = 0$$

$$-P + \tfrac{1}{2}S_1 = 0$$

from which $S_1 = +2P$ and $S_2 = -\sqrt{3}\,P$. Thus, the bar 1 carries a tensile force equal to $2P$, while the bar 2 carries a compressive force equal to $\sqrt{3}\,P$. In using these values in subsequent calculations, we should consider the sign as an integral part of the result.

Upon proceeding to the hinge B and projecting all forces on the same orthogonal axes, we see that the equations of equilibrium will become

$$+S_2 - S_6 = 0$$

$$-P + S_3 = 0$$

Upon substituting for S_2 its previously determined value $-\sqrt{3}\,P$, we obtain from these equations $S_3 = +P$ and $S_6 = -\sqrt{3}\,P$ (tension and compression, respectively). For the hinge C it will be most convenient to project all forces onto the orthogonal axes x' and y' directed as shown. For such axes, the equations of equilibrium become

$$-\frac{\sqrt{3}}{2} S_3 - \frac{\sqrt{3}}{2} S_5 = 0$$

$$-S_1 - \tfrac{1}{2}S_3 + \tfrac{1}{2}S_5 + S_4 = 0$$

Using $S_3 = +P$ in the first of these, we find $S_5 = -P$, after which the second equation gives $S_4 = +3P$. It is left as an exercise for the reader to consider the hinges D and E and complete the analysis of the truss.

The foregoing procedure in the analysis of a simple truss is called the *method of joints*. It always can be applied either graphically or analytically to any truss the bars of which are assembled in accordance with the rule given on page 53, i.e., to any *simple truss*. This follows from the fact that in any such truss there must exist at least one joint (the last one added in accordance with the rule) at which only two bars meet. Hence the axial forces in these two bars can be determined from the two conditions of equilibrium existing for that joint and the two bars replaced by the reactions that they exert on two other hinges of the truss. Then, again, there must be one joint (the next to the last one established in accordance with the rule) where only two bars with unknown forces will be encountered, and these forces can be determined. Thus, by considering the joints of the truss one by one in the reverse order from which they were established, we shall find at each joint only two bars with unknown forces, and the analysis proceeds without difficulty. It must be pointed out, of course, that it will often be necessary to determine the external reactions at the points of support as a separate problem before the analysis of the truss proper can be commenced.

PROBLEMS

1 Determine the axial force in each bar of the simple truss supported and loaded as shown in Fig. 2.12a.
2 Make a complete analysis of each of the simple trusses supported and loaded as shown in Fig. 2.13.
3 Referring to the roof truss shown in Fig. 2.14, make a complete analysis for each of the indicated conditions of loading.

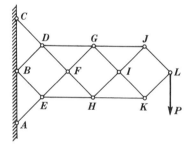

FIG. 2.18

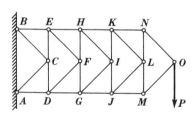

FIG. 2.19

4 Make a complete analysis, by the method of joints, of the simple truss shown in Fig. 2.18. All inclined bars are at 45° with the horizontal.
5 Make a complete analysis, by the method of joints, of the K truss shown in Fig. 2.19. The inclined bars are at 45° with the horizontal, and the panel distances are uniform.

2.4 MAXWELL DIAGRAMS

Referring to Fig. 2.16, in which the analysis of a truss has been made by constructing a separate force polygon for each hinge, we note that each axial-force vector appears in two different force polygons. To avoid this duplication of vectors, the separate polygons of forces, under certain conditions, can be superimposed to form one composite diagram called a *Maxwell diagram* for the truss.   For example, the three polygons of forces shown in Fig. 2.16, when superimposed, make the composite diagram shown in Fig. 2.20b.   Such superposition is desirable since it reduces the amount of necessary construction and also makes a more compact record of the final results.   However, in order to avoid duplication of any vector, the constructions must be carried out in a definite manner, which we shall now consider.

We begin with the simplest case of a triangular frame ABC, which is in equilibrium under the action of three external forces P, Q, and R acting in the plane of the triangle as shown in Fig. 2.21a.   These three forces, being in equilibrium, must intersect in one point D, and their free vectors must build a closed triangle abc as shown in Fig. 2.21b.   This done, a closed triangle of forces for each hinge can be superimposed directly on this triangle as shown. For example, the vectors $\overline{ab}$, $\overline{bd}$, and $\overline{da}$ directed in accordance with the arrows inside the $\triangle abd$ represent the forces that are in equilibrium at the hinge A. Similarly, $\triangle bcd$ and $\triangle cad$ with vectors directed in accordance with the inside arrows are closed triangles of forces for the hinges B and C, respectively.

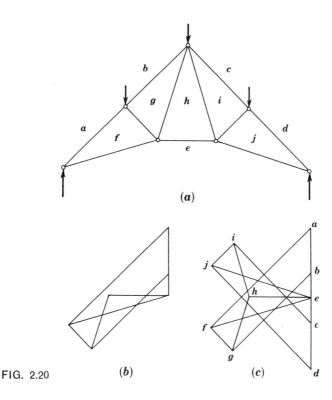

(a)

FIG. 2.20   (b)   (c)

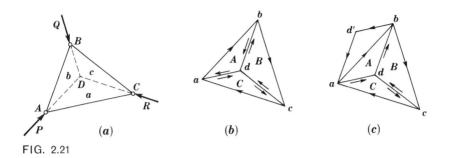

FIG. 2.21

Thus, in Fig. 2.21*b*, all triangles of forces are compactly superimposed, and no vector is duplicated. This will be possible only if each polygon of forces has its vectors assembled in the same order by which the forces that they represent are encountered in going around the corresponding hinge consistently in one direction (either clockwise or counterclockwise). We may note now that the basic triangle *abc* assembles the external forces in the order *PQR* obtained by going around the truss in a clockwise direction. Thus, in the construction of the remaining force polygons that are superimposed on the △*abc*, we must go around each hinge in a clockwise direction and take the forces in the order in which they are so encountered. Only by this consistent procedure can we avoid duplication of some vectors. For example, if we go clockwise around the hinges *B* and *C* but counterclockwise around the hinge *A*, we obtain the composite diagram shown in Fig. 2.21*c*, in which there is duplication of the vectors $\overline{bd}$ and $\overline{da}$.

A study of the diagrams in Fig. 2.21*a* and *b* shows that they bear a definite relationship to each other. In order to define this relationship between the two figures, let us visualize each one as the plane projection of a four-faced polyhedron. The polyhedron in Fig. 2.21*a*, for example, has the faces *ACD*, *ABD*, *BCD*, and *ABC*, which we designate, respectively, by the lowercase letters *a*, *b*, *c*, *d*, and the vertices *A*, *B*, *C*, *D*. Similarly, the polyhedron in Fig. 2.21*b* has the faces *abd*, *bcd*, *acd*, and *abc*, designated by *A*, *B*, *C*, *D*, and the vertices *a*, *b*, *c*, *d*. Thus, for each face of the polyhedron in Fig. 2.21*a*, there is a corresponding vertex to the one in Fig. 2.21*b*, for each vertex of the first, a corresponding face to the second, and their edges are mutually parallel and equal in number. Two such polyhedrons are said to be *reciprocal*, and the two plane figures representing their projections on a common plane are called *reciprocal figures*. It follows at once from such reciprocity that if forces represented in magnitude by the lines of one such plane figure are made to act between the extremities of the corresponding lines of the reciprocal figure, the points of the reciprocal figure will all be in equilibrium under the action of these forces. This follows from the fact that the forces meeting in any

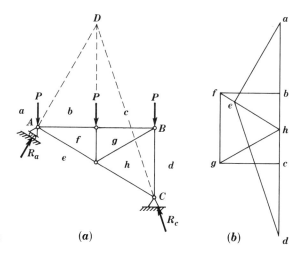

FIG. 2.22   (a)   (b)

one point of the second figure are proportional to the sides of a closed polygon in the first figure. This observation was made in 1864 by Clerk Maxwell in discussing the significance of reciprocal figures to problems of statics.[1] Because Maxwell was the first to point out the reciprocity between diagrams like those in Fig. 2.21, the composite vector diagram is called a *Maxwell diagram* for the truss. For the truss in Fig. 2.20a, the complete Maxwell diagram is shown in Fig. 2.20c. In a more complex case of this kind it is practically impossible to visualize the corresponding polyhedrons, but this is of no consequence so long as the two diagrams fulfill the requirements of reciprocal figures.

In the construction and use of Maxwell diagrams for the analysis of trusses, a system of notations called *Bow's notation* is convenient. In this system the spaces between the lines of action of the forces acting on the joints of the truss are given a lowercase letter. Then, any force is correspondingly designated by the letters of the two spaces separated by its line of action. Consider, for example, the simple truss supported and loaded as shown in Fig. 2.22a. In accordance with Bow's system, we letter the spaces between the five external forces a, b, c, d, e and those between the bars of the truss f, g, h, as shown. Thus, reading clockwise around the truss, we refer to the first load P on the left as $\overline{ab}$, the second as $\overline{bc}$, the external reaction at C as $\overline{de}$, etc. Likewise, the reaction of the vertical bar on the hinge C is $\overline{hd}$; that of the horizontal bar on the hinge A is $\overline{bf}$; etc.

We are now ready to consider the construction of a Maxwell diagram (Fig. 2.22b), which begins with a closed polygon *abcde* for the balanced system of forces external to the truss. With this basic polygon, the reciprocal diagram

[1] See Clerk Maxwell, On Reciprocal Figures and Diagrams of Forces, *Phil. Mag.*, vol. 26, p. 250, 1864.

is completed simply by drawing through each of its vertices lines parallel to all those which bound the corresponding space in the truss diagram. For example, through points b and e we draw horizontal and inclined lines parallel, respectively, to AB and AC of the truss. Since these two lines also help to bound space f, their intersection determines the vertex f of the reciprocal diagram. Then, through points f and c, we draw vertical and horizontal lines, respectively, and their intersection determines the vertex g of the diagram. Finally, through points g and e, we draw the inclined lines whose intersection h on the line ad determines the final vertex, and the diagram is completed. The reader will do well to identify in this diagram the separate polygon of forces for each hinge of the truss.

Bow's notation is particularly advantageous when we come to decide whether a given bar of the truss is in tension or in compression. Let us consider, for example, the force in the bar BC that is represented in magnitude by the length of the line hd in the Maxwell diagram. Going around the hinge B in a clockwise direction, the reaction that this bar exerts on the hinge will be read as dh. Now, in the Maxwell diagram, the vector $\overline{dh}$ is directed upward, indicating pressure on the hinge B, and we conclude that the bar BC is in compression. If, instead, we choose to consider the reaction of this same bar on the hinge C, reading clockwise around C, we have hd instead of dh, and in the Maxwell diagram the vector $\overline{hd}$ is directed downward, indicating pressure on C and consequently compression, as before.

PROBLEMS

1   Construct a Maxwell diagram for the truss shown in Fig. 2.23, and determine from it the axial force in each bar.
2   Construct a Maxwell diagram for the truss shown in Fig. 2.18, and determine from it the axial force in each bar.
3   Construct a Maxwell diagram for the truss shown in Fig. 2.24, and determine from it the axial force in each bar.
4   Construct a Maxwell diagram for the truss in Fig. 2.19, and determine from it the axial force in each bar.
5   Construct a Maxwell diagram for the truss shown in Fig. 2.25, and determine from it the axial force in each bar.

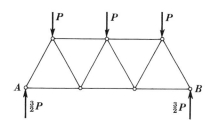

FIG. 2.23

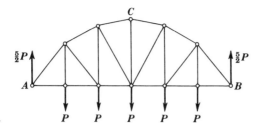

FIG. 2.24

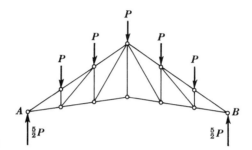

FIG. 2.25

2.5 METHOD OF SECTIONS

We shall now consider another method of analysis of trusses, the use of which makes it possible to determine the axial force in some chosen bar without going through successive considerations of the equilibrium of all hinges as was done in the two preceding articles. Referring to the truss shown in Fig. 2.26a, let us assume that it is required to determine the axial forces in the bars 10, 11, and 12, due to the loading shown. Instead of considering the equilibrium of the hinges A, H, B, I, C, and J in succession, as would be necessary by the method of joints, we imagine that a section mn cuts the truss into two parts and then consider the conditions of equilibrium of the part to the left of this section (Fig. 2.26b). Acting upon this free body we have the vertical reaction at A, three vertical loads P, and the three unknown forces S_{10}, S_{11}, and S_{12}, representing the axial forces in the bars that were cut by the section mn. The directions of these forces must, of course, coincide with the axes of the bars so that only their magnitudes remain unknown. Thus we obtain altogether a system of coplanar forces in equilibrium, and Eqs. (1.2) (page 11) can be employed to determine the magnitudes of the three unknown forces. For example, equating to zero the algebraic sum of moments of all forces with respect to point D, we obtain

$$-S_{10}h + Pa + P2a + P3a - \tfrac{7}{2}P3a = 0$$

from which $S_{10} = -9Pa/2h$. The negative sign, of course, indicates compression instead of tension as assumed. In a similar manner, by taking point J as a moment center, we find $S_{12} = +4Pa/h$. S_{11} can be evaluated most readily by equating to zero the algebraic sum of projections of all forces on a vertical axis. Thus, we obtain

$$\tfrac{7}{2}P - 3P - S_{11} \frac{h}{\sqrt{a^2 + h^2}} = 0$$

from which $S_{11} = +P\sqrt{a^2 + h^2}/2h$.

The foregoing procedure in the analysis of trusses is called the *method of sections*. It consists, essentially, in the isolation of a portion of the truss by a section so chosen as to cause those internal forces which we wish to evaluate to appear as external forces on the isolated free body. By this procedure, we usually obtain the general case of a coplanar system of forces in equilibrium, and Eqs. (1.2) can always be used in evaluating the unknowns as was done above. The success or failure of the method rests entirely upon the choice of section. In general, a section should cut only three bars, since only three unknowns can be determined from three equations of equilibrium. However, there are occasional exceptions to this rule, some of which are illustrated below.

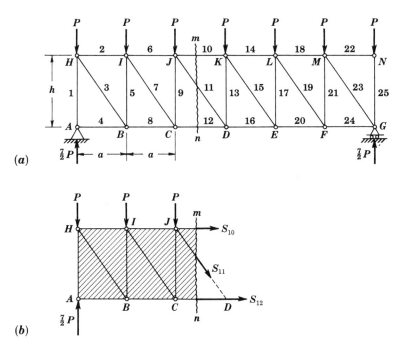

(a)

(b)

FIG. 2.26

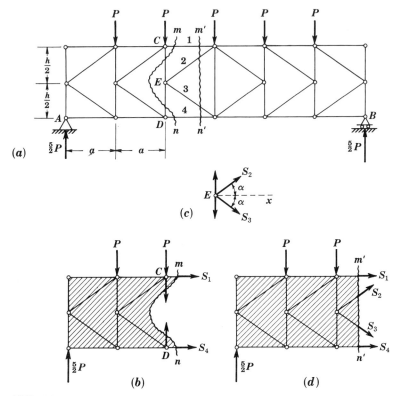

FIG. 2.27

Sometimes, in order to obtain the desired results, it may be necessary to make more than one section or to use the method of sections in conjunction with the method of joints. Suppose, for example, that it is required to find the axial force in each of the bars 1, 2, 3, 4 of the simple K truss shown in Fig. 2.27a. To accomplish this, we consider two sections and one joint as indicated by the free-body diagrams (b), (c), and (d). Beginning with Fig. 2.27b and using points D and C successively as moment centers, we obtain $S_1 = -4Pa/h$ and $S_4 = +4Pa/h$. Then, considering the equilibrium of the hinge E (Fig. 2.27c) and projecting all forces onto a horizontal x axis, we conclude that the forces in the bars 2 and 3 must be of equal magnitude but opposite sign, that is, $S_2 = -S_3$. Keeping this condition in mind and proceeding to Fig. 2.27d, we have only to project all forces onto a vertical axis to find $S_3 = -S_2 = \frac{1}{4}P \csc \alpha$.

It is sometimes advantageous to be able to employ the method of sections in a purely graphical manner; this can be done with very little trouble. By way of illustration, we take the truss shown in Fig. 2.28a and assume that we wish to evaluate graphically the axial forces in the bars 1, 2, and 3. Then as a first step we consider the equilibrium of the entire truss and make the polygon of forces (Fig. 2.28b) and the corresponding funicular polygon (Fig. 2.28c) from which we find the reactions at the supports A and B as shown. This done, we isolate that portion of the truss to the left of the section mn and consider its conditions of equilibrium. It will be remembered from the discussion of Art. 1.9 that the resultant of all external forces to the left of section mn is a vertical force R acting through the intersection q of the sides 3 and 9 of the funicular polygon as shown. This follows from the fact that the rays 9 and 3 in Fig. 2.28b are components of R and must intersect on its line of action. Since the internal forces S_1, S_2, and S_3 must hold the force R in equilibrium, we see that our problem is simply one of resolution of a given force R' (the equilibrant of R) into three components having specified lines of action (the axes of the bars 1, 2, and 3). This is a completely determinate problem and may be carried out graphically as follows: In Fig. 2.28a, we extend the line of action of S_1 to its intersection C with the resultant force R. At this point the equilibrant of R can be resolved into two components acting along the lines CD and CE, respectively, and having the magnitudes S_1 and Q as shown in Fig. 2.28d. Then, in turn, the force Q can be transmitted to point E and there resolved into components S_2 and S_3 coinciding with the axes of the bars 2 and 3. Finally, ignoring the force Q, we have in Fig. 2.28d the closed polygon of forces for that portion of the truss to the left of mn.

Sometimes the analysis of a truss can be made in a very simple manner by

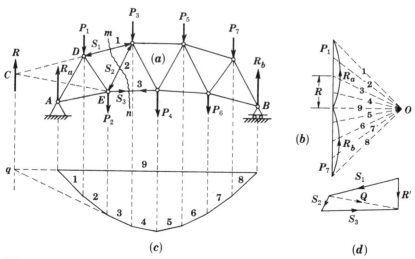

FIG. 2.28

considering it as a beam and using conventional bending-moment and shearing-force diagrams as discussed in Art. 1.4.   Consider, for example, the simple truss with parallel top and bottom chords loaded as shown in Fig. 2.29a. Making a vertical section mn and writing equations of equilibrium for that portion of the truss to the left of this section, we obtain

$$S_1 = -\frac{R_a 4a - P_1 2a}{h} \qquad (a)$$

$$S_2 = +\frac{R_a - P_1}{\sin \alpha} \qquad (b)$$

$$S_3 = +\frac{R_a 3a - P_1 a}{h} \qquad (c)$$

An examination of these equations now shows that the numerators represent, respectively, the bending moment at point E, the shearing force at the section mn, and the bending moment at point D, when we consider the truss as a beam. The corresponding axial forces S_1, S_2, and S_3 are seen to be proportional to these quantities.   Since similar conclusions may be reached for any section other than mn, we conclude that a bending-moment diagram and a shearing-force diagram are all that is needed for a complete analysis of the truss.

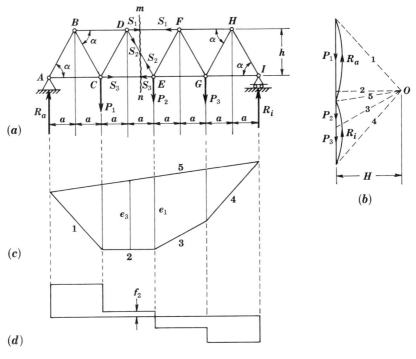

FIG. 2.29

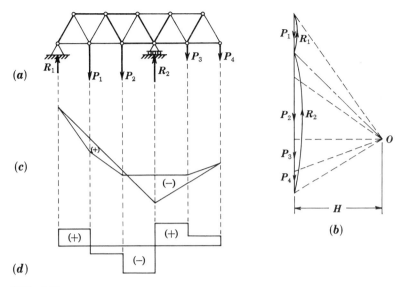

FIG. 2.30

In such cases it is expedient to work graphically. First we determine the reactions as shown in Fig. 2.29b, and thereby we obtain the desired bending-moment diagram as represented by the closed funicular polygon in Fig. 2.29c. A shearing-force diagram (Fig. 2.29d) can always be constructed without difficulty. As was shown in Art. 1.9, the bending moment for any point on the truss is obtained simply by multiplying the corresponding ordinate of the closed funicular polygon by the pole distance H. Thus, for example, the ordinate e_1 (Fig. 2.29c) when multiplied by H (Fig. 2.29b) gives the bending moment with respect to point E, that is, the numerator of expression (a). We conclude then that the force H when multiplied by the factor e_1/h gives directly the axial force S_1. Similarly, the force H multiplied by e_3/h gives the axial force S_3, etc. We obtain the force S_2 simply by multiplying the ordinate f_2 of the shearing-force diagram by the factor csc α.

The bending-moment and the shearing-force diagrams for a truss are sometimes helpful in distinguishing between tension and compression members. In general, for trusses with parallel chords, it may be observed that for positive bending moment, top chord members will be in compression and bottom chord members in tension, as the extreme fibers of a beam. For negative bending moment, these conditions are simply reversed. For positive shear, web members sloping down to the right will be in tension, and those sloping up to the right will be in compression. For negative shear, these conditions also are reversed. An example, illustrating the foregoing remarks, is shown in Fig. 2.30. Here compression members are shown by heavy lines and tension members by fine lines. With the aid of the bending-moment and shearing-

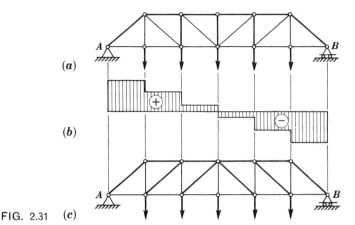

(a)

(b)

FIG. 2.31   (c)

force diagrams shown below the truss, the reader should verify these results for himself.

Another example is shown in Fig. 2.31. For a uniform loading of this truss, we see from the shearing-force diagram (Fig. 2.31b) that for the arrangement of web members shown in Fig. 2.31a, we shall have tension in each diagonal and compression in each vertical, whereas for the arrangement shown in Fig. 2.31c, these conditions will be reversed. For a steel truss, the arrangement in Fig. 2.31a is better because the short verticals can carry compression more efficiently than the longer diagonals, which may have a tendency to buckle. On the other hand, for a wooden truss, with respect to which the question of buckling is not likely to be significant, the arrangement of web members in Fig. 2.31c is ideal, especially if steel rods are used for the verticals.

PROBLEMS

1   Referring to Fig. 2.26 and using the method of sections, find the axial forces in the bars 2, 5, and 8. Assume $P = 10,000$ lb, $a = 9$ ft, $h = 12$ ft.
    Ans. $S_2 = -1.875P$, $S_5 = -2.5P$, $S_8 = +1.875P$.

2   Using the method of sections, compute the axial forces in the bars 1, 2, and 3 of the truss shown in Fig. 2.32.
    Ans. $S_1 = +2.25P$, $S_2 = -0.75P$, $S_3 = -2.25P$.

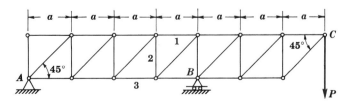

FIG. 2.32

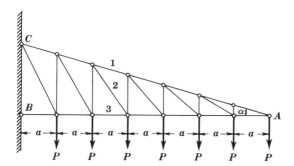

FIG. 2.33

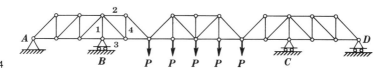

FIG. 2.34

3 Construct bending-moment and shearing-force diagrams for the truss in Fig. 2.32, and distinguish between tension and compression members accordingly.

4 Referring to Fig. 2.33, prove that the axial force in the nth vertical from the free end is $S_n = -[(n-1)/2]P$.

5 With the aid of bending-moment and shearing-force diagrams, distinguish between tension and compression members in the bridge loaded as shown in Fig. 2.34.

2.6 COMPOUND TRUSSES

In preceding articles we have considered only simple trusses formed in accordance with the rule given on page 53. Another kind of plane truss, called a *compound truss*, can be formed by interconnecting two or more simple trusses in accordance with the requirements for complete constraint of a rigid body in one plane (see page 58). The trusses in Fig. 2.35, for example, are of this kind. In Fig. 2.35a two simple trusses ADC and CEB (shaded in the figure) are hinged together at C and otherwise interconnected by the bar DE. Likewise, in Fig. 2.35b, the same two simple trusses are interconnected by three bars so arranged that their axes neither are parallel nor intersect in one point. Although such interconnection of two simple trusses always makes a rigid and statically determinate system, it frequently happens that such a truss cannot be completely analyzed by the method of joints alone.

Consider, for example, the compound truss shown in Fig. 2.36a, which consists of two shaded simple trusses hinged together at C and also connected by a bar DE. As a first step in the analysis of this truss, we determine the

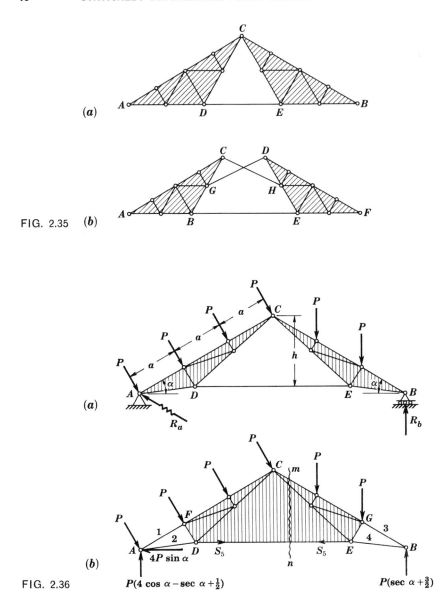

FIG. 2.35   (a)

(b)

FIG. 2.36   (a)

(b)

$P(4 \cos \alpha - \sec \alpha + \tfrac{1}{2})$ $P(\sec \alpha + \tfrac{3}{2})$

external reactions at A and B as shown in Fig. 2.36b.   This done, we can find the axial forces in the bars 1, 2, 3, 4 without difficulty by the method of joints, but beyond this no progress can be made by this method because there is no joint where we encounter less than three unknown internal forces.   Thus the shaded portion $DFCGE$ (Fig. 2.36b) does not lend itself to analysis by the method of joints, and to proceed further we must resort to the method of sections. Making a section mn as shown and considering the equilibrium of that portion of the truss to the right of this section, we take C as a moment center and write

$$(P \sec \alpha + \tfrac{3}{2}P)\,3a \cos \alpha - Pa \cos \alpha - 2Pa \cos \alpha - S_5 h = 0$$

from which $S_5 = +(3Pa/h)(1 + \tfrac{1}{2}\cos \alpha)$. As soon as S_5 is known, the analysis may be completed by the method of joints without further difficulty.

If we undertake to construct a Maxwell diagram for this truss loaded as shown in Fig. 2.37a, we shall, of course, encounter the same difficulty. As soon as the constructions indicated by heavy lines in Fig. 2.37c have been completed, we shall be unable to finish the reciprocal figure in the usual manner. Consequently, to proceed further, we introduce the section mn as

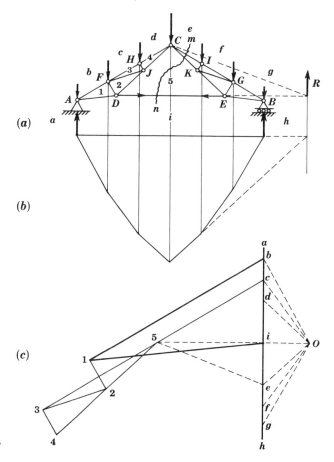

FIG. 2.37

shown and complete the polygon of forces $efghi5e$ for that portion of the truss to the right of this section.   These constructions, indicated by dashed lines, are carried out as explained in connection with Fig. 2.28 (see page 73) and serve to establish the apex 5 of the reciprocal diagram.   Point 5 having been established, the remainder of the diagram as indicated by fine lines can be constructed in the usual manner without further difficulty.

In Fig. 2.38a we have a compound truss for which the method of joints fails at the very beginning because there is no joint to which less than three bars are attached.   It also appears at first glance that there is no possibility of using the method of sections, since we cannot make any section that cuts only three bars that do not meet in one point.   However, if we note that the truss consists essentially of two triangles AEF and BCD, which are interconnected by three bars that neither are parallel nor intersect in one point, we see at once how to proceed with the analysis.   After the external reactions at A and B have been found as shown, we isolate the triangle BCD as shown in Fig. 2.38b.   In this way we obtain a statically determinate system of coplanar forces in equilibrium and by using Eqs. (1.2) (page 11) can find the three unknown forces S_1, S_2, and S_3 without difficulty.   As soon as these forces are known, the remainder of the analysis can be made by the method of joints.

Another method of forming a compound truss, different from those con-

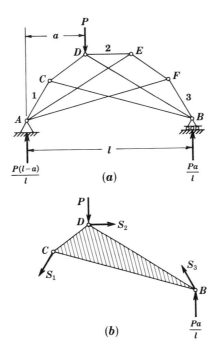

FIG. 2.38

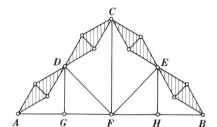

FIG. 2.39

sidered above, is illustrated in Fig. 2.39. Here we have several simple trusses (shaded in the figure) that together with single bars are arranged in accordance with the rule for assembling the bars of a simple truss. It is obvious that any such arrangement of bars and simple trusses must constitute a rigid and statically determinate system. However, such compound trusses usually require special methods of analysis. We have already seen that compound trusses like those in Fig. 2.35 cannot be completely analyzed by the method of joints alone but that it is necessary to employ also the method of sections. Similarly, for a compound truss like that shown in Fig. 2.39, it may happen that the method of joints and the method of sections, even when used in conjunction, will be inadequate for a complete analysis. A general method of analysis applicable to all such cases will now be considered.

Referring to Fig. 2.39, we note that the simple truss elements in this system really serve two functions. They act as single bars in the main truss, and at the same time they function as *secondary trusses* to transfer their own loads to the joints at their ends. By separating these two functions, we always can make a complete analysis of the system without difficulty. In Fig. 2.40a, for example, suppose that ADE is a portion of a truss that has within it a secondary truss CE as shown. In the analysis of this system, then, we first replace the secondary truss by a fictitious bar CE and the system of loads P_1, P_2, . . . acting upon it by a statically equivalent system consisting of two parallel forces R_1 and R_2 at C and E as shown in Fig. 2.40b.[1] These substitutions will not affect any of the bars outside the secondary truss, and we may now proceed with the analysis of the main truss by any of the methods already discussed, thereby obtaining the axial force S in the fictitious bar. Now, from a study of Fig. 2.40b, it is evident that the forces shown at the hinges C and E must represent completely the action of the secondary truss on the remainder of the system. Hence, by reversing these forces, we obtain the reactions for the secondary truss as shown in Fig. 2.40c and can now make a complete analysis of this system. If there are other secondary trusses within the main truss, they may be handled in the same manner.

---

[1] Any coplanar system of forces can always be resolved into two parallel components applied at two given points in their plane of action.

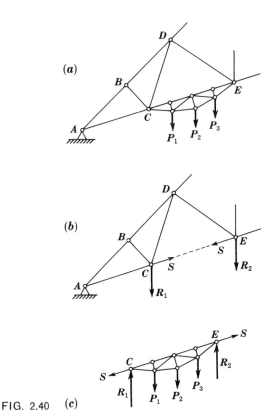

FIG. 2.40   (c)

A specific application of the foregoing procedure is illustrated in Fig. 2.41, in which we have a roof truss with secondary trusses for top chord members. We begin the analysis by replacing the actual system of loads (Fig. 2.41a) by the statically equivalent system shown in Fig. 2.41b. This leaves the secondary trusses free from all loads so that they function simply as single bars, and we obtain a simple truss as shown. A Maxwell diagram for this system, from which the axial forces in all major members can be scaled, is shown in Fig. 2.41c. Thus we are ready to consider the secondary trusses. Taking AF as a typical example, we see that the external forces can be broken down into two balanced systems, (1) the loads P together with their vertical reactions at A and F and (2) the equal, opposite, and collinear forces S_1 found from the Maxwell diagram in Fig. 2.41c. Under the action of this latter system, only the top chord members will be active, and we already have the corresponding axial force in this chord from Fig. 2.41c. Hence, in the remaining analysis of the secondary truss, we ignore the forces S_1 and make a Maxwell diagram for the vertical loading only, as shown in Fig. 2.41e. To obtain the total force in any bar of the compound truss (Fig. 2.41*a*), we simply superimpose the results from the two separate Maxwell diagrams.

The foregoing method of analysis of a compound truss is sometimes useful even in cases where it is not strictly necessary. Consider, for example, the truss shown in Fig. 2.42*a*. Although not necessary in this case, the notion of secondary-truss action can be used to advantage. Proceeding on this basis, we regard *ABC*, loaded as shown in Fig. 2.42*b*, as the basic truss. Super-

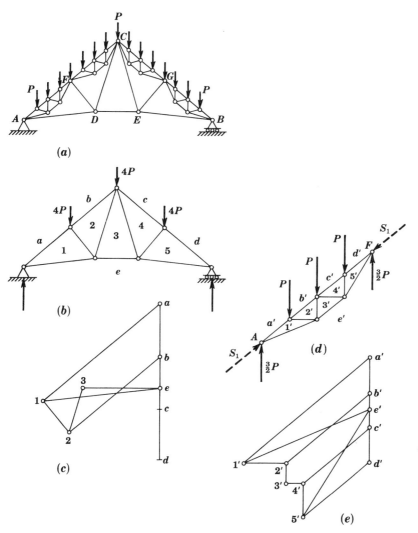

(a)

(b)

(c)

(d)

(e)

FIG. 2.41

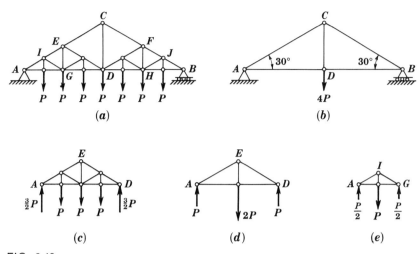

FIG. 2.42

imposed upon this are the two secondary trusses ADE and BFD, loaded as shown in Fig. 2.42c. Each of these secondary trusses again can be regarded as consisting of a main truss ADE (Fig. 2.42d) that has within it two smaller trusses as shown in Fig. 2.42e. Finally, then, by making a simple analysis by inspection of each of the trusses in (b), (d), and (e) and superimposing the results, we obtain a complete analysis of the compound truss in (a).

PROBLEMS

1   Make a complete analysis of the compound truss shown in Fig. 2.43. The triangles ABC and DEF are equilateral.

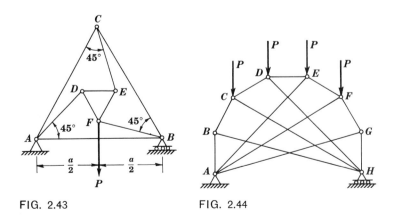

FIG. 2.43   FIG. 2.44

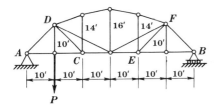

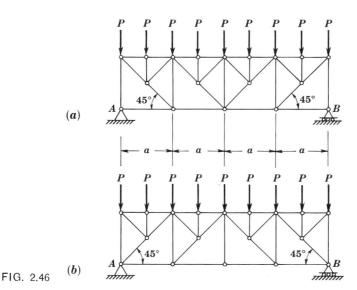

FIG. 2.45

(a)

(b)

FIG. 2.46

2 Make a complete analysis of the compound truss shown in Fig. 2.44. *ABCDEFGH* is a portion of a regular duodecagon.
3 Make a complete analysis of the compound truss shown in Fig. 2.45. Assume $P = 10$ kips.
4 Make a complete analysis of the compound truss shown in Fig. 2.46*a*, and compare with that in Fig. 2.46*b*.
5 Make a complete analysis of the compound truss shown in Fig. 2.46*b*, and compare with that in Fig. 2.46*a*.

2.7 GENERAL THEORY OF PLANE TRUSSES

We return now to the general problem of assembling a system of bars in one plane so as to form a rigid truss. In Art. 2.1 we have already seen that this can be done in two ways. In one case we begin with three bars pinned together at their ends in the form of a triangle and attach each joint thereafter by means of two additional bars. By this procedure we obtain a simple truss

(Fig. 2.3a) for which there will always exist, between the number of members m and the number of joints j, the relationship

$$m = 2j - 3 \qquad (2.1a)$$

The rigidity of such a truss is, of course, entirely independent of any attachment to a foundation. In the other case, we begin directly with a foundation and establish each joint by means of two intersecting bars as shown in Fig. 2.3b. In this way, we obtain a simple truss the rigidity of which depends on its interconnection with points of the foundation and for which, instead of Eq. (2.1a), we have

$$m = 2j \qquad (2.1b)$$

As we have already seen in Art. 2.2 any simple truss of the first kind requires, for the completion of its constraint in one plane, three additional bars or their equivalent, whereas for any simple truss of the second kind the constraint is already complete. Thus, in either case we come finally to the same conclusion: namely, for the complete constraint of j pins in one plane we must interconnect them between themselves and the foundation by $m = 2j$ bars or equivalent constraints.

A great variety of plane trusses satisfying the foregoing general requirement of rigidity can be obtained by variously rearranging the bars of a simple truss

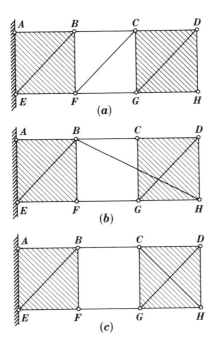

FIG. 2.47

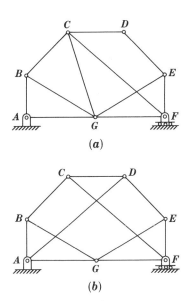

FIG. 2.48

(a)

(b)

in such a way that neither the total number of bars nor the total number of joints is changed. Consider, for example, the simple truss shown in Fig. 2.47a. Regarding this as a system of two simple trusses that are interconnected by three bars that neither are parallel nor intersect in one point, we conclude that we can substitute for the bar CF a bar BH and obtain the rigid truss shown in Fig. 2.47b. By this substitution we change neither the number of bars nor the number of joints, but we now have a compound truss instead of a simple truss.

As a second example, consider the simple truss shown in Fig. 2.48a. Replacing the bar CG by a bar AD, we obtain the truss shown in Fig. 2.48b. This arrangement of bars and external constraints still satisfies the relationship $m = 2j$ but otherwise fails to fulfill either the definition of a simple truss or that of a compound truss. Such a system is called a *complex truss*.

It must not be concluded from the foregoing discussion that we can indiscriminately interconnect $2j$ bars with j joints and expect to obtain a rigid system. That is, the condition $m = 2j$ is not alone a complete criterion of rigidity. Consider again, for example, the simple truss shown in Fig. 2.47a. If we remove the diagonal FC from the middle panel, we destroy the rigidity of the system and introduce the possibility of relative translation between the two rigid shaded portions. A bar BH as shown in Fig. 2.47b prevents such distortion and is therefore a legitimate substitute for the bar FC. In fact, as already noted, we now have a compound truss. On the other hand, if we replace the bar FC by a second diagonal CH in the end panel, as shown in Fig. 2.47c, we do not restore the rigidity of the truss; there is still the same freedom for relative translation between the two shaded portions.   Thus, notwithstanding the fact that $m = 2j$, the system in Fig. 2.47c is not a rigid one. Accordingly, we conclude that we must modify our criterion of rigidity and say that $2j$ bars are necessary and, *when properly arranged*, sufficient for the rigid interconnection between themselves and the foundation of j joints in one plane.

We shall now consider a further significance of the relationship $m = 2j$. In Fig. 2.49, we take any completely constrained plane truss (simple, compound, or complex) comprised of m bars and j joints and load it in its own plane and at the joints only as shown.   Then, to make a complete analysis of the truss, we must determine the axial force in each of the m bars.   Replacing each bar by the two equal but opposite reactions that it exerts on the pins at its ends, we obtain j systems of concurrent coplanar forces for each of which there exist two conditions of equilibrium [Eqs. (1.1), page 3].   Hence, we have altogether $2j$ simultaneous equations involving m unknown axial forces; and we see that, if $m = 2j$, there are exactly as many unknowns as there are equations of statics.   Thus, in all but exceptional cases, to be considered later, these equations give a definite solution to the problem.   For this reason any completely constrained plane truss that satisfies the condition $m = 2j$ is said to be *statically determinate*.   That is, the axial forces in the bars can be found from equations of statics alone; it is unnecessary to take account of the elastic deformations throughout the system.   Consider, for example, the system shown in Fig. 2.50a, for which $m = 2j$.   Under the action of a load P applied as shown, we see that the bars AC and AD are inactive, while BC and BD carry, respectively, tension and compression the magnitudes of which can be found from statical considerations of the hinge B.   Owing to these internal forces, BC will be slightly elongated, while BD will be shortened; consequently, the joint B moves slightly downward and to the right, while the joint A remains stationary.   Thus, the distance AB is greater after loading than before; but this small elastic distortion of the system does not affect the internal forces, and we need take no account of it.

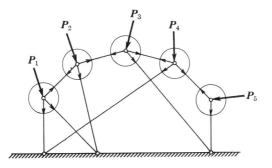

FIG. 2.49

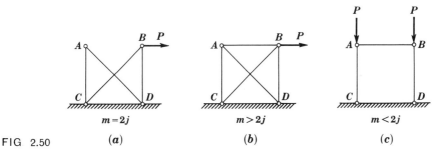

FIG 2.50   (a)   (b)   (c)

If $m > 2j$, there will, of course, be more unknown axial forces than there are independent equations of statics, and these equations fail to yield a unique solution.   Accordingly, the truss is said to be *statically indeterminate*.   Such a case is shown in Fig. 2.50b, which is identical with Fig. 2.50a except for the extra bar AB.   In this case, owing to the presence of the bar AB, the joint B cannot move relative to the joint A, as before, without stretching the bar AB and thus inducing some movement of A, also.   Thus, part of the load P will be transmitted to the joint A, and the bars AC and AD also become active. The way in which P is divided between B and A in this case depends on the relative rigidities of the bars.   For example if AB is very flexible in comparison with the other four bars, most of the load will be carried at B; in the extreme case where AB has no rigidity, all the load is carried at B as in Fig. 2.50a. On the other hand, if AB is relatively very rigid, it will remain practically constant in length, and A and B will have to move about the same amount. Accordingly, the load will be about equally divided between these two joints. Thus, we see that when a truss is statically indeterminate $(m > 2j)$, the distribution of internal forces depends on the elastic deformations throughout the system, and, to make an analysis, these deformations must be taken into account.[1]

If $m < 2j$ (Fig. 2.50c), the system is not rigid and can be in equilibrium only under certain conditions of external loading.   That is, since there are more equations of statics than unknown axial forces, it follows that these equations will determine the unknowns and, in addition, impose certain limitations on the system of external loads.   In Fig. 2.50c, for example, we can have equilibrium for vertical loads as shown, but any lateral loads will cause the frame to collapse.

In following the various rules of formation of plane trusses, already discussed, there is always the possibility of accidentally obtaining a so-called *critical form*, i.e., a certain configuration of the truss that is nonrigid, whereas

[1] Various methods of analysis of statically indeterminate trusses will be discussed in Chap. 7.

adjacent configurations are rigid. Sometimes these critical forms are self-evident; sometimes they are not. We consider first the obvious example of a critical form of the simple truss shown in Fig. 2.51. The configurations (*a*) and (*c*) of this truss are completely rigid, but between them lies the possibility of the critical form (*b*). Here the bars *CE* and *DE* are collinear, and appreciable movement of the joint *E* relative to the other joints can result from the most minute changes in the lengths of the bars or from slight play in the hinges. In short, such a truss is not completely rigid. In the same way, the compound truss shown in Fig. 2.52*a* has a critical form when the bars 1, 2, and 3 are parallel as shown in Fig. 2.52*b* or intersect in one point as shown in Fig. 2.52*c*. In each of these latter cases, there is a limited freedom for relative lateral translation between the two shaded portions, and we must regard them as nonrigid forms. Such critical forms in the case of a compound truss are, of course, completely similar to the incompletely rigid systems of support illustrated in Fig. 2.10.

Another peculiarity of the critical form is that it is always statically indeterminate notwithstanding the fact that the condition $m = 2j$ is satisfied. Consider, for example, the critical form of simple truss shown in Fig. 2.51*b*. Loaded as shown in Fig. 2.53*a*, this system behaves as the truss in Fig. 2.50*b*, and we conclude accordingly that it is statically indeterminate. That is, the portion of the load *P* that is transmitted to *CD* (which functions as one bar in this case) depends on the relative elastic deformations of the bars. When loaded as shown in Fig. 2.53*b*, we see, by making a free body of the hinge *E*, that the bars *CE* and *DE* must carry infinite tensions in order to balance the vertical component of the external force *P*; and this, of course, is

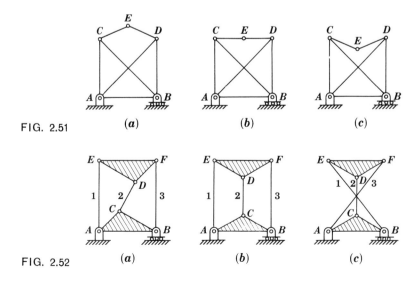

FIG. 2.51   (*a*)   (*b*)   (*c*)

FIG. 2.52   (*a*)   (*b*)   (*c*)

physically impossible.   Actually, upon application of the load P, all bars of the system will deform slightly, allowing the hinge E to assume an appreciably lower position whereby CE and DE become sufficiently inclined to balance the load P with finite tensions.   However, these elongations and consequently the final configuration of equilibrium of the system depend on the elastic deformations of the bars, and these deformations must be taken into account in the analysis of the truss.   Thus, again, the truss is statically indeterminate.

In the more general case of a complex truss, it is not always possible to detect a critical form by inspection.   The complex truss in Fig. 2.54b, for example, has a critical form, whereas the one in Fig. 2.54a has not.   In such cases a general method of detecting a critical form of truss can be based on a consideration of the *determinant* of the system of 2j equations of equilibrium for its j joints.   If this determinant is different from zero, the equations yield a unique solution: namely, there is one and only one set of values for the axial forces that can satisfy the conditions of equilibrium at each joint, and the truss is rigid and statically determinate.   On the other hand, if the determinant happens to be zero, the equations of equilibrium fail to yield a unique solution, and this will always be an indication that the truss has a critical form.   This suggests, then, a convenient method of testing for critical form, generally known as the *zero-load test*.   With no loads on the truss, we see at once that one possible solution satisfying the conditions of equilibrium at each joint will be obtained by assuming all bars to be inactive, i.e., with zero axial force.   Hence, if under the same condition of loading we can find another set of values different from zero that also satisfy the conditions of equilibrium at each joint, we shall know that the truss has a critical form.

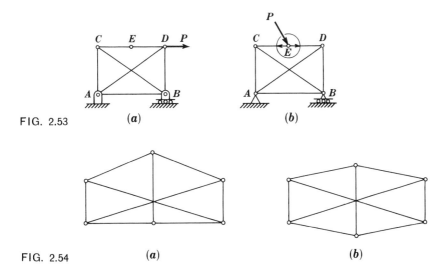

FIG. 2.53   (*a*)   (*b*)

FIG. 2.54   (*a*)   (*b*)

Consider, for example, the truss in Fig. 2.51*b*. With no external forces at the joints, we assume a tension S in the bar CE and an equal tension in the bar DE. Then, with the same tension S in each of the bars AC, BD, and AB and with a compression $\sqrt{2}\,S$ in each of the diagonal bars, we can satisfy the conditions of equilibrium at all joints. Thus, under zero load, we may have forces in the bars different from zero, and this indicates that the truss has a critical form. Since the determinant mentioned above depends only on the configuration of the truss and not at all on how it is loaded, we conclude that a truss of critical form will always be statically indeterminate regardless of how it may be loaded.

PROBLEMS

1   The plane truss in Fig. 2.55 has one redundant member; that is, $m = 2j - 3 + 1$. If BE is removed, we shall have a simple truss. What kind of truss shall we have if AB is removed: CD, BD, etc., for each bar in turn?

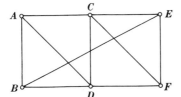

FIG. 2.55

2   Using the zero-load test, prove that the complex truss in Fig. 2.48*b* is statically determinate.
3   Test each of the compound trusses in Fig. 2.52 for critical form by the method of zero loads.
4   Apply the zero-load test to each of the complex trusses shown in Fig. 2.54, and prove that (*b*) has a critical form while (*a*) has not.

2.8 COMPLEX TRUSSES: HENNEBERG'S METHOD

In previous articles, we have considered the analysis of simple and compound trusses by the method of joints and the method of sections. These are very useful methods of analysis for trusses and are applicable in the majority of practical cases. However, in the case of a complex truss, it usually happens that these elementary methods of analysis are not directly applicable. In such cases, of course, we can always proceed with the solution of $2j$ simultaneous equations of equilibrium for the j joints of the system, but this will

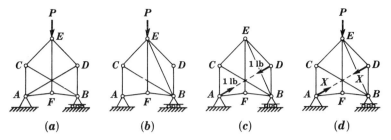

FIG. 2.56

usually prove highly impracticable. The first workable method of analysis for complex trusses was developed by Henneberg[1] and will now be explained.

As a specific example, let us consider the complex truss supported and loaded as shown in Fig. 2.56a. We note at once that, the reactions at A and B having been found, no further progress with the analysis can be made by either the method of joints or the method of sections. We observe, however, that by substituting for the bar AD a bar BE, we obtain a simple truss as shown in Fig. 2.56b. A complete analysis of this simple truss under any given condition of loading can be made by the method of joints. Let us assume, then, that this simple truss, corresponding to the given complex truss, has been completely analyzed for two particular conditions of loading, as follows: (1) the same loading as that on the given complex truss (Fig. 2.56b) and (2) two equal and opposite unit forces acting between A and D (Fig. 2.56c). Let S_i' denote the axial force in any bar of the simple truss due to the loading of the first case (Fig. 2.56b) and s_i' the corresponding axial force due to the loading of the second case (Fig. 2.56c). In the second case, if we have forces of magnitude X instead of unit forces, it is obvious that the axial force in any bar will be simply $s_i' X$ instead of s_i'. Finally, then, by superposition of these two cases, we conclude that for the combined loading shown in Fig. 2.56d the axial force in any bar of the truss will be

$$S_i = S_i' + s_i' X \tag{a}$$

and that in the particular case of the substituted bar BE, for which we shall use the subscript a, it will be

$$S_a = S_a' + s_a' X \tag{b}$$

Now, if we choose X of such magnitude that S_a from Eq. (b) becomes zero, the substituted bar BE becomes inactive and may be removed, and the truss in Fig. 2.56d is then identical with the given truss (Fig. 2.56a) except that the

[1] See L. Henneberg, "Statik der Starren Systeme," Bergsträsser, Darmstadt, Germany, 1886.

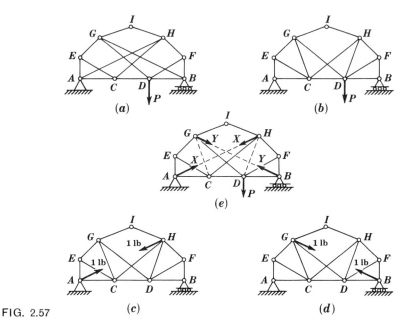

FIG. 2.57

action of the bar AD on the rest of the system is replaced by the forces X. Hence, we conclude that that value of X which makes S_a equal to zero in Eq. (b) represents the true axial force in the bar AD. Proceeding in this manner, we write

$$S_a' + s_a' X = 0 \tag{c}$$

from which

$$X = -\frac{S_a'}{s_a'} \tag{d}$$

With the value of X from Eq. (d), the force in any other bar of the given complex truss can be found by using Eq. (a).

A similar procedure may be used in the analysis of a complex truss like that in Fig. 2.57a, where, to arrive at a simple truss, it is necessary to replace two bars AH and BG by fictitious bars GC and HD, respectively, as shown in Fig. 2.57b. Considering three conditions of loading of this simple truss as shown in (b), (c), and (d), we can find the corresponding axial forces S_i', s_i', and s_i'' in each bar of the truss without difficulty by the method of joints. Denoting, then, by X and Y the unknown forces in the bars AH and BG, respectively, of the given complex truss and using the idea of superposition, we find for the axial force in any bar of the fictitious truss loaded as shown in Fig. 2.57*e* the following:

$$S_i = S_i' + s_i' X + s_i'' Y \tag{e}$$

For the fictitious bars *GC* and *HD*, denoted, respectively, by the subscripts *a* and *b*, we have

$$S_a = S_a' + s_a' X + s_a'' Y$$
$$S_b = S_b' + s_b' X + s_b'' Y \tag{f}$$

Setting these values of S_a and S_b equal to zero, as before, in order to realize by the superimposed systems the case of the given complex truss, we obtain

$$X = \frac{s_b'' S_a' - s_a'' S_b'}{s_b' s_a'' - s_a' s_b''}$$
$$Y = \frac{s_b' S_a' - s_a' S_b'}{s_a' s_b'' - s_b' s_a''} \tag{g}$$

As soon as the values of X and Y have been found from Eqs. (*g*), the axial force in any bar of the complex truss is found from Eq. (*e*).

In the case of a complex truss of critical form we shall find that the denominator of expression (*d*) or of expressions (*g*) becomes zero. This, of course, indicates that the system is statically indeterminate.

As a specific application of the Henneberg method, let us consider now a complete analysis of the complex truss in Fig. 2.58*a*. Assuming $P = 1{,}000$ lb, $a = 5$ ft, $h = 9$ ft, we begin with the corresponding simple truss and make a complete analysis (1) for the loading shown in Fig. 2.58*b* and (2) for the unit forces acting along the line *AD* in Fig. 2.58*c*. These analyses can readily be made by the method of joints, and the results are recorded in columns 2 and 3, respectively, of Table 2.1.

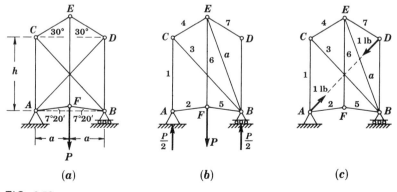

FIG. 2.58

TABLE 2.1

Bar (1)	S_i' (2)	s_i' (3)	$s_i'X$ (4)	S_i (5)
1	-500	-0.574	-546	$-1,046$
2	0	-0.749	-714	-714
3	$+455$	$+0.522$	$+498$	$+953$
4	-391	-0.488	-427	-818
5	0	-0.749	-714	-714
6	$+1,000$	-0.191	-182	$+818$
7	0	-0.858	-818	-818
8	0	-1.098	$-1,046$	$-1,046$
a	-872	$+0.915$	$+872$	0

Using the values of S_a' and s_a' in Eq. (d), we find

$$X = -\frac{-872}{+0.915} = +953 \text{ lb}$$

Having the value of X, we may now fill in column 4 of the table, and then from Eq. (a) the axial force for each bar of the given truss may be calculated and recorded in column 5. It will be noted that we obtain zero for the force in the fictitious bar a, which serves as a partial check on the calculations.   In this particular case, we obtain a further check by observing that the results in column 5 satisfy the conditions of symmetry in Fig. 2.58a.

PROBLEMS

1 Determine the axial forces in the bars of the complex truss supported and loaded as shown in Fig. 2.59.   Each inclined bar makes an angle of 30° with the horizontal.
2 Using Henneberg's method, make a complete analysis of the complex truss supported and loaded as shown in Fig. 2.60.

Hint   Only the portion *CDEF* of this truss is of complex form.

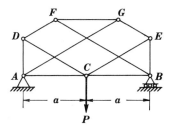

FIG. 2.59

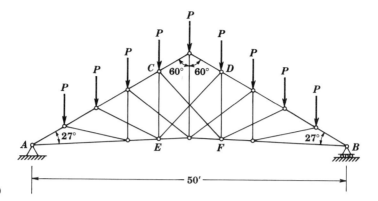

FIG. 2.60

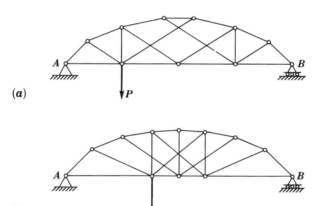

(a)

(b)

FIG. 2.61

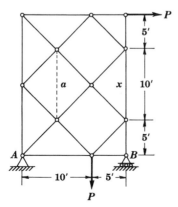

FIG. 2.62

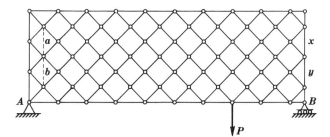

FIG. 2.63

3 Using Maxwell diagrams in conjunction with Henneberg's method, make a complete analysis of each of the complex trusses supported and loaded as shown in Fig. 2.61.
4 Make a complete analysis of the complex truss supported and loaded as shown in Fig. 2.62. To reduce this system to a simple truss, remove the bar x and substitute a bar a as indicated by the dashed line.
5 Make a complete analysis of the lattice truss supported and loaded as shown in Fig. 2.63. All diagonals are inclined at 45° with the horizontal, and the small subdivisions are squares.

> *Hint*   To reduce this truss to a simple truss, it is necessary to remove the bars x and y and add the bars a and b.

2.9 METHOD OF VIRTUAL DISPLACEMENTS

In many cases, the principle of virtual displacements, as discussed in Art. 1.10, can be used to advantage in the analysis of statically determinate trusses. To find the axial force in a given bar of a truss by this method, we imagine that bar to be removed and its action on the rest of the truss represented by two equal and opposite forces S. In this way, we obtain a nonrigid system with one degree of freedom to which the principle of virtual displacements can be applied.[1]

As a first example, consider the simple truss shown in Fig. 2.64a, and let it be required to find the axial force in the bar AD. Replacing this bar by collinear forces S at A and D, we obtain a nonrigid system with one degree of freedom as shown in Fig. 2.64b. A virtual displacement of this system can be defined by an infinitesimal horizontal displacement δ of the upper portion of the truss. We see from the figure that under this displacement each of the applied loads P_1, P_2, P_3, . . . produces a work $P_i \delta$, while the force S at D

---

[1] The use of the principle of virtual displacements in the analysis of trusses was introduced by Otto Mohr. See his papers, Beiträge zur Theorie des Fachwerks, *Z. Architekten-Ingr. Ver. Hannover*, 1874, p. 509, and 1875, p. 17; also Beitrag zur Theorie des Fachwerks, *Zivilingenieur*, 1885, p. 289.

produces a work $-S \delta \cos \alpha$. The force S at A produces no work because its point of application does not move. Thus, the equation of virtual work for the system becomes

$$(P_1 + P_2 + P_3) \delta - S \delta \cos \alpha = 0 \qquad (a)$$

from which we find $S = (P_1 + P_2 + P_3) \sec \alpha$.

To obtain the force S in the vertical bar FD, we proceed in a similar manner, replace this bar by collinear forces S at D and F, and obtain the nonrigid system shown in Fig. 2.64c. In this case, a virtual displacement of the system is best defined by the infinitesimal angle of rotation $\delta\theta$ of the upper portion of the truss as shown. The corresponding displacements of points G, E, and F, respectively, are $2h \ \delta\theta$, $h \ \delta\theta$, and $a \ \delta\theta$, and the equation of virtual work becomes

$$P_1 2h \ \delta\theta + P_2 h \ \delta\theta + Sa \ \delta\theta = 0 \qquad (b)$$

from which $S = -(h/a)(2P_1 + P_2)$.

From the preceding examples, we see that, in general, the determination of the axial force in any one bar of a truss by the method of virtual work necessitates the evaluation of the virtual displacements of the points of application of all active forces. If there are forces at almost every joint of the truss, the amount of calculation required to determine analytically all necessary virtual displacements may be considerable. In such cases, displacement diagrams as discussed in Art. 1.10 will be found helpful.

While there is usually little advantage in employing the method of virtual work in the analysis of simple or compound trusses, it is often valuable in the case of a complex truss. By way of illustration, let us consider the complex truss shown in Fig. 2.65a. If we succeed in finding the force in any one bar of this truss by the method of virtual work, the remainder of the analysis can be made without difficulty by the method of joints. In this case, we select the bar FC, replace it by collinear forces S at F and C, and obtain the nonrigid

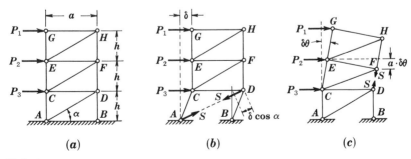

(a)   (b)   (c)

FIG. 2.64

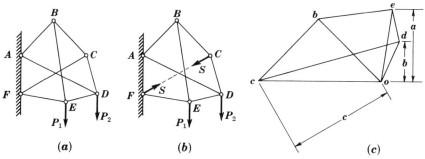

(a)   (b)   (c)

FIG. 2.65

system shown in Fig. 2.65*b*. A displacement diagram for this system (constructed as explained in Art. 1.10) is shown in Fig. 2.65*c*. Using the displacements $\overline{oe}$, $\overline{oc}$, $\overline{od}$, or rather their projections c, a, b (Fig. 2.65*c*) on the corresponding forces S, P_1, P_2 (Fig. 2.65*b*), we obtain the equation of virtual work,

$$Sc - P_1a - P_2b = 0$$

from which

$$S = \frac{P_1a + P_2b}{c}$$

The displacement diagram must, of course, be constructed to scale and the distances a, b, and c measured from it.

Besides displacement diagrams of the kind shown in Fig. 2.65*c*, there is another graphical method for determining a set of compatible displacements for the hinges of a truss from which one bar has been removed. To demonstrate this method, we consider first the simple example in Fig. 2.66. Here we have a rigid triangle *ABC* supported by two hinged bars so that the system

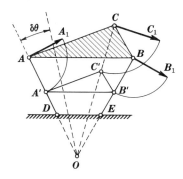

FIG. 2.66

has one degree of freedom.   In such a case, a virtual displacement of the system can be defined by an infinitesimal angular displacement $\delta\theta$ around the instantaneous center O.   The corresponding linear displacements $\overline{AA_1}$, $\overline{BB_1}$, and $\overline{CC_1}$ of the hinges A, B, and C are proportional to the radii OA, OB, and OC and perpendicular to them, respectively, as shown.   If we rotate each of these displacement vectors clockwise by $90°$, we obtain the points A', B', and C' on the corresponding radii as shown.   The figure $A'B'C'$, so obtained, is geometrically similar to the figure ABC, since by virtue of the ratios $AA':BB':CC' = OA:OB:OC$, corresponding sides of the two figures are parallel.   This conclusion holds for the virtual displacement of any rigid plane figure with one degree of freedom.   Reversing the above procedure, we conclude that a set of compatible virtual displacements for the joints of any rigid plane system having one degree of freedom can be obtained by assuming the magnitude of the displacement of one joint and then constructing the proper similar figure like $A'B'C'$ in Fig. 2.66.

Take, for example, the simple truss already considered in Fig. 2.64, and suppose that the vertical bar BD is removed as shown in Fig. 2.67a.   In such a case the truss can rotate around the hinge A, and we can define a virtual displacement of the system by any arbitrary linear displacement δs_d of the hinge D normal to AD.   Rotating this displacement vector clockwise by $90°$, we obtain the point D' on the line AD.   Corresponding displacements of the other joints are now obtained simply by constructing on AD' the figure $AD'C'F'E'H'G'$ with its sides parallel, respectively, to those of the given truss. Thus, GG' represents in magnitude the displacement of point G, HH' that of point H, etc.   If the bar AD of the truss is removed (Fig. 2.67b), the virtual displacement of the system is defined by an arbitrary horizontal displacement δs_d of point D; and, proceeding as before, we obtain the similar figure $ABC'D'E'F'G'H'$ as shown.

The foregoing procedure can be applied also in the case of a complex truss.

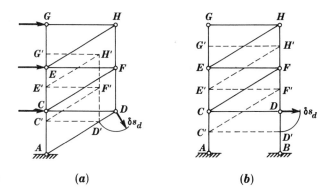

FIG. 2.67   **(a)**   **(b)**

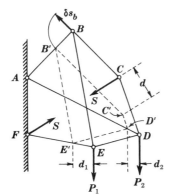

FIG. 2.68

For the truss shown in Fig. 2.65b, for example, we can define a virtual displacement of the system by an arbitrary linear displacement δs_b at right angles to AB as shown in Fig. 2.68. Rotating this displacement vector by 90°, we obtain the point B' on the line AB. BE being a rigid body, the corresponding displacement of E, as defined by EE', will be obtained by drawing the dashed line $B'E'$ parallel to BE. Then, having the displacement of E corresponding to the assumed displacement of B, we obtain the corresponding displacement of D, as defined by DD', by drawing $E'D'$ parallel to ED, since ED also is a rigid body. Finally, the displacement of C, as represented by CC', is found by drawing $B'C'$ and $D'C'$ parallel, respectively, to BC and DC.

Having compatible displacements for all joints of the truss, the unknown force S can now be found by writing the equation of virtual work for the system as before. In this case, however, it can be noted from the figure that since the displacements have all been rotated by 90° from their true directions, the corresponding works of the various forces acting on the joints can be obtained by taking their moments with respect to the points E', D', C'. Thus, for example, the work of the force P_1 on the true displacement of the joint E is identical with the moment of P_1, with respect to point E', etc. Upon using this conclusion, we obtain the equation for determining S:

$$-\Sigma P_i d_i + Sd = 0 \qquad (c)$$

from which

$$S = \frac{\Sigma P_i d_i}{d} \qquad (d)$$

It should be noted that the value of S as given by Eq. (d) is not changed if all the distances such as BB', EE', ... are decreased or increased in the same proportion. Thus, any figure $AB'C'D'E'F$ with sides parallel to those of the figure $ABCDEF$ can be used in writing Eq. (c) above.

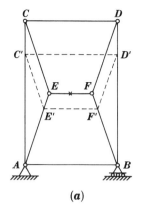 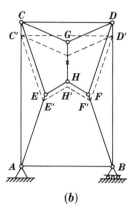

FIG. 2.69   (a)   (b)

The graphical constructions illustrated in Fig. 2.68 are also helpful in detecting a critical form of complex truss. Referring to Eq. (d), we see that the truss of Fig. 2.68 can have an indeterminate form only if the distance d is zero, i.e., if the line FC' coincides with the line FC. We can generalize this observation as follows: If, upon removal of one bar of a complex truss, a figure such as $AB'C'D'E'F$ (Fig. 2.68), defining compatible virtual displacements of the joints of the remaining system, has all its sides (including the one corresponding to the removal bar) parallel to those of the given figure, then the truss has a critical form and is statically indeterminate. Two such examples are shown in Fig. 2.69.

PROBLEMS

1 Using the method of virtual displacements, find the axial force S_x in the bar x of the complex truss supported and loaded as shown in Fig. 2.70.
    Ans. $X = 0$.

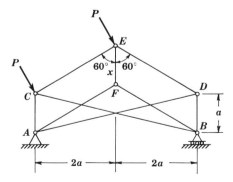

FIG. 2.70

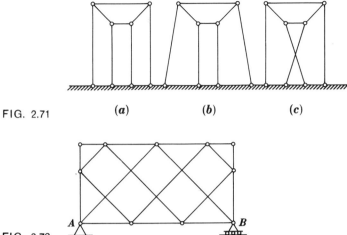

FIG. 2.71   **(a)**   **(b)**   **(c)**

FIG. 2.72

2 Using the method of virtual displacements, prove that the complex truss in Fig. 2.54a is completely rigid, while the one in Fig. 2.54b is not.

3 Test each of the complex trusses shown in Fig. 2.71 for rigidity, and identify those which have a critical form.

4 Study the lattice truss shown in Fig. 2.72, and prove that it has a critical form.

5 Prove that the statically determinate complex truss shown in Fig. 2.54a will become statically indeterminate if a hinge is introduced at the center.

Chapter 3

Influence lines

3.1 MOVING LOADS AND INFLUENCE LINES

Engineering structures in general and bridges in particular are frequently submitted to the action of various systems of moving loads such as trucks, trains, automobile traffic.   These loads are called *live loads* to distinguish them from *dead loads* such as the weight of a structure itself.   Dead loads are always fixed in magnitude and position, whereas live loads, although fixed in magnitude, can have a variety of positions on the structure.   One of the most common examples of live load with which we have to deal in the design of railroad bridges is represented by the wheel loads from a pair of 213-ton locomotives, followed by a uniform train of 3 tons per lineal foot, as shown in Fig. 3.1. This particular system of loads is known as a *standard train* or *Cooper's E*-60 *loading*.   The wheels are numbered consecutively from left to right, and the distances between them are as shown.   It must be understood that these distances between wheels are fixed so that the system can move only as a unit.

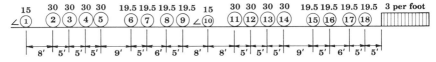

FIG. 3.1

The numbers directly above the wheels represent the load concentrations in kips per rail or tons per track.

A tabulation of useful numerical data pertaining to the standard train above and known as a *moment table* for Cooper's E-60 loading is shown on page 107. Besides the information given in Fig. 3.1, the first two horizontal lines of this table give the distance of each wheel from either end of the locomotive system, while the third and fourth lines give successive summations of loads up to and including any chosen wheel from either end of the system. The fifth horizontal line gives the sum of moments, with respect to wheel ①, of all loads back to and including any chosen wheel. Thus, for example, the sum of moments, with respect to wheel ①, of all loads back to and including wheel ⑧, is 4,040 kip-ft. The remaining lines of the table give sums of moments, with respect to each wheel, of all loads between that wheel and any other chosen wheel ahead of it. Thus, for example, the sum of moments of wheels ③, . . . , ⑮ with respect to wheel ⑮ is 12,500 kip-ft. To find this figure in the table, we follow vertically downward, under wheel ⑮, to the bottom of the table and then move horizontally to the left and read 12,500 under wheel ③. Examples illustrating the use of the moment table will be discussed later.

The analysis of structures under the action of live loads presents two major problems not encountered in connection with dead loads. First, the moving loads may have a dynamic effect on the structure, tending to produce vibrations, shock, or other undesirable effects. Second, even the purely statical effect of a system of moving loads is continually changing owing to change in position of the loads, and it becomes necessary to consider the problem of how to place them on the structure in order to realize the most severe stresses. It is only this latter aspect of the problem that we shall consider here.[1]

Sometimes we are able to determine by inspection how to place a given system of loads on a structure so as to realize the most severe stresses. In other cases, it may be necessary to resort to mathematical criteria for maxima and occasionally to trial-and-error procedures. In all cases, however, the problem can be greatly simplified by the use of *influence lines*, which show graphically just how changing the position of a single load on a structure influences various significant quantities such as reactions, bending moments,

---

[1] For discussions of the dynamic action of live loads on structures, see Chap. 12. See also C. E. Inglis, "A Mathematical Treatise on Vibrations in Railway Bridges," Cambridge University Press, New York, 1934.

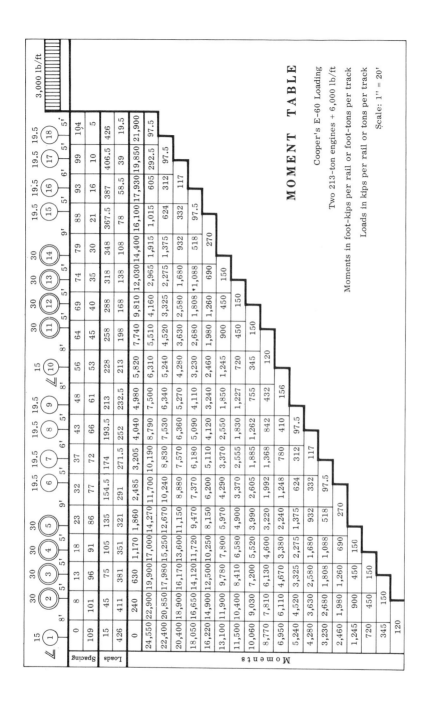

MOMENT TABLE

Cooper's E-60 Loading

Two 213-ton engines + 6,000 lb/ft

Moments in foot-kips per rail or foot-tons per track

Loads in kips per rail or tons per track

Scale: 1″ = 20′

3,000 lb/ft

Axle loads and spacings

Wheel	1	2	3	4	5	6	7	8	9	10	11	12	13	14	15	16	17	18
Load	15	30	30	30	30	19.5	19.5	19.5	19.5	15	30	30	30	30	19.5	19.5	19.5	19.5
Spacing (ft)	—	8′	5′	5′	5′	9′	5′	6′	5′	8′	8′	5′	5′	5′	9′	5′	6′	5′

Table data (columns = wheels 1–18)

	1	2	3	4	5	6	7	8	9	10	11	12	13	14	15	16	17	18
Spacing	0	8	13	18	23	32	37	43	48	56	64	69	74	79	88	93	99	104
	109	101	96	91	86	77	72	66	61	53	45	40	35	30	21	16	10	5
Loads	15	45	75	105	135	154.5	174	193.5	213	228	258	288	318	348	367.5	387	406.5	426
	426	411	381	351	321	291	271.5	252	232.5	213	198	168	138	108	78	58.5	39	19.5
Moments	0	240	630	1,170	1,860	2,485	3,205	4,040	4,980	5,820	7,740	9,810	12,030	14,400	16,100	17,930	19,850	21,900
	24,550	22,900	19,900	17,000	14,270	11,700	10,190	8,790	7,500	6,310	5,510	4,160	2,965	1,915	1,015	605	292.5	97.5
	22,400	20,850	17,980	15,250	12,670	10,240	8,830	7,530	6,340	5,240	4,520	3,325	2,275	1,375	624	312	97.5	
	20,400	18,900	16,170	13,600	11,150	8,880	7,570	6,360	5,270	4,280	3,630	2,580	1,680	932	332	117		
	18,050	16,650	14,120	11,720	9,470	7,370	6,180	5,090	4,110	3,230	2,680	1,808	1,088	518	97.5			
	16,220	14,900	12,500	10,250	8,150	6,200	5,110	4,120	3,240	2,460	1,980	1,260	690	270				
	13,100	11,900	9,780	7,800	5,970	4,290	3,370	2,550	1,850	1,245	900	450	150					
	11,500	10,400	8,410	6,580	4,900	3,370	2,555	1,830	1,227	720	450	150						
	10,060	9,030	7,200	5,520	3,990	2,605	1,885	1,262	755	345	150							
	8,770	7,810	6,130	4,600	3,220	1,992	1,368	842	432	120								
	6,950	6,110	4,670	3,380	2,240	1,248	780	410	156									
	5,240	4,520	3,325	2,275	1,375	624	312	97.5										
	4,280	3,630	2,580	1,680	932	332	117											
	3,230	2,680	1,808	1,088	518	97.5												
	2,460	1,980	1,260	690	270													
	1,245	900	450	150														
	720	450	150															
	345	150																
	120																	

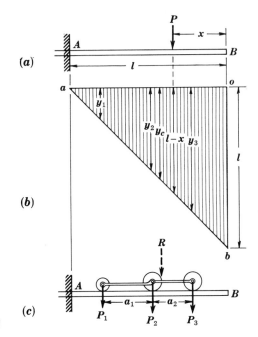

FIG. 3.2

shearing forces, and deflections.   Consider, for example, the cantilever beam shown in Fig. 3.2*a*.   In the design of this beam, we shall be especially interested in the bending stresses at the built-in end, since this is the dangerous section. Thus, a diagram showing how the bending moment at A varies with change in position of a load P on the beam will be helpful in deciding the most critical position of that load.   Such a diagram may be constructed as follows: First let the load have any position on the beam as defined by the distance x from the free end.   Then the bending moment at the built-in end A is

$$M_a = -P(l - x)$$

and the factor $-(l - x)$ by which the load P is multiplied is called the *influence coefficient* for M_a.   Being a linear function of x, it can be represented graphically by the straight line *ab* as shown in Fig. 3.2*b*[1] and this line is called the *influence line* for bending moment at A.   Correspondingly, the diagram *abo* is called the *influence diagram*.   The influence diagram for bending moment must not be confused with a *bending-moment diagram* for the beam.   Whereas the latter shows by each ordinate the bending moment at the corresponding section due to *fixed loads*, the influence diagram shows by each ordinate that factor by which a correspondingly placed load P must be multiplied to give the bending

[1] We take the ordinates of the influence line down if the influence coefficient is negative.

moment at a *fixed cross section*.   The ordinates of a bending-moment diagram have the dimension of *force* $\times$ *length;* the ordinates of an influence diagram for bending moment, as shown in Fig. 3.2*b*, have the dimension of *length*.   Thus, only when multiplied by the load P do they give the proper dimension for bending moment.   Numerically, however, the ordinates in Fig. 3.2*b* may be considered as representing the bending moment at A due to a correspondingly placed *unit load*, and we shall often use them in this sense.

   We see at once from the influence diagram in Fig. 3.2*b* that for maximum bending moment at A the load P should be placed in correspondence with the largest ordinate, i.e., at the free end of the beam, and that the corresponding bending moment at A is $-Pl$.   In this particular case such conclusions, obtained with the aid of the influence diagram, are rather obvious; but for more complicated systems, we shall find that this diagram can be of more substantial help.   For example, if we have a system of concentrated loads as shown in Fig. 3.2*c* and if y_1, y_2, and y_3 are the ordinates of the influence line corresponding to a certain position of this system of loads on the beam, it follows from simple statical considerations that the corresponding bending moment at A is

$$M_a = -(P_1 y_1 + P_2 y_2 + P_3 y_3) \tag{a}$$

Since the ordinates y_1, y_2, and y_3 will all be increased by moving the system of loads to the right, we conclude that the most critical condition of loading in this case will be obtained by placing the load P_3 at the free end of the beam. Using the corresponding values of y_1, y_2, and y_3, we obtain the desired maximum bending moment at A from Eq. (*a*).

   If R is the resultant of the loads P_1, P_2, and P_3 and y_c is the corresponding ordinate of the influence line, we have

$$R y_c = P_1 y_1 + P_2 y_2 + P_3 y_3 \tag{b}$$

To prove this, we need only recall that the moment of the resultant with respect to any point is equal to the algebraic sum of the corresponding moments of its components.   Equation (*b*) follows directly from this statement together with the fact that the ordinates y_1, y_2, y_3, and y_c are proportional to their distances from the built-in end of the beam.   Such replacement of a system of loads by their resultant, as in Eq. (*b*), always holds if the influence line is rectilinear and is very useful in establishing criteria for the most critical position on a structure of a complicated system of loads such as the standard train in Fig. 3.1.

   The influence diagram also can be used to advantage in dealing with uniformly distributed live load.   Suppose, for example, that we wish to calculate the bending moment at the built-in end of a cantilever beam partly covered by

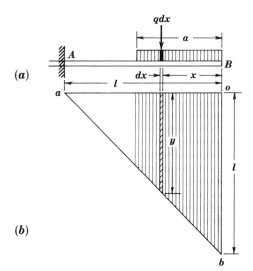

(a)

(b)

FIG. 3.3

a uniform load of intensity q as shown in Fig. 3.3a.   Considering such loading as a series of infinitesimal concentrated loads each of magnitude $q\ dx$ and at the distance x from the free end of the beam, we conclude, by the same reasoning as used above for the case of three loads, that the total bending moment at A is

$$M_a = \int_0^a qy\ dx \tag{c}$$

where y is the ordinate of the influence line corresponding to x.   Since

$$\int_0^a qy\ dx = q \int_0^a y\ dx = q[\text{area}]_0^a$$

we conclude that the bending moment at A due to any partial distribution of uniform load on the beam is obtained simply by taking the area of the corresponding portion of the influence diagram and multiplying it by the intensity of load q.   This fact is useful because it enables us to ascertain by inspection of the influence diagram just what portion of the beam should be uniformly loaded to obtain the most severe bending moment at a chosen section.   In the case illustrated in Fig. 3.3, of course, we obtain the greatest negative bending moment at A by loading the entire span.

As mentioned above, we can construct an influence line for any quantity that varies with change in position of load on a structure.   Consider, for example, the beam AB supported as shown in Fig. 3.4a.   If a single load P acts on this beam as shown, the tension induced in the tie rod CD will be

$$S = P\frac{x}{a} \sec \alpha$$

Here, again, the influence coefficient (x/a) sec α, by which the load P must be multiplied to give the corresponding tensile force S in the tie rod, is a linear function of x, and the corresponding influence line has the form shown in Fig. 3.4b.   We see that as x varies from zero to l, the influence coefficients, which in this case are pure numbers, vary from zero to (l/a) sec α.

In the two preceding examples, the influence lines happened to be rectilinear, but they may not always be so.   Consider, for example, an influence line for deflection δ at the free end of a cantilever beam of uniform flexural rigidity EI (Fig. 3.5).   For a load P at the distance x from the built-in end, this deflection is

$$\delta = P\left[\frac{x^3}{3EI} + \frac{x^2}{2EI}(l - x)\right]$$

and the influence coefficient obviously is not a linear function of x.   According-ly, the influence line has the curvilinear form shown in Fig. 3.5b.   It will be noted that the ordinates of this line have the dimension of *length* $\div$ *force*, e.g., inches per pound.   Thus, when multiplied by the load P, they give the proper dimension *(length)* for δ.   Since, for small deflections, the effects of several loads on the beam will be independent of each other, we can conclude at once that, for the loading shown in Fig. 3.5c, the deflection at the free end

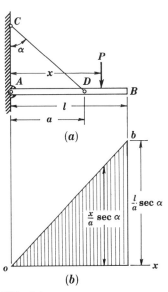

FIG. 3.4

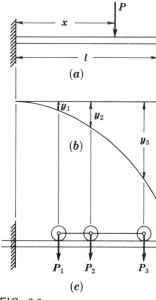

FIG. 3.5

will be

$$\delta = P_1y_1 + P_2y_2 + P_3y_3 \tag{d}$$

where y_1, y_2, and y_3 are the ordinates of the influence line corresponding to the positions of the loads P_1, P_2, and P_3, respectively. Equation (b) must not be used in this case because of the nonrectilinear character of the influence line.

3.2 INFLUENCE LINES FOR BEAM REACTIONS

Influence lines can often be used to advantage in the determination of simple beam reactions. Consider, for example, the simply supported beam shown in Fig. 3.6a. If a load P acts on this beam at the distance x from the right support, the vertical reactions at A and B are

$$R_a = P\frac{x}{l} \qquad R_b = P\left(1 - \frac{x}{l}\right) \tag{a}$$

which we shall consider positive when directed upward. The factors x/l and $1 - x/l$, by which P must be multiplied to give the corresponding reactions, are the influence coefficients and can be represented graphically by the influence lines oa and ba as shown in Fig. 3.6b and c.

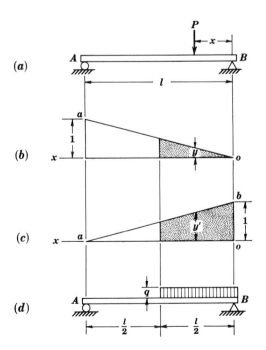

FIG. 3.6

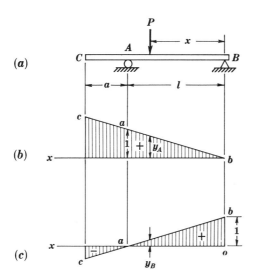

FIG. 3.7   (c)

By using these influence lines and proceeding as explained in the previous article, we can obtain the reactions for any given system of loads on the beam. For example, if there are several loads P_1, P_2, . . . acting on the beam and y_1, y_2, . . . are the corresponding ordinates of the influence line for R_a (Fig. 3.6b), we may write

$$R_a = \Sigma(P_i y_i) \qquad\qquad (b)$$

In the same way, denoting by y_1', y_2', . . . the corresponding ordinates of the influence line for R_b (Fig. 3.6c), we have

$$R_b = \Sigma(P_i y_i') \qquad\qquad (b')$$

If a portion of the span carries a uniformly distributed load of intensity q, each reaction will be obtained by multiplying by q the corresponding area of the proper influence diagram. Thus, for a uniform load that extends from B to mid-span (Fig. 3.6d), we obtain

$$R_a = q\,\frac{1}{4}\frac{l}{2} = \frac{1}{8}\,ql \qquad R_b = q\,\frac{3}{4}\frac{l}{2} = \frac{3}{8}\,ql$$

where $\frac{1}{4}l/2$ and $\frac{3}{4}l/2$ are the shaded areas shown in Fig. 3.6b and c, respectively.

In the case of a simply supported beam with overhang (Fig. 3.7a), expressions (a) for the reactions due to a moving load P still hold. However, since the value of x can now vary from zero to $l + a$, we obtain the influence lines shown in Fig. 3.7b and c. For values of x between l and $l + a$, we see that the influence coefficient for R_a becomes greater than unity, while that for R_b becomes negative. Thus, their sum remains constant and equal to unity. The negative ordinates for R_b simply indicate that when the load is on the overhang, this reaction is directed downward.

Since the influence coefficients x/l and $1 - x/l$ in expressions (a) can be regarded numerically as the reactions that would be produced at A and B by a *unit load* in place of the load P, we can devise a very simple method of construction of influence lines for reactions. As a first example, let us reconsider the influence line for the reaction R_b in Fig. 3.7c. If we imagine a *unit load* placed at B, the reaction R_b obviously has the magnitude of unity; when the unit load is at A, it is zero. Thus, having the key points b and a and keeping in mind that the reaction is a linear function of x, we construct the straight line *bac* through these key points, and the diagram is completed.

The procedure above can be used also in more complicated cases where the writing of analytical expressions for the reactions may become involved. Consider, for example, the compound beam ACD supported as shown in Fig. 3.8a. To construct the influence lines for the vertical reactions at A, B, and D in this case, we proceed as follows: Beginning with the reaction at A, we note that this force must have magnitudes of unity and zero, respectively, as a unit load successively takes positions at A and B. Thus, through the key points a and b (Fig. 3.8b) we can construct the straight line abc. When the load is at D, the reaction R_a is again zero, and we complete the influence diagram with the straight line cd. The same procedure is used in the construction of the influence lines for R_b (Fig. 3.8c) and R_d (Fig. 3.8d).

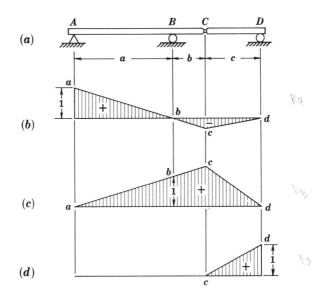

FIG. 3.8

Although influence lines for reactions are hardly necessary for such simple beams as those shown in Figs. 3.6 and 3.7, they may prove very helpful in more complicated cases like that shown in Fig. 3.8. In such a case, we can see clearly from the influence diagrams just how to place given loads on the beam in order to obtain maximum values of the reactions. For example, under uniform load, we see that the most severe uplift on the reaction at A will be obtained when only that portion of the beam between B and D is loaded. Again, it is evident at a glance that loads on the beam AC have no effect on the reaction at D. For the maximum reaction at B, we must put as many loads as possible on the entire beam, etc.

The principle of virtual displacements as discussed in Art. 1.10 can be used to advantage in the construction of influence lines for reactions. Consider, for example, the simply supported beam ABC with overhang loaded as shown in Fig. 3.9a. To find the reaction at A by the method of virtual displacements, we remove the constraint at A and replace it by a vertical force R_a as shown in Fig. 3.9b. This leaves the rigid bar AC free to rotate around the fixed hinge B. Defining such a virtual displacement of the system by a linear displacement $\overline{AA'}$* of point A, we see that all other points on the axis of the beam must have displacements as shown by the ordinates to the dashed line $A'C'$. Thus, the equation of virtual work becomes

$$R_a\overline{AA'} - Py = 0$$

from which

$$R_a = P\frac{y}{\overline{AA'}} \qquad (c)$$

where y is the displacement of the point of application of the load P. From

---

* Actually the displacements are infinitesimal circular arcs that we can consider as coincident with their own vertical projections; thus, the projection AA' for the arc AA'', etc.

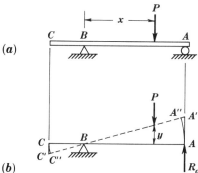

FIG. 3.9 **(b)**

(a)

expression (*c*), we conclude that by taking AA' = unity, we can consider the dashed line $A'C'$ as the influence line for the reaction R_a. The negative ordinates to the left of B indicate that this reaction will be directed downward when the load is on the overhang.

The procedure above can be used also in more complicated cases such as that shown in Fig. 3.10*a*, where we have a statically determinate compound beam AG on four supports. To obtain an influence line for the vertical reaction at C, we simply remove the constraint at C and make a positive (upward) displacement $\overline{CC'}$ of this point as shown in Fig. 3.10*b*. By taking CC' equal to unity, the ordinates to the dashed lines defining the new configuration of the system will represent the corresponding influence coefficients for R_c. In the same manner, removal of the constraint at G and a subsequent positive unit displacement of this point as shown in Fig. 3.10*c* leads to the influence line for R_g, as shown by dashed lines. Thus, we see that to obtain an influence line for any statically determinate reaction, it is necessary only to remove the corresponding constraint and make a positive unit displacement of its point of application. Then the new configuration of the system defines the required influence line. It is left as an exercise for the reader to construct influence lines for the reactions at B and F by this procedure.

We have now discussed several methods of constructing influence lines for reactions. Their application in the analysis of beams under various systems of live loads can best be illustrated by an example. For this purpose, we take the simple beam with overhang as shown in Fig. 3.11*a* and assume that we wish to evaluate the maximum reaction which can be induced at B by the standard train shown in Fig. 3.1. With the aid of the influence line for R_b (Fig. 3.11*b*), we see that in this case the most critical position of the train will be obtained

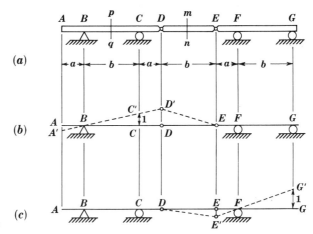

FIG. 3.10

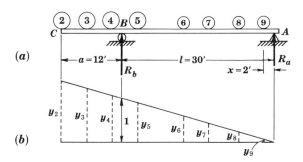

FIG. 3.11

by placing wheel ② at C as shown. That is, as the train moves slowly across the bridge from right to left, the reaction R_b will have its largest value after the wheel ① leaves the bridge and just as wheel ② reaches the end. Thus, the question of placement of the loads having been disposed of, we are ready to consider the numerical calculation of R_b for the chosen condition of loading. This calculation can be made in two ways: In one case, we scale the influence coefficients y_2, y_3, y_4, . . . , multiply each by the corresponding wheel load, and use the formula

$$R_b = \Sigma(P_i y_i) \tag{d}$$

as explained on page 113. An easier and more accurate method, however, will be to discard the influence diagram completely as soon as the critical position of the loads has been selected and to calculate R_b simply by equating to zero the algebraic sum of moments of all forces with respect to point A. Thus, denoting by ΣM_a the sum of moments of all loads on the beam with respect to A, we have

$$R_b = \frac{\Sigma M_a}{l} \tag{e}$$

The numerical calculations indicated by Eq. (e) can be made in a very simple manner by using the *moment table* for Cooper's E-60 loading as shown on page 107. To use this table, we first write expression (e) in the equivalent form

$$R_b = \frac{\Sigma M_{⑨} + (\Sigma P_i)x}{l} \tag{e'}$$

where $\Sigma M_{⑨}$ denotes the sum of moments of all loads on the beam with respect to wheel ⑨ and ΣP_i denotes the summation of all loads on the beam, x being the distance between A and wheel ⑨. Taking the numerical values of $\Sigma M_{⑨}$ and ΣP_i directly from the moment table and using $l = 30$ ft and $x = 2$ ft as shown in Fig. 3.11a, we have

$$R_b = \frac{4,520 + 198 \times 2}{30} = 163.5 \text{ kips}$$

This discussion assumes that the bridge consists of two parallel beams and that there is a single track, i.e., that the load on each girder is the same as that for one rail.

PROBLEMS

1 Construct an influence line for the axial force in the strut CD supporting the horizontal beam AB as shown in Fig. 3.12.

2 Construct influence lines for the axial forces developed in the bars AF, BE, and BD, which support the beam ABC as shown in Fig. 3.13.

3 Construct influence lines for the reactions at A and B of the simply supported beam shown in Fig. 3.14.   Using a standard train (Cooper's E-60), calculate the greatest possible value of R_b if $a = 10$ ft, $l = 30$ ft, and $b = 12$ ft.

   Ans.   Max R_b = 322 kips.

4 Construct influence lines for the reactions at A, C, and D of the compound beam shown in Fig. 3.15.   How should a standard train be placed to make R_a a maximum?   What is this maximum value of R_a if a, b, and l have the same numerical values as in Prob. 3?

   Ans.   Max R_a = 189.1 kips.

5 Construct influence lines for the reactions at A, B, and C of the system shown in Fig. 3.16.

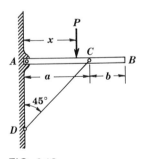

FIG. 3.12

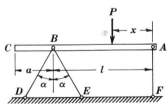

FIG. 3.13

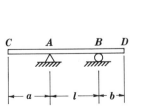

FIG. 3.14

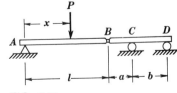

FIG. 3.15

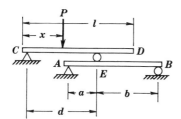

FIG. 3.16

3.3 INFLUENCE LINES FOR SHEARING FORCE

In the case of a simply supported beam (Fig. 3.17*a*), an influence line for shearing force at a given section *mn* can be obtained as follows: When a load *P* is to the right of the section *mn*, we note that the shearing force at the section is positive and numerically equal to the reaction R_a. Likewise, when the load is to the left of the section, the shearing force is negative and numerically equal to the reaction R_b. Hence, we obtain the influence diagram for shearing force at *mn* simply by taking the shaded portions of the two influence diagrams for the reactions R_a and $-R_b$ as shown in Fig. 3.17*b*. Any ordinate of this diagram is numerically equal to the shearing force at the fixed section *mn* when a unit load has that position on the beam corresponding to the chosen ordinate. As this load crosses the section from right to left, the shearing force changes abruptly from a maximum positive value b/l to a maximum negative value a/l.

From the influence diagram (Fig. 3.17*b*), it is evident that under the action of a single load *P* the maximum shearing force at any chosen section will occur with the load at that section (theoretically, an infinitesimal distance to one side). Likewise, under uniform load, the numerical maximum of shearing

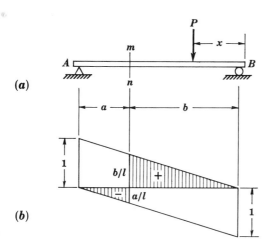

(a)

(b)

FIG. 3.17

force at a given section occurs when the distribution is continuous between that section and the more distant support.   The magnitude of such shearing force will be obtained as the product of the intensity of load q and that area of the influence diagram corresponding to the loaded portion of the beam. For example, in the case represented in Fig. 3.17, the uniform load should extend from the section *mn* to the support B, and the corresponding shearing force at *mn* is

$$V_{mn} = q \frac{b}{l} \frac{b}{2} = \frac{qb^2}{2l}$$

The principle of virtual displacements can be used also in the construction of influence lines for shearing forces in beams.   To illustrate, we consider the simply supported beam with overhang as shown in Fig. 3.18a.   Assuming that we are interested in the shearing force at the section *mn*, we imagine the resistance to transverse sliding at this section to be destroyed and replace it by shearing forces V as shown.   At the same time, the resistance to bending at the section *mn* is assumed to remain intact.   To realize such conditions, we imagine that at the section *mn* one element of the beam of length dx is replaced by two links *mm'* and *nn'* as shown in Fig. 3.18b.   This preserves the resistance against relative angular displacement between the two portions of the beam and yet allows a small relative transverse displacement as shown in Fig. 3.18c.

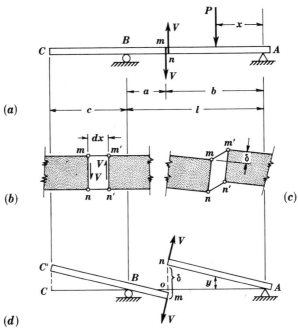

FIG. 3.18   (d)

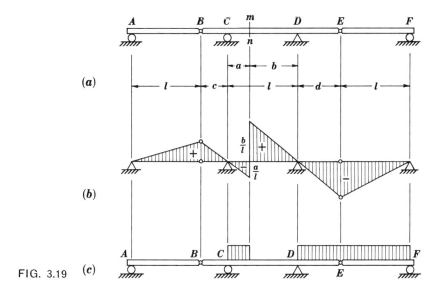

FIG. 3.19

Thus we introduce one degree of freedom into the system and can define a corresponding virtual displacement by a small relative displacement δ as shown in Fig. 3.18d.[1] Noting that the two portions of the beam have to remain parallel, we conclude that the displaced system must satisfy the condition $om:on = a:b$, and the configuration is completely determined. Since only the shearing forces V and the applied load P produce work during the displacement, the equation of virtual work becomes

$$V\delta - Py = 0$$

from which

$$V = P\frac{y}{\delta} \tag{a}$$

We see now that the numbers represented by the ratios y/δ are influence coefficients for shearing force at the section mn. Thus, the diagram in Fig. 3.18d has the shape of an influence diagram, and to use it as such we need only select a vertical scale that makes $\delta = 1$.

The above procedure is perfectly general and applicable to more complicated cases. Consider, for example, the compound beam shown in Fig. 3.19a, and assume that we require an influence diagram for shearing force at the section mn. To obtain this by the usual methods of statics will involve considerable labor because of the necessity of first finding all reactions. Only the principle of virtual displacements offers a method of approach by which we can ignore the reactive forces. By this method, we simply induce a unit transverse sliding

---

[1] It should be kept in mind that we are discussing displacements of infinitesimal magnitude and that we exaggerate the distortion only for the sake of clarity in the figure.

displacement at the section *mn*, keeping all other constraints (both external and internal) intact. The corresponding configuration of the system as shown in Fig. 3.19*b* defines an influence diagram for shearing force at the section *mn*. With the aid of such a diagram it is easy to see how to place given loads on the beam in order to obtain maximum shearing force at this section. The distribution of uniform load illustrated in Fig. 3.19*c*, for example, is selected to give maximum negative shearing force at *mn*.

In the case of a beam submitted to the action of a series of concentrated loads like the standard train in Fig. 3.1, the condition of loading for maximum shearing force at a given section is not always self-evident. However, with the aid of an influence diagram, it is possible to develop general criteria to determine the most critical position of the loads in any given case. These criteria follow directly from a consideration of the fluctuations in shearing force at a given section as a series of concentrated loads moves across the span. To illustrate, let us suppose that a standard train moves from right to left across the simply supported beam shown in Fig. 3.20*a*. As it does so, we see from the influence line that the shearing force at the section *mn* increases steadily until wheel ① reaches this section, since the influence coefficients under the loads will be increasing both in number and in magnitude. As wheel ① crosses the section, there will be an abrupt drop in the shearing force by an amount equal to the load on this wheel; but, with further movement to the left (Fig. 3.20*b*), the positive shearing force at *mn* continues its gradual increase since the positive ordinates of the influence line are increasing and the negative ordinate under the wheel ① is decreasing. This condition prevails until wheel ② crosses the section, when there is again a corresponding abrupt drop in the shearing force, followed by another gradual rise, etc. This indicates that there will be as many maxima of shearing force as there are wheels and that each maximum occurs just as some wheel reaches the section. Thus, *as a first criterion for maximum shearing force at a chosen section, the system of loads must be placed so that one of the wheels is at this section.*

To determine which load of the series should be placed at the given section in order to obtain a maximum shearing force, we begin with the first wheel at the section and consider the *change in shearing force* as each new wheel is moved up. The total increase in shearing force during an advance of the loads is evidently

$$\Delta V = \Delta R_a - \Delta P \tag{3.1}$$

where ΔR_a is the increase in the reaction R_a due to the advance and ΔP is the increase of total load to the left of the section. If expression (3.1) is positive, it indicates that the shearing force at the section has been increased by advancing the loads. Hence, the procedure is repeated until there is a change in sign of expression (3.1), which indicates that the greatest maximum of shearing

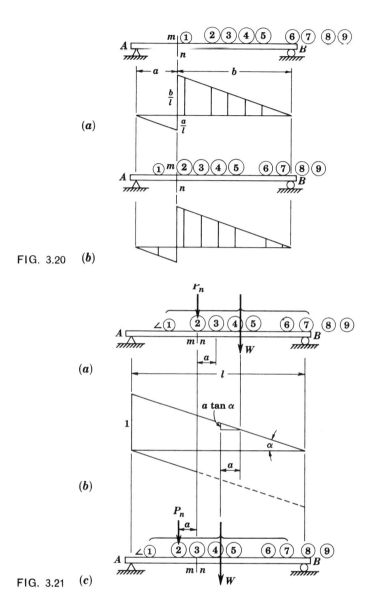

FIG. 3.20   **(b)**

FIG. 3.21   **(c)**

force has been passed. Thus, *we may regard a change in sign of expression* (3.1) *as the second criterion for maximum shearing force.*

If no loads enter or leave the span during one of the advances discussed above, the changes ΔR_a and ΔP may be calculated in a very simple manner. Suppose, for example, that we are advancing the loads from the position shown in Fig. 3.21*a* to that shown in Fig. 3.21*c*. From the influence line for R_a

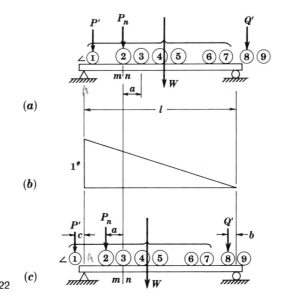

FIG. 3.22

(a)

(b)

(c)

(Fig. 3.21b), we see that if W is the resultant of all loads on the span and a the distance the loads are advanced, the change in R_a will be

$$\Delta R_a = Wa \tan \alpha = \frac{Wa}{l} \qquad (b)$$

where $\tan \alpha = 1/l$ is the slope of the influence line. Also, when no load leaves the span, ΔP is simply P_n, the load which crosses the section. Thus, expression (3.1) becomes

$$\Delta V = \frac{Wa}{l} - P_n \qquad (3.1a)$$

and a change in sign of this expression may be taken as the second criterion for maximum shearing force.

Loads entering or leaving the span complicate the calculation of ΔR_a. In such a case (Fig. 3.22), let W be the resultant of all loads on the span before the advance, Q' a load that enters the span a distance b, and P' a load that goes beyond A a distance c. Then, for the change in R_a as the loads are advanced from the position shown in Fig. 3.22a to that shown in Fig. 3.22c, we have

$$\Delta R_a = \frac{Wa}{l} - P'\left(1 + \frac{c}{l}\right) + \frac{Q'b}{l} \qquad (c)$$

In this expression, the first term Wa/l represents the increase in R_a, if we assume that there is sufficient overhang at the left to carry the load P' which has gone beyond A, whereas the second term simply corrects for the fact that there is no such overhang. The third term represents the increase in R_a due to the appearance on the span of the load Q', which was not included in W.

The load P' leaving the span also affects the expression for increase of total load to the left of the section so that

$$\Delta P = P_n - P' \tag{d}$$

Substituting expressions (c) and (d) into Eq. (3.1), we obtain

$$\Delta V = \frac{Wa}{l} - P_n - \frac{P'c}{l} + \frac{Q'b}{l} \tag{3.1b}$$

Since the ratios c/l and b/l are usually small compared with unity and since they are of opposite signs, the last two terms in expression $(3.1b)$ can be neglected, in which case it coincides exactly with expression $(3.1a)$.

As an application of the foregoing criteria, we shall now determine the maximum shearing force that a Cooper's E-60 loading can induce at the section mn of the simple beam shown in Fig. 3.23. Beginning with wheel ① at the section and moving up wheel ②, we have, by Eq. $(3.1a)$,

$$\Delta V = \frac{213 \times 8}{70} - 15 = +9.34 \text{ kips}$$

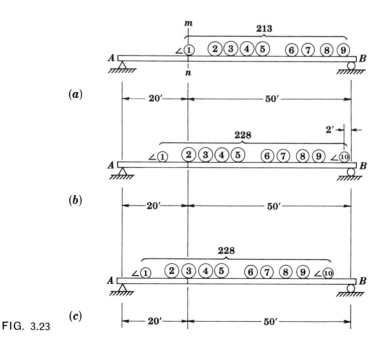

FIG. 3.23

This being positive, the shearing force has been increased, and we start again with wheel ② at the section and move up wheel ③. Then, by Eq. (3.1a),

$$\Delta V = \frac{228 \times 5}{70} - 30 = -13.7 \text{ kips}$$

This being negative, the shearing force has been reduced by the second advance, and we put wheel ② at the section for maximum shearing force there (Fig. 3.23b). Now, to calculate this maximum shearing force, we use the formula[1] $V = R_a - 15$. Calculating R_a with the aid of the moment table (page 107) as explained in the preceding article, this becomes

$$V = \frac{M_{⑩} + 228 \times 2}{70} - 15 = \frac{6,950 + 456}{70} - 15 = 90.8 \text{ kips}$$

It must be emphasized here that the procedure above, i.e., the use of Eq. (3.1) as a criterion for maximum shearing force, is applicable only to the case of a simply supported beam without overhang. In more complicated cases, the influence line should always be drawn and used as a guide in selecting the most critical condition of loading.

PROBLEMS

1   A simply supported girder has a clear span of 20 ft. What maximum shearing force can be induced by a standard train (Cooper's E-60), and at what cross section does such shearing force occur?
     Ans. $V_{max} = 75$ kips.
2   A simply supported beam has a clear span of 90 ft. Construct the influence line for shearing force at a cross section 20 ft from the left support. How should Cooper's E-60 loading be placed on the beam to give maximum shearing force at this section, and what is this maximum shearing force?
     Ans. $V_{max} = 126.9$ kips.
3   A simply supported beam with an overall length of 44 ft has a clear span of 32 ft with a 12-ft overhang on one end. Construct an influence line for shearing force at a cross section that is 22 ft from either end of the beam. How should Cooper's E-60 loading be placed on the beam to give maximum shearing force at this section? Evaluate this shearing force.
     Ans. $V_{max} = 57.1$ kips.
4   Assuming a uniform live load of 6 kips per lineal foot and a uniform dead load of 2 kips per lineal foot, what maximum uplift must be provided for at the support D of the compound beam shown in Fig. 3.15? Assume $l = 30$ ft, $a = 10$ ft, and $b = 20$ ft.

---

[1] We assume that wheel ② is just to the right of the section.

5   Construct an influence line for shearing force on the pin B of the system shown in
Fig. 3.15.   What maximum shearing force can be induced in this pin by a Cooper's
E-60 loading?   By a uniform live load of 6 kips per lineal foot?   Use the same
numerical data as in Prob. 4.

3.4   INFLUENCE LINES FOR BENDING MOMENT

The question of variation in bending moment at a chosen section of a beam or
girder with change in position of a system of moving loads is one of great
practical importance.   Consider, for example, a simply supported beam AB
under the action of a moving load P as shown in Fig. 3.24a.   In such a case,
we conclude that so long as the load is to the right of a given section mn, the
bending moment at this section will be $R_a a$.   Likewise, when the load has any
position to the left of the section, the bending moment at the section will be
$R_b b$.   In both cases, the bending moment is positive.   Thus, as in the case of
shearing force, we obtain the influence line for bending moment at the given
section mn directly from the influence lines for the reactions R_a and R_b.   For
the portion of the beam to the right of the section, we use the influence line for
R_a and simply multiply each ordinate by the length a.   Similarly, for the
portion of the beam to the left of the section, we use the influence line for R_b
and multiply each ordinate by the length b.   Thus the complete influence
diagram for bending moment at the section mn is represented by the shaded
triangle acb shown in Fig. 3.24b.   We see that the ordinates of an influence line
for bending moment always have the dimension of length.   Thus, the product
between one of these ordinates and the load P has the proper dimension
(*force* × *length*) for bending moment.

From the constructions indicated in Fig. 3.24b, it can be seen that the maxi-

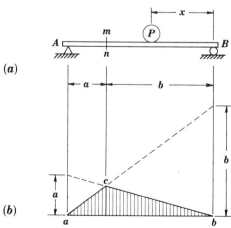

FIG. 3.24   (*b*)

mum ordinate of the diagram occurs under the section mn and has the magnitude ab/l. Thus, for maximum bending moment due to a single concentrated load P, the load should be placed at the section, and the corresponding bending moment is Pab/l. For maximum bending moment due to uniformly distributed load, the entire span should be covered. Since the area of the diagram is $ab/2$, the corresponding magnitude of this maximum bending moment will be $qab/2$, where q is the intensity of load. If we take $a = b = l/2$, this reduces to the well-known expression $ql^2/8$.

The influence line for bending moment in a beam can also be obtained by using the principle of virtual displacements. Consider, for example, the simply supported beam with overhangs as shown in Fig. 3.25a. To construct an influence line for bending moment at the section mn, we imagine that an element of the beam at this section is replaced by an ideal hinge as shown in Fig. 3.25b. This allows relative rotation between the two portions of the beam as shown in Fig. 3.25c but at the same time keeps the resistance to shear and direct tension intact. Thus, we obtain a system with one degree of freedom as shown in Fig. 3.25d. Now to this movable system we apply at any point a load P and at the hinge two equal and opposite couples M as shown. Obviously, the relation between P and M for equilibrium of this fictitious system represents the desired relation between P and the bending moment at the section mn of the original beam in Fig. 3.25a. This relation is found by

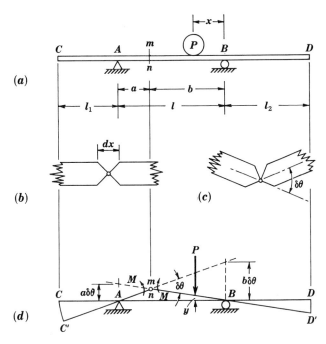

FIG. 3.25

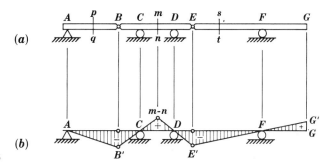

FIG. 3.26

assuming a virtual displacement of the system as shown in Fig. 3.25d and equating to zero the corresponding virtual work.   Thus,

$$M\,\delta\theta - Py = 0$$

where $\delta\theta$ is the total angular displacement between the two parts of the beam and y is the vertical displacement of the point of application of the load P. From this equation of virtual work, we find

$$M = \frac{Py}{\delta\theta}$$

and we see that the lengths $y/\delta\theta$ are the influence coefficients for bending moment at the section mn.   Hence, the diagram in Fig. 3.25d has the shape of an influence diagram, and to use it as such we need only magnify the vertical scale in the ratio $1:\delta\theta$.   Thus, if $\delta\theta = \frac{1}{10}$ rad, we use a magnification factor of 10.

The conclusion above is general and can be used to great advantage in more complicated cases.   Consider, for example, the compound beam shown in Fig. 3.26a, and let it be required to construct an influence line for bending moment at the section mn.   To accomplish this, we simply introduce an imaginary hinge at this section (Fig. 3.26b) and make, between the two portions of the beam BE, a relative angle of rotation in such a direction that positive bending moment at mn will do positive work.   The corresponding configuration of the system, compatible with all remaining constraints, defines the required influence line from which any desired influence coefficient can be scaled directly.

With the aid of the influence line in Fig. 3.26b, we can see at once how to place given loads on the structure so as to obtain the maximum bending moment at the section mn.   The maximum negative bending moment under the action of a single load P, for example, occurs with the load at the hinge B.   Again, under uniform live load, the worst condition will be realized when the spans AC and DF of the system are loaded, and this condition of loading also induces negative bending moment at the section mn.

We shall consider now the question of how to place a series of concentrated loads such as a standard locomotive on a simply supported girder so as to induce the greatest possible bending moment at a given section. We begin with the influence line ACB for bending moment at a section mn as shown in Fig. 3.27 and allow the system of loads $P_1, \ldots, P_n$ to move onto the span from right to left. Then, for any position of the loads as shown in the figure, the bending moment at the section will be obtained simply by taking the sum of moments produced by the individual loads. Thus,

$$M = P_1 y_1 + P_2 y_2 + P_3 y_3 + \cdots + P_n y_n \qquad (a)$$

where $y_1, y_2, \ldots$ are the influence coefficients as shown in the figure. Now imagine that the loads are moved a short distance δx to the left. Then the corresponding change δM in bending moment at the section can be expressed as the algebraic sum of the individual changes in the terms $P_i y_i$ of the expression (a). Denoting by R_1 the resultant of all loads to the left of the section and by R_2 the resultant of all loads to the right, we can express the change δM as follows,

$$\delta M = \delta x (R_2 \tan \alpha_2 - R_1 \tan \alpha_1) \qquad (b)$$

where α_1 and α_2 are the slopes of the lines AC and BC, respectively, as shown. Since $\tan \alpha_1 = b/l$ and $\tan \alpha_2 = a/l$, expression (b) can be written in the form

$$\delta M = \frac{ab}{l}\, \delta x \left(\frac{R_2}{b} - \frac{R_1}{a} \right) \qquad (c)$$

In this expression, the terms R_2/b and R_1/a represent, respectively, the *average loads* on the right and left portions of the span. Thus, we conclude from expression (c) that the bending moment at the section will continue to increase with movement of the loads to the left so long as

$$\frac{R_2}{b} > \frac{R_1}{a} \qquad (3.2)$$

i.e., so long as the average load on the right portion of the span is greater than

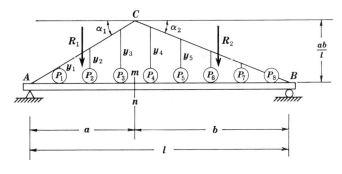

FIG. 3.27

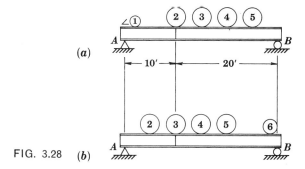

FIG. 3.28   (b)

that on the left.   As soon as this condition is reversed, the bending moment will begin to decrease.

If, during movement of the loads to the left, a new load enters the span from the right, R_2/b will be increased, while R_1/a will remain unaffected.   Hence, to reach a maximum bending moment at mn, further movement to the left is indicated.   Likewise, if a load leaves the span on the left, R_1/a will be decreased, and R_2/b will be unaffected, so that in this case also further movement to the left is indicated.   We conclude, then, that the entrance of a load on the right or the exit of a load on the left cannot invalidate the conclusion of the preceding paragraph and is not significant in determining the position of the loads for greatest bending moment at the section mn.   On the other hand, each time a load crosses the section mn there will be a sudden increase in R_1/a and a corresponding decrease in R_2/b, which may reverse condition (3.2). From this we conclude that the maximum bending moment at mn will occur with some load at the section.   The proper load will be that one which, when moved across the section, reverses condition (3.2).

As a full series of loads moves from right to left across the span, there may be several reversals of condition (3.2).   This simply means that the bending moment at the section passes through several maxima, as we have already seen for shearing force (page 122).   In such a case, each maximum (with some load at the section) must be evaluated, and then the one that is numerically greatest will be used as a basis for design.   An example will serve to illustrate these remarks.

In Fig. 3.28, we have a short girder AB for which it is required to determine the maximum bending moment at the third point under the action of a Cooper's E-60 loading (see Fig. 3.1, page 106).   With wheel ② just to the right of the section (Fig. 3.28a), expression (3.2) becomes

$$\frac{120}{20} > \frac{15}{10}$$

while, with the same wheel just to the left of the section, we have

$$\frac{90}{20} = \frac{45}{10}$$

This condition of equality indicates that the bending moment remains constant as wheel ② crosses the section and up to the time when wheel ① leaves the span. As wheel ③ comes up to the section (Fig. 3.28*b*), condition (3.2) becomes

$$\frac{109.5}{20} > \frac{30}{10}$$

which indicates that the bending moment is still increasing; but as this wheel crosses the section, condition (3.2) drops to

$$\frac{79.5}{20} < \frac{60}{10}$$

and the bending moment begins to decrease. Hence, for maximum bending moment at the third point, we place the loads as shown in Fig. 3.28*b*. The corresponding bending moment $M = 556.5$ kip-ft can be found very easily with the help of the moment table (page 107).

ABSOLUTE MAXIMUM BENDING MOMENT   Previously, we have considered how to position a given system of loads on a beam in order to realize the maximum bending moment at some chosen section. We shall now consider a method of determining that particular cross section of the beam for which the maximum bending moment is greater than for any other cross section. That is, as a given system of loads moves across the span, what is the maximum bending moment that occurs in the beam and at what cross section does it occur? This particular cross section is called the *dangerous section*, and the maximum bending moment occurring there is called the *absolute maximum bending moment*. It is, of course, for the case of a beam of uniform cross section, the bending moment that should be used as a basis for design.

To establish a criterion of loading for such absolute maximum bending moment, consider the beam in Fig. 3.29*a*. We conclude, by inspection, that to obtain an absolute maximum bending moment we should place as many heavy loads on the beam as possible. Then, for any assumed position of these loads, we know that the maximum bending moment will occur under that load where the shearing force in the beam changes sign. Let us assume in Fig. 3.29 that this load is P_i, and let R denote the resultant of all the loads on the span and x its distance from the support B. Also, let M denote the sum of moments of all loads to the left of P_i with respect to the point of application of P_i; and,

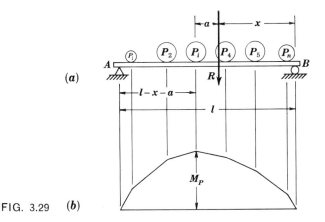

FIG. 3.29   (b)

finally, let a denote the distance between R and P_i as shown. With these notations, the bending moment under the load P_i can be expressed as follows:

$$M_p = \frac{Rx}{l}(l - x - a) - M \qquad (d)$$

We assume now that we can vary x slightly without any loads going on or off the span. Then, within these limits, M_p can be regarded as a continuous function of x which will be a maximum when $dM_p/dx = 0$. This gives

$$\frac{R}{l}(l - 2x - a) = 0$$

from which

$$l - x - a = x \qquad (e)$$

This expression shows that M_p will be an absolute maximum when the load P_i and the resultant of all the loads on the span are equidistant from the ends of the beam. The foregoing conclusions can be summarized by the following criterion: *The maximum bending moment in a simply supported beam under a series of concentrated loads occurs under that load where the shear changes sign and is an absolute maximum when the loads are so placed that the mid-point of the span bisects the distance a between this load and the resultant R of all the loads on the beam.*

In using the criterion above for absolute maximum bending moment, it must be kept in mind that as a given series of loads moves across the beam, there may be several absolute maxima of bending moment as different wheels occupy the middle region of the span. However, experience shows that the section of absolute maximum bending moment, i.e., the dangerous section, is never far removed from the middle cross section. Thus, we can often reduce the amount of labor in calculation by first determining the position of the loads for maximum bending moment at the middle cross section. This done, the loads can be shifted slightly to satisfy the criterion for absolute maximum bending moment, and then the moment can be evaluated. For all practical purposes it can be taken for granted, without further investigation, that this will be the greatest possible absolute maximum bending moment.

PROBLEMS

1 A simply supported girder AB has a clear span of 60 ft. Under the action of a standard Cooper's E-60 loading, what is the maximum bending moment that can occur (a) at the mid-point of the span, (b) at a third point?
     Ans. (a) 1,907.5 kip-ft. (b) 1,738.7 kip-ft.

2 A simply supported beam 30 ft long has a clear span of 24 ft with a 6-ft overhang at one end. What maximum bending moment can be produced by a standard train (a) at the mid-point of the 24-ft span, (b) at the overhung support?
     Ans. (a) 412.5 kip-ft. (b) −210.0 kip-ft.

3 Find the absolute maximum bending moment in the simple beam loaded as shown in Fig. 3.30. How does this compare with the maximum bending moment at the mid-point of the span?

4 Determine the absolute maximum bending moment in a simply supported beam having a clear span of 46 ft if the live load is a standard train (Cooper's E-60).
     Ans. 1,243 kip-ft.

5 Determine the absolute maximum bending moment induced in the beam CD of the system shown in Fig. 3.31.

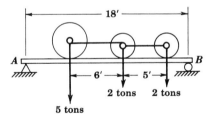

FIG. 3.30

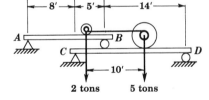

FIG. 3.31

3.5 GIRDERS WITH FLOOR BEAMS

In those cases where long-span girders are used in bridge construction, the live loads are rarely applied directly to the girder. Instead, as illustrated in Fig. 3.32a, the main girders AB carry several crossbeams at a, b, c, . . . which are called *floor beams*, and these in turn carry a series of *stringers ab, bc, cd*, . . . by which the floor system of the bridge is supported. Those portions of the main girder between the floor beams are called *panels*, and the points *a*, *b*, *c*, . . . are called *panel points*. It follows from such construction that a load *P* applied to any stringer will be transmitted to the main girder only at the two corresponding panel points. Such division of the load between two panel points has no effect upon the reactions at *A* and *B*, and the influence lines for these quantities will be the same as for a girder without floor beams. In the construction of influence lines for shearing force and bending moment, however, it becomes necessary to modify slightly our previous discussions.

We begin with the question of influence lines for shearing force. Since loads can be transmitted to the girders only at panel points, we conclude at once that, for any condition of loading on the stringers, the shearing force in a girder will be constant throughout any one panel. Thus, without ambiguity, we may speak of the *shearing force in a panel* instead of the shearing force at any particular cross section of that panel. With this idea in mind, we shall now consider the construction of an influence line for shearing force in the panel *cd* of the girder shown in Fig. 3.32*a*. For any position of the load *P* to the left of panel point *c*, the shearing force in the panel *cd* is negative and numerically equal to R_b, whereas for any position of *P* to the right of *d*, it is positive and equal to R_a. Thus, for the portions *de* and *ac* of the span, we use directly the corresponding portions *d'e'* and *a'c'* of the influence lines for R_a and R_b, respectively, as shown in Fig. 3.32*b*.

Now let the load *P* have any position within the panel *cd* as defined by the distance *x*. Then, at *c* and *d*, the corresponding panel-point loads are,

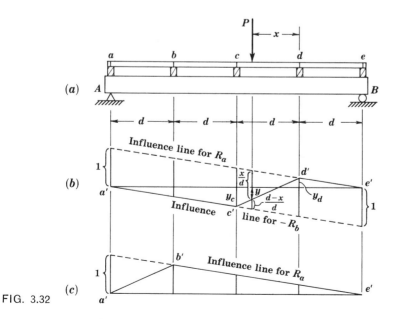

FIG. 3.32

respectively,

$$P_c = P\frac{x}{d} \quad \text{and} \quad P_d = P\frac{d-x}{d} \tag{a}$$

where d is the panel distance as shown. Using the corresponding influence coefficients y_c and y_d, we find that the shearing force in the panel is

$$V = y_c P\frac{x}{d} + y_d P\frac{d-x}{d} \tag{b}$$

This expression is a linear function of x and reduces to Py_d when $x = 0$ and to Py_c when $x = d$. Hence, to obtain that portion of the influence line corresponding to positions of the load within the panel cd, we need only connect the established points c' and d' by a straight line as shown (Fig. 3.32b). By the same procedure, we obtain the influence diagram for shearing force in the panel ab as shown in Fig. 3.32c.

To construct an influence line for bending moment at some given cross section mn of a girder with floor beams (Fig. 3.33a), we proceed in a similar manner. Again we note that for any position of the load P to the right of d, we have at the section mn the bending moment $R_a a$, while, for any position to the left of point c, we have a bending moment $R_b b$. Hence, as for a girder without floor beams, we obtain the portions $a'c'$ and $e'd'$ of the desired influence

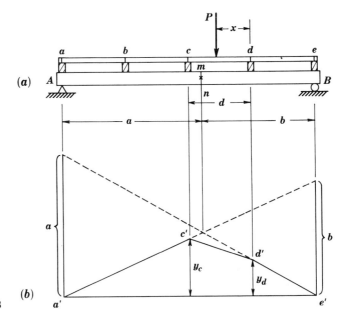

FIG. 3.33

diagram (Fig. 3.33b) simply by multiplying by a and b, respectively, the corresponding ordinates of the influence lines for R_a and R_b. Now, let the load have any position within the panel as defined by the distance x. Then, as before, the panel-point loads at c and d are given by expressions (a); and using these, together with the established influence coefficients y_c and y_d, we find for the bending moment at the section mn

$$M_{mn} = y_c P \frac{x}{d} + y_d P \frac{d - x}{d} \qquad (c)$$

Like expression (b), this is a linear function of x, reducing to Py_d when $x = 0$ and to Py_c when $x = d$. Accordingly, we conclude that the straight line $c'd'$ in Fig. 3.33b completes the influence diagram for bending moment at the section mn.

In general, we can state that in the case of a girder with floor beams, any influence line can be obtained directly from the corresponding influence line for a girder without floor beams. It is necessary only to connect by a straight line the points of the latter influence line corresponding to the ends of the panel under consideration. This follows from the fact that if the load is applied at any panel point, it is transmitted directly to the girder, whereas for any position of the load within a panel, the shearing force and bending moment at a given section vary linearly with change in position of the load.

In the case of a girder with floor beams the development of criteria for the placement of concentrated load systems to produce maximum effects does not require much additional discussion. Since the shearing force in an end panel will always be greater than in any intermediate panel and since the influence line (Fig. 3.32c) in such a case has the same form as an influence line for bending moment, we may use the criteria already developed in Art. 3.4 for maximum bending moment at a given section. Again, in the case of actual bending moment, the maximum will occur at one of the panel points since loads are transmitted to the girder only at such points. Thus, in this case, also, the criteria already developed for maximum bending moment at a given section are applicable, and the question of absolute maximum moment need not be considered.

As an example illustrating the numerical calculation of maximum live-load shearing force and maximum live-load bending moment in the case of a girder with floor beams, we assume that Fig. 3.34a represents a single-track plate-girder railroad bridge having a span of 88 ft and subdivided into four equal panels as shown. We assume also that the live load is a standard Cooper's E-60 loading.

For shearing force in an end panel, we have the influence diagram shown in Fig. 3.32c and can use, as a criterion of maximum, the reversal of condition (3.2) as discussed on page 131. With wheel ④ just to the right of panel point b

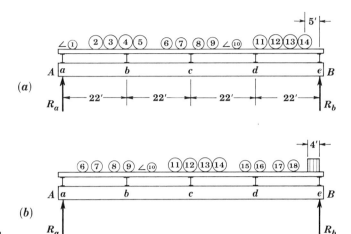

FIG. 3.34

(Fig. 3.34*a*), expression (3.2) becomes

$$\frac{273}{66} > \frac{75}{22}$$

whereas with this wheel just to the left of *b*, we have

$$\frac{243}{66} < \frac{105}{22}$$

Thus, there is a reversal of condition (3.2) as wheel ④ crosses the section, and we place this wheel at *b* for maximum shearing force in the end panel *ab*.   The corresponding value of this shearing force is

$$V_{ab} = R_a - P_a$$

where R_a is the reaction at *A* and P_a is the panel-point load at *a*.   Using the moment table for Cooper's E-60 loading (page 107), we find

$$R_a = \frac{13,100 + 348 \times 5}{88} = 168.5 \text{ kips}$$

$$P_a = \frac{720}{22} = 32.7 \text{ kips}$$

so that
$$V_{ab} = 168.5 - 32.7 = 135.8 \text{ kips}$$

For maximum bending moment, which will occur at the panel point *c*, we put wheel ⑫ at this point (Fig. 3.34*b*) because, as this wheel crosses mid-span, condition (3.2) changes from

$$\frac{180}{44} > \frac{123}{44} \quad \text{to} \quad \frac{150}{44} < \frac{153}{44}$$

The corresponding value of the reaction at A is (see moment table)

$$R_a = \frac{11,700 + 291 \times 4 + 12 \times 2}{88} = 146.3 \text{ kips}$$

and the bending moment at c then becomes

$$M_c = 146.3 \times 44 - 2,605 = 3,840 \text{ kip-ft}$$

With the foregoing maxima of shearing force and bending moment, a trial section can be chosen for the girder on the basis of which more detailed investigations of stresses can be made.

Sometimes the maximum live-load shearing force in an intermediate panel of a girder with floor beams will be required. For such cases, a criterion for placing the loads can be developed as follows: Referring to Fig. 3.35 and assuming that we require the maximum shearing force in the panel bc as a standard train moves from right to left across the span, we denote by W the resultant of all loads on the girder and by x its distance from B as shown. Likewise, let W' be the resultant of all loads within the panel bc and x' its distance from the panel point c. Then, by statics, the shearing force in the panel bc is

$$V_{bc} = \frac{Wx}{l} - \frac{W'x'}{d} \tag{d}$$

If the loads are now advanced a distance Δx to the left, the shearing force becomes

$$V'_{bc} = \frac{W}{l}(x + \Delta x) - \frac{W'}{d}(x' + \Delta x) \tag{e}$$

and we see that the change in shearing force is

$$\Delta V = \left(\frac{W}{l} - \frac{W'}{d}\right)\Delta x \tag{f}$$

As long as this expression is positive, i.e., as long as

$$\frac{W}{l} > \frac{W'}{d} \tag{3.3}$$

the shearing force in the panel bc continues to increase as the loads advance

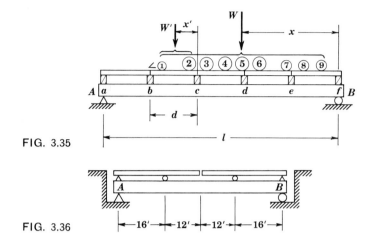

FIG. 3.35

FIG. 3.36

from right to left.   Thus, a maximum value of V_{bc} will be reached only when there is a reversal of condition (3.3), and from Fig. 3.35 we see that this will occur just as some wheel enters the panel bc.   Consequently, for maximum shearing force in the panel bc, we place at panel point c that wheel which upon entering the panel bc reverses condition (3.3).

PROBLEMS

1 How should a standard train be placed on the girder in Fig. 3.34 to produce a maximum shearing force in the panel bc?   Evaluate this maximum shearing force.
    Ans.   65.9 kips.
2 Evaluate the maximum bending moment at the panel point b of the girder in Fig. 3.34 if the loading is a standard Cooper's E-60 train.
    Ans.   2,990 kip-ft.
3 Determine the greatest floor-beam reaction (i.e., panel-point load) produced by the passage of a Cooper's E-60 train across the girder shown in Fig. 3.34.
    Ans.   105.3 kips.
4 Evaluate the maximum live-load bending moment at the center of the span in Fig. 3.35 if $l = 50$ ft and $d = 10$ ft.   Assume a Cooper's E-60 loading.   Compare this with the maximum bending moment at c or d.
5 Referring to Fig. 3.36, find the maximum live-load shearing force and bending moment produced in the girder AB as a standard train (Cooper's E-60) crosses the span.

3.6 INFLUENCE LINES FOR THREE-HINGED ARCH RIBS

In discussing influence lines for three-hinged arches, we begin with the case of a nonsymmetrical arch ACB (Fig. 3.37a) and assume that a moving vertical load P acts directly upon the rib as shown. This load induces reactions at the supports A and B, each of which we resolve into two components, one vertical and the other directed along the line AB as shown. Then, by equating to zero the algebraic sum of moments of all forces with respect to the points A and B, we conclude that the vertical components R_a and R_b of the reactions are the same as for a simple beam of span l. Denoting by H' the components in the direction of AB and projecting all forces onto a horizontal axis, we conclude that these components are equal in magnitude and opposite in direction. The horizontal projection of H' is called the *horizontal thrust* of the arch, and we denote it by H, that is, $H = H' \cos \alpha$. To determine the magnitude of H, we consider the portion AC of the arch as a free body and equate to zero the algebraic sum of moments of all forces with respect to the hinge C. Thus, we write

$$R_a a - H'f \cos \alpha = 0$$

where f is the *vertical rise* of the arch as shown in the figure. From this equation we find

$$H' \cos \alpha = H = R_a \frac{a}{f} \qquad (a)$$

Observing that $R_a a$ is the bending moment that would be produced at the distance a from the left end of a simple beam of span l, we conclude that during motion of the load P along the arch, the horizontal thrust H is always proportional to this simple-beam bending moment. Hence, to obtain the influence

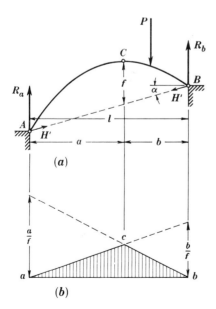

FIG. 3.37   (b)

line for H, we simply divide by f the ordinates of the corresponding influence line for bending moment at C in a simple beam, as shown in Fig. 3.37b.

If a system of vertical loads acts on the arch and it is required to find their position to make H a maximum, we simply use the criterion already developed for maximum bending moment at point C in a simple beam [see Eq. (3.2), page 130]. To obtain the horizontal thrust H when vertical load is uniformly distributed along the span of the arch, we simply multiply the area acb of the influence diagram by the intensity q of this load. Since the ordinates of the diagram are pure numbers in this case, the area acb has the dimension of length, and its product with intensity of load q has then the dimension of force.

Let us consider now the construction of an influence diagram for bending moment at some chosen cross section D of the unsymmetrical arch in Fig. 3.38a. If the position of this cross section is defined by its distance c from the reaction R_a, the bending moment for the loading shown may be expressed as follows:

$$M_d = R_a c - H y_d \qquad (b)$$

The first term on the right side of this expression represents the corresponding bending moment in a simple beam of span l, while the second term represents the moment contributed by the horizontal thrust H. Hence, the influence diagram for M_d is obtained by subtracting, from the ordinates of the influence line for bending moment in a simple beam, the ordinates of the influence line for H (Fig. 3.37b) multiplied by y_d. The result of such subtraction is shown by the shaded areas in Fig. 3.38b. This influence diagram can be represented in a somewhat simpler form by plotting the ordinates from a horizontal base ab as shown in Fig. 3.38c. To obtain this simplified diagram, we note that the zero point e must lie on the vertical through E (Fig. 3.38a) where the lines BC and AD intersect. This follows from the fact that when the load P passes through point E, the total reaction at A evidently passes through point D, and M_d vanishes. Observing further that the points d and c are on verticals through D and C and that at the left end of the diagram the ordinate of the straight line ced must be equal to c, we can readily make the simplified constructions shown in Fig. 3.38c.

The shearing force produced at the cross section D (Fig. 3.39a) by a vertical load P on the arch is given by the equation

$$V_d = R_a \cos \phi - H' \sin (\phi - \alpha) = R_a \cos \phi - H \frac{\sin (\phi - \alpha)}{\cos \alpha} \qquad (c)$$

where ϕ is the angle that the tangent to the center line at D makes with the horizontal and α is the angle between the horizontal and the line AB as shown. The first term on the right side of expression (c) represents the corresponding simple-beam shearing force at D multiplied by $\cos \phi$, while the second term

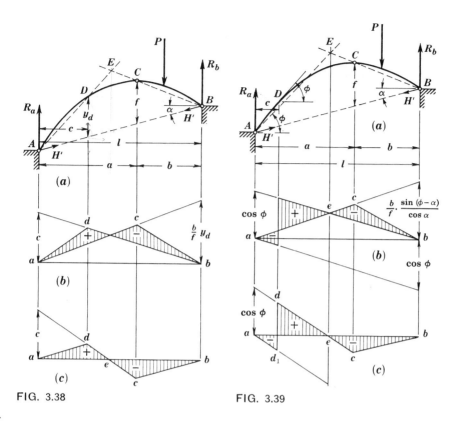

FIG. 3.38   FIG. 3.39

represents the contribution to shearing force made by the horizontal thrust H. Thus, the ordinates of the influence diagram for shearing force at D are obtained as differences between corresponding ordinates for shearing force in a simple beam multiplied by $\cos \phi$ and for thrust H multiplied by $\sin (\phi - \alpha)/\cos \alpha$. These differences are shown by ordinates of the shaded areas in Fig. 3.39b. Here, again, the influence diagram can be presented in simpler form by plotting the ordinates from a horizontal base line ab as shown in Fig. 3.39c. In this case, we obtain the simplified diagram by noting that the zero point e must lie on the vertical through E obtained as the intersection between the line BC and the line through A which makes the angle ϕ with the horizontal. This follows from the fact that the total reaction at A is parallel to the tangent at D when the load P passes through E. Having the zero point e and noting further that the straight line ced has the ordinate $\cos \phi$ at the left end of the span, we can make the constructions in Fig. 3.39c without difficulty.

Arches are usually so designed that there can be no direct transmission of live load to the rib as assumed throughout the preceding discussion; instead, the loads are applied to a system of floor beams supported by the arch as shown in Fig. 3.40a.   Under such conditions, forces can be transmitted to the arch proper only at the panel points I, J, K, . . . , and in the construction of influence lines we must proceed in the same manner as for a girder with floor beams (see Art. 3.5).   That is, we construct first the influence lines as for an arch without floor beams and then connect by straight lines those points which correspond to the extremities of the panel under consideration.   For example, to obtain the influence line for horizontal thrust H of the arch in Fig. 3.40a, we begin in Fig. 3.40b with the influence line acb, which assumes direct transmission of the load P (see Fig. 3.37b), and then join by a straight line the points j and k corresponding to the panel points J and K as shown.   Thus, the

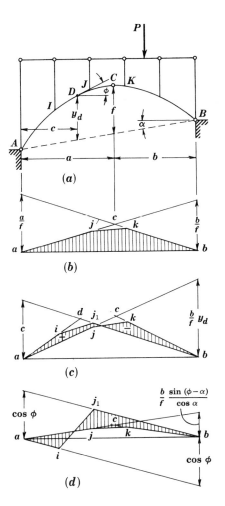

FIG. 3.40   (d)

ordinates of the line *ajkb* represent the required influence coefficients for
horizontal thrust H. The correctness of this procedure follows directly from
the fact that H, as we already have seen from Eq. (a), is proportional to the
simple-beam bending moment at C, and C is contained within the panel JK.
If the floor beams are so arranged that the hinge C becomes a panel point, the
influence line for H will be the same as for direct transmission of the load P.

The influence diagram for bending moment at the section D of the arch is
obtained in a similar manner as shown in Fig. 3.40c. The portions *acb* and
adb of this diagram are first constructed on the assumption of direct transmission of live load (compare with Fig. 3.38b), and then the points j, k and i,
j_1 corresponding to the panel points I, J, K are connected by straight lines as

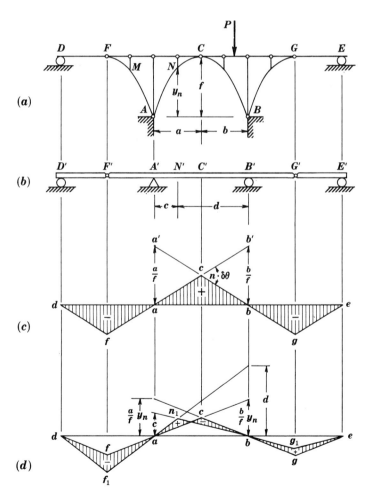

FIG. 3.41

shown. The ordinates of the shaded portions of the diagram represent the required influence coefficients for bending moment at D.

The influence diagram for shearing force at the cross section D, obtained by the same general procedure, is shown in Fig. 3.40d. It should be noted in connection with this latter diagram that, owing to the curvature of the arch rib, the shearing force is not constant throughout the panel IJ as in the case of a girder with floor beams.

Expressions (a), (b), and (c), developed for the case of a simple three-hinged arch, hold also for the arch with overhangs as shown in Fig. 3.41a. Accordingly, from Eq. (a) we conclude that the influence line for horizontal thrust H in this arch will be obtained by dividing by f the ordinates of an influence line for bending moment at C in a corresponding compound beam $D'F'G'E'$, supported as shown in Fig. 3.41b. To obtain this influence line, we use the method of virtual displacements and make at c (corresponding to C) such a relative angular displacement $n \, \delta\theta$ as shown in Fig. 3.41c that $aa' = a/f$ and $bb' = b/f$. The ordinates of the shaded diagram so obtained represent the required influence coefficients for horizontal thrust H of the arch. The influence diagram for bending moment at N is obtained in a similar manner, as shown in Fig. 3.41d. Here $df_1n_1g_1e$ represents the influence line for bending moment at N' of the corresponding compound beam (Fig. 3.41b), while $dfcge$ is simply the foregoing influence line for H with all ordinates multiplied by y_n. In accordance with Eq. (b), the differences in ordinates obtained by superposition of these two diagrams represent the required influence coefficients for bending moment at N in the arch of Fig. 3.41a. An influence diagram for shearing force at N can be obtained in a similar manner.

PROBLEMS

1 Construct an influence line for horizontal thrust H in a symmetrical three-hinged arch for which $l = 60$ ft and $f = 8$ ft. (a) Using this line, determine the magnitude of H produced by a uniformly distributed load of intensity $q = 1$ kip/ft and extending over the entire span. (b) Find the maximum value of H produced by a standard train (Cooper's E-60) assuming that the crown C is a panel point.
   Ans. (a) 56.25 kips. (b) 239 kips.

2 Assuming that the arch in Fig. 3.38a has the form of a parabola with vertical axis and vertex at C and that $a = b = l/2$, that is, that the arch is symmetrical, find the maximum positive bending moment at D due to a uniform live load of intensity q per unit length of span. Note that only the portion AE of the span should be loaded. The following numerical data are given: $l = 60$ ft, $f = 15$ ft, $c = 15$ ft, $q = 1$ kip/ft.
   Ans. 67.5 kip-ft.

3 Referring to Fig. 3.39 and assuming, as in the preceding problem, that the arch is a symmetrical parabola of span $l = 60$ ft and rise $f = 15$ ft, find the numerical maximum of shearing force at the quarter point D ($c = l/4$) under the action of a

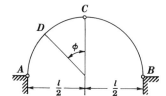

FIG. 3.42

uniform live load of intensity $q = 1$ kip per foot of span. Assume a direct transmission of load to the arch rib.

      Ans. 3.35 kips.

4 Construct influence diagrams for horizontal thrust H, bending moment M_d, and shearing force V_d in the case of a symmetrical semicircular three-hinged arch of span l as shown in Fig. 3.42. Assuming direct transmission of a uniformly distributed live load of intensity $q = 1$ kip per foot of span, find the maximum numerical value of each of the foregoing quantities. Assume $l = 60$ ft, $\phi = 30°$.

      Ans. $H = 15$ kips, $M_d = -104$ kip-ft, $V_d = 8.06$ kips.

5 Construct influence diagrams for shearing force at N and for bending moment at M of the arch shown in Fig. 3.41.

3.7 INFLUENCE LINES FOR SIMPLE TRUSSES

In the design of a truss we must find for each member the most unfavorable position of live load and then evaluate the corresponding axial force in that member. For such investigations, we shall see that influence lines can be used to advantage. We begin, for example, with the simple truss shown in Fig. 3.43a and assume that all loads are transmitted by means of floor beams to the joints $A, C, D, \ldots$ of the lower chord. Then, to construct an influence line for the axial force in an upper chord member such as EF, we assume a vertical load P acting on the truss and make a section mn as shown. Considering that portion of the truss to the left of this section as a free body and writing an equation of moments with respect to joint D, we obtain

$$R_a a + S_1 h_1 = 0$$

from which

$$S_1 = -\frac{R_a a}{h_1} \tag{a}$$

From this expression, we see that the compressive force S_1 is proportional to the bending moment $R_a a$ which would occur at the cross section D of a correspondingly loaded simple beam of span l. The same observation holds also if the load P is to the left of D. Hence, we conclude that the influence line for S_1 will be obtained by dividing by $-h_1$ the ordinates of an influence line for

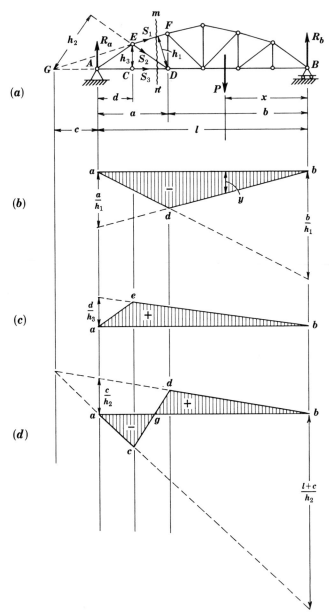

FIG. 3.43

bending moment at the cross section D of a simple beam AB. This construction is shown in Fig. 3.43b, and adb is the desired influence line for axial force in EF. Multiplying the load P by the ordinate y of this line, which is a pure number, we obtain the corresponding value of S_1. In the same way, if a uniformly distributed load extends over the entire span, the corresponding axial force S_1 is obtained as the product of the intensity q of this load and the area abd of the influence diagram. To find the maximum value of S_1 that can be induced by a system of loads such as the standard train in Fig. 3.1, we proceed in the same manner as to find the maximum bending moment at D of a simple beam (see page 130).

An influence line for the axial force in a lower chord member such as CD can be obtained in a similar manner. In this case, we use E as a moment center and note that the force S_3 is proportional to the simple-beam bending moment at this point. Hence, the desired influence line will be obtained by dividing by h_3 the ordinates of an influence line for bending moment at E of a simple beam of span l. This construction is shown in Fig. 3.43c, and we note that the influence coefficients are positive, indicating tension in the bar CD.

We shall now consider the construction of an influence line for axial force in the diagonal ED of the truss in Fig. 3.43a. Assuming first that the load P acts to the right of joint D and equating to zero the algebraic sum of moments of all forces to the left of mn with respect to point G, we obtain

$$S_2 = \frac{R_a c}{h_2} \tag{b}$$

Thus, so long as P is to the right of D, the ordinates of the influence line for S_2 can be obtained simply by multiplying by c/h_2 the ordinates of the influence line for R_a. In this way we obtain the portion bd of the required influence line as shown in Fig. 3.43d. When the load P is to the left of joint C, we consider the equilibrium of the right portion of the truss; and an equation of moments with respect to point G then gives

$$S_2 = -\frac{R_b(l + c)}{h_2} \tag{c}$$

Thus, for positions of the load to the left of C, the ordinates of the influence line for S_2 can be obtained by multiplying by $-(l + c)/h_2$ the ordinates of the influence line for R_b. This construction is shown in Fig. 3.43d by the straight line ac, having at b the ordinate $-(l + c)/h_2$. Now, when P is between C and D, we follow the same reasoning used in the case of a girder with floor beams (see page 134) and conclude that to complete the diagram we need only connect the established points c and d by a straight line as shown. We see that this influence diagram for a diagonal has a form similar to that for shearing force in an intermediate panel of a girder with floor beams (see Fig. 3.32b)

and that the axial force S_2 may be either tension or compression depending on the placement of the live load.   For example, to realize the maximum tensile force in ED due to uniformly distributed live load of intensity q, we must load only the portion gb of the span.   Then the corresponding magnitude of S_2 is obtained as the product between q and the area of the triangle gbd.   Similarly, the maximum compressive force in ED occurs when the distributed load extends only over the portion ag of the span.   In finding the maximum value of S_2 due to a series of concentrated loads such as a standard train, we proceed in a manner similar to that used in finding maximum shearing force in an intermediate panel of a girder with floor beams (see page 135).

The influence lines for vertical members of a truss will usually be constructed in a manner similar to that discussed above for diagonal members. For example, if we require an influence line for the axial force S in the vertical bar DF of the truss in Fig. 3.44a, we make the section mn as shown and then, with G as a moment center, write equations of equilibrium for the left and right portions of the truss as P is successively to the right of I and to the left of D. This gives

$$S = - \frac{R_a c}{a} \quad \text{and} \quad S = R_b \frac{l + c}{a} \tag{d}$$

from which we conclude that the required influence line for S will be obtained from the influence lines for R_a and R_b modified as shown in Fig. 3.44b.

The method of virtual displacements can often be used to advantage in the construction of influence lines for truss members.   Consider, for example, the truss shown in Fig. 3.45a, and assume that live load is transmitted to the joints

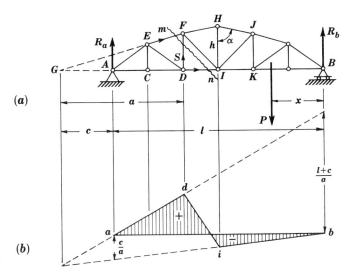

(a)

(b)

FIG. 3.44

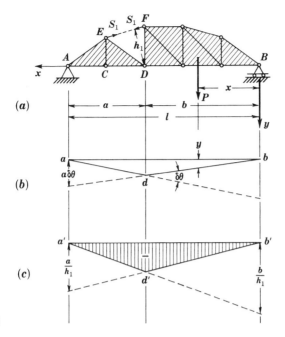

FIG. 3.45

of the lower chord.   Then, to obtain the influence line for a member EF of this truss, we imagine this bar to be removed and its action on the remainder of the truss represented by two equal but opposite forces S_1 as shown.   In this way, we obtain a system with one degree of freedom, as represented by the possibility for relative rotation about joint D between the two shaded rigid portions.   A virtual displacement of this system can be defined by the line adb (Fig. 3.45b), the ordinates of which represent the vertical deflections of points. on the lower chord corresponding to a small relative angular displacement $\delta\theta$ between the two rigid portions.   If y denotes the deflection of the point of application of the load P and Δ the shortening of the distance EF during the assumed virtual displacement, the equation of virtual work becomes

$$S_1\Delta + Py = 0$$

and we obtain

$$S_1 = -\frac{Py}{\Delta} \qquad\qquad (e)$$

We see from this expression that S_1 is proportional to y, and hence the deflection line adb gives us the general shape of the required influence diagram.   To obtain the influence coefficients to scale, we need only divide the ordinates y of this diagram by $-\Delta$.   To do this, we note from the figure that for the portion bd of the line we can write $y = xa\ \delta\theta/l$ and also that $\Delta = \delta\theta\ h_1$.

Hence, for positions of the load P to the right of D, the influence coefficients are

$$- \frac{y}{\Delta} = - \frac{xa}{h_1 l}$$

In Fig. 3.45c, then, the corresponding portion $b'd'$ of the true influence line for S_1 must have the ordinate a/h_1 when $x = l$ as shown.   In the same manner, we can show that for the left portion of the truss the line $a'd'$ must have at b' the ordinate b/h_1.   The same procedure can be used in constructing the influence line for any lower chord member.

To obtain an influence line for the diagonal ED by the method of virtual displacements, we first replace this bar by forces S_2 as shown in Fig. 3.46a. Then a virtual displacement of the system can be defined by a relative angular displacement $\delta\theta$ between the two rigid shaded portions.   This relative rotation must take place about the instantaneous center G in such a manner that the supported points A and B of the truss do not move vertically.   To accomplish this, we assume first that the support at B is removed and rotate the entire truss as a rigid body about the hinge A.   Small vertical displacements of the lower chord corresponding to this rotation are indicated in Fig. 3.46b by the straight line ab_1, and we see that, while b goes to b_1, the instantaneous center

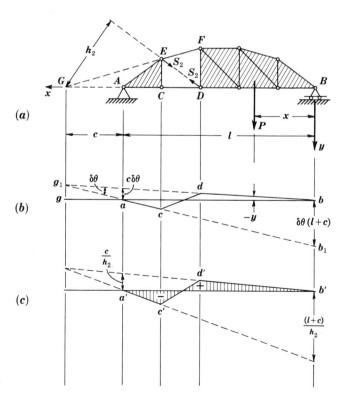

FIG. 3.46

g goes to g_1. Now, keeping the left portion of the truss stationary, we rotate the right portion about g_1 by such an angle $\delta\theta$ that point B comes back to its original position, i.e., in Fig. 3.46b, point b_1 comes back to b. The final configuration of the bottom chord, then, is represented by the line $acdb$ as shown. Denoting by y the vertical displacement of the load P corresponding to the assumed virtual displacement of the system, the equation of virtual work becomes

$$S_2\Delta + Py = 0$$

from which

$$S_2 = -\frac{Py}{\Delta} \qquad\qquad (f)$$

where Δ, as before, is the shortening of the distance ED corresponding to $\delta\theta$. Again, we see that S_2 is proportional to y and conclude that the line $acdb$ gives us the general shape of the required influence line for S_2.

To get influence coefficients $-y/\Delta$ to scale, we note from Fig. 3.46b that

$$-y = c\,\delta\theta\,\frac{x}{l} \qquad \text{and} \qquad \Delta = \delta\theta\,h_2$$

Hence, for the right portion of the truss, the influence coefficients are

$$-\frac{y}{\Delta} = \frac{x}{l}\frac{c}{h_2}$$

and the corresponding portion $b'd'$ of the true influence line has, at $x = l$, the ordinate c/h_2 as shown in Fig. 3.46c. In the same manner, we conclude that the line $a'c'$ must have at b' the ordinate $-(l+c)/h_2$ as shown. Comparing Fig. 3.46c with Fig. 3.43d, we see that the influence line obtained by the method of virtual displacements is identical with that previously obtained by the method of sections.

In the analysis of trusses, we often use influence diagrams only to find the most unfavorable positions of live load and then calculate the corresponding axial forces in the members without further reference to these diagrams. For such purpose, it is evident that we do not need the actual magnitudes of the influence coefficients but only the general shapes of the diagrams, which, as we have just seen, can be obtained very easily by the method of virtual displacements.

PROBLEMS

1 Referring to Fig. 3.43 and assuming that live load is transmitted to the lower-chord joints, find (a) the maximum possible axial force in CD with a uniformly distributed live load of intensity $q = 1$ kip/ft, (b) the maximum possible axial force in ED with a standard Cooper's E-60 loading. Assume that $l = 120$ ft, $h_3 = 18$ ft, $c = 30$ ft.

     Ans. (a) 66.7 kips. (b) 80.2 kips.

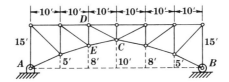

FIG. 3.47

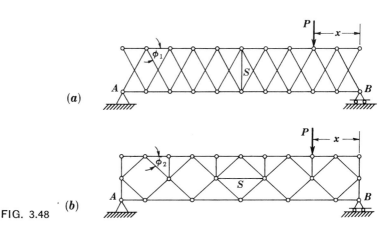

(a)

(b)

FIG. 3.48

2   Using the method of sections, construct influence diagrams for the axial forces S_1, S_2, S_3 in the truss shown in Fig. 2.32.   Assume that the live load is transmitted to the upper-chord joints.   What are the numerical maxima of these axial forces for a uniform live load of intensity $q = 1$ kip/ft?   Assume $a = 10$ ft.
    Ans. $S_1 = +33.75$ kips, $S_2 = -26.25$ kips, $S_3 = -33.75$ kips.

3   Using the method of virtual displacements, construct influence lines for the axial forces S_1 and S_2 in CD and DE, respectively, of the truss in Fig. 3.47.   Assume live load applied to the joints of the upper chord.   For a live load of uniform intensity $q = 1$ kip/ft, what are the possible numerical maxima of these axial forces?
    Ans. $S_1 = 36.7$ kips, $S_2 = -26.4$ kips.

4   Assuming that live load is transmitted to the joints of the upper chord, construct an influence line for the middle vertical of the simple trusses shown in Fig. 2.27, page 72.   Assume $a = 10$ ft, $h = 12$ ft.   For a uniform live load of intensity $q = 1$ kip/ft, evaluate the maximum value of this axial force.
    Ans. $S = -5$ kips.

5   Construct an influence line for axial force S in the middle bar of each of the simple trusses shown in Fig. 3.48.   Assume $\phi_1 = 60°$, $\phi_2 = 45°$.

3.8   INFLUENCE LINES FOR COMPOUND TRUSSES

A compound truss with subdivided panels like that shown in Fig. 3.49a may be considered as consisting of a basic simple truss (Fig. 3.49b) on which are superimposed several secondary trusses (Fig. 3.49c).   In the analysis of such a system under dead load, we determine first the axial forces in the bars of the basic truss and then add algebraically the forces in the corresponding bars of the secondary truss (see Art. 2.6). The same procedure can be used in the construction of influence lines for the compound truss. We begin with the influence lines for the bars of a secondary truss as shown in Fig. 3.49c. These are shown, respectively, in Fig. 3.49d for the vertical member, Fig. 3.49e for

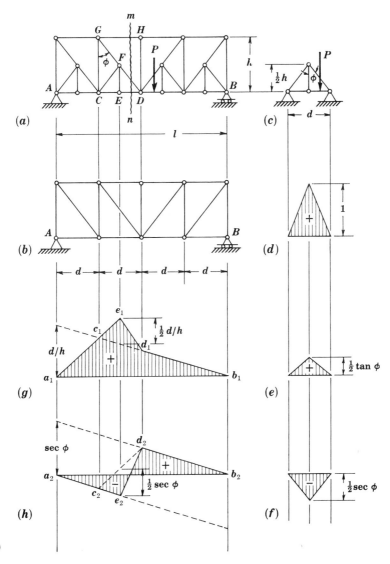

FIG. 3.49

the horizontal member, and Fig. 3.49f for either inclined member. With these secondary diagrams, the influence diagram for any bar of the compound truss can easily be obtained. Consider, for example, the member CD. For the corresponding member of the basic truss (Fig. 3.49b) the influence diagram is represented by the triangle $a_1c_1b_1$ shown in Fig. 3.49g. Now on the ordinates of this diagram we must superimpose the ordinates of the diagram in Fig. 3.49e. Since $\frac{1}{2} \tan \phi = \frac{1}{2}d/h$, this is accomplished simply by extending the line a_1c_1 to point e_1 and then connecting points e_1 and d_1 by a straight line as shown. The figure $a_1e_1d_1b_1$ obtained in this way represents the required influence diagram for the member CD of the given compound truss.

To obtain the influence diagram for the lower portion FD of a diagonal of the compound truss, we construct first the influence diagram $a_2c_2d_2b_2$ (Fig. 3.49h) for the corresponding diagonal of the basic truss. Then, on the ordinates of this diagram, we superimpose the ordinates of the secondary diagram in Fig. 3.49f as shown. In this way, we obtain the shaded diagram $a_2e_2d_2b_2$ (Fig. 3.49h), the ordinates of which represent the required influence coefficients for the member FD of the given compound truss. The upper portions of the diagonals as well as the verticals and upper chord members of the compound truss will, of course, have the same influence lines as the corresponding members of the basic truss. Thus in Fig. 3.49h, for example, the line $a_2c_2d_2b_2$ may be used as the influence line for the member GF of the compound truss.

In the case of a compound truss like that in Fig. 3.49a, the influence diagrams in Fig. 3.49g and h can also be constructed by direct application of the method of sections as in the preceding article. If the load P is to the right of joint D, we consider the equilibrium of that portion of the truss to the left of the section mn (Fig. 3.49a) and find that the lines b_1d_1 and b_2d_2 must be the same as for the basic truss (Fig. 3.49b). Likewise, if the load P is to the left of joint E, we consider the equilibrium of that portion of the truss to the right of the section mn and find the lines a_1e_1 and a_2e_2 as shown. Then, to complete the constructions, it remains only to draw the straight lines e_1d_1 and e_2d_2 corresponding to positions of the load within the panel ED.

Influence diagrams for various members of the cantilever truss shown in Fig. 3.50a can be readily constructed by considering the compound beam in Fig. 3.50b as the corresponding basic system. Let us consider, for example, the influence diagram for the upper-chord member CD of this truss. Making a section mn as shown and writing an equation of moments with respect to the joint E, we conclude that for any position of the load P on the lower chord the axial force S in the bar CD is obtained by dividing by $-h$ the corresponding bending moment at E' of the compound beam shown in Fig. 3.50b. Hence, the desired influence diagram for S is obtained by dividing by h the ordinates of an influence diagram for bending moment at E' as shown in Fig. 3.50c. Influence diagrams for members of the lower chord of the cantilever truss can be constructed in a similar manner.

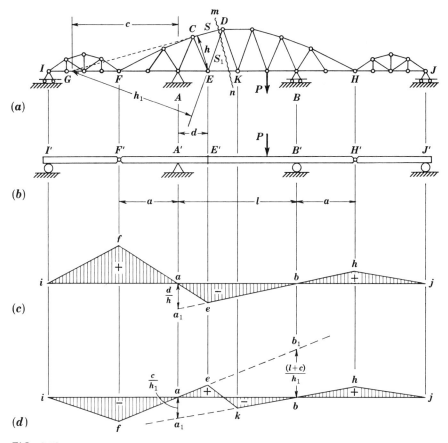

FIG. 3.50

In the case of a diagonal member DE, the axial force S_1 is obtained by using the same section mn and writing an equation of moments with respect to point G (Fig. 3.50a). If the load P is to the right of joint K, this equation gives

$$S_1 = -\frac{R_a c}{h_1} \tag{a}$$

and we see that the corresponding portion of the influence diagram for S_1 can be obtained by multiplying by $-c/h_1$ the ordinates of an influence line for the reaction R_a of the compound beam in Fig. 3.50b. This construction is represented by the line $jhbk$ in Fig. 3.50d. If the load P is to the left of joint E, we consider the equilibrium of the portion of the truss to the right of the section *mn* and obtain

$$S_1 = R_b \frac{l + c}{h_1} \qquad (b)$$

Thus, in Fig. 3.50*d*, we obtain the portion *ife* of the required diagram by multiplying by $(l + c)/h_1$ the ordinates of an influence line for the reaction R_b

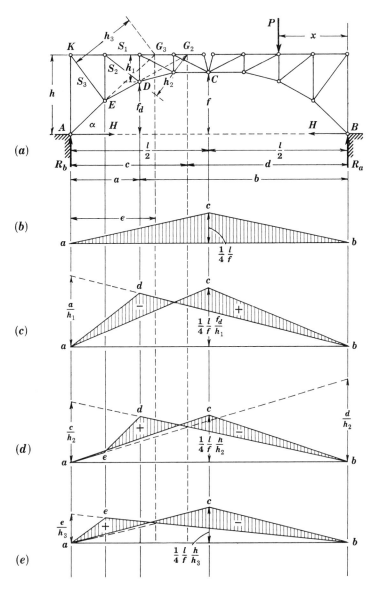

FIG. 3.51

of the compound beam in Fig. 3.50*b*.   Finally, for positions of the load *P* within the panel *EK*, we draw the straight line *ek*, and the required influence diagram *ifekhj* for S_1 is completed.

In the case of a three-hinged arch under vertical load as shown in Fig. 3.51*a*, we note that the reactive forces at *A* and *B* differ from those for a simply supported truss *AB* only by the presence of the horizontal thrust *H*.   Hence, we conclude that the axial force S_i in any bar of the system can be obtained by superimposing on the axial force $\mathcal{S}_i$, calculated as for a simply supported truss, the additional axial force induced by the thrust action *H*.   Thus, for the system in Fig. 3.51*a*,

$$S_1 = \mathcal{S}_1 + H\frac{f_d}{h_1} \qquad S_2 = \mathcal{S}_2 - H\frac{h}{h_2} \qquad S_3 = \mathcal{S}_3 - H\frac{h}{h_3}$$

From these expressions, we see now that to obtain an influence diagram for the axial force S_i in any bar of the three-hinged arch, we need only to construct the corresponding $\mathcal{S}_i$ influence line, as for a simply supported truss, and then superimpose on it a certain modification of the *H* influence line shown in Fig. 3.51*b*.   In Fig. 3.51*c*, for example, the line *adb* with negative ordinates is the influence line for the axial force $\mathcal{S}_1$ in a simply supported truss, and *acb* is the influence line for *H* with all ordinates multiplied by f_d/h_1.   The shaded areas obtained by superposition of these two diagrams represent the desired influence diagram for the axial force S_1 in the three-hinged arch.   The influence diagrams for S_2 and S_3 are obtained in a similar manner as shown in Fig. 3.51*d* and *e*, respectively.

PROBLEMS

1   Construct influence diagrams for the axial forces S_1, S_2, and S_3 in each of the compound trusses shown in Fig. 3.52.

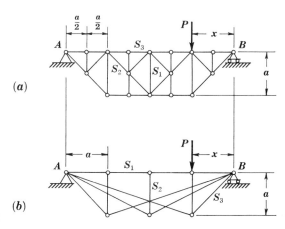

(*a*)

(*b*)

FIG. 3.52

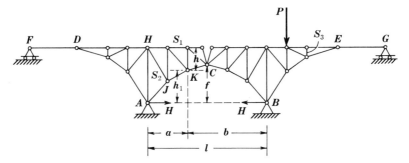

FIG. 3.53

2   Construct influence lines for S_1, S_2, S_3, S_4 of the cantilever bridge shown in Fig. 2.34, page 77. The height of the truss is 15 ft, and the panel distances are uniform at 15 ft each. What is the maximum value of S_1 that can be produced by a Cooper's E-60 loading?

    Ans. $S_1 = 449$ kips.

3   Referring to Fig. 3.51, find the maximum horizontal thrust H that can be produced in the arch by a uniformly distributed live load of intensity $q = 1$ kip/ft. Assume $l = 120$ ft and $f = 20$ ft. What maximum thrust can occur in the arch under the action of a standard train?

    Ans. $H = 90$ kips. $H = 344.5$ kips.

4   Construct an influence diagram for the vertical member AK of the three-hinged arch shown in Fig. 3.51a. What maximum compressive force can be induced in this member by a uniform live load of intensity $q = 3$ kips/ft? Assume $l = 120$ ft, $f = 20$ ft, $h = 30$ ft, and $\tan \alpha = \frac{3}{4}$.

    Ans. 55.4 kips.

5   Construct influence diagrams for the axial forces S_1, S_2, and S_3 in the structure shown in Fig. 3.53.

    Hint   Construct first the influence lines for S_1, S_2, and S_3 as in a cantilever truss and then modify for the effect of the horizontal thrust H as was done in Fig. 3.51c.

Chapter 4

Statically determinate space structures

4.1 CONCURRENT FORCES IN SPACE

If several forces in space have the same point of application, they can always be reduced to a single resultant force by using the principle of the parallelogram of forces as discussed in Art. 1.1. Consider, for example, the three concurrent forces F_1, F_2, and F_3, represented by the vectors $\overline{OA}$, $\overline{OB}$, and $\overline{OD}$ in Fig. 4.1a. Considering, first, only the vectors $\overline{OA}$ and $\overline{OB}$ and using the principle of the parallelogram of forces, we find their resultant $\overline{OC}$ as shown. Now, taking this *partial resultant* together with the remaining force F_3 and again applying the principle of the parallelogram of forces, we find their resultant as represented by the diagonal $\overline{OE}$ of the parallelogram $ODEC$. Obviously, this force $\overline{OE}$, which we denote by R, is the resultant of the three given forces; and we note that it is obtained as the diagonal of the parallelepiped formed on the three given vectors. The same resultant R can also be obtained as the closing side $\overline{O'E'}$ of the *space polygon of forces* $O'A'C'E'$ shown in Fig. 4.1b. This follows from the fact that the space figure $O'A'C'E'$ is identical with the space figure $OACE$ in Fig. 4.1a. Since the constructions shown in Fig. 4.1 can readily be extended to any number of concurrent forces in space, we conclude that the resultant of such a system can always be obtained as the geometric sum of the given forces and that its line of action will always act through the point of concurrence of the given forces.

It may be noted here that if a system of concurrent forces in space (Fig. 4.1a) and the corresponding space polygon of forces (Fig. 4.1b) are orthogonally projected onto any plane, we obtain in the plane of projection a polygon of forces the sides of which are equal to the corresponding projections of the given forces. From this fact, we conclude that any projection of the resultant of the given forces is identical with the resultant of the corresponding projections of the forces themselves. In the particular case where the given system of forces in space is in equilibrium, it follows that their orthogonal projections on any plane will represent a coplanar system of forces in equilibrium. As we shall see later, this observation can often be used to advantage in dealing with equilibrium of space systems.

From the foregoing discussion, we can conclude at once that the projection on any axis of a resultant of several concurrent forces in space will be equal to the algebraic sum of the projections of the given forces on the same axis. From this it follows that if the given forces are in equilibrium, the algebraic sums of their projections on mutually orthogonal axes x, y, and z must vanish. Thus we arrive at the well-known *equations of equilibrium*

$$\Sigma X_i = 0 \qquad \Sigma Y_i = 0 \qquad \Sigma Z_i = 0 \tag{4.1}$$

where X_i, Y_i, and Z_i are the orthogonal projections of any force F_i, and the summations are understood to include all forces in the system.

On the basis of Eqs. (4.1) several general observations can be made that will prove useful in later discussions. (1) Three concurrent forces that do not lie in one plane cannot be in equilibrium unless all three forces are zero. To prove this statement, consider the three forces in Fig. 4.1a, and equate to

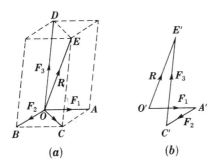

FIG. 4.1   (*a*)   (*b*)

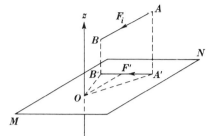

FIG. 4.2

zero the algebraic sum of their projections on an axis normal to the plane AOB. Then, since F_3 is the only force that has such a projection different from zero, we conclude that $F_3 = 0$. In the same way, by successively projecting the forces onto axes that are normal, respectively, to the planes AOD and BOD, we conclude that $F_2 = 0$ and that $F_1 = 0$. (2) If two of four concurrent forces that are not all in one plane are collinear, equilibrium can exist only if the other two forces are zero. The two collinear forces, of course, must be equal in magnitude and opposite in direction. This statement may be proved by projecting the system onto a plane normal to the line of action of the two collinear forces. Then, in this plane of projection there are only two forces that are not collinear, and two such forces cannot be in equilibrium unless they are both zero. (3) If all but one of any number of concurrent forces in space are coplanar, equilibrium can exist only if this odd force is zero. This is proved by equating to zero the algebraic sum of the projection of all forces on an axis normal to the coplanar forces. (4) If the known lines of action of all but two of any number of concurrent forces in equilibrium are coplanar and the magnitude of one of these two is known, the magnitude of the other can always be found by projecting all forces onto an axis normal to the coplanar forces.

In dealing with space systems, the notion of *moment of a force with respect to an axis* is often useful. To obtain the moment of a force F_i with respect to an axis z (Fig. 4.2), we first project the force onto a plane MN that is normal to the axis z and then take the moment of this projection F' with respect to the point O where the axis pierces the plane. This moment of the projection F' with respect to the point O is equal to the doubled area of the triangle $A'OB'$ and is considered positive when directed as shown in the figure. From this definition of moment of a force with respect to an axis, we see that the moment vanishes if the force is parallel to the axis or intersects it. We see also that, if any system of concurrent forces in space is in equilibrium, the algebraic sum of their moments with respect to any axis must be zero, since, by the theorem of moments,[1] the algebraic sum of moments of the given forces is equal to

[1] S. Timoshenko and D. H. Young, "Engineering Mechanics," 4th ed., p. 180, McGraw-Hill Book Company, New York, 1956.

the corresponding moment of their resultant, and when the forces are in equilibrium, the resultant vanishes.

Let us now turn our attention for a moment to the purely geometrical question of the complete constraint of a point in space. Referring to Fig. 4.3a, we see that the attachment of a point O to a rigid foundation by means of two bars OA and OB serves only to establish constraint of the point in the plane AOB of the bars and that there remains the possibility of rotation of this plane about the axis AB. To remove this possibility of rotation, a third bar OC (Fig. 4.3b) that is not in the plane AOB of the other two is necessary. If all three bars by which the point O is attached to the foundation lie in one plane, complete constraint is not realized. In the case represented in Fig. 4.3c, for example, the ends A, C, and B of the three bars all lie on one axis, and there is the same unlimited freedom of rotation about this axis as in the case represented in Fig. 4.3a. Again, in the case shown in Fig. 4.3d, it is evident that considerable movement of point O in the direction normal to the plane ABC of the bars can take place without appreciable changes in the lengths of the bars. Thus, in this case, also, we have unsatisfactory constraint of the point O in space. From this discussion, we can conclude that complete and satisfactory constraint of a point in space can always be realized by attaching it to a foundation by three bars the axes of which do not lie in one plane.

Let us assume now that an external force P is applied to the completely constrained point O in Fig. 4.4. Under the action of this load, axial forces

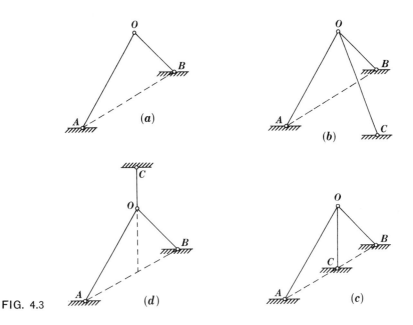

FIG. 4.3

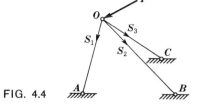

FIG. 4.4

will be induced in the three supporting bars, and accordingly each bar will exert on the joint O a reaction S_i directed along the axis of the bar and representing in magnitude the corresponding axial force. Thus, at O we have a system of four concurrent forces that are in equilibrium; and since all lines of action are given, we see that the only unknown elements in the system are the magnitudes S_1, S_2, and S_3. Hence, regardless of the magnitude or direction of the applied force P, the corresponding magnitudes of the three reactions can always be found by using Eqs. (4.1). For this reason the system is said to be *statically determinate*. If the point O is attached to the foundation by more than three bars, i.e., if there are *redundant supports*, the three necessary and sufficient conditions of equilibrium represented by Eqs. (4.1) will be insufficient to determine the unknown elements, and the system is said to be *statically indeterminate*. If there are fewer than three supporting bars or three bars in one plane, the system is nonrigid and will not remain in equilibrium under the action of an applied force P that does not coincide with the plane of the bars.

Confining our attention to statically determinate systems, we shall now consider various practicable methods of application of the conditions of equilibrium represented by Eqs. (4.1). As a first example, we take the simple space structure shown in Fig. 4.5. This system consists of a strut AO hinged at O to a vertical wall MN and supported at A by guy wires AB and AC as shown. Under the action of an external force P at A, the analysis of this system can be made without difficulty by direct application of Eqs. (4.1). We begin with a free-body diagram of point A, which is acted upon by the external force P, and the three reactions S_1, S_2, and S_3, representing the axial forces in the bars. We assume each of these unknown reactions to be directed away from the joint so that in our final results plus signs will indicate tension and minus signs compression. Equating to zero the algebraic sum of the projections of all forces at A on each of the orthogonal axes x, y, and z, directed as shown in the figure, Eqs. (4.1) become, respectively,

$$-S_1 - \tfrac{12}{13}S_2 - \tfrac{12}{13}S_3 = 0$$

$$-P + \tfrac{3}{13}S_2 = 0 \qquad (a)$$

$$\tfrac{5}{13}S_3 - \tfrac{4}{13}S_2 = 0$$

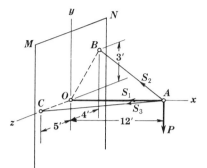

FIG. 4.5

from which we find $S_1 = -7.20P$, $S_2 = +4.33P$, $S_3 = +3.47P$. The negative sign for S_1 indicates that the strut is under compression, whereas the guy wires each carry tension.

The same results can be found in another way by using the notion of moment of force with respect to an axis. For example, if we equate to zero the algebraic sum of moments of all forces with respect to the z axis, we obtain

$$-P \times 12 + \tfrac{3}{13}S_2 \times 12 = 0$$

from which, as before, we find $S_2 = +4.33P$.

Sometimes the analysis of a space structure can be handled to advantage by working with one or more plane projections of the given system. Consider, for example, the simple space system shown in Fig. 4.6a. We recall that, in general, if a system of concurrent forces in space is in equilibrium, their projections on any plane will also be in equilibrium. This idea can be used to advantage in the present case. Projecting onto the vertical plane AEB, we

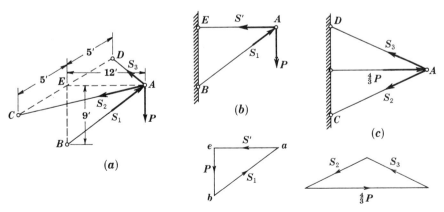

FIG. 4.6

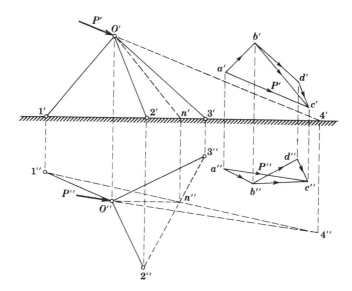

FIG. 4.7

obtain the coplanar system shown in Fig. 4.6b, the analysis of which is indicated by the accompanying triangle of forces *eba*.   From this triangle, the compressive force in the strut is seen to be $S_1 = \frac{5}{3}P$.   In the same way, by projecting the system onto the horizontal plane *ACD* (Fig. 4.6c) and using the previously determined value of S_1, the horizontal projection of which is equal but opposite to the force S' in Fig. 4.6b, we find the tensions in the two guy wires to be $S_2 = S_3 = 0.722P$.

In dealing with a system of concurrent forces in space, we may often encounter difficulty in determining analytically the projections or moments of the forces with respect to various axes.   In such cases, a graphical method may be helpful.   For example, the axial forces produced in the bars *O*1, *O*2, and *O*3 of the system in Fig. 4.7 can be found graphically by resolving the given force P, defined by its orthogonal projections P' and P'', into three components acting along *O*1, *O*2, *O*3.   We begin with a determination of the line of intersection of the plane defined by the bar *O*1 and P with the plane defined by the bars *O*2 and *O*3.   One point on this line of intersection is obviously point *O*.   Another point on the same line is the point *n* obtained by using the intersection of the lines 1″4″ and 2″3″ in the horizontal projection.   With the points *O* and *n*, the required line of intersection is completely defined by its projections *O′n′* and *O″n″*.   We next resolve the load P into two components, one along the axis of the bar *O*1 and one along the line *On*, the projections of which we have just found.   The triangles of forces *a′b′c′* and *a″b″c″* represent the vertical and horizontal projections, respectively, of the corresponding triangle of forces *abc* in space.   The side $\overline{ab}$ of this triangle gives the component of P that acts along $O1$, and the side $\overline{bc}$, the component that acts along On. Finally, since the line On is in the plane $O23$, this latter component of P can be resolved into two components $\overline{bd}$ and $\overline{dc}$ that act, respectively, along the axes of the bars $O3$ and $O2$ as shown. With the orthogonal projections $\overline{a'b'}$, $\overline{b'd'}$, $\overline{d'c'}$ and $\overline{a''b''}$, $\overline{b''d''}$, $\overline{d''c''}$ of the three components of P, the components themselves can be obtained without difficulty. As already mentioned, the axial forces in the bars can be found directly from these components. We see that in this case the bar $O1$ will be in tension, whereas the bars $O2$ and $O3$ are in compression.

PROBLEMS

1 Three bars of equal length l are joined together at A and supported at B, C, and D, as shown in Fig. 4.8. Find the axial force induced in each bar due to a vertical load P at A, if $OB = OC = OD = l$.

     Ans. $S_1 = -2P/3$, $S_2 = -2P/3$, $S_3 = +P/3$.

2 The legs of a tripod are of equal length l and are supported at points A, B, and C, which form an equilateral triangle with sides of length l in a horizontal plane. Find the compressive force S induced in each leg by a vertical load P applied at the apex of the tripod.

     Ans. $S = -P/\sqrt{6}.$

3 Assuming that the legs of the tripod in Prob. 2 are supported on a frictionless horizontal plane and that they are prevented from spreading by a string ABC, find the tension induced in this string.

     Ans. $S = +P/3\sqrt{6}.$

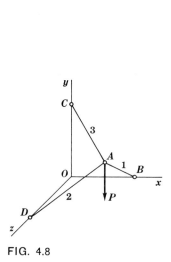

FIG. 4.8

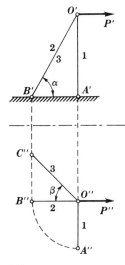

FIG. 4.9

4   Determine the axial forces S_1, S_2, and S_3 in the bars of the space system arranged and loaded as shown in Fig. 4.9.   Note that the distances $O''B''$ and $O''A''$ in the horizontal projection are equal.   Assume that $\beta = 45°$.

   Ans. $S_1 = -P \sec \alpha$, $S_2 = -2P \sec \alpha$, $S_3 = -P \sqrt{2 - \tan^2 \alpha}$.

5   How will the axial forces S_1, S_2, and S_3 in Fig. 4.9 be changed if the external force P is vertical instead of horizontal as shown?

4.2 SIMPLE SPACE TRUSSES: METHOD OF JOINTS

A system of bars in space, joined together at their ends in such a way as to form a rigid space structure, is called a *space truss*.   Many kinds of engineering structures such as radar telescopes, transmission-line towers, and cranes are of such construction.   In the fabrication of these structures, it is common practice to make the connections at the joints by either riveting or welding.   Of course, the rigidity of this type of connection is bound to interfere to some extent with the free adjustment of the system to applied loads so that some secondary bending of the bars will be induced.   However, in many practical cases, the presence of such secondary bending does not materially influence the primary action of the structure, and the axial forces can usually be calculated with good accuracy by ignoring the effect of the rigidity of the joints.[1]   Thus we generally assume that the bars are connected at their ends by *ideal spherical hinges* even though such connections can never be realized in practice.   In our further discussion here, we shall always assume such hinges.

   By way of establishing a criterion of rigidity for space trusses with ideal spherical hinges, we recall that the complete constraint of a point in space requires its attachment to a foundation by three bars the axes of which are not in one plane.   With this notion of complete constraint of one point in space, we can easily establish a method of assembling a system of bars in space so as to form a rigid structure.   Referring to Fig. 4.10, we begin with three bars AE, BE, and CE by which the joint E is rigidly attached to a foundation $ABCD$.   With the joint E completely constrained in space, it follows that by the three bars EF, DF, and AF the joint F is completely constrained in space. E and F now being fixed points like A, B, C, and D, we conclude that the joint G can be rigidly connected to the rest of the structure by the three bars EG, FG, and CG.   Since this procedure may be carried on indefinitely, we may state the following rule: *A rigid space truss can always be formed by attaching the first joint to a foundation by means of three bars that do not lie in one plane and establishing each additional joint thereafter by three more bars that do not lie in one*

---

[1] In some cases, the presence of secondary bending in a space structure may greatly affect its behavior under load, and it becomes necessary to consider this effect in detail.   Several such examples are discussed by A. Föppl in his book "Vorlesungen über technische Mechanik," vol. II, p. 276, B. G. Teubner, Leipzig, 1912.

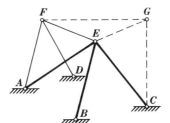

FIG. 4.10

plane. Those three bars by which any joint after the first is attached to the existing structure may be joined either to the foundation or to previously established joints. Any space system formed in accordance with this rule is called a *simple space truss*. Several examples of such space trusses are shown in Fig. 4.11. In each case the joints have been set up in alphabetical order, the first joint being attached to the foundation by three bars not in one plane and succeeding joints being attached to the existing structure in the same manner. It should be noted that in general the rigidity of such structures is not independent of their connection to the foundation. That is, none of the systems shown in Fig. 4.11 will represent a rigid body if disconnected from the foundation points A', B', C', ...

Suppose now that any one of the space trusses in Fig. 4.11 is subjected to the action of several applied loads. Under the influence of these external forces, internal forces will be induced in the various bars, and the determination of these internal forces constitutes the analysis of the truss. In dealing with such problems, we make the same idealizing assumptions that we did for plane trusses; namely, (1) the bars themselves are weightless, (2) they are connected at their ends by ideal hinges, and (3) external forces are applied only at the joints. On the basis of these assumptions, it follows that each bar will suffer only simple tension or compression without bending, and thus the equal but

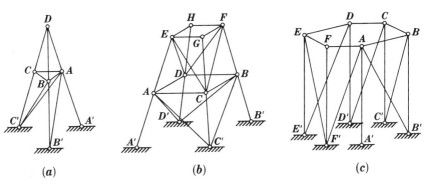

FIG. 4.11

opposite reactions that it exerts on the joints at its two ends will be directed along the axis of the bar. We have then at each joint a system of concurrent forces in space, the lines of action of which are known and to which the three conditions of equilibrium represented by Eqs. (4.1) can be applied directly.

The analysis of space trusses by which we apply successively to each joint the conditions of equilibrium represented by Eqs. (4.1) is called the *method of joints*. To illustrate, let us consider the analysis of the space system arranged and loaded as shown in Fig. 4.12. Beginning with the joint D and denoting by S_1, S_2, and S_3, respectively, the axial forces in the bars 1, 2, and 3, we see that these three forces can be evaluated without difficulty by one of the methods discussed in the preceding article. Assuming then that S_1, S_2, and S_3 have been determined, we find at the joint C only three unknowns, namely, S_4, S_5, and S_6, and these three magnitudes can be found without difficulty. When this has been done, there will remain only three unknown forces at B, and the equilibrium of this joint can be considered next. Finally, we may proceed to the joint A, where all forces except S_{10}, S_{11}, and S_{12} will be known; and when these are found, the analysis of the truss is completed.

In general, we see that to be successful with the method of joints we must, at the beginning, find at least one joint of the truss to which only three bars not in one plane are attached. Then, when the forces in these three bars have been determined, there must be another joint where only three unknowns will be encountered, etc., until the analysis is completed. Recalling the method of formation of a simple space truss where each joint is attached to the existing portion of the structure by three bars not in one plane, we see that the method of joints must always be applicable to such trusses. It is necessary only to begin the analysis with the last joint added to the structure and then consider the joints successively in the reverse order from which they were set up.

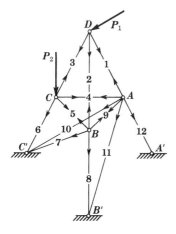

FIG. 4.12

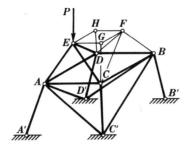

FIG. 4.13

By such procedure we encounter only three unknowns at each new joint, and the analysis proceeds without difficulty.

As a preliminary step in the analysis of any space truss, we can often simplify the problem by examining the system for *inactive members*, i.e., bars, which, under a given condition of loading, do not carry either tension or compression. Consider, for example, the space truss constructed and loaded as shown in Fig. 4.13. Beginning with the joint G, we see that there is no external load here, and only three bars not in one plane. Hence the axial forces in these three bars must all be zero since, as we have already pointed out, three concurrent forces can be in equilibrium only if they are coplanar. The same reasoning may be applied to the joint H. Then, since no forces are exerted on the joint F by the bars HF and GF, we conclude that the three remaining bars DF, BF, and CF must also be inactive since they are three bars not in one plane and since no external force acts at F. Thus, the inactive bars (represented in the figure by fine lines) can be removed, leaving, for further analysis, only that portion of the structure represented by heavy lines.

In Fig. 4.14 we have another example of a simple space truss in which several of the bars are inactive for the particular case of loading shown. In this case we do not begin the analysis at once with a consideration of the joint F to which only three bars are attached. Instead, let us consider the joint B at which there

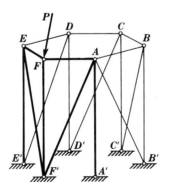

FIG. 4.14

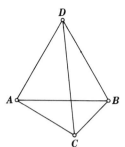

FIG. 4.15

is no external load and four bars, three of which are in one plane. From this fact it follows that the bar *AB* must be inactive. Similar reasoning with respect to the joints *C*, *D*, and *E* leads us to conclude that the bars *BC*, *CD*, and *DE* also are inactive. Let us imagine, then, that these inactive bars *AB*, *BC*, *CD*, and *DE* are removed from the structure. As soon as this is done, we see that at each of the joints *B*, *C*, and *D* there remain only two bars which are not collinear. From this we conclude that the bars *BB′*, *BC′*, *CC′*, *CD′*, *DD′*, and *DE′* are also inactive since two forces can be in equilibrium only if they are collinear in action. Finally, then, if all inactive bars (represented by fine lines) are removed from the system, we have for further analysis only that portion of the truss represented by heavy lines.

We have already noted that the rigidity of such simple space trusses as those in Fig. 4.11 is not independent of their attachment to a foundation. Sometimes, as in the case of a dirigible, it is desirable to have a rigid space structure independent of any foundation. To assemble a system of bars in space so as to form a self-contained rigid framework independent of any foundation, we can proceed as follows: Beginning with three bars in the form of a triangle *ABC* (Fig. 4.15), we attach to these a fourth joint *D* by means of the three bars *AD*, *BD*, and *CD* that do not lie in one plane. In this way we obtain a rigid tetrahedron that cannot be distorted by any system of external forces applied to its joints.[1] This tetrahedron represents the simplest form in which a system of bars in space can be interconnected to make a self-contained rigid body. Any such tetrahedron can readily be extended by attaching new joints to the existing system, each by means of three bars the axes of which do not lie in one plane. Several examples of more extended forms are shown in Fig. 4.16; such systems also are called *simple space trusses*. In each case we begin with a triangle *ABC* and establish succeeding joints in alphabetical order, each by means of three bars not in one plane.

Whenever any self-contained simple space truss like those shown in Fig. 4.16 is submitted to the action of a balanced system of external forces applied

[1] We neglect, of course, any slight change in shape that accompanies the small elastic deformations of the bars under axial load.

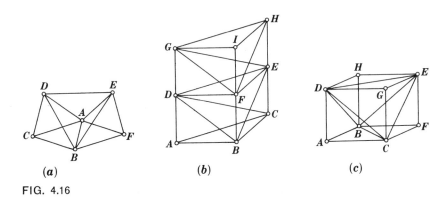

FIG. 4.16

to its joints, we can always make a complete analysis by the method of joints. This follows at once from the manner of formation of such trusses; we see that in the process of analysis it is necessary only to consider the joints in the reverse order from which they were set up in the formation of the system. By way of illustration, let us consider the simple space truss shown in Fig. 4.17a. This system has the form of a cube; at the corners A and H are applied two equal and opposite forces P that act along the diagonal AH, as shown. That the cube as a whole is in equilibrium under the action of two such collinear forces is self-evident, and we may proceed at once with the analysis. Beginning with the joint H and successively projecting all forces there onto axes coinciding with HF, HE, and HG, we find that each of these bars carries an axial compression equal to $P/\sqrt{3}$, as shown in Fig. 4.17b. Conditions at A being identical with those at H, we conclude the same for the bars AB, AC, and AD. Then, at each of the joints G and F, we find four forces in equilibrium, three of which are in one plane. Accordingly, we conclude that GD and FD are

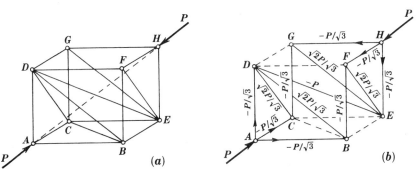

FIG. 4.17

inactive bars, as shown by dashed lines in Fig. 4.17b. Also, we find that $GE = FE = +\sqrt{2}\,P/\sqrt{3}$ (tension), and $GC = FB = -P/\sqrt{3}$ (compression). This done, there remain at each of the joints C and B only three bars with unknown axial forces, and we find $CD = DB = +\sqrt{2}\,P/\sqrt{3}$, while $BC = 0$ and $CE = BE = 0$, as shown by dashed lines in Fig. 4.17b. Finally, from a consideration of the conditions of equilibrium either at D or at E, we conclude that $DE = -P$, and the analysis is completed.

Although the method of joints is always applicable in the analysis of a simple space truss, we need not follow it too rigorously in all cases. That is, it is not always necessary to begin the analysis with the last joint and then systematically proceed through the structure joint by joint until all axial forces have been found. Instead, we can take a somewhat more general view of the problem as follows: Since the joint-by-joint procedure is always applicable and must lead to a definite and unique solution of the problem, we conclude that a simple space truss is always *statically determinate*; i.e., for a given condition of loading there is one and only one set of values for the axial forces that can satisfy the conditions of equilibrium at each and every joint. Hence, if by some indirect procedure, such as guessing, we can succeed in finding a set of values for the axial forces that satisfy the conditions of equilibrium at all joints, we may rest assured that this constitutes the true solution of the problem. Consider, for example, the simple space truss loaded as shown in Fig. 4.18. In this system, the triangle ABC is equilateral with sides of length a, the triangle $A'B'C'$ is equilateral with sides of length $2a$, and the distance between the horizontal planes ABC and $A'B'C'$ is a. If we remove the bars 7, 8, and 9 from this system, we see that the conditions at the joints A, B, and C will be identical. Accordingly, we conclude, after a consideration of the joint C, that a complete solution, satisfying the conditions of equilibrium of all joints, will be obtained by taking $S_7 = S_8 = S_9 = 0$, $S_4 = S_5 = S_6 = -2P/\sqrt{3}$ (compression), and $S_1 = S_2 = S_3 = -\frac{1}{3}P$ (compression).

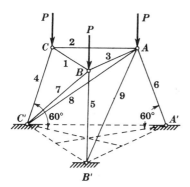

FIG. 4.18

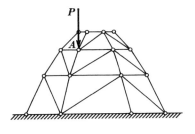

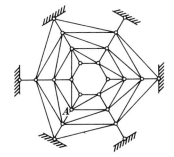

FIG. 4.19

PROBLEMS

1   Examine the simple space truss shown in plan and elevation in Fig. 4.19, and identify, by inspection, the bars that are inactive under the action of a single vertical load P applied at A as shown.

2   In Fig. 4.11b, $EGFH$ and $ACBD$ are two squares with parallel sides of lengths a and $2a$, respectively. The vertical distance between their two horizontal planes is also $2a$. Make a complete analysis of the upper story of this structure if there is a vertical load P at each of the four top joints.

3   Make a complete analysis of the cube shown in Fig. 4.16c under the action of two equal, opposite, and collinear forces P applied to the joints C and H.

4   Make a complete analysis of the space truss in Fig. 4.18 if there is a vertical load P at C only.

5   Make a complete analysis of the space truss in Fig. 4.11b if a tensile force P is introduced in a bar HG (not shown) by means of a turnbuckle. For dimensions of the structure, see Prob. 2.

4.3 STATICALLY DETERMINATE CONSTRAINT OF A RIGID BODY IN SPACE

In the general case, a system of forces acting on a rigid body may be neither concurrent nor coplanar. Such a system of forces can always be reduced to a *resultant force* and a *resultant couple*. Consider, for example, any single force F_i

applied at point A of a body (Fig. 4.20). This force can be transformed into an equal and parallel force F_i' at the origin O together with a couple formed by the given force F_i at A and equal and opposite force F_i'' at O. This is done simply by introducing at O the two equal and opposite forces F_i' and F_i'', which, being themselves in equilibrium, do not alter the action of the given force F_i at A. Following the same procedure for each force of the system, we conclude that, in general, any system of forces can be transformed into a system of forces concurrent at O together with a system of couples the moments of which are equal to the corresponding moments of the given forces with respect to point O.

We can have equilibrium of two such systems only if the resultant force and the resultant couple are both zero. For the resultant force to vanish, we must have the algebraic sums of projections of the given forces on the coordinate axes x, y, and z equal to zero; for the resultant couple to vanish, we must have the algebraic sums of moments of the given forces with respect to the three coordinate axes equal to zero. Thus, the conditions of equilibrium for a system of forces in space may be expressed as follows:

$$\Sigma X_i = 0 \qquad \Sigma Y_i = 0 \qquad \Sigma Z_i = 0$$
$$\Sigma M_x = 0 \qquad \Sigma M_y = 0 \qquad \Sigma M_z = 0 \tag{4.2}$$

These equations will determine any six unknown elements pertaining to a completely general system of forces in equilibrium.

With the foregoing equations of equilibrium in mind, let us now consider the general problem of attaching a rigid body to a foundation in such a way that it will be completely constrained in space. Consider, for example, the rigid body having the form of a rectangular parallelepiped as shown in Fig. 4.21a. As we already know, to fix completely any point A of the body in space, we need *three bars* the axes of which do not lie in one plane, as shown. With such attachment to the foundation, it is evident that freedom of motion of the body is limited to rotation about point A. Under such conditions any other point in the body is free to move on the surface of a sphere with center at A and having a radius equal to the distance from A to the point in question.

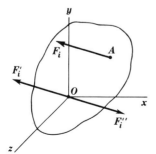

FIG. 4.20

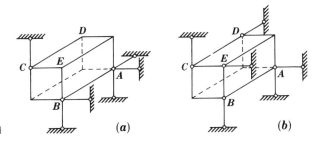

FIG. 4.21   (*a*)   (*b*)

Hence, further constraint of the body can be obtained by completely constraining a second point *B* in a plane which is tangent to the sphere on which *B* would otherwise be free to move. This, we know, can be accomplished by *two bars* at *B* arranged as shown in the figure. Freedom of motion of the body is now limited to rotation about the axis *AB*, and in this case any point in the body can move only along the arc of a circle the plane of which is normal to the axis *AB* and the center of which lies on this axis. Thus, at a third point *C*, *one bar*, the axis of which does not intersect *AB*, will complete the constraint of the body in space. We conclude then that at least *six bars* are necessary for the complete constraint of a rigid body in space. It is not necessary, however, for them to be arranged exactly as in Fig. 4.21*a*. For example, we can replace one of the bars at *A* by a parallel bar at *D* and one of the bars at *B* by a parallel bar at *E* (Fig. 4.21*b*) and still have complete constraint of the body.

It must not be concluded from the discussion above that six bars will always be adequate for the constraint of a rigid body in space. For example, if the bars are all parallel or lie in parallel planes as shown in Fig. 4.22*a*, it is evident that there is some freedom for endwise motion without inducing appreciable changes in the lengths of the supporting bars. Hence, six bars so arranged cannot be said to furnish complete constraint. In Fig. 4.22*b*, we have another case where six bars are not satisfactorily arranged for the complete constraint of a rigid body. In this case four of the bars are attached to one point *A*, and the other two can be arranged in any manner whatsoever. Under such conditions the axis of the bar at *C* and the point *A* define a plane, and the axis

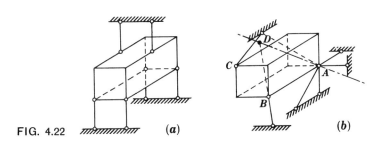

FIG. 4.22   (*a*)   (*b*)

of the bar at B intersects this plane at some point D as shown or is parallel to it. Hence all six bars intersect the axis AD; and if externally applied forces give a moment with respect to this axis, the six supporting bars will be unable to develop a balancing moment, and the rigid body will rotate to some other position. Such incomplete constraint of a rigid body in space is analogous to that of a rigid body in a plane where the axes of three bars are parallel or intersect in one point (see page 58).

From the foregoing discussion, we conclude that a system of supports consisting of six bars so arranged that their axes cannot all be intersected by a straight line is always necessary and usually sufficient[1] for the complete constraint of a rigid body in space. Any bars in excess of this number will constitute *redundant constraints*.

Let us assume now that either of the constrained bodies shown in Fig. 4.21 is subjected to the action of a system of external forces. Under the action of these loads, axial forces will be induced in the supporting bars, and each bar will exert a reaction on the body at the point of attachment and coincident in direction with the axis of the bar. Considering both active and reactive forces together, we have the general case of a system of forces in equilibrium. The forces are not concurrent, coplanar, or parallel. For such a system we have six equations of equilibrium as represented by Eqs. (4.2), and we see that these six equations will determine the magnitudes of the six reactive forces exerted on the body by the supporting bars. Thus, the six bars that are both necessary and sufficient for the complete constraint of the rigid body also represent a *statically determinate* system of supports. If there are more than six supporting bars, i.e., if there are redundant constraints, the six equations of statics will be insufficient to completely determine the reactive forces, and the system of supports is said to be *statically indeterminate*. In special cases like those shown in Fig. 4.22, where there are only six bars but so arranged that their axes can all be intersected by a straight line, the determinant of the six equations of equilibrium will vanish and the system of supports will again prove to be statically indeterminate.

In the analysis of a system of supports of a rigid body in space, we first replace the supporting bars by the reactions that they exert on the body, thus obtaining a free-body diagram. Since the six reactive forces coincide with the axes of the bars that exert them, their directions are known, and, generally speaking, the six unknown magnitudes can always be determined by Eqs. (4.2). However, in the solution of practical problems, we shall not always adhere rigorously to the use of this system of equations. Since the body is in equilibrium, it follows that the algebraic sum of the moments of all the forces with respect to any axis (not necessarily x, y, or z) must be zero and likewise that the algebraic sum of the projections of all forces on any axis must be zero.

---

[1] In exceptional cases, the determinant of Eqs. (4.2) may vanish even when all six bars do not intersect one axis; this will always be an indication of incomplete constraint.

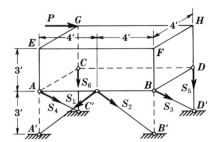

FIG. 4.23

Thus, in writing the equations of equilibrium, it is usually possible, by a proper choice of axes, to obtain six equations in each of which only one or two of the unknown forces appear. In this way we avoid the difficulties connected with the solution of six simultaneous equations with as many unknowns, and our problem is greatly simplified.

To illustrate the application of the foregoing general discussion, let us consider the rectangular parallelepiped $ABCDEFGH$ supported and loaded as shown in Fig. 4.23. To make a free-body diagram, we replace the six supporting bars by the reactions which they exert on the body, remembering that each force must act along the axis of the bar which produces it. We assume all bars to be in tension as shown so that any negative signs obtained during calculation will simply indicate that the corresponding bars are in compression. Writing first an equation of moments with respect to the vertical axis BF, which is parallel to or intersects all bars except 4, we obtain

$$-\tfrac{4}{5}S_4 \times 8 - P \times 4 = 0$$

from which $S_4 = -\tfrac{5}{8}P$. In the same way, by equating to zero the algebraic sum of moments of all forces with respect to the axis AE, we find $S_3 = +\tfrac{5}{8}P$. Since we already know the value of S_4, this latter result may also be obtained directly by equating to zero the algebraic sum of projections of all forces on the axis AC.

Now, taking moments of all forces, first with respect to the axis AB and again with respect to the axis $C'D'$, we conclude, successively, that

$$S_5 = -S_6 \quad \text{and} \quad S_1 = -S_2$$

Then, equating to zero the algebraic sum of the projections of all forces on the axis AB, we obtain

$$-\tfrac{4}{5}S_1 + \tfrac{4}{5}S_2 + P = 0$$

from which $S_1 = -S_2 = \tfrac{5}{8}P$.

Finally, we equate to zero the algebraic sum of moments of all forces with respect to the axis AC and obtain

$$\tfrac{3}{5}S_1 \times 4 + \tfrac{3}{5}S_2 \times 4 + \tfrac{3}{5}S_3 \times 8 + S_5 \times 8 + P \times 3 = 0$$

from which, using the previously determined values of S_1, S_2, and S_3, we find $S_5 = -S_6 = -\tfrac{3}{4}P$, and the analysis is completed.

Sometimes a problem involving a general system of forces in space can be simplified by introducing an *equivalent loading*. Consider, for example, the rigid body supported by six bars as shown in Fig. 4.24a and subjected to a horizontal force P in the end plane ABE. We begin by adding to the given system at A the two equal, opposite, and collinear forces P as shown in the figure. Two such forces being in equilibrium do not alter in any way the action of the system, but we may now consider that we have a force P at A together with a couple consisting of the force P at E and the opposite force P at A. This couple, the moment of which in the end plane of the body is Pb, can be transferred to the opposite end of the body and represented by the vertical forces Pb/a at C and D as shown in Fig. 4.24b. The system of three applied loads shown in Fig. 4.24b is equivalent in action to the single load P at E in Fig. 4.24a and will induce in the supporting bars the same axial forces. However, in Fig. 4.24b we have at A, C, and D three simple systems of concurrent forces that can be analyzed by the most elementary procedures. By inspection, we conclude that $S_3 = S_5 = 0$, while $S_4 = -S_6 = Pb/a$. Considering the remaining forces at A and projecting successively onto horizontal and vertical axes, we find $S_1 = P \csc \alpha$, and $S_2 = -P \cot \alpha$.

In Fig. 4.25 we have a plan and elevation of an equilateral triangular slab supported in a horizontal plane by six bars of equal length arranged as shown. It is required to find the axial forces induced in these bars by a couple of moment M acting in the plane of the slab as shown. We begin with a free-body diagram of the slab as indicated in the figure. Then, taking AB as an axis of moments, we see that only the reactions S_3 and S_4 have moments different from zero with respect to this axis. Hence, we conclude that these

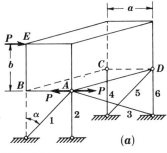

FIG. 4.24

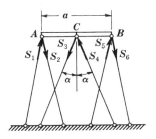

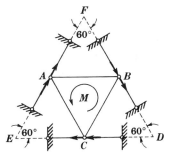

FIG. 4.25

forces, which are equally inclined to the vertical, must be equal in magnitude and represent, respectively, tension in one bar and compression in the other as indicated by the arrows in the figure.[1]   By similar considerations of moments about the axes AC and BC, we conclude that S_5 and S_6 as well as S_1 and S_2 are equal in magnitude and directed as shown.   Now, by successively equating to zero the algebraic sums of projections of all forces on the axes AD and BE, we conclude that the six reactive forces must all be equal in magnitude. Finally, then, by balancing moments with respect to a vertical axis through the centroid of the triangle, we obtain

$$6S \sin \alpha \times \frac{2}{3} \frac{\sqrt{3}}{2} a = M$$

from which $S = \sqrt{3}\, M/(6a \sin \alpha)$, where S is the magnitude of axial force in any one of the bars.

PROBLEMS

1   A strut AB is hinged to a vertical wall at B and supported horizontally by two guy wires arranged as shown in Fig. 4.26.   Find the tension induced in each guy wire by a vertical load P applied at A.
    Ans. $S_1 = 3.15P$, $S_2 = 5.96P$.

[1] For expediency, we depart here from our usual rule of arbitrarily assuming, to begin with, that all bars are in tension.

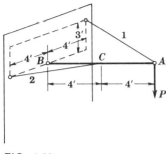

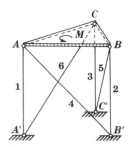

FIG. 4.26   FIG. 4.27

2   An equilateral triangular slab is supported in a horizontal plane by six bars arranged as shown in Fig. 4.27. Each side of the triangle is of length a, and the vertical bars also are of length a. If the weight of the slab is W, what must be the moment of a couple M, acting in the plane of the slab as shown, for the vertical bars to be inactive?

> *Ans.* $M = Wa/2 \sqrt{3}$.

3   Using the notion of equivalent loading, make an analysis of the system of supports in Fig. 4.24a if the load P at E is vertical.

> *Ans.* $S_1 = S_3 = S_5 = 0, S_2 = S_4 = -S_6 = -P$.

4   Make a complete analysis of each system of supports in Fig. 4.21 under the action of a vertical load P at D. Assume in each case that the rectangular parallelepiped has dimensions a, a, and $2a$.

5   Analyze the system of supports in Fig. 4.23 under the action of a vertical load P at E.

> *Ans.* $S_1 = S_2 = -\frac{5}{6}P, S_3 = S_4 = 0, S_5 = -S_6 = \frac{1}{2}P$.

4.4   COMPOUND SPACE TRUSSES: METHOD OF SECTIONS

In the preceding article, we saw how a rigid body can be completely constrained in space by means of six bars so arranged that their axes cannot all be intersected by one straight line. On this basis, we conclude that any self-contained simple space truss such as those shown in Fig. 4.16 can be rigidly attached to a foundation in the same manner. Consider, for example, the system shown in Fig. 4.28, where we have a simple space truss $ABCDEFGH$ attached to the foundation by six bars arranged as shown. In this way, we obtain a rigid and statically determinate structure capable of holding in equilibrium any system of externally applied loads such as $P_1, P_2, \ldots$. Such a structure will be called a *compound space truss*. In the analysis of a compound truss, we shall generally find that the method of joints alone is inadequate. For example, in this case (Fig. 4.28) we cannot begin the analysis by the method of joints

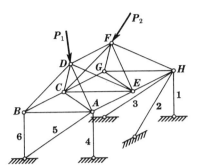

FIG. 4.28

because there is no joint to which less than four bars are attached. Consequently, we must first consider the entire portion $ABCDEFGH$ as a free body and, using the six equations of equilibrium of the preceding article [Eqs. (4.2)], find the axial forces in the six supporting bars. Such procedure in the analysis of a space truss is usually called the *method of sections*. As soon as we know completely the balanced system of forces external to the simple truss as a whole, the remainder of the analysis can be made without difficulty by the method of joints.

In Fig. 4.29, we have an example of a self-contained compound space truss. To obtain this structure, we take two simple space trusses, as represented by the shaded portions of the system, and interconnect them by six bars arranged in accordance with the requirements for complete constraint of a rigid body in space. It must be self-evident, then, that the resulting system is rigid and statically determinate. However, under the action of a balanced system of external forces, we again may be unable to make a complete analysis by the method of joints. To begin the analysis in this case, we make a section cutting the six numbered bars and isolate one of the simple trusses as a free body. Then, with the help of the six available equations of equilibrium, we determine the axial forces in these six interconnecting bars, after which the two simple trusses can be analyzed without difficulty by the method of joints.

If desired, the simple truss $ABCDEFGH$ of Fig. 4.28 can be considered as a compound truss like that in Fig. 4.29. It is necessary only to regard it as two

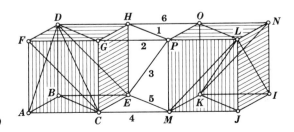

FIG. 4.29

simple tetrahedrons $ABCD$ and $EFGH$ interconnected by the six bars AE, CE, DE, CF, DF, and CG. Accordingly, we conclude that the axial forces in these bars, also, can be found by the method of sections, leaving for analysis by the method of joints only the two tetrahedrons. In the same way, the simple space truss shown in Fig. 4.11a can be considered as a compound space truss consisting of the simple tetrahedron $ABCD$ attached to the foundation by six bars arranged in a manner satisfying the conditions of complete constraint of a rigid body in space. On the other hand, no such conclusion can be made for the simple space truss in Fig. 4.11b. In the first place, the portion $ABCDEFGH$ of this structure does not represent a rigid body; and, second, to separate it from the foundation we should have to cut eight bars instead of six. Under such circumstances, the method of sections cannot be used.

The identification of any space structure as a simple or compound truss will always be an indication that it is rigid and statically determinate, i.e., that under any given condition of loading there will be one and only one set of values for the axial forces that can satisfy the conditions of equilibrium at each and every joint. Whether or not we rigorously follow the method of joints in finding this set of values is of no importance. Any procedure by which we succeed in finding a solution that satisfies all conditions of equilibrium is a valid procedure.

As an example, let us consider the analysis of the compound space truss shown in Fig. 4.30. This structure consists of a rigid equilateral prism $ABCDEF$, with edges of length l, that is attached to the foundation by six bars arranged as shown and then subjected to the action of a vertical load P at A. The orthodox procedure in the analysis of this compound space truss would be to find the axial forces in the six supporting bars by the method of sections and then use the method of joints for the simple truss $ABCDEF$. While such a procedure will involve no particular difficulty, it will be somewhat more advantageous in this particular case to find the forces in the supporting bars by using the notion of equivalent loading, which was discussed on page 181. Introducing at C two equal and opposite vertical forces P that, being in equi-

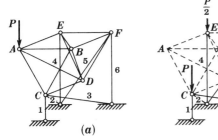

(a)

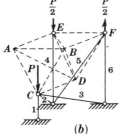

(b)

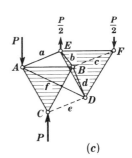

(c)

FIG. 4.30

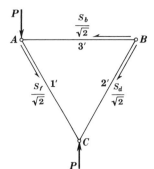

FIG. 4.31

librium, do not affect the system, we see that the given loading can be considered as a vertical load P at C together with a counterclockwise couple $Pl/2$ in the end plane ABC of the structure. Transferring this couple to the end plane DEF where we represent it by two vertical forces $P/2$ at E and F, we obtain the equivalent loading shown in Fig. 4.30b. Regarding this notion of equivalent loading, it must be emphasized here that the loading in Fig. 4.30b is equivalent to that in Fig. 4.30a only in so far as the axial forces induced in the supporting bars are concerned. The forces induced in the other bars of the system will be completely different in the two cases. From Fig. 4.30b, we see by inspection that the supporting bars 2, 3, and 5 are inactive, while the axial forces in the other three are as follows: $S_1 = -P$, $S_4 = -P/2$, $S_6 = +P/2$. Returning, now, to the true loading and replacing the six supporting bars by the reactions that they exert on the simple truss $ABCDEF$, we obtain, for further analysis, the system shown in Fig. 4.30c. This simple truss, however, can also be considered as a compound truss consisting of the rigid triangles ABC and DEF, which are interconnected by the six bars a, b, c, d, e, and f, as shown. As can be seen by inspection of the joints C and F, the bars e and c of these six are inactive and can be removed from the system. Making a section that cuts the four remaining bars and projecting onto the plane of the triangle ABC all forces that act upon it, we obtain a coplanar system of forces in equilibrium as shown in Fig. 4.31. Successively equating to zero the algebraic sums of moments of these forces with respect to the points A, B, and C, we find

$$S_d = +\sqrt{\tfrac{2}{3}}\,P \qquad S_f = -\sqrt{\tfrac{2}{3}}\,P \qquad \text{and} \qquad S_b = -\sqrt{\tfrac{2}{3}}\,P$$

To find S_a, we return to Fig. 4.30c and use the method of joints. Projecting all forces at A onto an axis coinciding with AE, we obtain $S_a = +P/\sqrt{3}$. The two triangles ABC and DEF may now be analyzed as any other plane truss. In Fig. 4.31, for example, we see that $S_1' = S_2' = -P/\sqrt{3}$, while $S_3' = +P/\sqrt{3}$.

PROBLEMS

1 The compound space truss in Fig. 4.32 consists of a rigid square pyramid $ABCED$ attached to the foundation by seven bars arranged as shown. Then, by means of a turnbuckle F, a tensile force P is induced in the bar CC'. What axial forces will be induced in the other bars of the system?

$Ans.$ $AA' = CC' = +P, BB' = EE' = -P, DC = DA = + \sqrt{2}\, P,$
$DB = DE = - \sqrt{2}\, P, AB = BC = CE = EA = +P/\sqrt{2},$
$AE' = AB' = EC' = 0, AC = -2P.$

2 The rigid cube shown in Fig. 4.33 is formed by interconnecting the two shaded tetrahedrons by means of six bars the axes of which cannot all be intersected by one straight line. Make a complete analysis of this system under the action of two equal, opposite, and collinear forces P acting along the diagonal AG as shown.

$Ans.$ $S_1 = S_6 = +P/2 \sqrt{3}, S_2 = S_3 = S_4 = S_5 = -P/2 \sqrt{3}.$

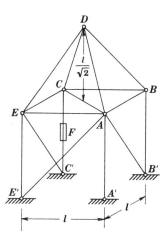

FIG. 4.32

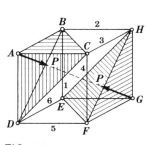

FIG. 4.33

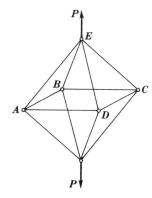

FIG. 4.34

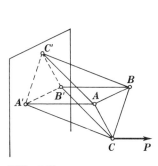

FIG. 4.35

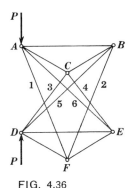

FIG. 4.36

3   Prove that the system of bars shown in Fig. 4.34 constitutes a compound space truss, and make a complete analysis of the system under the action of two equal and opposite forces P acting as shown. The system has the form of a regular octahedron.

4   Make a complete analysis of the compound space truss loaded as shown in Fig. 4.35. Assume that ABC and $A'B'C'$ are equilateral triangles and that $A'B'BA$ is a square.

Ans. $A'C = B'C = +P/\sqrt{2}$, $C'A = C'B = -P/\sqrt{2}$, $A'A = B'B = +P/2$, $CA = CB = -P/2$, $AB = +P/2$.

5   In Fig. 4.36, the triangles ABC and DEF are equilateral with sides of length a, and the distance between their parallel planes is also a. Find the axial forces in the six bars that interconnect these two triangles if two equal and opposite collinear forces P are applied to the system as shown.

Ans. $S_1 = S_6 = -P/\sqrt{2}$, $S_2 = -S_5 = +P/\sqrt{2}$, $S_4 = -S_3 = +P/\sqrt{2}$.

4.5   GENERAL THEORY OF STATICALLY DETERMINATE SPACE TRUSSES

In this article, we shall consider the general problem of how to assemble a system of bars in space so as to form a completely rigid space truss. We have already seen in Art. 4.2 that a *simple space truss* can be formed by beginning with a rigid foundation to which the first joint is attached by means of three bars not in one plane; thereafter, succeeding joints are attached to the foundation or to previously established joints in the same manner. The truss in Fig. 4.37a has been formed in this way, beginning with joint A and setting up the other joints in alphabetical order. From the rule of formation of a simple space truss, it follows that, between the number of members m and the number of joints j, there must exist the relationship

$$m = 3j \qquad\qquad (4.3a)$$

since we use three bars for each joint.

While the foregoing rule of formation of a space truss is a very simple one, it does not represent the only way in which a system of bars can be assembled to form a rigid space structure. For example, if we remove the bars CC' and BD' of the simple truss in Fig. 4.37a and introduce instead the bars DC and EF as shown in Fig. 4.37b, we obtain a *compound space truss* like that shown in Fig. 4.28. That is, the portion $ABCDEFGH$ of the structure now represents a self-contained simple space truss which is attached to the foundation by six bars the axes of which cannot all be intersected by one straight line. Since, by the above rearrangement of bars, we change neither the number of bars m nor the number of joints j, we conclude that the compound space truss in Fig. 4.37b also satisfies Eq. (4.3a). Still another type of rigid space truss can be derived from the simple truss in Fig. 4.37a simply by changing the directions of the diagonals in the two side panels as shown in Fig. 4.37c. In this way, we obtain a system that, although it still satisfies the relationship $m = 3j$, can no longer be classed either as a simple truss or as a compound truss. Many of our engineering structures are of this latter form, which is called a *complex space truss*.

From the preceding examples, we may draw the general conclusion that $3j$ bars are always necessary and, when properly arranged, sufficient for the rigid interconnection between themselves and the foundation of j joints in space. This observation holds also for any self-contained space truss that is attached to a foundation by the six bars necessary and sufficient for the complete constraint of a rigid body in space. To demonstrate this, we recall from Art. 4.2 the rule of formation of a self-contained simple space truss, by which we begin with three bars and three joints in the form of a triangle and attach succeeding

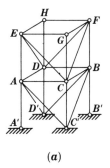

(a)

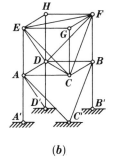

(b)

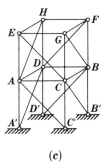

(c)

FIG. 4.37

joints, each by means of three bars not in one plane. Since, by this rule, we use three bars for each joint except the first three, for which there is only one bar for each joint, we conclude that between the total number of bars m and the total number of joints j of a self-contained simple space truss there must exist the relationship

$$m = 3j - 6 \qquad\qquad (4.3b)$$

Then the six additional bars required to complete the constraint of a rigid body in space bring us to $m = 3j - 6 + 6$, or simply $m = 3j$ as before.

In arranging a system of bars to form a rigid space truss, it is often desirable, for purposes of utility, to avoid any obstruction of the inner space. Regarding space structures without internal diagonals, it can be proved that if any self-contained space truss has the form of a closed polyhedron the plane faces of which are triangular or subdivided into triangles, then Eq. (4.3b) will be satisfied, and, generally speaking, the truss will represent a completely rigid body. To prove this statement, we begin with a general theorem of stereometry that is due to Euler. This theorem states the relationship between the number of faces, edges, and apices of any closed polyhedron and may be established on the basis of the following reasoning: Beginning with one face, represented by any polygon, we see that we have, to start with, an equal number of edges and apices. Now, when we come to add a second face to the first, there will be one of its edges and two of its apices already existing. Again, when we come to add a third face to the first and the second, two of its edges and three of its apices will already exist, etc. Thus, in general, the addition of each face after the first entails the addition of one more new edge than new apex; and as we proceed, the total number of edges gains on the total number of apices by exactly the number of faces that up to any moment have been added to the first, or starting, face. Hence, we conclude that, at any stage of construction, the number of edges must be equal to the number of apices plus the number of added faces, i.e., all except the starting face. This relationship holds until we come to the last, or closing, face, the addition of which entails no new edges and no new apices; thus, we acquire a second extra face. Denoting by m the number of edges, by j the number of apices, and by f the number of faces, we have, then, for any closed polyhedron the relationship

$$m = j + (f - 2) \qquad\qquad (a)$$

and this equation expresses the theorem of Euler mentioned above. The foregoing arguments apply to the general case of any closed polyhedron. In the particular case of a closed polyhedron the faces of which are triangular or divided into triangles, we can express a further relationship between the number of faces and the number of edges, i.e., between f and m. Every edge being common to two faces and all faces being triangles, we see that there

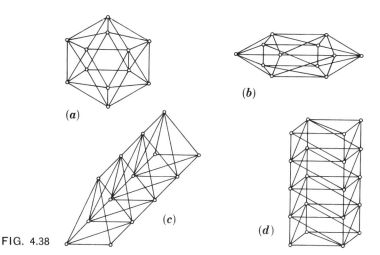

FIG. 4.38

(a)

(b)

(c)

(d)

must be exactly half as many edges as three times the number of faces. That is,

$$m = \tfrac{3}{2}f \qquad (b)$$

Eliminating f between Eqs. (a) and (b), we obtain $m = 3j - 6$ as expressed by Eq. (4.3b). Thus, we conclude that any self-contained space truss the bars of which represent the edges of a closed polyhedron having triangular faces and being without internal diagonals must satisfy Eq. (4.3b). Several examples of such structures are shown in Fig. 4.38, and we see that they must be classified as complex trusses. As already stated, these forms have the practical advantage that their inner space is free from obstruction; for this reason, they are commonly employed in all kinds of structural work.

We have seen now that there are three general classes of space trusses, *simple, compound,* and *complex,* and that in each case $m = 3j$ is a general requirement of rigidity and complete constraint. We shall now discuss another general significance of the relationship $m = 3j$. Consider, for example, any completely constrained space truss comprised of m bars and j joints and submitted to external loads applied only at the joints, as shown in Fig. 4.39. Under the action of such applied loads, axial forces will, in general, be induced in all the m bars of the system, and the determination of these internal forces constitutes the analysis of the truss. If we are dealing with a simple or compound truss, we know that the analysis can always be made by the method of joints or by the method of sections; such procedures have already been discussed in detail in Arts. 4.2 and 4.4. In the case of a complex truss, however, these methods of analysis may fail. In the present case, for example, we see that there are four bars meeting at each joint, and so the method of joints cannot be used. Likewise, there is no possibility of employing the

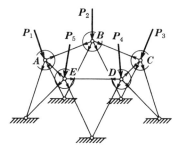

FIG. 4.39

method of sections because no section can be conceived which cuts only six bars that do not all intersect one straight line. Under such circumstances, we must take a more general view of the problem as follows: Replacing each of the m bars by the two equal but opposite reactions that it exerts on the joints at its ends, we obtain j systems of concurrent forces in equilibrium as shown. Then, for each joint we write three equations of statics ($\Sigma X_i = 0$, $\Sigma Y_i = 0$, $\Sigma Z_i = 0$) and obtain $3j$ simultaneous equations involving m unknowns. We see now that, if $m = 3j$, there are exactly as many unknowns as there are equations and that in all but exceptional cases,[1] where the determinant of these equations vanishes, the system of equations of statics must yield a unique solution to the problem. For this reason, any completely constrained space truss that satisfies the condition $m = 3j$ is said to be *statically determinate*. That is, under any condition of loading, the axial forces in all bars can be found from equations of statics alone, and there is no necessity to take account of the elastic deformations of the bars. The solution of $3j$ simultaneous equations involving as many unknowns is, of course, a problem in itself, but we shall content ourselves for the moment with the knowledge that the axial forces can be found by equations of statics alone if $m = 3j$.

If $m > 3j$, there will, of course, be more unknown axial forces than there are independent equations of statics, and the system of $3j$ equations cannot yield a unique solution. Accordingly, the truss is said to be *statically indeterminate*. Under such conditions, the elastic deformations of the bars must be taken into account to determine the way in which the internal forces adjust themselves to meet the conditions of equilibrium of the joints. On the other hand, if $m < 3j$, the structure is not rigid and will probably collapse under the action of externally applied loads.

Returning to the case where $m = 3j$, let us consider the exceptional trusses for which the determinant of the $3j$ equations of statics vanishes and the equations do not yield a definite solution for the axial forces. This circumstance will always be an indication that the truss is nonrigid and therefore unsuitable for structural purposes. Such exceptions are called *critical forms*. A critical form will be obtained, for example, in the formation of a simple

[1] Such exceptional cases will be discussed later.

space truss if we forget that those three bars by which any joint is attached to the rest of the system must not all lie in one plane.   Thus the self-contained simple truss in Fig. 4.40a has a critical form if the joint E lies in the plane ABD, and we see that under such conditions there is a limited freedom for relative movement of this joint in the direction perpendicular to the plane ABD.   Likewise, the compound space truss in Fig. 4.40b has a critical form because the six bars by which the rigid tetrahedron $ABCD$ is attached to the foundation are so arranged that they all intersect the vertical axis BD or are parallel to it.   Thus, again, there is a limited freedom for rotation of the tetrahedron around this axis.

Such critical forms as those shown in Fig. 4.40 are easily detected by inspection and, in fact, can be avoided by careful observation of the rules of formation of simple and compound space trusses.   In the case of a complex truss, however, we may be unable to discover a critical form by inspection, and it is for such trusses that they are most likely to occur.   A general method of detection of critical form is based on a consideration of the $3j$ equations of statics for the j joints of the system.   If the determinant of these equations is different from zero, we have a statically determinate system, and there is no critical form.   If the determinant is zero, the system is statically indeterminate, and we do have a critical form.

The actual evaluation of the above-mentioned determinant is, of course, impracticable.   However, since it depends only on the configuration of the truss and not at all on how the truss is loaded, it follows that if for any assumed loading we can find, without ambiguity, the axial forces in all bars, the determinant evidently is not zero, and the truss is rigid.   On the other hand, if under an assumed loading we can discover some ambiguity regarding the internal forces, the determinant evidently is zero, and the truss has a critical form.   In undertaking such an investigation, the simplest procedure is to assume a zero load at each joint.   Then, one obvious solution satisfying the conditions of equilibrium at the joints is obtained by taking all bars with zero axial forces. If no other set of values different from zero can be found to satisfy the conditions of equilibrium at the joints, the truss is rigid and statically determinate; but if, under zero loading, a set of axial forces different from zero can be found to satisfy the equilibrium of the joints, the solution is ambiguous, and

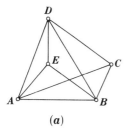
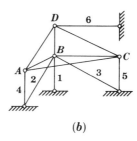

FIG. 4.40   *(a)*   *(b)*

the truss has a critical form. Such analysis of a truss under zero load for the purpose of detecting a critical form is known as the *zero-load test*.

As an example, we consider the complex space truss shown in plan and elevation in Fig. 4.41. This system consists of a square frame *ABCD* supported in a horizontal plane by eight bars attached to the foundation as shown, and we see that the condition $m = 3j$ is satisfied. Now, with zero load at each joint, we assume an arbitrary tension in *AE* and, at the same time, an equal compression in *AF*. Then, the resultant of these two forces at *A* will lie in the plane of the square *ABCD* and will be perpendicular to its diagonal *AC*. Hence, it can be balanced by a proper tension in *AB* and an equal compression in *AD*, and all conditions of equilibrium for the joint *A* are satisfied. Similar arguments can be made for the joints *B*, *C*, and *D*. Thus, we conclude, finally, that under zero loads a set of axial forces different from zero can exist in the bars of the truss as shown. Consequently, the solution is ambiguous, and the truss has a critical form.

The nonrigidity of this system can also be seen physically by considering the plan view shown in Fig. 4.41*c*. From this figure, it is clear that the joints *A*, *B*, *C*, *D* can move in or out along the diagonals of the square without changes in the length of any of the bars. Thus, the truss can take the distorted form as indicated, and we have a nonrigid system unsatisfactory for practical use.

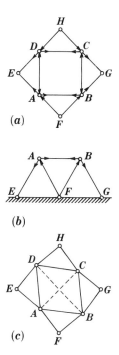

FIG. 4.41   *(c)*

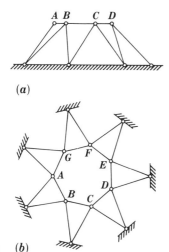

FIG. 4.42   (b)

PROBLEMS

1 Apply the zero-load test to the complex truss shown in Fig. 4.37c, and prove that
   it is rigid and statically determinate.
2 Using the zero-load test, prove that the complex space truss shown in plan and
   elevation in Fig. 4.42 is rigid and statically determinate notwithstanding its general
   resemblance to the nonrigid system shown in Fig. 4.41.
3 Show in general that a complex space truss like those in Figs. 4.41 and 4.42 will
   be rigid and statically determinate if the regular polygon $ABCDE \cdots$ has an odd
   number of sides, and nonrigid and statically indeterminate if there is an even number of sides.

4.6 ANALYSIS OF COMPLEX SPACE TRUSSES

In the preceding article, we have discussed the general problem of formation of
space trusses and a criterion for the detection of critical forms.   We shall now
turn our attention to the problem of analysis of various complex trusses that
have been proved to be rigid and statically determinate.

One of the most useful methods of analysis of space trusses, in general, is
the method of joints, which we have already discussed in Art. 4.2.   This
method, it will be remembered, is generally applicable only to simple trusses,
but there are cases where it can be used successfully in the analysis of a complex
truss.   The truss in Fig. 4.43, for example, is of this kind and can be completely
analyzed by the method of joints.   We begin with joint A and find the axial
forces in the bars 1, 2, and 3.   Then, replacing these bars by the reactions
that they exert on the remainder of the structure at B, C, and D, we find that

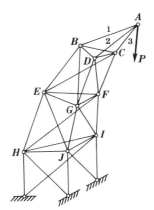

FIG. 4.43

there are still four unknown axial forces at each of these joints. However, at
D, three of the bars are in one plane, and so the axial force in the fourth bar
BD can be found by projecting all forces at D onto an axis normal to the plane
DCF. As soon as the force in BD is known, we can proceed to the joint B,
where there will now be only three bars (BG, BE, and BC) with unknown axial
forces, and these can be found. Then, knowing the action of BC on the joint
C, we can consider the equilibrium of this joint and find the forces in CE, CF,
and CD. After this, we return to D and find the remaining unknown forces
there (DF and DG). Beginning with G, the same procedure may be employed
at the joints G, E, and F, and so on, throughout the truss until the analysis is
completed. It will be seen that success with this complex truss by the
method of joints rests on the fact that, whenever all but one of the unknown
forces of a concurrent system lie in one plane, this one force can always be
found by projecting the system onto an axis normal to the plane defined by
the lines of action of the other unknown forces, no matter how many (see
page 163).

Sometimes the analysis of a complex space truss can be greatly simplified
by taking advantage of the symmetry of the system. Consider, for example,
the structure shown in Fig. 4.44, and suppose that there is a vertical load at
each joint and that all loads on any one horizontal ring are equal. Under such
conditions of symmetry, a complete analysis of the truss can be made in a very
simple manner. We begin with the zero-load test for complete rigidity. At
each joint of the top ring there are four bars, three of which lie in one plane.
Hence, under zero load, the bars of this ring must be inactive and can be
removed from the system. This leaves only two bars at each joint that are
not collinear, and we conclude accordingly that these bars also are inactive
and may be removed. Repeating this reasoning for the joints of succeeding
rings, we conclude that no axial forces different from zero can exist in the

system under zero load. Hence, it is rigid and statically determinate. This indicates that if under external loads different from zero we can find, by any convenient means, a set of axial forces that satisfy the conditions of equilibrium of the joints, we may be sure that we have the true solution.

Keeping the foregoing general remarks in mind, let us consider now any meridian $ABCD$ of the structure, as shown in Fig. 4.45a. Noting that the external loads P_1, P_2, and P_3 lie in the vertical plane of the meridian, we conclude that this one rib of the structure can be in equilibrium only if at each joint the forces exerted by the bars entering from the two sides have a resultant H which lies in the plane of the meridian. Furthermore, we see that this condition can be realized by assuming that all diagonals are inactive and that all bars comprising any one horizontal ring have equal axial forces. Proceeding on this basis, we isolate the rib $ABCD$ and project all forces onto the plane of the meridian as shown in Fig. 4.45b. Then, beginning with the joint A, we can construct the polygon of forces for each of the joints A, B, and C, as shown in Fig. 4.45c. By this procedure, we determine the axial forces S_1, S_2, and S_3 in the bars of the rib as well as the resultants H_1, H_2, and H_3 of the two equal horizontal ring-bar forces at each joint. This done, we find the axial forces in the ring bars themselves simply by resolution of H_1, H_2, and H_3 into components parallel to the corresponding bars as indicated by the equilateral triangles in Fig. 4.45c. Since the conditions along each meridian are identical, the diagram of forces in Fig. 4.45c constitutes a complete analysis of the truss.

Frequently, the analysis of a complex space truss can be simplified by reducing it to the analysis of several plane trusses. Consider, for example, the space truss shown in Fig. 4.46a. This complex system is obtained by

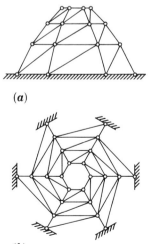

(a)

(b)

FIG. 4.44

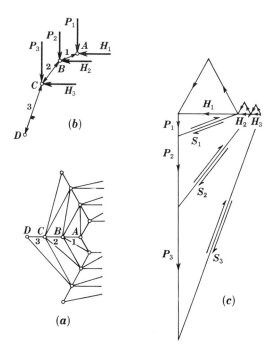

FIG. 4.45

removing from an otherwise rigid parallelepiped $AA'BB'EE'FF'$ the bar EF' and introducing instead the extra bar g in the system of supports. In the analysis of this system under the action of a horizontal load P at D, we begin at the joint F, where, by inspection, we see that $S_1 = 0$. Then, proceeding to the joint F' and projecting all forces onto an axis coinciding with FF', we conclude that $S_2 = 0$. We may now consider the joint D, where we find that S_3 is the only unknown force which lies out of the plane $ABFE$. Hence, by projecting all forces at D onto an axis normal to this plane, we find $S_3 = -P$. Now, knowing the action of the bar 3 on the joint D' and projecting all forces at D' onto an axis coinciding with DD', we find $S_4 = +P \sec \alpha$. Continuing in this way and considering the equilibrium of the joints B and B' in succession, we find $S_5 = -P$ and $S_6 = P \sec \beta$. In this way we find the forces in all web members of the top panel.

To find the axial forces in the web members of the bottom panel, we must first find the force in the bar e of the system of supports. This we accomplish by considering the entire parallelepiped as a free body and equating to zero the algebraic sum of moments of all forces acting on it with respect to an axis coinciding with AB. This gives

$$S_e \cos \gamma \times 2a + Pa = 0$$

from which $S_e = -(P/2)$ sec γ. Then, starting at E' and considering, in
succession, the joints E', E, C', C, and A' of the bottom panel, we find $S_7 = 0$,
$S_8 = +(P/2)$ sec α, $S_9 = -P/2$, $S_{10} = +(P/2)$ sec α, and $S_{11} = -P/2$.
Finally, replacing the web members of the top and bottom panels by the
reactions that we have just found them to exert on the joints of the two side
panels, we obtain for further analysis the two plane trusses loaded as shown
in Fig. 4.46b and c.   The analysis of these plane systems will be a straight-
forward procedure and need not be discussed here.   Although we have chosen
in the example a very simple case of external loading consisting of a single
force P, it should be understood that the same general procedure can be used in
case of a more elaborate system of loads.

   In general, the resolution of a space truss into several statically determinate
plane trusses represents a very practicable method of analysis.   As another
example, let us consider the complex system loaded as shown in Fig. 4.47a.
This truss satisfies the condition $m = 3j$ and, as can easily be demonstrated
by the zero-load test, is rigid and statically determinate.   Hence, we conclude
that under the given loading there is one and only one set of values for the
axial forces which can satisfy the conditions of equilibrium of the joints and
that any procedure by which we can obtain such axial forces will be a valid
one.   We begin by resolving the applied load at A into three components that
coincide, respectively, with the lines AA_3, AB, and AE as shown.   Then,
making a separate analysis of the system for each of these components and

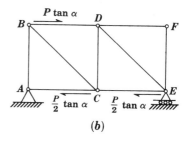

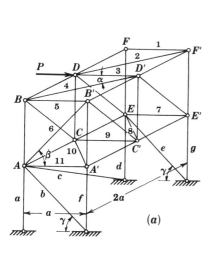

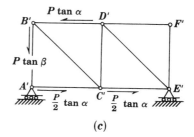

FIG. 4.46

superimposing the results, we shall obtain the desired axial forces induced by the given load P.

First, we consider only the component P_1, which coincides with AA_3, and conclude that, under such load, all bars except AA_1, A_1A_2, and A_2A_3 are inactive and that these three bars each carry a compressive force numerically equal to P_1. This done, we consider next the component P_2 which coincides with AB. Again, for this loading it can be seen that only those bars comprising the panel ABA_3B_3 will be active, and our problem reduces to the analysis of a plane truss loaded as shown in Fig. 4.47b. We make this analysis and record the results as shown. In the same way, we conclude that, under the action of the force P_3 alone, only the bars of the panel AEA_3E_3 will be active, and we again have a simple problem of analysis of a plane truss as shown in Fig. 4.47c. Now, to obtain the axial force in any bar under the original loading (Fig. 4.47a), we simply add algebraically the results already obtained. Thus, for example, in the bar AA_1, we have a force $S = -P_1 + P_3 \tan \alpha$; in the bar A_1A_2, we have $S = -P_1 + P_2 \tan \alpha + 2P_3 \tan \alpha$; etc. If there are applied loads at the other joints, they can be handled in the same way.

The method of resolution of a space truss into several plane trusses can be used to advantage in the analysis of the complex system shown in plan and elevation in Fig. 4.48. This structure is seen to satisfy the condition $m = 3j$; but, as a preliminary to its analysis under load, we must first rule out the possibility of a critical form. Using for this purpose the zero-load test, we

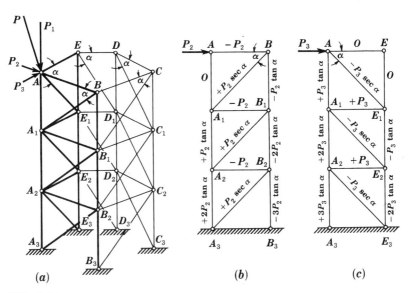

FIG. 4.47

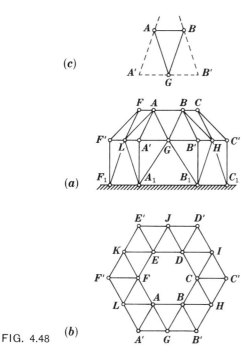

(c)

(a)

(b)

FIG. 4.48

begin by isolating the triangle ABG as shown in Fig. 4.48c. Since all bars that join this triangle at G lie in one plane that intersects the plane of the triangle itself in a horizontal line $A'B'$ through G, it follows that any action exerted on the triangle by such bars must lie along this line of intersection of the two planes. In the same way, all bars that join the triangle at A lie in one plane that intersects the plane of the triangle along AA'; hence, the resultant of any action of these bars on the triangle at A must lie along AA'. Likewise, any action on the triangle at B must lie along BB'. Now, since three coplanar forces can be in equilibrium only if they are concurrent and since the lines AB, AA', and BB' do not intersect in one point, we conclude that no such forces can exist at A, B, and G. This leaves the statically determinate triangle free from external forces, and hence no internal forces different from zero can exist in the three bars AB, AG, and BG. What is true for the triangle ABG holds for the other triangles like it, and we conclude accordingly that, under zero load, no axial forces different from zero can exist in the system. Thus, the system does not have a critical form and will be rigid and statically determinate under any system of applied loads.

Now, let us consider an analysis of the system under the action of a vertical load P applied at A as shown in Fig. 4.49. As in the preceding example, we first resolve this force into three components, P_1 coinciding with AA', P_2

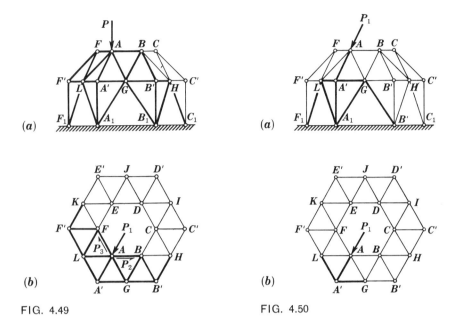

FIG. 4.49   FIG. 4.50

coinciding with AB, and P_3 coinciding with AF. Then, making a separate analysis of the system for each of these components and superimposing the results, we shall obtain the required axial forces induced by the given load P.

We begin with the component P_1 acting along AA' as shown in Fig. 4.50. Since this force does act along AA', our previous reasoning regarding such triangles as ABG (see Fig. 4.48c) is still valid, and we conclude accordingly that the load P_1 is carried entirely by the bar AA'. Thus, owing to P_1, only the bars shown by heavy lines in Fig. 4.50 are active, and the axial forces in such bars can be found without difficulty by the method of joints.

Now, considering only the component P_2, which acts along AB (Fig. 4.51), and proceeding as for the case of zero load, we again conclude that all bars except those shown by heavy lines are inactive. Then, to proceed further, we isolate the triangle ABG again as shown in Fig. 4.51c and consider its conditions of equilibrium. In this case, we conclude that the resultant of P_2 and the reaction R_a acting along AA' must pass through the point B' where the known lines of action of R_b and R_g intersect. Thus, the polygon of forces in Fig. 4.51d determines the reactions R_a, R_b, and R_g, and a complete analysis of the triangle ABG can now be made without difficulty by the method of joints. Furthermore, since the adjacent triangles AFL and BCH are inactive, we conclude that the reactions R_a and R_b represent, respectively, the axial forces in AA' and BB'. Knowing these forces and applying the method of joints first to the hinges A' and B' and then to the hinges G, L, and H, we find the forces in the remaining active bars as indicated by heavy lines in Fig. 4.51. An analysis of the system under the action of the component P_3 that acts along AF can be made in the same manner. Then, adding algebraically the axial forces in any bar due to each of the three components P_1, P_2, and P_3, we shall obtain the required axial forces due to the given load P. If there are loads at the other joints of the structure, the same general procedure may be used.

As a last example, let us consider the complex space truss loaded as shown in Fig. 4.52. This system, as we have already seen in Art. 4.5, is rigid and statically determinate, and we may proceed directly with its analysis. As a first step in this direction, we consider the conditions of equilibrium of such joints as B, C, D, and E, at each of which there is no external load and only four bars. Since the two bars that support the ring $ABCDE$ at B, for example, define a plane that intersects the plane of the ring itself in a horizontal line as shown, it follows that the resultant of the reactions exerted at B by the supporting bars must lie along this line. Thus, projecting all forces at B onto a horizontal axis normal to this line, we conclude that $S_1 = -S_2$. Similar arguments can be made with respect to the joints C, D, and E, and we conclude accordingly that $S_1 = -S_2 = S_3 = -S_4 = S_5$. Now, knowing that $S_1 = S_5$ and projecting all forces at A onto an axis that is normal to the plane $A'AE'$, we may determine S_1 and S_5 without difficulty, after which the remainder of the system can easily be analyzed by the method of joints. If there are external loads at the other joints, we make a separate analysis for each load, as above, and then superimpose the results.

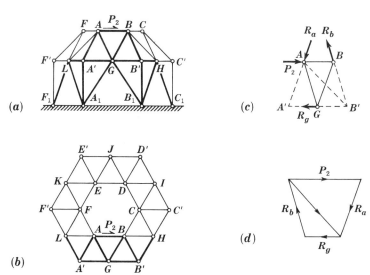

(a)

(b)

(c)

(d)

FIG. 4.51

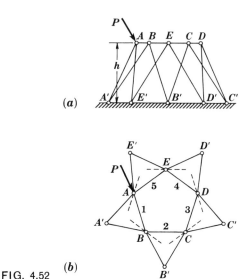

FIG. 4.52

It will be noted that, in each of the last two examples, we have managed the analysis by taking advantage of the fact that whenever a system of concurrent forces in space is such that the forces all lie in two intersecting planes, the resultant of those forces in either plane must lie along the line of intersection of the two planes. This, of course, follows from the fact that, for equilibrium, the resultant of the forces in one plane must be equal, opposite, and collinear with the resultant of the forces in the other plane. In general, this conclusion is very helpful in the analysis of complex space trusses.

PROBLEMS

1   Make a complete analysis of the structure in Fig. 4.44*b* under the action of a single vertical load *P* applied to one joint of the top ring. For simplification, assume that the stories are of equal height, the ribs being straight and inclined by 60° with the horizontal.

2   Make a complete analysis of the system in Fig. 4.46 under the action of a horizontal force *P* at each of the joints *B*, *D*, and *F*, instead of only at *D* as shown. For simplification, assume $\alpha = \beta = \gamma = 45°$, that is, that all panels are subdivided into squares.

3   Make a complete analysis of the structure in Fig. 4.49 under the action of a single vertical load *P* at *A* as shown. Using the results of this analysis, compute the axial force in each bar of the system when there is a vertical load *P* at each joint of the top ring.

4   Make a complete analysis of the complex system in Fig. 4.52 if the load *P* at *A* is vertical. Assume the following numerical data: $AB = BC = \cdots = 10$ ft,

$A'B' = B'C' = \cdots = 15$ ft, and $h = 12.5$ ft.   Using the results of this analysis, compute the axial force in each bar of the system when there is a vertical load P at each joint of the ring $ABCDE$.

4.7 HENNEBERG'S METHOD

Not infrequently, Henneberg's method of analysis can be used to advantage in working with complex space trusses.   This method has already been discussed in Art. 2.8 for the case of plane trusses, but here we shall review briefly a general outline of the procedure.   Suppose, for example, that Fig. 4.53a represents a complex space truss to which none of the methods of analysis discussed in the preceding article seems to apply, but that by removing the bar x and substituting a bar a as shown in Fig. 4.53b, we obtain a truss which can be analyzed by elementary methods.   This may mean, for example, that the substitution of the bar a for the bar x reduces the system to a simple space truss or to another complex truss which can be more readily analyzed.   This fictitious truss we now analyze under each of two separate conditions of loading: (1) the given system of loads $P_1, P_2, \ldots$ as shown in Fig. 4.53b and (2) two equal and opposite unit forces acting along the axis of the removed bar x as shown in Fig. 4.53c.   Let S_i' be the axial force in any bar due to the P loading (Fig. 4.53b) and s_i' the axial force in any bar due to the unit-force loading (Fig. 4.53c).   Now, it is obvious that if we have forces of magnitude X instead of unit forces in Fig. 4.53c, the axial force in any bar will be simply $s_i'X$ instead of s_i'.   Next we superimpose this latter condition of loading on that in Fig. 4.53b and conclude that the corresponding axial force in any bar of the fictitious truss under the combined X and P loading will be

$$S_i = S_i' + s_i'X \tag{a}$$

In the particular case of the added bar a, then, we have

$$S_a = S_a' + s_a'X \tag{b}$$

Now, if we choose X of such magnitude as to make $S_a = 0$, the bar a becomes

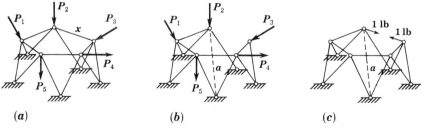

(a)   (b)   (c)

FIG. 4.53

inactive and can be removed, leaving the fictitious truss identical with the given truss except that the bar x is replaced by forces X. Hence, we conclude that the value of X which makes S_a in Eq. (b) equal to zero represents the true axial force in the bar x of the given truss (Fig. 4.53a). Proceeding in this manner, we write

$$S_a' + s_a'X = 0$$

from which

$$X = -\frac{S_a'}{s_a'} \qquad\qquad (c)$$

Using this value of X in Eq. (a), we may now calculate the axial force S_i in any other bar of the given truss without further difficulty.

If in the procedure above we should find $s_a' = 0$, the value of X defined by Eq. (c) becomes indeterminate or infinite depending on whether S_a' is zero or different from zero, and the truss is statically indeterminate. This idea can sometimes be used to advantage in testing a complex truss for critical form.

Let us now consider the application of Henneberg's method to several particular cases. As a first example, we take the octahedron loaded as shown in Fig. 4.54a. To define the configuration of this system, we assume that $ABCD$ is a square with edges of length 8 ft, while each of the other eight bars has a length of 9 ft. This makes the diagonals of the square $AC = BD = 8\sqrt{2}$ ft, and the vertical diagonal $EF = 14$ ft. The equal and opposite loads P are assumed to act along the diagonal AC of the square so that the system as a whole is in equilibrium.

If we remove the bar EC (marked x) and substitute a bar AC (marked a), we obtain a simple space truss as shown in Fig. 4.54b. Without difficulty, we can now make a complete analysis of this fictitious truss under the action of the applied loads P (Fig. 4.54b) and again under the action of two equal and opposite unit forces acting along the axis EC of the removed bar x (Fig. 4.54c).

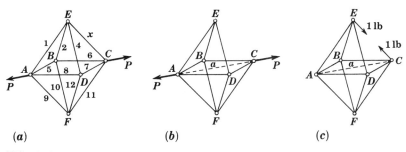

(a) (b) (c)

FIG. 4.54

TABLE 4.1

Bar (1)	S_i' (2)	s_i' (3)	$s_i'X$ (4)	S_i (5)
1	0	$+1.000$	$+0.397P$	$+0.397P$
2	0	-1.000	$-0.397P$	$-0.397P$
x		$+1.000$	$+0.397P$	$+0.397P$
4	0	-1.000	$-0.397P$	$-0.397P$
5	0	$+0.889$	$+0.353P$	$+0.353P$
6	0	$+0.889$	$+0.353P$	$+0.353P$
7	0	$+0.889$	$+0.353P$	$+0.353P$
8	0	$+0.889$	$+0.353P$	$+0.353P$
9	0	$+1.000$	$+0.397P$	$+0.397P$
10	0	-1.000	$-0.397P$	$-0.397P$
11	0	$+1.000$	$+0.397P$	$+0.397P$
12	0	-1.000	$-0.397P$	$-0.397P$
a	$+P$	-2.515	$-1.000P$	0

The results of such analyses are shown in the second and third columns of Table 4.1. Using the values of S_a' and s_a' from this table in Eq. (c) above, we obtain

$$X = -\frac{+P}{-2.515} = +0.397P$$

Having this value of X, we may now fill in column 4 of the table, and then the values of S_i in column 5 are obtained from Eq. (a).

In using Henneberg's method, we naturally raise the question as to which bar of the system to remove and where to place the added bar a. In general, any bar can be taken as x, but the added bar a must then be so placed as to restore the rigidity of the frame, since otherwise the fictitious truss would be statically indeterminate. There is usually more than one possibility for the added bar a, and we try to make a choice that will render the fictitious truss as easy to analyze as possible. For example, by placing the bar a between the joints A and C in the example above, we obtained a very simple case where all bars except a were inactive under the P loading. A bar a between the joints B and D would have served our general purpose just as well, but then the analysis of the system under the P loading would have been a little more complicated.

As a second example, let us consider the rectangular parallelepiped supported and loaded as shown in Fig. 4.55. We have already seen in Fig. 4.46 (see page 199) that if the bar EF' of this truss is removed and a bar g introduced between the points E' and H', we obtain a system which can be readily

analyzed by resolution into plane trusses.   Hence, if we take the truss in
Fig. 4.46 as the fictitious truss, we already have the results of the analysis under
the P loading and can at once fill in column 2 of Table 4.2.   This done, we next
consider the analysis of the fictitious truss (Fig. 4.46) under the action of two
equal and opposite unit forces applied at E and F' and acting along the line
joining these two points.   This analysis can be carried out in about the same
manner as that already discussed in connection with Fig. 4.46, and we give
simply the final results in column 3 of the table.   Using now the values of
S_g' and s_g' from the last line of this table in Eq. (c), we find

$$X = + \frac{P}{2\sqrt{2}} = +0.354P$$

With X known, the values of S_i as given in column 5 of the table can now be
computed from Eq. (a), and the analysis is completed.
   Sometimes, in order to reduce a given complex space truss to a form that can
be readily analyzed, it may be necessary to remove several bars $x_1, x_2, \ldots$
and substitute as many others $a_1, a_2, \ldots$.   Then, in application of Henneberg's method, we proceed as before and make a complete analysis of the
fictitious truss under each of the following conditions of loading: (1) the given
P loading, (2) a pair of unit forces replacing the bar x_1, (3) a pair of unit forces
replacing the bar x_2, etc.   Then, denoting by S_i' the axial force in any bar due
to the P loading and by $s_i', s_i'', \ldots$, the axial forces due to each pair of unit

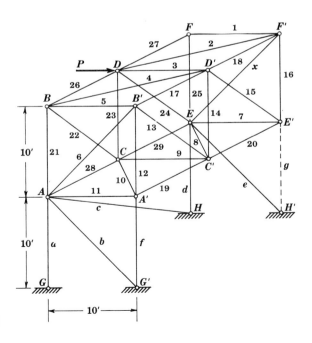

FIG. 4.55

TABLE 4.2

Bar (1)	S_i' (2)	s_i' (3)	$s_i'X$ (4)	S_i (5)
1	0	0	0	0
2	0	-1	$-0.354P$	$-0.354P$
3	$-P$	$+1/\sqrt{2}$	$+0.250P$	$-0.750P$
4	$+\sqrt{2}\,P$	-1	$-0.354P$	$+1.06P$
5	$-P$	$+1/\sqrt{2}$	$+0.250P$	$-0.750P$
6	$+\sqrt{2}\,P$	-1	$-0.354P$	$+1.06P$
7	0	0	0	0
8	$+P/\sqrt{2}$	-1	$-0.354P$	$+0.353P$
9	$-P/2$	$+1/\sqrt{2}$	$+0.250P$	$-0.250P$
10	$+P/\sqrt{2}$	-1	$-0.354P$	$+0.353P$
11	$-P/2$	$+1/\sqrt{2}$	$+0.250P$	$-0.250P$
12	$-3P/2$	$+\sqrt{2}$	$+0.500P$	$-1.00P$
13	$+P/\sqrt{2}$	-1	$-0.354P$	$+0.353P$
14	$-P/2$	$+1/\sqrt{2}$	$+0.250P$	$-0.250P$
15	$+P/\sqrt{2}$	-1	$-0.354P$	$+0.353P$
16	0	$-1/\sqrt{2}$	$-0.250P$	$-0.250P$
17	$-P/2$	$+1/\sqrt{2}$	$+0.250P$	$-0.250P$
18	0	$+1/\sqrt{2}$	$+0.250P$	$+0.250P$
19	$-P/2$	$+1/\sqrt{2}$	$+0.250P$	$-0.250P$
20	$-P/2$	$+1/\sqrt{2}$	$+0.250P$	$-0.250P$
21	$+P/2$	$-1/\sqrt{2}$	$-0.250P$	$+0.250P$
22	$-P/\sqrt{2}$	$+1$	$+0.354P$	$-0.353P$
23	$+P/2$	$-1/\sqrt{2}$	$-0.250P$	$+0.250P$
24	$-P/\sqrt{2}$	$+1$	$+0.354P$	$-0.353P$
25	0	0	0	0
26	$-P/2$	0	0	$-0.500P$
27	0	0	0	0
28	0	0	0	0
29	0	0	0	0
x		$+1$	$+0.354P$	$+0.354P$
g	$+P/2$	$-\sqrt{2}$	$-0.500P$	0

loads, we find by superposition that

$$S_i = S_i' + s_i'X_1 + s_i''X_2 + \cdots \qquad (d)$$

where $X_1, X_2, \ldots$ are so chosen as to satisfy the equations

$$S_{a_1} = S_{a_1}' + s_{a_1}'X_1 + s_{a_1}''X_2 + \cdots = 0$$
$$S_{a_2} = S_{a_2}' + s_{a_2}'X_1 + s_{a_2}''X_2 + \cdots = 0 \qquad (e)$$
$$\cdots\cdots\cdots\cdots\cdots\cdots\cdots\cdots$$

TABLE 4.3

Bar (1)	S_i' (2)	s_i' (3)	s_i'' (4)	s_i''' (5)	s_i'''' (6)	$s_i'X_1$ (7)	$s_i''X_2$ (8)	$s_i'''X_3$ (9)	$s_i''''X_4$ (10)	S_i (11)
1	$-1.414P$	0			-1.414	0			$+0.707P$	$-0.707P$
2	$+1.414P$	$+1.414$			$+2.828$	$-0.177P$			$-1.414P$	$-0.177P$
3	$-1.732P$	-1.732			-1.732	$+0.217P$			$+0.866P$	$-0.650P$
4		-1.414	0			$+0.177P$				$+0.177P$
5		$+2.828$	$+1.414$			$-0.354P$				$-0.354P$
6		-1.732	-1.732			$+0.217P$				$+0.217P$
7			-1.414	0				0		0
8			$+2.828$	$+1.414$				$+0.177P$		$+0.177P$
9			-1.732	-1.732				$-0.217P$		$-0.217P$
10				-1.414	0			$-0.177P$	0	$-0.177P$
11				$+2.828$	$+1.414$			$+0.354P$	$-0.707P$	$-0.354P$
12				-1.732	-1.732			$-0.217P$	$+0.866P$	$+0.650P$
13	$-1.414P$	-1.414			-2.828	$+0.177P$			$+1.414P$	$+0.177P$
14	$-1.000P$	-1.000			-2.000	$+0.125P$			$+1.000P$	$+0.125P$
15		-2.828	-1.414			$+0.354P$				$+0.354P$
16		-2.000	-1.000			$+0.250P$				$+0.250P$
17			-2.828	-1.414				$-0.177P$		$-0.177P$
18			-2.000	-1.000				$-0.125P$		$-0.125P$
19				-2.828	-1.414			$-0.354P$	$+0.707P$	$+0.354P$
20				-2.000	-1.000			$-0.250P$	$+0.500P$	$+0.250P$

21		0				−4.000	−0.500P	+1.000P	+0.375P
22	+1.000P	+1.000				+2.000	−0.125P	−1.000P	−0.125P
23	+2.828P	+2.828			+4.243	0		−2.121P	+0.707P
24	−3.000P	+1.000	−2.828	−1.414	+4.243	−4.000	+0.250P	+2.000P	−0.750P
25		+2.000	+1.000			−4.000	−0.250P		−0.250P
26		+4.243	+2.828	−2.828	−1.414	−0.530P	−0.177P		−0.707P
27		−4.000	+1.000	+1.000		+0.500P	+0.125P		+0.625P
28		+2.000	+1.000				+0.125P		+0.125P
29		+4.243	+2.828	−2.828	−1.414		+0.707P		+0.707P
30		4.000	−3.000	+1.000	+1.000	−0.500P	−0.250P		−0.750P
31			+2.000	+1.000		+0.125P	+0.250P		−0.250P
32	−1.414P	−1.414	+4.243	+2.828	−2.828	+2.828	+0.177P	+0.530P	−0.707P
a_1	−1.000P	−1.000	−3.000	−1.000		+0.500P	−0.125P	+0.500P	0
a_2		−1.000	−3.000	−1.000		+0.125P		+0.500P	0
a_3	−2.000P	−1.000	−3.000	−1.000		−0.500P		+0.500P	0
a_4		−1.000	−1.000	−3.000	−1.000	+0.125P		+2.000P	0
x_1									−0.125P
x_2									0
x_3									+0.125P
x_4									−0.500P

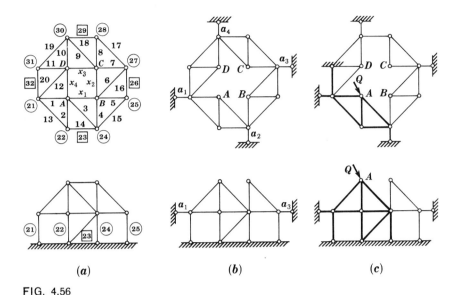

(a)   (b)   (c)

FIG. 4.56

As a specific example, let us consider the complex space truss consisting of 12 joints and 36 bars arranged as shown in Fig. 4.56a. This is a rigid and statically determinate system, but one that does not lend itself to ready analysis by elementary methods. However, if we remove the four bars x_1, x_2, x_3, and x_4 that form the top ring and introduce instead the horizontal constraints a_1, a_2, a_3, and a_4, as shown in Fig. 4.56b, we obtain a simple space truss that can readily be analyzed by the method of joints. We begin with the observation that, under the action of any applied load Q at the joint A, only the bars indicated in Fig. 4.56c by heavy lines will be active. Furthermore, owing to the symmetry of the system, we conclude that if we analyze this heavy-line portion under the action of each of three unit-force components as shown in Fig. 4.57a, b, c, respectively, we can easily obtain from this the axial force in any bar of the system due to any combination of loads applied to the joints A, B, C, D of the top ring. For example, let us assume that the actual loading on the given truss is limited to a single vertical load P at A. Then, by using the results from Fig. 4.57a, the value of S_i' for each bar of the system will be as shown in column 2 of Table 4.3. Likewise, if we want the values of s_i' due to two equal and opposite unit forces replacing the bar x_1, we use the results from Fig. 4.57b and c and obtain the values shown in column 3 of this table. In the same way, the values for s_i'', s_i''', and s_i'''', as shown in columns 4 to 6, are obtained. Now, using the values from the table for the fictitious bars

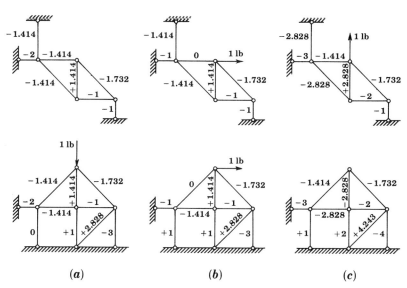

FIG. 4.57

a_1, a_2, a_3, and a_4 in Eqs. (e) on page 209, we may write

$$S_{a_1} = -P - 4X_1 - X_2 - X_4 = 0$$
$$S_{a_2} = 0 - X_1 - 4X_2 - X_3 = 0$$
$$S_{a_3} = 0 - X_2 - 4X_3 - X_4 = 0$$ \hfill (e')
$$S_{a_4} = -2P - X_1 - X_3 - 4X_4 = 0$$

from which we readily find

$$X_1 = -\frac{P}{8} \qquad X_2 = 0 \qquad X_3 = +\frac{P}{8} \qquad X_4 = -\frac{P}{2}$$

Finally, using these values in Eq. (d), we obtain the desired axial forces S_i as recorded in column 11 of the table. This completes the analysis of the given system under the action of a single vertical load P at A.

PROBLEMS

1 Using Henneberg's method, make a complete analysis of the complex space truss loaded as shown in Fig. 4.58. To obtain a truss easily analyzed by elementary methods, remove the bar EC and substitute a fictitious bar AB'. $ABCD$ is a square, and each inclined bar makes an angle of $45°$ with the vertical.

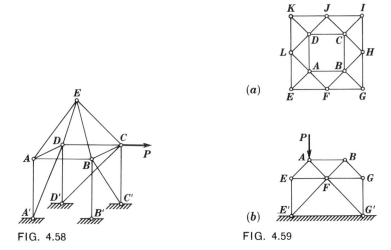

(a)

(b)

FIG. 4.58   FIG. 4.59

2   Repeat the analysis of the system shown in Fig. 4.58 if there is a vertical load P at E instead of a horizontal load P at C as shown.

3   Using Henneberg's method, make a complete analysis of the complex space truss shown in plan and elevation in Fig. 4.59, (a) under the action of a single vertical load P at A as shown, (b) under the action of a vertical load P at each of the joints A, B, C, and D.

4   Repeat the analysis of the system in Fig. 4.59, assuming a horizontal force P applied at E and acting to the right.

5   Make a complete analysis of the complex system shown in Fig. 4.56a if there is a horizontal force P applied at A and acting to the right in the direction coinciding with AB.

Chapter 5

General theorems relating
to elastic systems

5.1 STRAIN ENERGY IN TENSION, TORSION, AND BENDING

To a certain extent, all structural materials are elastic and deform slightly under the action of applied loads. This means that the loaded configuration of any structure, such as a truss or arch rib, is slightly different from its unloaded configuration. However, if the structure is statically determinate, this extremely small change in configuration has no significant effect on its geometry, and it is entirely justifiable to use the unloaded configuration as a basis of calculation of internal forces. In the case of a statically indeterminate system, however, such small deformations have a significant effect on the distribution of internal forces and must be taken into account. We therefore turn our attention now to various relationships pertaining to elastic deformations of structural elements under load.

Within limits, most structural materials can be considered as perfectly elastic, and they can be assumed to obey Hooke's law. In the case of a

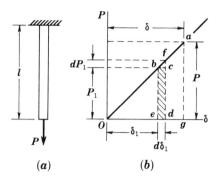

FIG. 5.1   (*a*)   (*b*)

prismatic bar in simple tension (Fig. 5.1*a*), this means that the load-deflection curve *Oa* is a straight line as shown in Fig. 5.1*b*.   When such a bar elongates under the action of a gradually increasing tensile load *P*, the load does work, and this work is stored in the bar in the form of *strain energy*.   To calculate the amount of this strain energy, we consider the state in which the load has the magnitude P_1, and the elongation the corresponding magnitude δ_1.   This state is represented in Fig. 5.1*b* by the point *b*.   If at this point an increment dP_1 is added, the elongation of the bar will increase by the amount $d\delta_1$, and the load P_1, which was already acting on the bar, will produce the work $P_1 \, d\delta_1$. This work is represented in the figure by the area of the shaded rectangle *bcde*.   The work of the small increment dP_1 of the load on the small dis-placement $d\delta_1$ can be neglected as a small quantity of second order.   The total work done by the load during its gradual increase from zero to the final value *P* is obtained as the sum of all such elemental areas as that shown in Fig. 5.1*b* and is represented by the area of the triangle *Oag*.   Thus, denoting by *U* the strain energy that is stored in the bar during its extension, we have

$$U = \frac{P\delta}{2} \qquad\qquad (a)$$

Using the known expression

$$\delta = \frac{Pl}{AE} \qquad\qquad (b)$$

for the elongation of a prismatic bar of length *l*, cross-sectional area *A*, and modulus of elasticity *E*, we can represent the strain energy (*a*) either as a function of the load *P* or as a function of the elongation δ.   These two forms for the strain energy are

$$U = \frac{P^2 l}{2AE} \qquad\qquad (5.1a)$$

$$U = \frac{AE\delta^2}{2l} \qquad\qquad (5.1b)$$

The strain energy of torsion of a prismatic shaft (Fig. 5.2a) can be obtained from the torsion-test diagram shown in Fig. 5.2b. This diagram shows the relation between the twisting moment, or *torque*, T and the corresponding angle of twist ϕ. We see that within the elastic range, the angle of twist is proportional to the torque as represented by the straight line Oa. Again, the shaded elemental area in the figure represents the work done by the torque during an infinitesimal increase $d\phi$ of the angle of twist ϕ, and the area of the triangle Oab represents the total work done by the torque as it increases gradually from zero to T. This work is equal to the strain energy stored in the shaft during torsion, and we have

$$U = \frac{T\phi}{2} \tag{c}$$

Using, for the angle of twist, the known formula

$$\phi = \frac{Tl}{C} \tag{d}$$

in which l is the length of the shaft and C its *torsional rigidity*,[1] we obtain

$$U = \frac{T^2 l}{2C} \tag{5.2a}$$

or $\qquad U = \frac{\phi^2 C}{2l} \tag{5.2b}$

In the first of these formulas, the strain energy is represented as a function of the torque T and in the second as a function of the angle of twist ϕ.

In the case of *pure bending* of a prismatic bar in a *principal plane* (Fig. 5.3a), the angle θ of rotation of one end with respect to the other is proportional to

[1] See S. Timoshenko, "Strength of Materials," 3d ed., vol. I, p. 290, D. Van Nostrand Company, Inc., Princeton N.J., 1955.

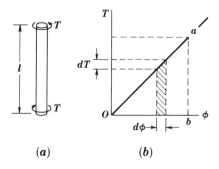

FIG. 5.2   **(a)**   **(b)**

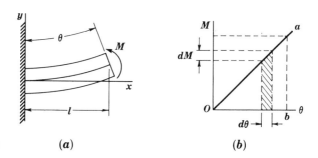

FIG. 5.3   (*a*)   (*b*)

the bending moment M as shown in Fig. 5.3*b*. Hence, we conclude that the strain energy of bending, equal to the total work produced by the moment M, is

$$U = \frac{M\theta}{2}$$ (*e*)

Using for θ the known formula

$$\theta = \frac{Ml}{EI}$$ (*f*)

in which l is the length of the beam and EI its flexural rigidity, we can represent this strain energy in either of the following two forms:

$$U = \frac{M^2 l}{2EI}$$ (5.3*a*)

or $$U = \frac{\theta^2 EI}{2l}$$ (5.3*b*)

Again, we see that the strain energy can be represented either as a function of the acting forces, in this case the bending moment M, or as a function of the quantity θ defining the deformation.

   In the case of a prismatic beam subjected to the action of transverse loads in a plane of symmetry, we have strain energy due to both bending and shear deformation. However, for beams of usual proportions, it can be shown that the strain energy due to shear is small compared with that due to bending, and the former is usually neglected in structural analysis.[1] Considering only bending, we obtain the strain energy in an element of the beam of length dx from Eqs. (5.3) simply by substituting dx for l and $d\theta/dx$ for θ/l. Thus, for one element,

$$dU = \frac{M^2\, dx}{2EI}$$ (*g*)

$$dU = \frac{EI}{2}\left(\frac{d\theta}{dx}\right)^2 dx$$ (*h*)

[1] For a complete discussion of this question, see *ibid.*, p. 318.

Then, to obtain the strain energy in the entire beam, we have only to sum expressions (g) and (h) over the entire length l of the beam. Noting that, for small deformation, $\theta \approx dy/dx$, we obtain in this way

$$U = \int_0^l \frac{M^2 \, dx}{2EI} \tag{5.4a}$$

$$U = \frac{EI}{2} \int_0^l \left(\frac{d^2 y}{dx^2}\right)^2 dx \tag{5.4b}$$

These formulas can be used also for a beam of variable cross section if the moment of inertia I can be expressed as a known function of x.

PROBLEMS

1 Two identical prismatic beams, one simply supported, the other with built-in ends, are bent by equal concentrated loads transversely applied at the middle. In what ratio are the amounts of strain energy stored?
   Ans. $4:1$.
2 A wooden cantilever beam having a rectangular cross section 8 in. deep and 5 in. wide and a length of 6 ft carries a uniform load of 200 lb/ft. Calculate the amount of strain energy in the beam if $E = 1.5(10)^6$ psi.
   Ans. $U = 42$ lb-in.
3 Compare the strain energy of torsion of a prismatic bar of circular cross section with that of pure bending of the same bar if the twisting moment and the bending moment are equal in the two cases, that is, if $T = M$. Assume that $E = 2.5G$.
   Ans. $U_T/U_M = \frac{5}{4}$.

5.2 PRINCIPLE OF SUPERPOSITION

We consider now the case where a structural member is subjected to the simultaneous action of several loads, as shown, for example, in Fig. 5.4. In such a case, if the bar is prismatic in form and the material obeys Hooke's law, the total elongation will be

$$\delta = \frac{(P_1 + P_2 + P_3)l_1}{AE} + \frac{(P_2 + P_3)(l_2 - l_1)}{AE} + \frac{P_3(l_3 - l_2)}{AE}$$

$$= \frac{P_1 l_1}{AE} + \frac{P_2 l_2}{AE} + \frac{P_3 l_3}{AE} \tag{a}$$

which is seen to be a linear function of the external forces. The first term on the right side of Eq. (a), for example, is the elongation $P_1 l_1/AE$ produced by the force P_1 acting alone. The second and third terms, likewise, are the elongations of the bar produced by the forces P_2 and P_3, respectively. Thus,

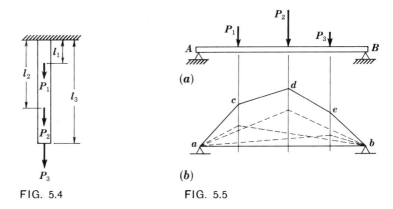

FIG. 5.4   FIG. 5.5

we see that the total elongation is obtained simply by summing up the elongations produced by the individual forces.

As a second example, let us consider bending of a simply supported beam AB under the action of transverse loads P_1, P_2, P_3, as shown in Fig. 5.5a.   In calculating deflections of the beam, we consider in Fig. 5.5b the *conjugate beam ab* loaded by the bending-moment area *acdeb*.   It is known[1] that the bending moments of this conjugate beam give, to a certain scale, the deflections of the actual beam.   Now, from simple statical considerations, it follows that the total moment area *acdeb* can be obtained by summing up the triangular areas indicated in the figure by dashed lines and representing, respectively, the moment areas for the individual loads.   Thus, the total fictitious load *acdeb* on the conjugate beam is the sum of the fictitious triangular loads corresponding to the individual forces P_1, P_2, and P_3 acting on the beam AB.   Repeating the same reasoning in calculating the bending moment at any cross section of the conjugate beam, we conclude that the bending moment produced by the total load *acdeb* is equal to the sum of the bending moments produced by the component triangular loads.   Hence, the deflection at any cross section of the actual beam AB is equal to the sum of the deflections produced at the same cross section by the individual loads P_1, P_2, and P_3.   Further, since these latter deflections are proportional to the corresponding forces, it can be concluded that the total deflection of any cross section of the beam AB will be a linear function of the forces P_1, P_2, and P_3 and is obtained by summing up the corresponding deflections produced by the individual loads.

In all cases of composite loading where deflections are linear functions of the applied forces, the above conclusion holds, and we obtain the total deflection of any point simply as the sum of the deflections produced by the individual forces.   This statement is called the *principle of superposition.*

[1] See *ibid.*, p. 147.

Under ordinary circumstances, a linear relationship between deflections and applied forces rests solely on the assumption that the material of a structure follows Hooke's law. However, there are certain cases in which this assumption alone will not be sufficient, and the deflections will not be linear functions of the applied forces even though the material does follow Hooke's law. One such example we have in the case of a bar submitted to the simultaneous action of axial and lateral forces. Considering, for example, the bending of the beam AB loaded as shown in Fig. 5.6a, we conclude that the deflection under the load P is no longer proportional to the load. Specifically, it can be represented by the formula[1]

$$\delta \approx \frac{Pl^3}{48EI} \frac{1}{1 - S/S_{cr}} \tag{b}$$

in which the first factor represents the deflection produced by the lateral load if acting alone, and the second factor represents the effect on this deflection of the axial compressive force S. The magnitude of this effect depends on the magnitude of the ratio S/S_{cr} in which $S_{cr} = \pi^2 EI/l^2$ is the critical load for buckling of the beam in the plane of the figure. Since S is proportional to P, expression (b) is no longer a linear function of the load, and the relation between δ and P is no longer linear. Representing this relation graphically, we obtain the curve shown in Fig. 5.6b. It is seen that the deflection is no longer proportional to the load and that it begins to increase very rapidly as the compressive force in the beam approaches the critical value. Thus, if we double the load P, the deflection will always be more than doubled, and the principle of superposition does not hold.

As another example where the principle of superposition does not hold, let us consider the system of two identical horizontal bars hinged together, as shown in Fig. 5.7a. Under the action of a vertical load P the bars will undergo some extension, and the hinge C will move down by an amount $\overline{CC_1} = \delta$. Assuming that this deflection is small, we find for the correspondingly small

See *ibid.*, vol. II, p. 52.

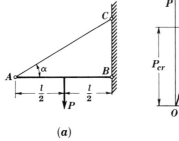

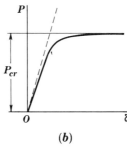

FIG. 5.6   (*a*)   (*b*)

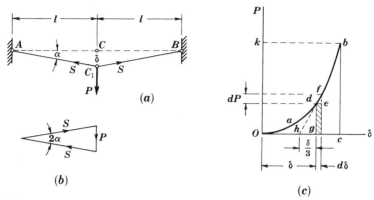

FIG. 5.7

angle α and for the tensile force S in each bar the following values:

$$\alpha \approx \frac{\delta}{l} \tag{c}$$

$$S \approx \frac{P}{2\alpha} \tag{d}$$

Considering, now, the unit elongation of each bar, we find

$$\epsilon = \frac{\sqrt{l^2 + \delta^2} - l}{l} \approx \frac{1}{2}\frac{\delta^2}{l^2}$$

The same elongation, if we use Hooke's law, is

$$\epsilon = \frac{S}{AE}$$

and we obtain

$$\frac{1}{2}\frac{\delta^2}{l^2} = \frac{S}{AE} = \frac{P}{2\alpha AE} = \frac{Pl}{2\delta AE} \tag{e}$$

from which

$$\delta = l\sqrt[3]{\frac{P}{AE}} \tag{f}$$

and $\qquad P = \dfrac{\delta^3 AE}{l^3} \tag{g}$

Again we see that the deflection δ is not proportional to the load although the material follows Hooke's law. This case differs from the preceding one in that with increasing deflection the system becomes stiffer, and the relation between δ and P is represented by the curve shown in Fig. 5.7c. It is typical of the behavior of a system of *critical form* as discussed in Art. 2.7 (page 89).

Following the same reasoning as for the case of simple tension, it can be shown that the area $OabcO$ in Fig. 5.7c represents the work done by the load P during the deflection δ and that it is equal to the strain energy stored in the bars AC and CB. The expression for this energy is obtained by summing up all such elemental areas as the shaded strip shown in the figure. This gives

$$U = \int_0^\delta P \, d\delta = \frac{AE}{l^3} \int_0^\delta \delta^3 \, d\delta = \frac{AE\delta^4}{4l^3} \tag{5.5a}$$

or
$$U = \frac{lP^{\frac{4}{3}}}{4 \sqrt[3]{AE}} \tag{5.5b}$$

It is seen that these expressions for strain energy are no longer second-degree functions of the displacement or force such as we had in those examples for which the law of superposition holds.

Considering what is characteristic of the examples represented in Figs. 5.6 and 5.7, we see that in each case the action of the external forces is appreciably affected by small deformations that take place in the system. The axial force S in Fig. 5.6 produces only compression of the beam AB if acting alone. However, when it acts in conjunction with the transverse load P, it produces not only compression but also some additional bending. In the case represented in Fig. 5.7, the tensile forces S in the bars depend on the deformation and are inversely proportional to the deflection δ that takes place. Always when we have such conditions that the action of external forces is affected by small deformations produced in the system, stresses and deformation will not be linear functions of the applied forces, and the principle of superposition does not hold. Thus, in conclusion, it can be said that the material must follow Hooke's law if the principle of superposition is to be applicable; but this requirement alone is insufficient. We have to consider also whether or not the action of the applied forces will be affected by small deformations of the structure. If such effect is substantial and must be taken into account, in calculating internal forces or stresses, the principle of superposition does not hold.

5.3 STRAIN ENERGY IN GENERALIZED FORM

In Art. 5.1, it was seen that expressions for strain energy in an elastic bar were second-degree functions either of the applied forces or of the displacements. It will now be shown that the same conclusion holds equally well for any elastic structure, provided that the principle of superposition can be applied. Let us consider, for example, an elastic body supported as shown in

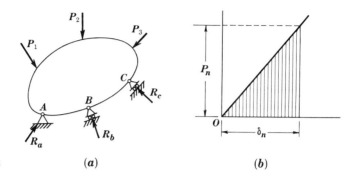

FIG. 5.8   (a)   (b)

Fig. 5.8a and submitted to the action of external forces P_1, P_2, P_3, ...
Since the amount of strain energy stored in the body depends not on the order
in which the forces are applied but only on their final magnitudes, we can
simplify our further discussion by assuming that all the forces are applied
simultaneously and then gradually increased in the same proportion.   Then,
if the principle of superposition holds, the displacements will be linear functions
of the forces, and during loading they increase in the same proportion as the
forces do.   In calculating the work of any force P_n, we shall be interested not
in the total displacement of its point of application but only in that component
in the direction of the force.   Let δ_n denote this component of displacement.
Then, during the assumed gradual loading, δ_n increases in the same proportion
as P_n, and the relation between these two quantities can be represented by the
diagram shown in Fig. 5.8b.   Hence, we conclude that the work produced by
the load P_n is $P_n \delta_n / 2$.   The total work of all external forces, equal to the
strain energy stored in the deformed body, is obtained by summing up the works
of the individual forces, which gives[1]

$$U = \tfrac{1}{2}(P_1\delta_1 + P_2\delta_2 + P_3\delta_3 + \cdots) \tag{5.6}$$

The reactions R_a, R_b, and R_c do not appear in this expression, because for the
conditions of support illustrated in Fig. 5.8, their work is zero.
    Since the displacements δ_1, δ_2, . . . are homogeneous linear functions of
the forces P_1, P_2, . . . , it follows that if these functions are substituted in
expression (5.6), we shall find the strain energy to be represented by a
homogeneous second-degree function of the external forces P_1, P_2, ...
Likewise, if we express the forces as linear functions of the displacements and
then substitute these functions in expression (5.6), we shall find that the strain

[1] The statement that the strain energy stored in an elastic body is equal to half of the
sum of the products of external forces by the corresponding displacements is sometimes
called *Clapeyron's theorem*.   It is mentioned in Lamé's "Theory of Elasticity," seventh
lecture.   See also Maxwell, "Scientific Papers," vol. I, p. 598, and Todhunter and Pearson,
"History," vol. I, p. 578, Cambridge University Press, London, 1886.

energy can also be represented as a homogeneous second-degree function of the displacements δ_1, δ_2, ... Both forms of representation of the strain energy will be useful in our further discussion.

It should be noted that the foregoing conclusions regarding the degree and homogeneity of the strain-energy function were obtained on the assumption that the principle of superposition holds. If this principle does not hold, the strain energy will no longer be a second-degree function of the forces or of the displacements, as can be seen, for example, from Eqs. (5.5) of the preceding article.

Expression (5.6) for strain energy can be made more general by using the notion of *generalized forces*.[1] Any group of statically interdependent forces that can be completely defined by one symbol can be considered as a generalized force. For example, in the case of axial extension of a bar (Fig. 5.9*a*), we have two equal and opposite forces acting along the axis of the bar, and one symbol P defines entirely this pair of balanced forces. Again, in the case of pure bending (Fig. 5.9*b*), we have two equal and opposite couples that are in equilibrium, and one symbol M completely defines the system. In the case of a transverse load acting on a beam (Fig. 5.9*c*), we have a group of three forces that, being in equilibrium, are completely defined by the magnitude P of the applied load. In all such cases where we can define a group of forces by one symbol, we may treat that group as a *generalized force*.

In using the notion of generalized force, we have to generalize also the notion of displacement. In dealing with single forces (Fig. 5.8), we have already pointed out that not the total displacements of their points of application but

[1] The notions of *generalized force* and *generalized displacement* were introduced by Lagrange in his famous book "Mécanique analytique," Paris, 1788. In application to the deformations of elastic systems, they were extensively used by Lord Rayleigh. See, for example, his "Scientific Papers," vol. I, p. 255; "Theory of Sound," 2d ed., p. 91.

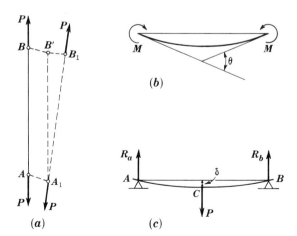

FIG. 5.9   (*a*)   (*c*)

only those components in the directions of the forces should be considered, since the work done by the forces depends only on such components. Thus, if δ_n is the component of the displacement of the point of application of the force P_n in the direction of that force, we say that δ_n is the displacement *corresponding* to the force P_n. If a small increment $\Delta\delta_n$ is given to this displacement, the work done by the force P_n is

$$P_n\,\Delta\delta_n \qquad\qquad (a)$$

Now, in using the notion of generalized force, the *corresponding generalized displacement* must be taken in such a way that the product of the generalized force and the increment of the corresponding generalized displacement gives the work. Take, for example, the case of simple tension (Fig. 5.9a). It is seen that the bar AB can be brought to any new position A_1B_1 by first moving it parallel to itself to the position A_1B' and then rotating it about the point A_1. During such displacement of the bar as a whole, the system of two equal and opposite forces does not produce any work. Work is produced only when the bar elongates by some amount δ. This elongation, then, is the generalized displacement corresponding to the generalized force consisting of two equal and opposite forces P. If an increment $\Delta\delta$ is given to the elongation δ, the generalized force P produces work of the amount $P\,\Delta\delta$, which is similar to expression (a) for the case of a single force. In the case of pure bending (Fig. 5.9b), the work produced by the couples M is entirely defined by the angle of rotation θ of one end of the bar with respect to the other. Hence this angle must be taken as the generalized displacement corresponding to the generalized force represented by the two equal and opposite couples. If θ obtains an increment $\Delta\theta$, the couples M produce the work $M\,\Delta\theta$ and again we obtain an expression similar to expression (a). In the case of a transverse load acting on a beam (Fig. 5.9c), the group of forces P, R_a, and R_b does not produce any work when the beam moves with its supports as a rigid body. Work is produced only when the beam deflects and point C moves perpendicular to AB. The deflection δ of the point C with respect to the line AB joining the ends of the beam axis is the generalized displacement in this case.

Sometimes the generalized displacement corresponding to a chosen generalized force may not be entirely self-evident. Consider, for example, the simply

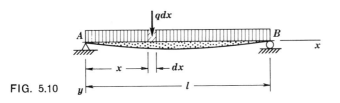

FIG. 5.10

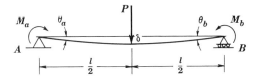

FIG. 5.11

supported beam under uniform load as shown in Fig. 5.10. If the intensity q of the load is taken as the generalized force, the corresponding generalized displacement will be the area between the chord AB and the deflection curve as shown in the figure. To show this, we give to the deflection y of each point on the axis of the beam a small increase Δy. Then the work done on each such additional displacement by the corresponding element of force $q\,dx$ is $q\,dx\,\Delta y$, and the entire load will produce the work

$$q\int_0^l \Delta y\,dx \tag{b}$$

Now, observing that the integral $\int_0^l \Delta y\,dx$ is an increment of the area between the chord AB and the deflected axis of the beam, we conclude, by definition, that such area is the generalized displacement corresponding to the generalized force q. It is well to note in this case that while the generalized force has the dimension of *force ÷ length*, the corresponding generalized displacement has the dimension of *length squared*, so that their product has the proper dimension for work. Since the work done by a generalized force on an increment of the corresponding generalized displacement has always the same form as expression (*a*) derived for a single load, we conclude that the total work produced by a generalized force during a gradual loading has the same form as that for single forces and is equal to half the product of the final magnitude of the generalized force and the final value of the corresponding generalized displacement. This means that expression (5.6) derived for isolated forces can be used also if the forces and the displacements are generalized.

As an example of the application of expression (5.6), let us calculate the strain energy in a simply supported beam of prismatic form that is loaded by a force P at the middle and by the two couples M_a and M_b applied at the ends as shown in Fig. 5.11. In such a case the system of forces acting on the beam can be represented in terms of three generalized forces, namely, the load P together with its reactions, and each of the couples M_a and M_b together with their reactions. The corresponding generalized displacements will be the deflection δ under the load and the angles of rotation θ_a and θ_b of the ends of the beam. The total strain energy stored in the beam, from expression (5.6), is

$$U = \tfrac{1}{2}(P\delta + M_a\theta_a + M_b\theta_b) \tag{c}$$

Using now the known expression for the deflection curve, we have

$$\delta = \frac{Pl^3}{48EI} + \frac{M_a l^2}{16EI} + \frac{M_b l^2}{16EI}$$

$$\theta_a = \frac{Pl^2}{16EI} + \frac{M_a l}{3EI} + \frac{M_b l}{6EI} \qquad (d)$$

$$\theta_b = \frac{Pl^2}{16EI} + \frac{M_a l}{6EI} + \frac{M_b l}{3EI}$$

Substituting these values of the displacements into expression (c), we obtain

$$U = \frac{l^3}{96EI} \left(P^2 + \frac{6}{l} PM_a + \frac{6}{l} PM_b + \frac{16}{l^2} M_a{}^2 + \frac{16}{l^2} M_b{}^2 \right.$$

$$\left. + \frac{16}{l^2} M_a M_b \right) \qquad (e)$$

It is seen that the strain energy is a homogeneous second-degree function of the generalized forces.

Solving Eqs. (d) for P, M_a, and M_b and substituting them in expression (c), we shall obtain the strain energy as a second-degree function of the generalized displacements.

PROBLEMS

1   Make a general expression for the strain energy stored in the beam shown in Fig. 5.11, assuming that $P = 0$, (a) expressed as a function of the end moments M_a and M_b, (b) expressed as a function of the angles of rotation θ_a and θ_b.

   Ans. (a) $U = \dfrac{l}{6EI} (M_a{}^2 + M_a M_b + M_b{}^2)$.

   (b) $U = \dfrac{2EI}{l} (\theta_a{}^2 - \theta_a \theta_b + \theta_b{}^2)$.

2   A thin steel strip of length l and uniform flexural rigidity EI is elastically bent into a complete circle by applied end moments.   Compute the strain energy U that is stored in the hoop.
   Ans. $U = 2\pi^2 EI / l$.

3   An elastic prismatic beam of length l has built-in ends and is subjected to the action of a transverse load P at the middle and of such magnitude that the deflection under the load is δ.   Assuming that the deflected axis of the beam has the form of a full wave of a cosine curve, calculate the strain energy stored in the beam.
   Ans. $U = EI\pi^4 \delta^2 / l^3$.

4   Using expression (5.6) and the notion of generalized force, compute the strain energy stored in the beam shown in Fig. 5.10.
   Ans. $U = q^2 l^5 / 240EI$.

5   An elastic body undergoes uniform compression under hydrostatic pressure p. If the pressure p is taken as the generalized force, what will be the corresponding generalized displacement?

5.4 CASTIGLIANO'S FIRST THEOREM

The principle of virtual displacements as discussed in Art. 1.10 for any ideally connected system of rigid bodies can readily be extended to apply to an elastic system. It is only necessary in this case to consider the virtual work of internal forces as well as that of applied external forces. As a model of an elastic body, we take a system of particles connected by springs as shown in Fig. 5.12, where the springs represent the elastic constraints between the various particles. Although not shown in the figure, we assume that there are suitable springs to resist relative rotation and sliding of the particles as well as direct changes in linear distances. Under the action of applied external forces, the model will be elastically deformed, and the springs will exert internal forces on the various particles of the system as shown in Fig. 5.12b. Thus, we obtain a very complex system of forces that, however, are in equilibrium and therefore subject to application of the principle of virtual displacements.

Let P_1, P_2, . . . denote external forces applied to the body and let δ_1, δ_2, . . . be the corresponding displacements. We may now define a virtual displacement of the system by any set of small changes $\Delta\delta_1$, $\Delta\delta_2$, . . . in the displacements δ_1, δ_2, . . . , and the principle of virtual work gives

$$\Sigma P_i \, \Delta\delta_i + \Delta T = 0 \qquad (a)$$

where ΔT denotes the work of the internal forces on the virtual displacements of the particles. Now, since we assume an elastic body, the springs all obey Hooke's law, and from this it follows that the work of internal forces on the virtual displacements of the particles in Fig. 5.12b is equal to the change in

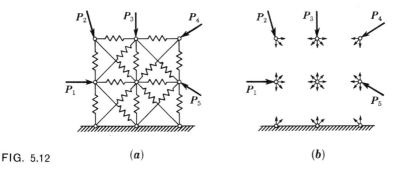

FIG. 5.12   (a)   (b)

strain energy in the springs with reversed sign, that is,

$$\Delta T = -\Delta U \qquad\qquad (b)$$

Substituting $-\Delta U$ for ΔT in Eq. (a), we obtain

$$\Sigma P_i\, \Delta\delta_i - \Delta U = 0 \qquad\qquad (c)$$

To calculate the increment ΔU, the strain energy must be represented first as a function of the displacements δ_1, δ_2, ... Then, in the usual way, the increment of U due to the increments $\Delta\delta_1$, $\Delta\delta_2$, . . . of the displacements is

$$\Delta U = \frac{\partial U}{\partial \delta_1}\Delta\delta_1 + \frac{\partial U}{\partial \delta_2}\Delta\delta_2 + \frac{\partial U}{\partial \delta_3}\Delta\delta_3 + \cdots \qquad\qquad (d)$$

In applying the principle of virtual displacements, we can select in any particular case a displacement that is most suitable for the solution of a given problem. For example, we can imagine a virtual displacement that affects only the displacement δ_n, corresponding to the load P_n, and leaves the displacements δ_1, δ_2, . . . unchanged. Under such conditions, $\Delta\delta_1$, $\Delta\delta_2$, . . . are all zero except $\Delta\delta_n$, and expression (d) for the increment of U reduces to

$$\Delta U = \frac{\partial U}{\partial \delta_n}\Delta\delta_n \qquad\qquad (e)$$

Using this expression in Eq. (c), we obtain

$$P_n\, \Delta\delta_n - \frac{\partial U}{\partial \delta_n}\Delta\delta_n = 0$$

which, upon canceling $\Delta\delta_n$, reduces to

$$\frac{\partial U}{\partial \delta_n} = P_n \qquad\qquad (5.7)$$

This equation states that if the strain energy of a deformed elastic body is represented as a function of the displacements δ_1, δ_2, . . . , a partial derivative of that function with respect to any chosen displacement gives the corresponding force. This statement is usually referred to as *Castigliano's first theorem*.[1] Although derived above for the case of single forces P_1, P_2, . . . , it holds equally well for generalized forces and corresponding generalized displacements.

As an example of the application of Eq. (5.7), let us consider a symmetrical system of three bars hinged together at D and loaded as shown in Fig. 5.13. Denoting by δ the vertical displacement of the hinge D, we find the elongation of each inclined bar to be $\delta \cos \alpha$, while for the vertical bar it will be δ. Assum-

---

[1] Alberto Castigliano, "Théorème de l'équilibre des systèmes élastiques et ses applications," Paris, 1879. The English translation of this book was made by E. S. Andrews, Scott, Greenwood & Son, London, 1919.

ing now that the cross-sectional areas and the moduli of elasticity of all three bars are equal, we find the strain energy of the system to be

$$U = \frac{AE}{2l}(\delta^2 + 2\delta^2 \cos^3 \alpha) \tag{f}$$

Now, using Eq. (5.7), we obtain

$$\frac{AE\delta}{l}(1 + 2\cos^3 \alpha) = P \tag{g}$$

and from this we find the axial force in the vertical bar to be

$$S = \frac{AE\delta}{l} = \frac{P}{1 + 2\cos^3 \alpha} \tag{h}$$

Thus, by using Castigliano's first theorem, we solve the statically indeterminate problem.

A consideration of the arguments used in the derivation of Castigliano's first theorem shows that its validity is in no way dependent upon the principle of superposition. The only requirement is that the system behave elastically. For this reason, the theorem is of particular value in dealing with systems of critical form like those discussed in Art. 5.2, for which the principle of superposition does not hold. As an example of this kind, we consider again the case of two bars arranged and loaded as shown in Fig. 5.7. Denoting by δ the deflection corresponding to the load P, we see that the elongation of each bar will be

$$\Delta l = \sqrt{l^2 + \delta^2} - l \approx \frac{\delta^2}{2l} \tag{i}$$

Then, by using Eq. (5.1b), we find that the strain energy of the system, expressed as a function of the displacement δ, becomes

$$U = 2\left(\frac{AE}{2l}\overline{\Delta l^2}\right) = \frac{AE\delta^4}{4l^3} \tag{j}$$

which we note is not a second-degree function of δ. Nevertheless, Eq. (5.7)

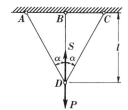

FIG. 5.13

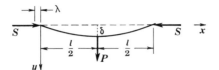

FIG. 5.14

applies, and we find, by differentiation,

$$\frac{AE\delta^3}{l^3} = P$$

from which

$$\delta = l\sqrt[3]{\frac{P}{AE}} \tag{k}$$

This result is seen to agree with expression (f) obtained on page 222.

As a last example, let us consider the case of a beam column simply supported at its ends and subjected to the simultaneous action of compressive forces S and a transverse force P as shown in Fig. 5.14. It is desired to find the magnitude of the deflection δ under the load P. To simplify the problem, we assume that the deflection curve can be represented with sufficient accuracy by a half sine wave, that is,

$$y = \delta \sin\frac{\pi x}{l}$$

Then the configuration of the system is entirely defined by δ, and the strain energy of bending[1] will be

$$U = \frac{EI}{2}\int_0^l \left(\frac{d^2y}{dx^2}\right)^2 dx = \frac{EI\pi^4\delta^2}{4l^3} \tag{l}$$

Associated with this bending, we see that the two ends of the beam come together by the amount

$$\lambda = \frac{1}{2}\int_0^l \left(\frac{dy}{dx}\right)^2 dx = \frac{\pi^2\delta^2}{4l} \tag{m}$$

To find now the generalized force corresponding to the displacement δ, we recall that by definition it is that quantity by which we must multiply the increment $\Delta\delta$ in order to obtain the corresponding virtual work. Making a

[1] It is unnecessary to consider the strain energy of direct compression since it remains constant and independent of δ.

small increase $\Delta\delta$ in δ, we see that this work is

$$P\,\Delta\delta + S\,\Delta\lambda = \left(P + S\,\frac{d\lambda}{d\delta}\right)\Delta\delta$$

Hence, the generalized force corresponding to δ is $P + S\,d\lambda/d\delta$. Now, using expressions (l) and (m), Eq. (5.7) becomes

$$\frac{EI\pi^4}{2l^3} = P + S\,\frac{\pi^2\delta}{2l}$$

from which

$$\delta = \frac{2Pl^3}{\pi^4 EI}\frac{1}{1 - Sl^2/\pi^2 EI} \tag{n}$$

Since the numerical factor $\pi^4/2 = 48.7$, we see that this approximate result compares very favorably with Eq. (b) on page 221.

PROBLEMS

1　Find the tensile force S in the vertical bar of the statically indeterminate system in Fig. 5.13 if its cross-sectional area is A while that of each inclined bar is $A/2$.
　　Ans. $S = P/(1 + \cos^3\alpha)$.

2　A prismatic beam with built-in ends has flexural rigidity EI and carries a transverse load P at the middle. Assuming that the deflection line can be represented with sufficient accuracy by the cosine curve

$$y = \frac{\delta}{2}\left(1 - \cos\frac{2\pi x}{l}\right)$$

calculate the magnitude of the deflection δ under the load.
　　Ans. $\delta = Pl^3/2\pi^4 EI$.

3　A rigid beam is supported by three vertical elastic bars as shown in Fig. 5.15. Each of the supporting bars has cross-sectional area A and modulus of elasticity E, but the middle bar is only half as long as the other two. Calculate the lateral deflection δ produced by the horizontal force P acting as shown. Assume in calculation that the deflection δ is a small quantity compared with the overall dimensions of the structure.
　　Ans. $\delta = \sqrt[3]{2Pl^3/AE}$.

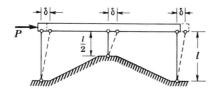

FIG. 5.15

5.5   CASTIGLIANO'S SECOND THEOREM

In the previous article, we used the expression for strain energy as a function of the displacements and found that a partial derivative of this function with respect to any generalized displacement gives the corresponding generalized force. Now let us consider the expression for strain energy as a function of the external forces and assume that the principle of superposition holds, in which case the strain energy is a homogeneous function of second degree. *Under such conditions, a partial derivative of the strain energy with respect to one of the external forces gives the displacement corresponding to that force.* This statement is usually called *Castigliano's second theorem.*[1]

To prove the second theorem, let us consider the case of an elastic body carrying the loads $P_1, P_2, P_3, \ldots$ as shown in Fig. 5.8a. During the application of these loads, deformations are produced, and a certain amount of strain energy U is stored within the body. If, subsequently, one of the forces, say P_n, receives an increment ΔP_n, some additional deformation of the body will ensue, and the strain energy U will obtain an increment

$$\Delta U = \frac{\partial U}{\partial P_n} \Delta P_n$$

so that the total strain energy becomes

$$U + \frac{\partial U}{\partial P_n} \Delta P_n \tag{a}$$

Now, suppose that instead of introducing the increment ΔP_n after the application of the loads $P_1, P_2, P_3, \ldots$, we reverse the procedure and apply first the infinitely small increment ΔP_n and afterward the loads $P_1, P_2, P_3, \ldots$. Since the infinitesimal load ΔP_n produces an infinitesimal displacement, the corresponding work is a small quantity of the second order and can be neglected. Further, during the subsequent application of the loads $P_1, P_2, P_3, \ldots$, we observe, by virtue of the principle of superposition, that the work of these forces will not be affected by the presence of the load ΔP_n and will be equal to its previous value U. At the same time the acting load ΔP_n rides through the displacement δ_n resulting from the application of the loads $P_1, P_2, P_3, \ldots$ and produces the work $\Delta P_n \delta_n$. Thus, in this case, the total work, equal to the total strain energy stored in the body, is

$$U + \Delta P_n \delta_n \tag{b}$$

Since the total amount of strain energy stored in the body does not depend on the order in which the loads are applied, we conclude that expressions (a)

[1] Alberto Castigliano, *Trans. Acad. Sci. Turin*, vol. 11, pp. 127–286, 1876. See also his treatise "Théorème de l'équilibre des systèmes élastiques et ses applications."

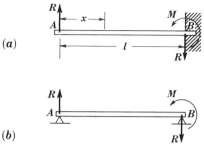

FIG. 5.16 (b)

and (b) must be equal. Thus,

$$U + \frac{\partial U}{\partial P_n} \Delta P_n = U + \Delta P_n \, \delta_n$$

from which

$$\frac{\partial U}{\partial P_n} = \delta_n \tag{5.8}$$

and the theorem is proved.

In Fig. 5.8a, P_1, P_2, P_3, . . . denote single forces; but the derivation holds also if they are generalized forces and δ_1, δ_2, δ_3, . . . are the corresponding generalized displacements. Thus, we can state that the partial derivative of the strain energy with respect to any generalized force gives the corresponding generalized displacement.

In the derivation of Castigliano's second theorem, we assumed that it is possible to give an arbitrary increment to one of the forces without changing the other forces. Thus, we consider these forces as independent. Such forces as statically determinate reactions do not satisfy this condition since their magnitudes are not independent of P_1, P_2, P_3, . . . and can be found from equations of statics.   From this consideration it follows that the strain energy U in Eq. (5.8) must be represented as a function of *statically independent* external forces.   Take, for example, the two beams shown in Fig. 5.16.   The same forces R and M are acting in both cases, and from statics we conclude that $M = Rl$. Thus, the strain energy can be represented in either of the following two forms:[1]

$$U = \frac{R^2 l^3}{6EI} \tag{c}$$

or $$U = \frac{M^2 l}{6EI} \tag{d}$$

If we use expression (c), we consider R as an independent external force and M as the reaction, as in the case of a cantilever beam (Fig. 5.16a).   In such a

[1] Both formulas are readily obtained from the general expression (5.4a) of the strain energy.

case the derivative of expression (c) with respect to R gives

$$\frac{\partial U}{\partial R} = \frac{Rl^3}{3EI}$$

which is the deflection of the end A of the cantilever beam built in at B. If expression (d) is used, we assume that M is the independent external force and R is the reaction as in the case of a simply supported beam (Fig. 5.16b). Then, taking the derivative of expression (d) with respect to M, we obtain

$$\frac{\partial U}{\partial M} = \frac{Ml}{3EI}$$

which is the angle of rotation of the end B of the simply supported beam. This example illustrates the significance of the requirement of representing the strain energy as a function of statically independent forces.

Castigliano's second theorem is very useful in calculating deflections of beams. Take, for example, the cantilever beam bent by a force and a couple applied at the end (Fig. 5.17a). The bending moment at any cross section is

$$M = M_a - Px \tag{e}$$

and the strain energy stored in the beam, as obtained from formula (5.4a), is

$$U = \int_0^l \frac{M^2 \, dx}{2EI} \tag{f}$$

The derivative of this expression with respect to P gives the displacement corresponding to P, that is, the deflection δ of the end A of the cantilever. Thus,

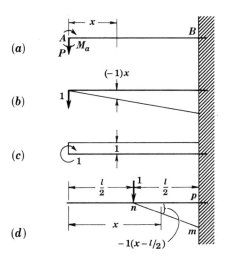

FIG. 5.17

we obtain

$$\delta = \frac{\partial U}{\partial P} = \int_0^l \frac{M}{EI} \frac{\partial M}{\partial P} \, dx = \frac{1}{EI} \int_0^l (M_a - Px)(-x) \, dx$$

$$= \frac{Pl^3}{3EI} - \frac{M_a l^2}{2EI} \quad (g)$$

The derivative of expression (f) with respect to the generalized force M_a gives the corresponding displacement, i.e., the angle of rotation θ_a of the end A of the cantilever, and we obtain

$$\theta_a = \frac{\partial U}{\partial M_a} = \int_0^l \frac{M}{EI} \frac{\partial M}{\partial M_a} \, dx = \frac{1}{EI} \int_0^l (M_a - Px)(1) \, dx$$

$$= \frac{M_a l}{EI} - \frac{Pl^2}{2EI} \quad (h)$$

In this application of Castigliano's theorem we did not calculate the final expression for strain energy as a function of external forces but used it in its general form (f), substituting the value of M only after differentiation under the integral signs in Eqs. (g) and (h). In this way a considerable simplification of calculation is accomplished, especially if there are several external forces.

It can be noted that the partial derivatives $\partial M/\partial P$ and $\partial M/\partial M_a$, which enter in the above calculations, have very simple meanings. The first of these derivatives represents the rate of change of bending moment in the beam with change of the load P. As shown in Fig. 5.17b, it can be visualized as the bending-moment diagram for a unit load at the end of the beam. The second derivative, representing the rate of change of the bending moment M with change of M_a, is shown in Fig. 5.17c. Using for these derivatives the notations M'_p and M'_m, we can write the expressions for the displacements in the following simplified forms:

$$\delta = \frac{1}{EI} \int_0^l MM'_p \, dx \quad (i)$$

$$\theta_a = \frac{1}{EI} \int_0^l MM'_m \, dx \quad (j)$$

We see that in each case we have to integrate along the length of the beam the product of the actual bending moment with the corresponding unit-load bending moment. This conclusion can be extended and applied to beams with any kind of lateral loading. If we have, for example (Fig. 5.18a), a simply supported beam carrying a uniform load q and a concentrated load P at the middle, the derivative $\partial M/\partial P$ is shown in Fig. 5.18b, and the deflection at the middle is

$$\delta = \frac{1}{EI} \int_0^l MM'_p \, dx = \frac{2}{EI} \int_0^{l/2} \left(\frac{P}{2} x + \frac{ql}{2} x - \frac{qx^2}{2} \right) \frac{x}{2} \, dx$$

$$= \frac{Pl^3}{48EI} + \frac{5}{384} \frac{ql^4}{EI}$$

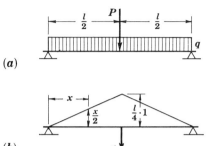

FIG. 5.18 (b)

It is seen that by applying Castigliano's theorem, we obtain the displacement corresponding to any of the forces acting on the elastic system, but there are cases where we need to find such displacements to which there are no corresponding forces acting. In such cases we add to the actual forces fictitious forces of infinitesimal magnitudes such that they do not change the actual displacement. We then obtain the required displacements by differentiation of the strain energy with respect to these added forces. Take, for example, the cantilever beam in Fig. 5.17a, and assume that it is required to calculate the deflection at the middle of the beam. Since there is no corresponding force, we assume an infinitesimal fictitious load Q applied at the middle. Then the required deflection is

$$\delta_1 = \frac{\partial U}{\partial Q} = \frac{1}{EI} \int_0^l M \frac{\partial M}{\partial Q} \, dx \qquad (k)$$

Since the added load Q is infinitesimal, we use for M the previous expression (e). The derivative $\partial M/\partial Q$, representing the rate of change of the bending moment M with change of the load Q, can be visualized by the unit-load bending-moment diagram nmp shown in Fig. 5.17d. Substituting these values into expression (k), we obtain

$$\delta_1 = -\frac{1}{EI} \int_{l/2}^l (M_a - Px)\left(x - \frac{l}{2}\right) dx = \frac{5Pl^3}{48EI} - \frac{M_a l^2}{8EI}$$

As a last example, we take the case of a slender cantilever beam of circular cross section, the axis of which is a circular quadrant of radius R in a horizontal plane, as shown in Fig. 5.19. Under the action of a vertical load P applied at A, such a bar will be subjected to both bending and torsion, and we have for any cross section, defined by the angular coordinate ϕ, a bending moment

$$M_\phi = PR \sin \phi \qquad (l)$$

and a twisting moment

$$T_\phi = PR(1 - \cos \phi) \qquad (m)$$

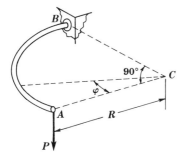

FIG. 5.19

Thus, neglecting the shear deformation associated with bending, the total strain energy of the system becomes

$$U = \int_0^{\pi/2} \frac{M_\phi^2 R}{2EI} \, d\phi + \int_0^{\pi/2} \frac{T_\phi^2 R}{2GJ} \, d\phi \tag{n}$$

To find the deflection δ corresponding to the load P, we have

$$\delta = \frac{\partial U}{\partial P} = \frac{R}{EI} \int_0^{\pi/2} M_\phi \frac{\partial M_\phi}{\partial P} \, d\phi + \frac{R}{GJ} \int_0^{\pi/2} T_\phi \frac{\partial T_\phi}{\partial P} \, d\phi \tag{o}$$

Substituting the values of M_ϕ and T_ϕ together with their derivatives from Eqs. (l) and (m) and performing the indicated integrations, we obtain

$$\delta = \frac{\pi P R^3}{4EI} + \frac{P R^3}{4GJ} (3\pi - 8) \tag{p}$$

In conclusion, we note that the derivation of Castigliano's second theorem was based on the principle of superposition. Hence, the expression for strain energy U must be a homogeneous second-degree function of the acting forces. If the principle of superposition does not hold and U is not a second-degree function of the acting forces, Castigliano's second theorem is not applicable. To illustrate this point, let us consider the example shown in Fig. 5.7. The strain energy in this case is given by expression (5.5b), which is not quadratic in P. Taking the derivative of that function with respect to P, we obtain

$$\frac{\partial U}{\partial P} = \frac{1}{3} \sqrt[3]{\frac{P l^3}{AE}}$$

which is only one-third of the true deflection δ as given by Eq. (f) on page 222. We have already seen that we get the correct result in this case by taking the strain energy U as a function of the displacement δ and using Castigliano's first theorem.

PROBLEMS

1 Using Castigliano's second theorem, find the angles of rotation at the ends of a simply supported beam AB of length l and flexural rigidity EI, due to a uniformly distributed load of intensity q.

> *Hint* Introduce equal infinitesimal moments M_Q at each end of the beam with respect to which the strain energy U can be differentiated.

> *Ans.* $\theta_A = \theta_B = ql^3/24EI$.

2 A continuous square frame $ABCD$ built in at A is loaded as shown in Fig. 5.20. Find the vertical deflection of point D if all three members have the same EI. Consider only strain energy of bending.

> *Ans.* $\delta = 5Pl^3/3EI$.

3 A continuous frame ABC hinged at A and supported by a roller at C is loaded as shown in Fig. 5.21. Find the horizontal displacement of point C if both members have the same length l and the same flexural rigidity EI.

> *Ans.* $\delta = 2Pl^3/3EI$.

4 Determine the horizontal and vertical displacements δ_h and δ_v of the free end A of the circular cantilever beam loaded in its own plane as shown in Fig. 5.22. Assume that the cross-sectional dimensions of the beam are small compared with the radius r, so that the straight-beam formula (5.4a) can be used in calculating the strain energy of bending. Neglect the strain energy due to direct and shearing stresses.

> *Ans.* $\delta_h = Pr^3/2EI,\ \delta_v = \pi Pr^3/4EI$.

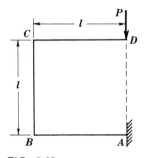

FIG. 5.20

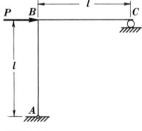

FIG. 5.21

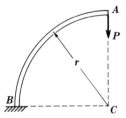

FIG. 5.22

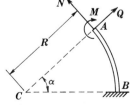

FIG. 5.23

5   The curved cantilever shown in Fig. 5.23 has a circular center line of radius R and subtends a central angle α. On the free end B there act an axial force N, a shear force Q, and a bending moment M, all in the plane of the figure. Develop a general formula for the angular rotation of the tangent to the elastic line at A.

$$Ans. \quad \theta = \frac{MR\alpha}{EI} + \frac{QR^2}{EI}(1 - \cos \alpha) - \frac{NR^2}{EI}(\alpha - \sin \alpha).$$

5.6 THEOREM OF LEAST WORK

In the preceding article we have considered applications of Castigliano's second theorem to statically determinate systems and found that the displacement of any point is obtained as the derivative of the strain energy of the system with respect to the corresponding force. Applying the theorem in the same way to a statically indeterminate system, we conclude that the derivative of the strain energy with respect to any redundant reaction or internal constraint must be zero since it is the function of such a reactive force to prevent any displacement at its point of application. Hence, if X, Y, Z, . . . denote the magnitudes of redundant forces and if the principle of superposition applies, we have

$$\frac{\partial U}{\partial X} = 0 \qquad \frac{\partial U}{\partial Y} = 0 \qquad \frac{\partial U}{\partial Z} = 0 \qquad \cdots \qquad (5.9)$$

where U is a second-degree function in X, Y, Z, ... We see that Eqs. (5.9) may be interpreted as conditions of a maximum or minimum of the strain-energy function U. By calculating the second derivatives and showing that they are always positive, it can be concluded that we have the case of a minimum. This means physically that the structure will deform under load in such a way as to keep its strain energy, equal to the work of applied forces, a minimum. This statement, called the *theorem of least work*, is very useful in the analysis of statically indeterminate structures. We simply derive the expression for strain energy as a function of the redundant forces and then find the magnitudes of these redundants from Eqs. (5.9). It is seen that there will always be exactly as many of these equations as there are redundants.

As an example, we take the case of a uniformly loaded beam built in at B and supported by a roller at A as shown in Fig. 5.24. For the determination of the unknown reactive forces Y_a, Y_b, M_b, in this case, we have only two equations of statics,

$$\Sigma Y = 0 \qquad \Sigma M = 0 \qquad\qquad (a)$$

and the problem is statically indeterminate. Choosing the vertical reaction Y_a at A as the redundant reaction, we obtain the case of a simple cantilever loaded as shown in Fig. 5.24b, where the reactions at the built-in end have been

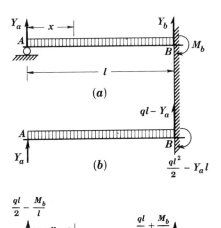

FIG. 5.24

expressed in terms of Y_a. Now, applying the theorem of least work to this system we may write

$$\frac{\partial U}{\partial Y_a} = \frac{\partial}{\partial Y_a} \int_0^l \frac{M^2 \, dx}{2EI} = \frac{1}{EI} \int_0^l M \frac{\partial M}{\partial Y_a} \, dx = 0 \qquad (b)$$

Substituting in this equation

$$M = Y_a x - \frac{qx^2}{2} \qquad \frac{\partial M}{\partial Y_a} = x$$

we find

$$\int_0^l \left(Y_a x - \frac{qx^2}{2} \right) x \, dx = \frac{Y_a l^3}{3} - \frac{ql^4}{8} = 0 \qquad (c)$$

which gives

$$Y_a = \tfrac{3}{8} q l$$

As an alternative approach to this same problem, we may take the simply supported beam shown in Fig. 5.24c as the primary system and consider the reactive moment M_b as the redundant. Then, again applying the theorem of least work, we see that the necessary equation for determining the magnitude of M_b becomes

$$\frac{\partial U}{\partial M_b} = \frac{\partial}{\partial M_b} \int_0^l \frac{M^2 \, dx}{2EI} = \frac{1}{EI} \int_0^l M \frac{\partial M}{\partial M_b} \, dx = 0 \qquad (d)$$

The bending moment at any cross section, represented as a function of M_b, is

$$M = \left(\frac{ql}{2} - \frac{M_b}{l}\right) x - \frac{qx^2}{2}$$

from which

$$\frac{\partial M}{\partial M_b} = -\frac{x}{l}$$

Substituting these values into Eq. (d), we obtain

$$\int_0^l \left[\left(\frac{ql}{2} - \frac{M_b}{l}\right) x - \frac{qx^2}{2}\right] \frac{x}{l} \, dx = 0$$

which gives

$$M_b = \frac{ql^2}{8}$$

Sometimes the internal forces acting between two adjacent portions of a structure will be chosen as the statically indeterminate quantities, rather than the reactions at the supports. In such cases the theorem of least work still holds and can be used to advantage. Consider, for example, the symmetrical rectangular frame shown in Fig. 5.25a. Taking a section through the horizontal plane of symmetry mn and considering the equilibrium of the upper part of the frame (Fig. 5.25b), we can represent the action of the lower part thereon by the vertical forces[1] $P/2$ and by the couples M_0, the magnitude of which cannot be determined from statics. From the symmetry of the deformation shown in Fig. 5.25a, we conclude that the cross sections on which the couples M_0 are acting in Fig. 5.25b do not rotate. Hence the derivative, with respect to M_0, of the strain energy stored in the upper part of the frame must vanish, and we can state, as before, that the magnitude of the statically indeterminate quantity M_0 is such as to make the strain energy a minimum. In

[1] From symmetry it can be concluded that there will be no shearing forces in the plane mn.

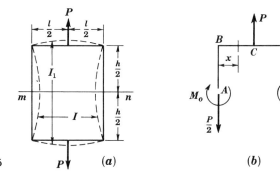

FIG. 5.25 (a) (b)

calculating this strain energy, we neglect the strain energy due to direct stress and assume that the effect of axial forces on bending can be neglected. Thus, the bending moment for the portion AB of the frame is M_0, while for the portion BC it is $M_0 - Px/2$. The strain energy of the upper half of the frame then is

$$U = \frac{M_0^2 h}{2EI} + \frac{1}{EI_1} \int_0^{l/2} \left(M_0 - \frac{Px}{2} \right)^2 dx$$

Applying the principle of least work, we now obtain

$$\frac{\partial U}{\partial M_0} = \frac{M_0 h}{EI} + \frac{2}{EI_1} \int_0^{l/2} \left(M_0 - \frac{Px}{2} \right) dx = 0$$

which gives

$$M_0 = \frac{Pl}{8[1 + (h/l)(I_1/I)]}$$

It is seen that when the cross-sectional moment of inertia I_1 of the horizontal bars of the frame is large in comparison with the corresponding quantity I for the vertical bars, the moment M_0 becomes small, and the condition of bending of the horizontal bars approaches that of simply supported beams. On the other hand, if I_1 is small in comparison with I, the moment M_0 approaches the value $Pl/8$ as for a beam with built-in ends.

As another example let us consider the circular ring shown in Fig. 5.26a and determine the moments M_0 and the increase in the vertical diameter of the ring under the action of forces P applied as shown. Proceeding as in the case of a rectangular frame (Fig. 5.25) and considering the equilibrium of the upper half of the ring, we conclude that

$$\frac{\partial U}{\partial M_0} = \frac{1}{EI} \frac{\partial}{\partial M_0} \int_0^{\pi r/2} M^2 \, ds = 0 \qquad (e)$$

Substituting in this equation

$$M = M_0 - \frac{Pr}{2} (1 - \cos \phi) \qquad \frac{\partial M}{\partial M_0} = 1$$

we obtain

$$\int_0^{\pi/2} \left[M_0 - \frac{Pr}{2} (1 - \cos \phi) \right] d\phi = 0$$

from which

$$M_0 = \frac{Pr}{2} \left(1 - \frac{2}{\pi} \right) = 0.182Pr \qquad (f)$$

To find the increase of the vertical diameter of the ring, we observe that the forces P in Fig. 5.26a represent the generalized force corresponding to the

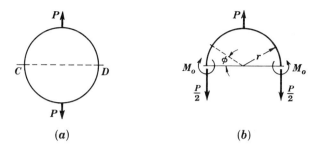

FIG. 5.26   *(a)*   *(b)*

increase δ of the diameter.   Hence, this increase[1] is

$$\delta = \frac{\partial U}{\partial P} = \frac{2}{EI} \frac{\partial}{\partial P} \int_0^{\pi/2} M^2 r \, d\phi$$

$$= -\frac{4r}{EI} \int_0^{\pi/2} \left[M_0 - \frac{Pr}{2} (1 - \cos \phi) \right] \frac{r}{2} (1 - \cos \phi) \, d\phi$$

If we use the value of M_0 from Eq. (*f*) above, this becomes

$$\delta = -\frac{Pr^3}{EI} \int_0^{\pi/2} \left(\cos \phi - \frac{2}{\pi} \right) (1 - \cos \phi) \, d\phi$$

$$= \frac{Pr^3}{EI} \left(\frac{\pi}{4} - \frac{2}{\pi} \right) = 0.149 \frac{Pr^3}{EI} \quad (g)$$

As another application of the method of least work, let us calculate the thrust H in the two-hinged arch under vertical load as shown in Fig. 5.27. The vertical reactions V_a and V_b can be obtained in the usual way from equations of statics; but the horizontal thrust H is a statically indeterminate quantity, and to find it we must use the theorem of least work, which requires that

$$\frac{\partial U}{\partial H} = 0 \qquad (h)$$

In the case of a flat arch, the strain energy due to direct stress is an important factor and cannot be neglected in comparison with the strain energy of bending. Thus, we take

$$U = \int_0^s \frac{M^2 \, ds}{2EI} + \int_0^s \frac{N^2 \, ds}{2AE} \qquad (i)$$

where M is the bending moment and N is the axial force at any cross section. The length of the axis of the arch is denoted by s.   The bending moment at any cross section can be considered as consisting of two parts: one representing

[1] In this calculation we assume that the strain energy due to direct and shearing stresses can be neglected in comparison with strain energy of bending.   This is justifiable only in the case of a thin ring.

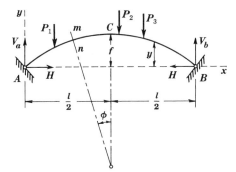

FIG. 5.27

the moment M_0, calculated as for a simple beam $(H = 0)$, and the other representing the moment due to the thrust H. Hence,

$$M = M_0 - Hy \qquad (j)$$

where y denotes the ordinates of the axis of the arch as shown in the figure. For a flat arch, the axial force N can be assumed, with good accuracy, as equal to the thrust H. Then,

$$U = \int_0^s \frac{(M_0 - Hy)^2 \, ds}{2EI} + \int_0^s \frac{H^2 \, ds}{2AE}$$

Substituting this expression in Eq. (h), we obtain

$$-\int_0^s \frac{(M_0 - Hy)y \, ds}{EI} + \int_0^s \frac{H \, ds}{AE} = 0$$

from which

$$H = \frac{\displaystyle\int_0^s \frac{M_0 y \, ds}{EI}}{\displaystyle\int_0^s \frac{y^2 \, ds}{EI} + \int_0^s \frac{ds}{AE}} \qquad (k)$$

This is a general formula from which H can be calculated if the loading and the dimensions of the arch are given.

In the case of an arch of homogeneous material and uniform cross section, E, I, and A are constants and can be taken from under the integral signs. Then,

$$H = \frac{\displaystyle\int_0^s M_0 y \, ds}{\displaystyle\int_0^s y^2 \, ds + i^2 \int_0^s ds} \qquad (l)$$

where i denotes the radius of gyration of the cross section with respect to its centroidal axis. The second term in the denominator represents the influence of the direct stress on the magnitude of H. If this influence is neglected, we obtain

$$H = \frac{\int_0^s M_0 y \, ds}{\int_0^s y^2 \, ds} \tag{m}$$

An especially simple expression for H is obtained in the case of a parabolic arch under the action of a load uniformly distributed along the horizontal span. In such a case

$$y = \frac{4fx}{l^2} (l - x)$$

$$M_0 = \frac{qx}{2} (l - x)$$

Then, substituting into Eq. (m), we obtain

$$H = \frac{ql^2}{8f}$$

where f is the vertical rise as shown in the figure.

PROBLEMS

1 Find, by using the theorem of least work, the bending moments M_a and M_b at the ends of a uniformly loaded beam with built-in ends and of uniform flexural rigidity EI.
   Ans. $M_a = M_b = -ql^2/12$.
2 Solve the preceding problem if the intensity of load along the length of the beam varies according to the linear law $q = q_0 x/l$.
   Ans. $M_a = -q_0 l^2/30$, $M_b = -q_0 l^2/20$.
3 Referring to Fig. 5.24a, calculate the reactive moment M_b if, instead of the uniform loading shown, the beam carries an isolated load P at the distance c from A.
   Ans. $M_b = Pc(l^2 - c^2)/2l^2$.
4 If, instead of the uniform loading shown in Fig. 5.24a, the beam AB is subjected to an active moment M_a at the end A, show by the theorem of least work that the corresponding moment induced at B will be $M_b = -M_a/2$.
5 Considering only strain energy of bending, calculate the horizontal thrust H in the case of a two-hinged semicircular arch rib of span l that carries a vertical load P at the crown. Assume a uniform flexural rigidity EI of the rib.
   Ans. $H = P/\pi$.

5.7 THE RECIPROCAL THEOREM

Let us begin with a simple example, the bending of a cantilever beam, and consider two loading conditions, (1) a load P at the free end (Fig. 5.28a) and (2) a load Q at any point C (Fig. 5.28b). In the first case, the deflection at C

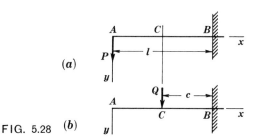

FIG. 5.28 (b)

is given by the equation

$$\delta_c = \frac{Pc^2}{6EI}(3l - c) \qquad (a)$$

In the second case the deflection at C is calculated as for a cantilever of length c and is equal to $Qc^3/3EI$. The part AC of the beam remains straight and is tangent to the deflection curve at C so that it has the slope $Qc^2/2EI$. Thus, the total deflection at point A in this case is

$$\delta_a = \frac{Qc^3}{3EI} + \frac{Qc^2}{2EI}(l - c) = \frac{Qc^2}{6EI}(3l - c) \qquad (b)$$

Comparing expressions (a) and (b), we see that when $P = Q$, these two deflections are equal, that is, a load P, placed at point A, produces at point C the same deflection as the load P, placed at C, produces at point A.* In a more general case when P and Q are not equal, the deflections (a) and (b) are no longer equal, but the work done by the force P on the corresponding displacement (b) is equal to the work done by the force Q on the corresponding displacement (a), that is,

$$P\delta_a = Q\delta_c$$

Let us consider now a general case of an elastic body subjected to two different conditions of loading. In the first case there act forces P_1 and P_2 (Fig. 5.29a), and in the second case the forces P_3 and P_4 (Fig. 5.29b). We shall designate the displacements of the points 1, 2, 3, and 4 in the directions of the forces for the first condition of loading by δ_1', δ_2', δ_3', and δ_4' and for the second condition of loading by δ_1'', δ_2'', δ_3'', and δ_4''. Assume, now, that all four forces are acting on the body simultaneously and that the principle of superposition holds. Then the displacements of points 1, 2, . . . corresponding to the forces P_1, P_2, . . . are obtained by superposition and are equal to $\delta_1' + \delta_1''$,

* This conclusion was obtained by J. C. Maxwell in considering deformation of trusses; see Maxwell, "Scientific Papers," vol. I, p. 602.

$\delta_2' + \delta_2''$, ... The total strain energy stored in the body is

$$U = \tfrac{1}{2}[(\delta_1' + \delta_1'')P_1 + (\delta_2' + \delta_2'')P_2 + (\delta_3' + \delta_3'')P_3$$
$$+ (\delta_4' + \delta_4'')P_4] \quad (c)$$

This amount of strain energy does not depend on the order in which the loads are applied. Let us assume, for example, that the loads P_1 and P_2 are applied first. Then, the corresponding amount of strain energy is

$$\tfrac{1}{2}(P_1\delta_1' + P_2\delta_2') \qquad (d)$$

Let us apply, now, the loads P_3 and P_4. Since the principle of superposition holds, the displacements produced during the application of P_3 and P_4 will not be affected by the presence of the previously applied loads P_1 and P_2 and will be equal to δ_1'', δ_2'', δ_3'', and δ_4'' as before. The work done by P_3 and P_4 during their gradual application will be

$$\tfrac{1}{2}(P_3\delta_3'' + P_4\delta_4'') \qquad (e)$$

At the same time, the previously applied loads P_1 and P_2 will produce work, on the displacements δ_1'' and δ_2'', equal to

$$P_1\delta_1'' + P_2\delta_2'' \qquad (f)$$

Upon summing up expressions (d), (e), and (f), the total amount of strain energy is obtained. Equating this energy to expression (c), we obtain

$$P_1\delta_1'' + P_2\delta_2'' = P_3\delta_3' + P_4\delta_4' \qquad (5.10)$$

This equation states that the work done by the forces of the first state of loading (Fig. 5.29a) on the corresponding displacements of the second state (Fig. 5.29b) is equal to the work done by the forces of the second state on the corresponding displacements of the first. This represents the so-called *reciprocal theorem*.[1]

[1] In its general form the reciprocal theorem has been proved by E. Betti, *Nuovo cimento*, ser. 2, vols. 7 and 8, 1872. See also Lord Rayleigh's paper in *Proc. London Math. Soc.*, vol. 4, pp. 357–368, 1873.

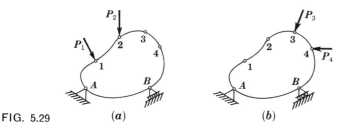

FIG. 5.29   (a)   (b)

The foregoing derivation of the reciprocal theorem holds also in the case of generalized forces. As an example, let us consider the two conditions of loading of the cantilever beam shown in Fig. 5.30. In the case of the load P applied at the end, the rotation of the end A is

$$\theta_a = \frac{Pl^2}{2EI}$$

Likewise, the deflection at A under the action of the couple M is

$$\delta_a = \frac{Ml^2}{2EI}$$

It is seen that these values of θ_a and δ_a satisfy the reciprocal theorem, i.e.,

$$M\theta_a = P\delta_a$$

As another example, let us consider the case of a rigid slab having the form of an equilateral triangle supported by three vertical and three inclined bars of equal cross-sectional areas A and hinged at the ends (Fig. 5.31). In one case, the slab is loaded by W at the center (Fig. 5.31a), and in another case it is loaded by a couple M acting in the plane of the slab (Fig. 5.31b). Owing to the action of the load W, the vertical bars will be compressed by the amount $Wh/3AE$; and since the lengths of the diagonals remain unchanged, the compression of the vertical bars will be accompanied by lateral distortions in the side planes of the structure as shown in Fig. 5.31c. Consequently, there will be rotation of the slab. In calculating the angle of rotation θ, we observe that the middle point s_1 between the hinges m_1 and n_1 moves along $m_1 n_1$ by the amount $Wh^2/3AEl$, and the angle of rotation of the slab is obtained by dividing this displacement by the distance $l/2 \sqrt{3}$ of the point s from the center O of the slab (Fig. 5.31a). This gives

$$\theta = \frac{Wh^2}{3AEl} \frac{2\sqrt{3}}{l} = \frac{2Wh^2}{AE\sqrt{3}l^2} \tag{g}$$

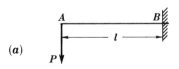

(a)

(b)

FIG. 5.30

As a result of the loading shown in Fig. 5.31b, we shall obtain not only rotation of the slab but also some vertical movement. To proceed with this case, we first replace the torque M by a statically equivalent system of three equal forces P coinciding with the three edges of the triangular slab. Then, since

$$3P \frac{l}{2\sqrt{3}} = M$$

we have

$$P = \frac{2M}{l\sqrt{3}}$$

Now each of these three forces P produces a compressive force Ph/l in the corresponding vertical bar as shown in Fig. 5.31d. Hence, the vertical displacement δ of the slab will be

$$\delta = \frac{Ph^2}{lAE} = \frac{2Mh^2}{l^2AE\sqrt{3}} \tag{g'}$$

Considering the rotation (g) in the first case of loading and the vertical displacement (g') in the second case, we see that the reciprocal theorem is satisfied, i.e.,

$$M\theta = W\delta$$

The reciprocal theorem is especially useful in the construction of influence lines for redundant reactions. Let us consider, for example, a beam on three

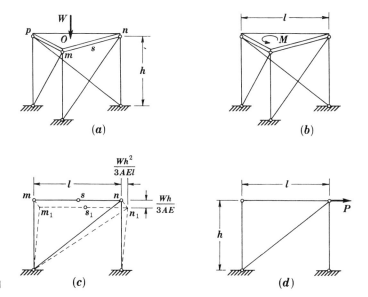

FIG. 5.31   (c)   (d)

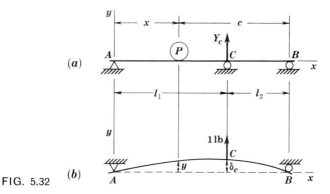

FIG. 5.32

supports as shown in Fig. 5.32a and investigate the change in the redundant reaction Y_c at the intermediate support with change of the distance x defining the position of a moving load P.   In applying the reciprocal theorem, we have always to compare two conditions of loading of the given structure.   As the first state, we take the actual loading, shown in Fig. 5.32a; as a second state, we select the fictitious loading shown in Fig. 5.32b, where the load P is removed and in place of the reaction Y_c a unit force acts.   This second state is statically determinate, and we can define the deflection curve AC by the equation[1]

$$y = \frac{(1 \text{ lb})l_2 x}{6(l_1 + l_2)EI}\left[(l_1 + l_2)^2 - l_2^2 - x^2\right] \tag{h}$$

A similar expression can be established for the right portion BC.   The deflection under the unit load is obtained by substituting $x = l_1$ in Eq. (h), which gives

$$\delta_c = \frac{(1 \text{ lb})l_1^2 l_2^2}{3(l_1 + l_2)EI} \tag{i}$$

Applying now the reciprocal theorem, we calculate first the work done by the forces of Fig. 5.32a on the corresponding displacements of Fig. 5.32b.   Such work evidently is

$$Y_c \delta_c - Py$$

Considering now the work of the forces of Fig. 5.32b on the corresponding displacements of Fig. 5.32a, we find that this work is zero since, for the unit load in Fig. 5.32b, the corresponding deflection in Fig. 5.32a is zero.   Hence, the reciprocal theorem gives

$$Y_c \delta_c - Py = 0$$

[1] See "Strength of Materials," vol. I, p. 145.

from which

$$Y_c = \frac{Py}{\delta_c} = \frac{3P(l_1 + l_2)EI}{(1 \text{ lb})l_1{}^2 l_2{}^2}\, y \qquad (j)$$

It is seen that when the load P is moving along the beam AB, the reaction at C varies in the same proportion as the ordinates y of the deflection curve ACB calculated for a unit load at C. Thus, this deflection curve can be taken as the *influence line* for the reaction Y_c. Having such an influence line, we can find the reaction Y_c for any system of vertical loads P_1, P_2, P_3, . . . in the usual way from the equation

$$Y_c = \frac{1}{\delta_c}\,(P_1 y_1 + P_2 y_2 + P_3 y_3 + \cdots)$$

where y_1, y_2, . . . are the ordinates of the influence line ACB corresponding to the forces P_1, P_2, ...

If we desire an influence line for bending moment M_c at the intermediate support C of the beam in Fig. 5.32a, we first cut the beam at this section and introduce the equal and opposite couples M_c as shown in Fig. 5.33a. The corresponding fictitious loading is shown in Fig. 5.33b. Now, using the reciprocal theorem, we find

$$M_c(\theta_1 + \theta_2) - Py = 0$$

from which

$$M_c = P\,\frac{y}{\theta_1 + \theta_2}$$

Upon substituting the known expressions for y, θ_1, and θ_2, we see that the influence coefficient for the left span becomes

$$\frac{x(l_1{}^2 - x^2)}{2l_1(l_1 + l_2)} \qquad (k)$$

The same expression can be used for the right span if we interchange the subscripts of l_1 and l_2 and measure x from B.

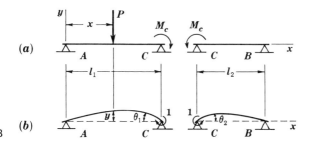

FIG. 5.33

If the derivation of an analytical expression for the influence line is not practicable as in the preceding examples, the line can always be obtained experimentally by making a test with a model of the actual structure. Suppose, for example, that we desire an influence line for the thrust H of the two-hinged arch shown in Fig. 5.34a. In the fictitious state of loading (Fig. 5.34b), we make the support B movable and apply to the arch two equal and opposite unit forces as shown. Let δ be the horizontal displacement of the support B produced in this fictitious case and y the vertical deflection of point C. Then the application of the reciprocal theorem gives

$$H\delta - Py = 0$$

from which

$$H = \frac{Py}{\delta} \qquad\qquad (l)$$

This result is similar to that in Eq. (j) obtained for the previous problem. Hence, we can state that the ratios y/δ for the case shown in Fig. 5.34b represent the influence coefficients for the thrust H. It is evident that, by making a model of the arch and loading it as shown in Fig. 5.34b, the influence coefficients can be obtained from the measured deflections y and δ.

The experimental determination of influence lines may be of practical interest in those cases where we have many redundant indeterminate quantities. Take, for example, the rectangular frame built in at the supports as shown in Fig. 5.35a. This is a structure with three redundant constraints. Removing the support at the right end and replacing it by reactive forces, we obtain the three statically indeterminate quantities H, V, and M_b as shown. To obtain for each of these quantities an influence line by experiment, we use a model of the frame and give in each case to the end B of the model a displacement *corresponding* to the force that we are planning to determine. If we are interested, for example, in the reaction H, we give to the end B of the model a horizontal displacement δ and at the same time by proper constraints we

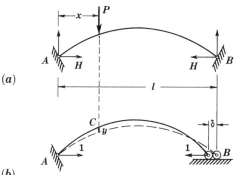

(a)

FIG. 5.34   (b)

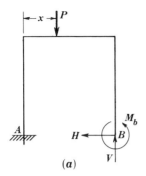 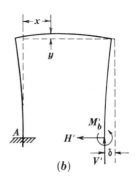

FIG. 5.35   (a)   (b)

prevent the cross section from both vertical and angular displacement. In this manner we obtain the deformation shown in Fig. 5.35b. Let H', V', and M'_b be the forces which we apply to the model at B to realize the above-described displacement. Now, applying the reciprocal theorem to the loading conditions shown in Fig. 5.35a and b and observing that only those displacements in the fictitious state (Fig. 5.35b) corresponding to the actual forces P and H are different from zero and that the displacements in Fig. 5.35a corresponding to the forces H', V', and M'_b are all zero, we obtain

$$H\delta - Py = 0$$

from which

$$H = \frac{Py}{\delta}$$

Again, the influence coefficients for H are obtained by dividing the deflections y by the displacement δ, and all these quantities can be measured in making the experiment with the model. Influence lines for V and M_b can be obtained in a similar manner. To get the influence line for V, we have to give to the end B of the model a vertical displacement and at the same time prevent any horizontal or rotational displacement. In the case of M_b we must give to the end B a rotation and at the same time prevent any horizontal or vertical motion. The measurements of deflections in these two cases give the information required for calculating the ordinates of the required influence lines.[1]

PROBLEMS

1   Referring to the two-span beam shown in Fig. 5.32 and using expression (k), find the maximum bending moment M_c at the intermediate support if $l_1 = 40$ ft, $l_2 = 20$ ft, and $P = 1,000$ lb.

  Ans.   Max $M_c = 5,125$ ft-lb.

[1] Special apparatus, known as *Begg's deformator gauges*, are available for controlling the deformations of models. For a description of these instruments, see *J. Franklin Inst.*, March, 1927, p. 375.

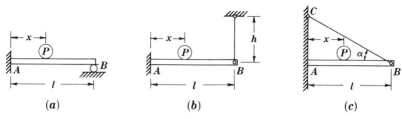

FIG. 5.36

2   Using the reciprocal theorem, derive an expression for the influence coefficient for end moment M_a in the case of a beam AB with built-in ends.   Where should a load P be placed on the beam to produce the maximum value of this end moment?
   Ans. $y = -(l^2x - 2lx^2 + x^3)/l^2$, $x = l/3$.

3   Referring to Fig. 5.36a and using the reciprocal theorem, derive an expression for the vertical reaction R_b for any position of the load P on the beam.   The beam has uniform flexural rigidity EI.

$$\text{Ans.}\quad R_b = \frac{Px^2}{2l^3}\,(3l - x).$$

4   Referring to Fig. 5.36b and using the reciprocal theorem, derive an expression for the tension S in the vertical tie rod BC for any position of the load P on the beam. The beam has uniform flexural rigidity EI and the tie rod has the same modulus of elasticity E, length h, and cross-sectional area A.

$$\text{Ans.}\quad S = \frac{Px^2}{6}\,\frac{3l - x}{l^3/3 + Ih/A}.$$

5   Referring to Fig. 5.36c and using the reciprocal theorem, derive an expression for the tension S in the inclined tie rod BC for any position of the load P on the beam. The beam has uniform flexural rigidity EI and the tie rod has the same modulus of elasticity E and cross-sectional area A.

$$\text{Ans.}\quad S = \frac{Px^2}{6}\,\frac{3l - x}{(l^3/3)\,\sin\alpha + (2Il/A)\,\csc 2\alpha}.$$

Chapter 6

Deflection of pin-jointed trusses

6.1 APPLICATIONS OF CASTIGLIANO'S THEOREM

Castigliano's theorem, discussed in Art. 5.5, can be used to advantage in studying the deflections of trusses, especially if the displacements of only a few joints are required. Consider, for example, the simple truss shown in Fig. 6.1a to which the vertical loads P, Q, and R are applied, and assume that it is required to determine the vertical deflection of the middle joint B of the lower chord. For this purpose, we must derive an expression for the strain energy of the truss as a function of the given loads P, Q, R and then calculate the partial derivative of this expression with respect to the force Q acting at joint B. The expression for strain energy in the case of a statically determinate pin-jointed truss with prismatic members is a very simple one. Let S_i be the force in any bar i due to the actual loading (Fig. 6.1a). Then, the strain energy stored in this bar is

$$\frac{S_i^2 l_i}{2A_i E} \tag{a}$$

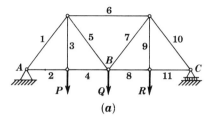

(a)

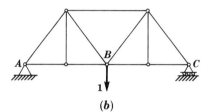

FIG. 6.1   (b)

where l_i is the length and A_i the cross-sectional area of the bar. Summing up expressions (a) for all bars of the truss, we obtain[1]

$$U = \sum \frac{S_i^2 l_i}{2A_i E} \tag{6.1}$$

In calculating the partial derivative with respect to the load Q, we observe that in expression (6.1) only the quantities S_i depend upon Q. Hence ordinary differentiation gives the required deflection in the following form:

$$\delta = \frac{\partial U}{\partial Q} = \sum \frac{S_i l_i}{A_i E} \frac{\partial S_i}{\partial Q} \tag{b}$$

Observing that the derivative $\partial S_i/\partial Q$ in this expression is the rate of change of the force S_i in any member i with respect to the load Q, we can determine the magnitude of this derivative in a very simple manner by considering the action on the truss of the unit load shown in Fig. 6.1b. Denoting by s_i the force produced in any bar i by this unit load, the magnitude of the derivative $\partial S_i/\partial Q$ is evidently equal to the ratio $s_i : 1$, and expression (b) for the deflection δ can be written in the following form:

$$\delta = \sum \frac{S_i l_i}{A_i E} s_i' \tag{6.2}$$

in which the factor $S_i l_i/A_i E$ in each term represents the elongation of the bar i

[1] It is assumed that the material of all bars is the same and that the modulus E is constant.

under the *actual loading* and s_i' is an abbreviation for the ratio $s_i : 1$, obtained for each bar from the fictitious loading shown in Fig. 6.1b.[1]   Since, in this case, the truss is statically determinate, the calculations of the quantities S_i and s_i' can be made without difficulty and the deflection δ can then be calculated from Eq. (6.2) provided that the dimensions of the bars and the modulus of elasticity E are given.

Assuming, for example, $P = Q = 16{,}000$ lb, $R = 8{,}000$ lb, and taking the lengths of the bars from column 2 of Table 6.1, we obtain for S_i and s_i' the values shown in columns 4 and 5, respectively, of the table.   Using now the cross-sectional areas, given in column 3, we obtain the figures in column 6. The sum of this last column, multiplied by 10^3 and divided by the modulus E, gives the required deflection δ as shown by Eq. (6.2).   Assuming that the truss is of structural steel and taking $E = 30 \times 10^6$ psi, we obtain

$$\delta = \frac{5{,}170 \times 10^3}{30 \times 10^6} = 0.1723 \text{ in.}$$

The calculations in Table 6.1 are made with four significant figures; but calculations with three significant figures, as given by an ordinary slide rule, will have sufficient accuracy for practical purposes.

If the horizontal displacement of the joint B is required, we add to the actual loads P, Q, R an infinitesimal force T acting in the direction corresponding to

[1] In our further discussion, we shall always denote the ratio $s_i : 1$ simply as s_i', but it should be kept in mind that when so used it must be considered as a pure number, which will be called the *influence number* for the bar i.

TABLE 6.1

i	l_i, in.	A_i, in.^{2}	S_i, lb	s_i'	$\dfrac{S_i s_i' l_i}{A_i 10^3}$	$s_i'' l_6$	$\dfrac{S_i l_i}{A_i} s_i''$
(1)	(2)	(3)	(4)	(5)	(6)	(7)	(8)
1	250	6	−27,500	−0.625	716.0	0.625	−2,387
2	150	3	16,500	0.375	309.4	−0.375	−1,031
3	200	2	16,000	0	0	0	0
4	150	3	16,500	0.375	309.4	−0.375	−1,031
5	250	2	7,500	0.625	585.9	0.625	1,953
6	300	4	−21,000	−0.750	1,181.0	0	0
7	250	2	12,500	0.625	976.6	−0.625	−3,255
8	150	3	13,500	0.375	253.1	0.375	844
9	200	2	8,000	0	0	0	0
10	250	6	−22,500	−0.625	585.9	−0.625	1,953
11	150	3	13,500	0.375	253.1	0.375	844

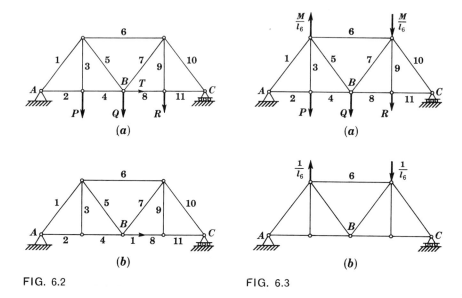

FIG. 6.2   FIG. 6.3

the required displacement (Fig. 6.2a). Then, the derivative $\partial U/\partial T$ gives the required horizontal displacement as follows:

$$\delta = \sum \frac{S_i l_i}{A_i E} \frac{\partial S_i}{\partial T} \tag{c}$$

Since T is an infinitesimal force, the values of S_i are the same as those already recorded in column 4 of Table 6.1. The values of the derivatives $\partial S_i/\partial T$, representing the rates of change of the forces S_i with respect to the force T, are obtained from the loading condition shown in Fig. 6.2b. For this latter condition of loading, only the bars 2 and 4 are active. Hence, in expression (c) only two terms are different from zero, and we obtain for the required horizontal displacement

$$\delta = \frac{S_2 l_2}{A_2 E} + \frac{S_4 l_4}{A_4 E} = 2\frac{16,500 \times 150}{3 \times 30 \times 10^6} = 0.055 \text{ in.}$$

which is evidently equal to the sum of the elongations of the bars 2 and 4.

Sometimes we have to find the angles of rotation of certain members of a truss during deflection. These angles can also be calculated by using Castigliano's theorem. To illustrate the procedure of such calculation, let us consider again the truss shown in Fig. 6.1a and find the angle of rotation of the bar 6 produced by the loads P, Q, and R. The generalized force corresponding to this rotation is the couple M applied as shown in Fig. 6.3a. This follows from the fact that such a group of forces produces work only during rotation of the bar 6 in the plane of the figure   If this bar moves parallel to itself or elongates, keeping its direction unchanged, the work of two such equal and opposite forces perpendicular to the axis of the bar vanishes.   Since the generalized force M corresponds to rotation of the bar 6, we obtain the angle of rotation by calculating the partial derivative $\partial U/\partial M$.   If we substitute for U its expression (6.1), the angle of rotation becomes

$$\theta = \frac{\partial U}{\partial M} = \sum \frac{S_i l_i}{A_i E} \frac{\partial S_i}{\partial M} \qquad (d)$$

Assuming that the couple M is infinitesimal, the forces S_i will have the same values as before and are given in column 4 of Table 6.1.   The derivatives $\partial S_i/\partial M$, representing the rates of change of the forces S_i with respect to the couple M, are obtained by applying to the truss the couple equal to unity as shown in Fig. 6.3b and then calculating the forces s_i'' produced in the members of the truss by this couple.   Thus,

$$\frac{\partial S_i}{\partial M} = \frac{s_i''}{1}$$

Since the right side of this equation has the dimension of force divided by moment of force, the partial derivatives $\partial S_i/\partial M$ have the dimension of $length^{-1}$, and the angle θ as obtained from expression (d) is a pure number.

Instead of the loads $1/l_6$ as shown in Fig. 6.3b, it is simpler to use unit loads, as before, and then divide corresponding axial forces $s_i''l_6$ by the length l_6 to obtain the numerical values of the derivatives $\partial S_i/\partial M$.   For the numerical data already assumed, the values of $s_i''l_6$ calculated for unit loads instead of $1/l_6$ as shown in Fig. 6.3b are given in column 7 of Table 6.1.   By using this column together with columns 2 to 4, we calculate the numbers in column 8. Summing up these numbers and dividing by E, we obtain, from Eq. (d), the required value of the angle of rotation θ.   For structural steel this value is

$$\theta = \frac{1}{E} \sum \frac{S_i l_i}{A_i} s_i'' = -\frac{2,110}{30 \times 10^6} = -70.3 \times 10^{-6} \text{ rad} \qquad (e)$$

The minus sign indicates that the bar 6 rotated in the direction opposite to the direction of the unit couple in Fig. 6.3b.

Castigliano's theorem can be used also to calculate the change in distance between two joints of a truss during deflection.   Assume, for example, that it is required to find the change in distance between the joints D and F (Fig. 6.4a) produced by the action of loads P, Q, and R.   The generalized force corresponding to this change in distance is evidently a group of two equal and opposite forces T applied at D and F and acting along the line DF as shown. Castigliano's theorem then gives

$$\delta = \frac{\partial U}{\partial T} = \sum \frac{S_i l_i}{A_i E} \frac{\partial S_i}{\partial T} \qquad (f)$$

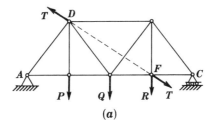

(a)

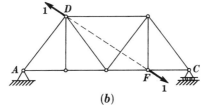

FIG. 6.4   (b)

If we assume again that T is an infinitesimal force, the forces S_i are those produced by the actual loads P, Q, and R. The values of the derivatives $\partial S_i/\partial T$ are obtained by calculating the forces produced in the truss members by unit forces acting as shown in Fig. 6.4b.

Reviewing the preceding examples, we see that in each case we need only to make two simple statical analyses of the truss: one under the actual loading and another under the action of a fictitious unit load or generalized force corresponding to the desired deflection or displacement. Then, with a little simple tabulation and the use of Eq. (6.2), the required deflection is easily found.

PROBLEMS

1   Using the data in Table 6.1, calculate the change in the distance DF of the truss shown in Fig. 6.4, due to the action of the applied loads P, Q, R.
     Ans. -0.0028 in.
2   Each bar of the simple truss shown in Fig. 6.5a has cross-sectional area $A_i = 1$ in.^{2}, and modulus of elasticity $E = 10(10^6)$ psi; $a = 10\sqrt{2}$ in., and $P = 10,000$ lb. Calculate the horizontal deflection δ_c of joint C.
     Ans. $\delta_c = 0.010$ in.
3   The simple truss shown in Fig. 6.5b has the form of a square $ABCD$ with sides 10 in. long, the diagonal AC being horizontal. Calculate the decrease δ in the vertical distance BD due to the applied load $P = 10,000$ lb. Each bar has cross-sectional area $A_i = 1$ in.^{2} and modulus of elasticity $E = 30(10^6)$ psi.
     Ans. $\delta = 0.0114$ in.
4   Find the vertical deflection of joint D of the simple truss loaded as shown in Fig. 6.6. Each bar has cross-sectional area $A_i = 2$ in.^{2}, and $E = 30(10^6)$ psi
     Ans. $\delta_d = 0.786$ in.

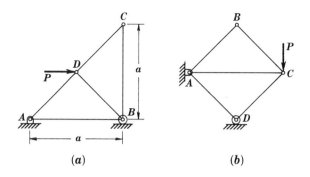

FIG. 6.5   (a)   (b)

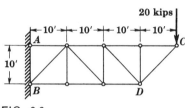

FIG. 6.6

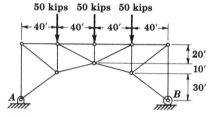

FIG. 6.7

5   Find the horizontal displacement of the roller-supported joint B of the simple truss loaded as shown in Fig. 6.7.   Each bar has cross-sectional area $A_i = 8$ in.², and modulus of elasticity $E = 30(10^6)$ psi.

  Ans. $\delta_b = 4.71$ in.

6.2 MAXWELL-MOHR METHOD OF CALCULATING DEFLECTIONS[1]

To explain this method, let us consider the truss shown in Fig. 6.8a and calculate the vertical deflection δ of a joint C produced by the given loads P and Q. This deflection can be obtained as the sum of the small deflections due to deformations of single bars of the truss.   To find the deflection at C due to the elongation of one single bar,[2] say bar CD, let us consider the system shown in Fig. 6.8b.   The bar CD is removed, and instead of the actual loads only a unit load is acting at joint C.   In this way we obtain a movable system consisting

[1] The method was developed by Maxwell in a paper published in *Phil. Mag.*, vol. 27, 1864. This paper did not come to the attention of engineers, and 10 years later in a paper published in *Z. Architekten-Ing. Ver.*, 1874, p. 223, O. Mohr developed the same method by using another way of reasoning.   Since Mohr's work was done independently of Maxwell's and since the method was accepted by engineers only after numerous applications shown by Mohr, it is customary to call it the *Maxwell-Mohr method*.

[2] The other bars are considered as rigid and their lengths unchanged.

of the two rigid portions, shaded in the figure, which can rotate with respect to each other. To ensure the equilibrium of this system, the forces s_i' must be added. These forces are replacing the action of the removed bar CD on the shaded portions of the truss and evidently are equal to the force produced in that bar by the unit load at joint C. We now have a simple geometrical problem, to find the deflection $\Delta\delta$ of the joint C resulting from the movement of the system by which the distance between the joints C and D increases by a small amount Δl_i. To solve this problem, we use the principle of virtual displacements. Since the unit force at C and the forces s_i' together with the reactions at the supports represent a system of forces in equilibrium, their work on the foregoing assumed small displacements must vanish; hence,

$$1\ \Delta\delta - s_i'\ \Delta l_i = 0 \qquad\qquad (a)$$

The reactions at the supports do not enter in this equation. They do not produce work since the support A does not move and the support B moves perpendicularly to the reaction at B. From Eq. (a), we obtain

$$\Delta\delta = \Delta l_i\ \frac{s_i'}{1} \qquad\qquad (b)$$

Thus we see that the deflection of the joint C is obtained by multiplying the change of distance Δl_i between the joints C and D by the ratio $s_i'/1$. Having this relation, we proceed now with the actual case of loading shown in Fig. 6.8a. Our previous notations being used, the elongation of a bar number i, which is the bar CD in our case, is $S_i l_i/A_i E$. From the relation (b), we now conclude that the deflection of joint C due to the elongation of the bar i is

$$\Delta\delta = \frac{S_i l_i}{A_i E}\frac{s_i'}{1} \qquad\qquad (c)$$

Proceeding in the same way with all other bars and summing up the cor-

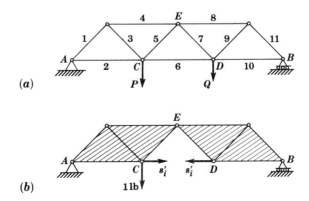

FIG. 6.8 (b)

responding small deflections,[1] we obtain the actual deflection of the joint C in the following form:

$$\delta = \sum \frac{S_i l_i}{A_i E} s_i' = \sum \Delta l_i s_i' \qquad (d)$$

It is seen that, for the determination of the deflection of any joint of a truss, we need to find the elongations Δl_i of all members of the truss under the actual load (Fig. 6.8a) and the forces s_i' produced in the same members by a unit load applied at the joint the deflection of which we have to find (Fig. 6.8b). Both these calculations can be easily performed in the case of a statically determinate truss and can be presented in tabular form as was done in the previous article (see Table 6.1, page 259).

Comparing expression (d) with expression (6.2), we see that the Maxwell-Mohr method gives the deflections in the form already obtained by applying Castigliano's theorem. This second derivation is given here because it makes it easier to grasp the purely geometrical character of the problem. It is evident that expression (d) holds independently of what causes the changes Δl_i in the lengths of the bars. Sometimes we have to consider the elongations of bars due to a rise in temperature from some specified temperature. If α_i is the coefficient of thermal expansion and t_i is the temperature increase, the corresponding elongation of the bar is $\alpha_i t_i l_i$. Sometimes the length of a bar can be changed by using some mechanical device such as a turnbuckle. The effect of such a change on the deflection of a truss can also be calculated from Eq. (d), provided that the change in length Δ_i is known. Superposing deflections produced in a truss by various causes, we can write expression (d) in a more general form,

$$\delta = \sum \left(\frac{S_i l_i}{A_i E} + \alpha_i t_i l_i + \Delta_i \right) s_i' \qquad (6.3)$$

in which not only elastic elongations of the bars but also elongations due to temperature changes and elongations produced by some special devices are considered.

Sometimes it is required to find not only deflections due to changes in the lengths of the bars of a truss but also deflections produced by some small movements of the supports. These additional deflections can be readily found from Eq. (6.3). We assume only that the hinges at the supports are attached to an immovable foundation by some fictitious bars, the changes in length of which are chosen in correspondence with the known displacements of the supports. Including these fictitious bars in the summation shown by expression (6.3), we automatically take into account the effect on the deflections of

[1] It is assumed that the principle of superposition holds for the small deformations produced in actual trusses.

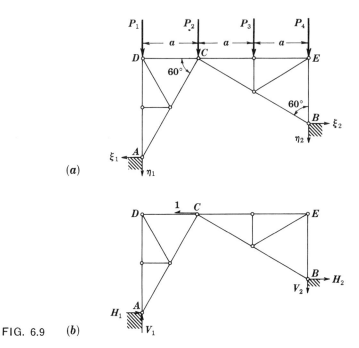

FIG. 6.9   (b)

the known movements of the supports. For example, let us consider an unsymmetrical arch with three hinges (Fig. 6.9a) and calculate the horizontal displacement of the upper hinge C produced by the loads $P_1, \ldots, P_4$, a uniform increase in temperature t, and the small movements of the supports the components ξ_1, η_1 and ξ_2, η_2 of which are shown to an enlarged scale in the figure. Assuming that each of the hinges A and B is attached to an immovable foundation by two fictitious bars, one vertical and one horizontal, we can consider that ξ_1, η_1 and ξ_2, η_2 represent the small shortening of these bars. Now, considering the same arch again, we assume that a horizontal unit load is applied at the upper hinge C (Fig. 6.9b) and calculate the reactions V_1, H_1, V_2, H_2 and the forces s_i' in the bars produced by this load. Applying, now, expression (6.3), we obtain the following value of the horizontal displacement of the hinge C:

$$\delta = \sum \left(\frac{S_i l_i}{A_i E} + \alpha t l_i \right) s_i' + \xi_1 H_1 + \eta_1 V_1 - \xi_2 H_2 - \eta_2 V_2$$

The summation in this expression includes all actual bars of the arch, and the last four terms correspond to the four fictitious bars. Since these bars are placed in such a manner that the displacements $\xi_1, \eta_1, \xi_2, \eta_2$ represent shortenings of the bars, we take all these displacements with negative signs. We take also with negative signs the reactions H_1 and V_1 since, from the directions of these reactions in Fig. 6.9b, we conclude that they represent compressive forces in the fictitious bars.

PROBLEMS

1 Referring to the truss in Fig. 6.9, calculate the vertical component of the deflection of the hinge C due to a uniform rise in temperature of 70°F. Assume that all bars are of steel whose coefficient of thermal expansion is $\alpha = 0.0000065$ (in./in.)/°F and that $a = 10$ ft.

    Ans. $\delta_v = 0.158$ in., up.

2 Each bar of the three-hinged arch truss in Fig. 6.9 has cross-sectional area $A_i = 2$ in.^{2}, modulus of elasticity $E = 30(10^6)$ psi, and $a = 10$ ft. The applied loads $P_1 = P_2 = P_3 = P_4 = 10,000$ lb. Calculate the vertical deflection of the hinge C if, in addition to the applied loads, the support B undergoes some settlement relative to the support A such that $\xi_1 = \eta_1 = 0$, $\xi_2 = \eta_2 = 0.01$ ft, and the temperature drops 40°F.

    Ans. $\delta_c = 0.223$ in., down.

6.3 GRAPHICAL DETERMINATION OF TRUSS DEFLECTIONS

From the discussion of the preceding article, we see that the analytical calculation of truss deflections requires consideration of a special loading of the truss for each joint whose deflection is desired. If the deflections of many joints are required, the foregoing calculations become tedious, and a graphical determination of the displacements can be used to advantage.[1] We begin with a very simple example consisting of a joint A attached to joints B and C by two bars 1 and 2, as shown in Fig. 6.10a. The displacements BB' and CC' of the joints B and C and the changes in length of the bars 1 and 2 are given; it is required to find the corresponding displacement of joint A. We first assume that the bars are disjointed at A and translate them to the positions $A'B'$ and $A''C'$ parallel to their initial positions and such that BB' and CC' represent the given displacements of the joints B and C. In these new positions, we keep the joints B' and C' fixed and give to the opposite ends of the bars the displacements $A'A_1'$ and $A''A_1''$ as shown by heavy lines. These latter displacements are equal to the given changes in the lengths of the bars; that is, $A'A_1'$ is the known elongation of the bar 1, and $A''A_1''$ is the known compression of the bar 2. Now, to finish the construction, we have to bring the points A_1' and A_1'' together by rotating the bar $B'A_1'$ with respect to the center B' and the bar $C'A_1''$ with respect to the center C'. Since we are dealing with small deformations and small angles of rotation, the arcs of the circles along which

---

[1] Such graphical constructions for the deflections of trusses are called *Williot diagrams.* See Williot, Notation pratique sur la statique graphique, *Publ. sci. ind.*, 1877.

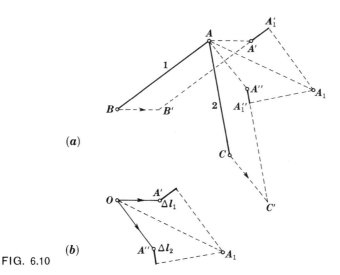

(a)

(b)

FIG. 6.10

the points A_1' and A_1'' travel during such rotations of the bars can be replaced by perpendiculars $A_1'A_1$ and $A_1''A_1$ the intersection of which gives the new position A_1 of the joint A. Thus, the vector $\overline{AA_1}$ represents the required displacement of the joint A.

Since the elongations of the bars and the displacements of the joints are very small in comparison with the lengths of the bars, it is necessary to represent these quantities to a large scale and to make all constructions in a separate diagram as shown in Fig. 6.10b. We take a pole O and lay out to the chosen scale the given displacements OA' and OA'' of the joints B and C. Then, from the points A' and A'' we draw the vectors Δl_1 and Δl_2, shown by heavy lines and representing the known changes in length of the bars 1 and 2. Due attention must be paid to the sign of these elongations. The bar 1 is increasing in length; hence, Δl_1 is put in the direction from B to A. The bar 2 is decreasing in length; hence, Δl_2 is put in the direction from A to C. Finally, perpendiculars constructed at the ends of the vectors Δl_1 and Δl_2 intersect at point A_1, defining the required displacement OA_1 of joint A. It will be noted that the displacement diagram in Fig. 6.10b is identical with the portion $AA'A_1'A_1A_1''A''$ of Fig. 6.10a, except that it can be constructed to a much larger scale if desired. Figure 6.10b represents the *Williot diagram* for the simple structure BAC of Fig. 6.10a.

The foregoing procedure can be used in the construction of displacement diagrams for all simple trusses formed in accordance with the rule given on page 53. As a first example, we consider the truss shown in Fig. 6.11a and assume that its various members are so stressed that they have changes in length Δl_i as recorded in Fig. 6.11b, where the plus signs indicate extension and the minus signs compression.   We begin with the displacement of joint C which is connected to A and B by the bars 1 and 2.   The hinges A and B being immovable, points a and b coincide with the pole O as shown in Fig. 6.11c. Then from a and b, we lay out, to a suitable scale, the vectors Δl_1 and Δl_2, representing extension of bar 1 and shortening of bar 2, respectively.   Constructing perpendiculars at the ends of these vectors, we obtain the intersection point c, which determines the displacement $\overline{Oc}$ of the hinge C.   Now, having points a and c in the diagram, we are ready to determine the displacement of joint D, which is connected to A and C by the bars 3 and 5.   Laying out from a the vector Δl_3 representing extension of bar 3, and from c the vector Δl_5 representing shortening of bar 5, and then constructing perpendiculars to these vectors, we obtain the intersection point d which determines the displacement $\overline{Od}$ of joint D.   Continuing in this way for joint E and, finally, for joint F, we obtain the completed Williot diagram as shown in Fig. 6.11c from which the displacement of each joint of the truss can be scaled.

As a second example, we take the case of a simply supported truss as shown in Fig. 6.12a and begin with a calculation of the length changes Δl_1, . . . , Δl_7 of all bars produced by the given load P.   These calculations can be made without difficulty since the system is statically determinate and all dimensions are known.   Starting now with joint A, which is fixed, we assume, for the beginning, that the bar AE retains its horizontal position during deformation. Hence, joint E has only a horizontal displacement equal to the elongation Δl_2 of the bar 2.   Knowing the displacements of the joints A and E, we can now find the displacement of the joint B, which is attached to these joints by the bars 1 and 4.   Proceeding as before, we start with an arbitrarily chosen pole O (Fig. 6.12b) and mark points a' and e', which correspond to the joints A and E.   Since joint A is fixed, a' coincides with the pole O.   The vector $\overline{Oe'}$, equal

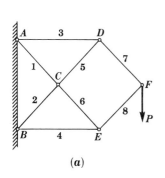

Bar	Δl_i, in.
1	$+0.05$
2	-0.05
3	$+0.10$
4	-0.10
5	-0.05
6	$+0.05$
7	$+0.05$
8	-0.05

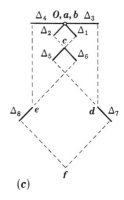

(a)   (b)   (c)

FIG. 6.11

to the elongation Δl_2 of the bar 2, is taken in the direction from A to E, indicating extension of the bar. From points a' and e' we draw in the proper directions the vectors Δl_1 and Δl_4, representing the shortening of bar 1 and the elongation of bar 4, respectively. Making the perpendiculars at the ends of these vectors, we obtain the intersection point b', which determines the displacement $\overline{Ob'}$ of the hinge B. Having now points e' and b' on the diagram, we can determine the position of the point c' and the displacement $\overline{Oc'}$ of the joint C, which is attached to joints B and E by the bars 3 and 5. For this purpose we draw from points b' and e' the vectors Δl_3 and Δl_5, representing, respectively, the shortening of bar 3 and the elongation of bar 5. The intersection of the perpendiculars drawn at the ends of these vectors determines the position of point c'. Proceeding further in the same way, we finally obtain the last point d' of the diagram. Vectors drawn from the pole O to the points e', b', c', and d' represent in both magnitude and direction the required displacements of the corresponding hinges of the truss. By using them to some reduced scale, we can construct the distorted shape of the truss as indicated by dashed lines in Fig. 6.12a.

Since we started with an arbitrary assumption that the bar AE remains horizontal, the deformed shape $AB'C'D'E'$ of the truss does not satisfy the condition at the support D. This support can move only horizontally, whereas the displacement DD', obtained from the diagram in Fig. 6.12b, is not horizontal. To satisfy the condition at the support, we must rotate the deformed truss, indicated by dashed lines in Fig. 6.12a, with respect to the hinge A by such an amount that the point D' will reach the horizontal line AD. In this way the conditions at both supports will be satisfied, and the true displacements of the hinges will be obtained by geometrically adding to the displacements found in Fig. 6.12b the displacements produced during such rotation. These latter displacements can be found as follows: Since the disorted shape $AB'C'D'E'$ of the truss is actually very close to its initial shape, it can be assumed with good accuracy that during rotation about the hinge A, the hinge D' moves perpendicularly to AD, hinge C' moves perpendicularly to AC, etc. Furthermore, the magnitudes of these displacements will be proportional to the radii AD, AC, etc. The required rotatory displacement of the point D' is evidently equal to the vertical component of the displacement DD' represented by the vector $\overline{Od'}$ in Fig. 6.12b. This rotatory displacement of D' having been obtained, the corresponding displacements of the other hinges are readily obtained from Fig. 6.12c, in which Od'' is taken equal to the vertical component of Od' in Fig. 6.12b and the other points are obtained by making the figure $Ob''c''d''e''$ geometrically similar to the figure $ABCDE$ of the truss but rotated by 90° with respect to that figure. The vectors $\overline{b''O}$, $\overline{c''O}$, $\overline{d''O}$, and $\overline{e''O}$ will then represent the rotatory displacements of all hinges of the truss. This follows from the geometric similarity that makes the vectors perpendicular to the corresponding radii and proportional to the lengths of these radii.

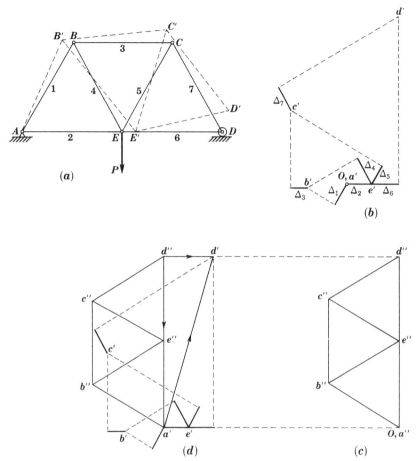

FIG. 6.12

Thus vector $\overline{b''O}$ in Fig. 6.12c is perpendicular to the radius AB in Fig. 6.12a, and $b''O:AB = d''O:AD$; vector $\overline{c''O}$ is perpendicular to the radius AC, and $c''O:AC = d''O:AD$; etc.   To simplify the geometric addition of the rotatory displacements to the displacements given by the diagram in Fig. 6.12b, we superimpose Fig. 6.12c on Fig. 6.12b so that the poles O coincide, as shown in Fig. 6.12d.   Then, the total displacements of the hinges B, C, D, E will be represented by the vectors $\overline{b''b'}$, $\overline{c''c'}$, $\overline{d''d'}$, and $\overline{e''e'}$.   To see this, let us take, for example, the hinge B.   Its displacement, corresponding to the dashed-line shape of the truss in Fig. 6.12a, is given in Fig. 6.12b by the vector $\overline{Ob'}$. The rotatory displacement of the same hinge is given by the vector $\overline{b''O}$; hence

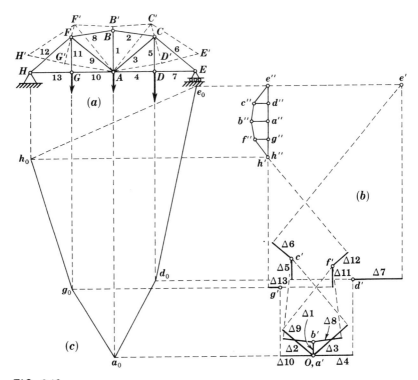

FIG. 6.13

the geometric sum of these two displacements, giving the true displacement of the hinge B, is the vector $\overline{b''b'}$. Similar reasoning holds for the other hinges.[1]

In the case of a truss with many bars, it may be anticipated that if we start the construction of the displacement diagram from the support, as we did in Fig. 6.12, the constructions will extend farther and farther away from the pole O, and the diagram may become unwieldy. In such cases, a more compact diagram can be obtained and the unavoidable inaccuracies of drawing can be reduced by starting the construction from the middle of the truss. Considering, for example, the truss in Fig. 6.13a, we begin with the bar AB. Assuming that the hinge A is immovable and that the hinge B moves only vertically, we find from the displacement diagram (Fig. 6.13b) that point a' coincides with the pole O and that point b' is vertically above O at a distance Ob' equal to the elongation Δl_1 of the bar 1. Having the points a' and b', we obtain the points corresponding to the other hinges in exactly the same manner as in Fig. 6.12.

---

[1] The foregoing method of correcting the Williot diagram to satisfy the conditions at the supports is due to Otto Mohr. See *Zivilingenieur*, vol. 33, p. 639, 1887. The corrected diagram should be called a Williot-Mohr diagram.

Considering the portion of the truss to the right of the bar AB, we obtain in the diagram in Fig. 6.13b the points c', d', and e'. For the left portion of the truss we obtain the points f', g', and h'. Vectors drawn from the pole O to these points give the displacements of the hinges of the truss during deformation if the middle bar AB is kept fixed. The corresponding distorted shape of the truss is indicated in Fig. 6.13a by dashed lines. Since our assumption regarding the bar AB was entirely arbitrary, the displacements obtained do not satisfy the conditions at the supports, which require that the hinge H be immovable and that the hinge E move only horizontally. To satisfy these two conditions, we have to perform two additional movements; first we have to move the distorted truss parallel to itself by the amount $H'H$, so that the condition at the left support H will be satisfied. Then, subsequently, we rotate the truss with respect to hinge H by such an amount that the point E' reaches the horizontal line HE in Fig. 6.13a. When the truss moves parallel to itself, all hinges suffer the same displacement given in Fig. 6.13b by the vector $\overline{h'O}$, and this must be geometrically added to the previously obtained displacements. This is readily accomplished by taking point h', instead of O, as the pole in Fig. 6.13b. Thus, for example, to obtain the result of superimposing the parallel motion represented by the vector $\overline{h'O}$ on the previously obtained displacement $\overline{Oe'}$ of the joint E, we have only to take the geometric sum of these two vectors, which is given by the vector $\overline{h'e'}$. Similar conclusions will be obtained for the other hinges. Hence, by taking point h', instead of O, as a pole, we accomplish the required geometric addition of the translatory displacement $\overline{h'O}$. After this operation, the displacement of the hinge E is represented by the vector $\overline{h'e'}$. Now, to satisfy the condition at the support E, we must rotate the truss with respect to the hinge H by such an amount that the rotatory displacement $\overline{e''h'}$ of the hinge E, when added geometrically to $\overline{h'e'}$, makes the resultant displacement $\overline{e''e'}$ of the hinge E horizontal (Fig. 6.13b). The corresponding rotatory displacements of the remaining hinges of the truss are then obtained by constructing the diagram $e''h''f''b''c''$ geometrically similar to the shape of the truss. The vectors $\overline{a''a'}$, $\overline{b''b'}$, $\overline{c''c'}$, . . . will then give the true displacements of the hinges of the truss.

Having the total displacements of the hinges, we can readily obtain, by projection, the vertical components of the displacements of the lower chord joints as shown by the polygon $h_0 g_0 a_0 d_0 e_0$ in Fig. 6.13c. Such a polygon is called the *deflection polygon* for the truss.

From the preceding examples it will be appreciated that in the case of simple trusses there is no difficulty in constructing the displacement diagram corresponding to known changes in the lengths of all bars. In proceeding with this construction, it is necessary only to repeat with each new hinge the construction illustrated in Fig. 6.10b. In the case of statically determinate trusses that are compound or complex in form, some additional considerations are required, which we shall now illustrate by a final example. For this purpose, we take the compound roof truss shown in Fig. 6.14*a* where tension members are marked with plus signs and compression members with minus signs. To construct the displacement diagram for this truss, we first disregard the web members on the right-hand side and consider *FGH* as one triangle. This means that temporarily we treat *FG*, *GH*, and *FH* as single bars, the length changes of which will be obtained simply by summing algebraically the known length changes in their component parts. In this manner, a simple truss is obtained for which the displacement diagram can be readily constructed. Such a diagram, constructed on the assumption that the hinge *B* remains immovable while the bar *BC* retains its original direction, is shown in Fig. 6.14*b*. Point *b* coincides with the pole *O*, and point *c* is obtained by constructing *Oc* parallel to *BC* and equal to the known shortening of that bar. Proceeding in this way, we finally obtain the points *a* and *h* defining the displacements $\overline{Oa}$ and $\overline{Oh}$ of the points of support *A* and *H*. To satisfy now the actual support conditions, we displace the truss parallel to itself by the amount $\overline{aO}$ so that the hinge *A* coincides with the fixed support and then rotate the truss about this support until the hinge *H* reaches the horizontal line through *A* in Fig. 6.14*a*. As already explained, the geometric addition of the translatory displacement is obtained simply by using *a* instead of *O* as a pole. The rotatory displacement of the hinge *H* is vertical and of such magnitude *h'a* that when geometrically added to the displacement $\overline{ah}$, it makes the resultant displacement $\overline{h'h}$ of the hinge *H* horizontal. The corresponding rotatory displacements of the other hinges are then obtained, as before, by constructing the figure *a'b'f'g'h'*

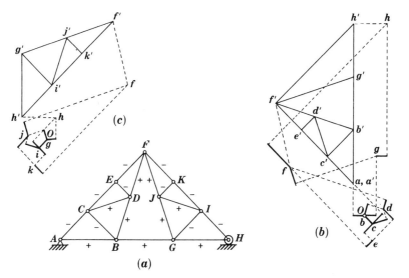

FIG. 6.14

in Fig. 6.14*b* geometrically similar to the truss but rotated by 90° as shown. The vectors measured on this diagram from the primed points to the corresponding unprimed points give then the true displacements of the hinges *A, B, C, D, E, F, G, H*.

To finish the problem, we have to consider the displacements of the hinges *I, J, K*, which were disregarded in the previous constructions. For this purpose, we make, in the usual way, the displacement diagram for the right-hand half of the truss, assuming that the hinge *G* remains stationary and that the bar *GI* retains its direction. This diagram is shown in Fig. 6.14*c*, from which we find the displacements $\overline{Of}$ and $\overline{Oh}$ of the hinges *F* and *H*. Naturally, these do not agree with the true displacements of these two hinges as already found in Fig. 6.14*b*, since we began the constructions on the basis of arbitrary assumptions regarding the hinges *G* and *I*. To correct the diagram, we first translate the right-hand half of the truss by the amount $\overline{f'O}$ such that $\overline{f'O} + \overline{Of} = \overline{f'f}$, taken from Fig. 6.14*b*. This translation is accomplished simply by taking *f'* in Fig. 6.14*c* as a new pole. Next, we must rotate the right-hand half of the truss about *F* until the hinge *H* attains its true horizontal displacement $\overline{h'h}$, taken again from Fig. 6.14*b*. Thus, the required rotatory displacement of *H* about *F* is represented in Fig. 6.14*c* by the vector $\overline{f'h'}$, and the corresponding rotatory displacements of the other hinges are found by constructing on *f'h'* the figure *f'g'h'i'j'k'*, geometrically similar to the right-hand half of the truss *FGHIJK*. A check on the accuracy of the work will be obtained at this point by noting that the vector $\overline{f'h'}$ in Fig. 6.14*c* should be perpendicular to the chord line *FH* in Fig. 6.14*a*.

Finally, the true displacements of all hinges of the truss will be obtained by scaling the vectors from the primed points to the corresponding unprimed points. That is, the true displacement of joint *D* is represented by the vector $\overline{d'd}$ in Fig. 6.14*b*, that of joint *I* by the vector $\overline{i'i}$ in Fig. 6.14*c*, etc.

PROBLEMS

1 The bars of the simple truss shown in Fig. 6.15 are of such cross-sectional areas that they elongate (or shorten) 0.01 in. per 1,000 lb of axial force. Construct a Williot diagram and find therefrom the horizontal and vertical components of the displacement of joint *E*.

   Ans. $\delta_h = 0.017$ in., $\delta_v = 0.080$ in.

2 Construct a Williot-Mohr diagram for the simple truss supported and loaded as shown in Fig. 6.16, assuming that each bar has a unit axial strain of 0.001. For maximum accuracy, begin the constructions on the assumption that joint *D* remains stationary and that *DC* remains vertical. What is the final vertical deflection of the hinge *D*?

   Ans. $\delta_v = 0.345$ in.

3 Construct a Williot diagram for the simple truss shown in Fig. 2.18, page 65, assuming that each bar has an axial strain of 0.001.

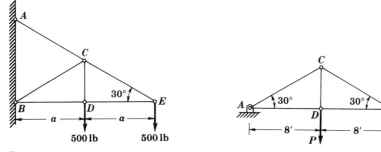

FIG. 6.15   FIG. 6.16

4 Construct a Williot diagram for the simple truss shown in Fig. 2.19, page 65, assuming that each bar has an axial strain of 0.001.

5 Construct a Williot-Mohr diagram for the compound truss shown in Fig. 2.45, page 85, if there is a vertical load P at each lower-chord joint and the cross-sectional areas of the bars are such that each bar has an axial strain of 0.001.

> *Hint* First, construct a separate displacement diagram for each half of the truss, assuming, for the left half, that joint C remains stationary while CD retains its direction and, for the right half, that joint E remains stationary while EF retains its direction.

6.4 METHOD OF FICTITIOUS LOADS

The graphical method of finding displacements described in the preceding article tends to become inaccurate in the case of a truss containing many bars. The unavoidable errors of construction increase rapidly with the number of graphical operations, especially if it is necessary to determine the intersections of lines that are too nearly parallel. In practical applications we often need to know only the vertical deflections of the chord joints of a truss. This limited problem can be solved by using a method of fictitious loads[1] similar to that applied in calculating deflections of beams. Take, for example, the truss in Fig. 6.17a, and assume that the elongations of all bars produced by the given loads P_1, P_2, . . . are known. Then, to calculate the vertical deflections of the joints resulting from an elongation Δl_i of one bar, say bar CD, we use the method explained in Art. 6.2. Accordingly, the deflection δ_m of any joint m (Fig. 6.17b) is obtained from the equation

$$\delta_m = \Delta l_i \frac{s_i'}{1} \tag{a}$$

[1] The application of fictitious loads in calculating deflections of trusses was introduced by O. Mohr, Beitrag zur Theorie des Fachwerks, *Z. Architekten-Ingr.-Ver. Hannover*, 1875, p. 17. See also his book "Abhandlungen aus dem Gebiete der technischen Mechanik," p. 377, 1906.

in which s_i' is the axial force in the bar CD due to a unit load at m. Since all bars, except CD, are considered rigid, the two portions of the truss, shaded in Fig. 6.17b, move as rigid bodies, rotating with respect to each other about the hinge m, and the vertical deflections of all joints are evidently given by the corresponding ordinates of the diagram amb in Fig. 6.17c. Observing that the axial force s_i' produced in the bar CD by the unit load at m is equal to the bending moment at m divided by the distance h, we conclude, from Eq. (a), that the deflection diagram in Fig. 6.17c can be considered as the bending-moment diagram for a fictitious beam AB acted upon by a fictitious load

$$\frac{\Delta l_i}{h} \tag{b}$$

as shown in Fig. 6.17d. In a similar manner the deflections resulting from a change in length Δl_i of any other chord member of the given truss can be found. Using, now, the method of superposition, we conclude that the deflection of the truss resulting from changes in length of all chord members can be calculated for each joint as the bending moment at the corresponding cross section

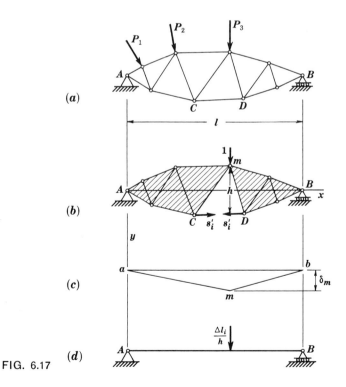

FIG. 6.17

of a simple beam subjected to fictitious loads as defined by expression (*b*).*
Regarding the sign of the fictitious loads, we observe that compression of any
upper chord member or elongation of any lower chord member results in a
downward deflection of the truss.   This indicates that shortening of the upper
chord or elongation of the lower chord implies a downward or positive fictitious
load.

Let us consider, now, the effect of changes in length of web members on
the deflection of a truss.   If only one bar, say the bar *DE* of the truss in Fig.
6.18*a*, changes in length by the amount Δl_i, the deflection of a joint *m* (Fig.
6.18*b*) is again obtained from Eq. (*a*).   Applying this equation to all joints in
succession, we conclude that their deflections are obtained by multiplying by
Δl_i the corresponding ordinates of the influence diagram for the bar *DE* as
shown in Fig. 6.18*c*.   To construct this influence diagram, we note that, for
any position of the unit load to the left of joint *E*, the force s_i' (Fig. 6.18*b*) is
obtained from the equation

$$s_i' = \frac{x}{l}\frac{a}{r} \tag{c}$$

in which the distances *a* and *r* are as shown in the figure.   If the unit load is to
the right of joint *D*, the force s_i' is given by the equation

$$s_i' = \frac{l+a}{r}\left(\frac{x}{l} - 1\right) \tag{d}$$

Thus, the influence diagram for s_i' has the form shown in Fig. 6.18*c*.   Upon
multiplying the ordinates of this diagram by Δl_i, we obtain the deflections of
the truss produced by the change in length Δl_i of the bar *DE* (Fig. 6.18*d*).   In
all cases where the influence diagram has the shape shown in Fig. 6.18*c*, the
shaded area in Fig. 6.18*d* can be considered as the bending-moment diagram
for a simply supported beam loaded as shown in Fig. 6.18*e*.   This loading
consists of two fictitious loads *P* and *Q* the magnitudes of which are obtained
from the conditions that the reactions at the ends of the beam are

$$R_a = \frac{a\,\Delta l_i}{rl} \quad \text{and} \quad R_b = -\frac{(a+l)\,\Delta l_i}{rl}$$

This gives

$$P = \frac{\Delta l_i}{r}\frac{l_2}{l_3} \quad \text{and} \quad Q = \frac{\Delta l_i}{r}\frac{l_1}{l_3} \tag{e}$$

where l_1, l_2, and l_3 are the distances indicated in Fig. 6.18*e*.   As a check, we
calculate the bending moment for a point of the beam to the left of the load *P*

---

* These loads, as we see, are pure numbers, and the corresponding bending moments have
the dimension of length, as should be the case.

and at a distance x from the support A (Fig. 6.18e). This moment

$$M = \frac{a}{r}\frac{x}{l}\,\Delta l_i$$

is seen to agree with expression (c) multiplied by Δl_i. In a similar manner, the bending moment for the portion of the beam to the right of the load Q is represented by expression (d) multiplied by Δl_i. This indicates that the bending-moment diagram for the beam in Fig. 6.18e is identical with the deflection diagram in Fig. 6.18d. We conclude, then, that by introducing for each web member the two fictitious loads, defined by expressions (e), and using the method of superposition, we obtain the deflections of the truss due to changes in length of all web members by calculating the bending moments in the corresponding simple beam carrying the above-mentioned fictitious loads.

Expressions (e) for the fictitious loads P and Q can be somewhat simplified as follows: Drawing verticals through the ends of the web member DE

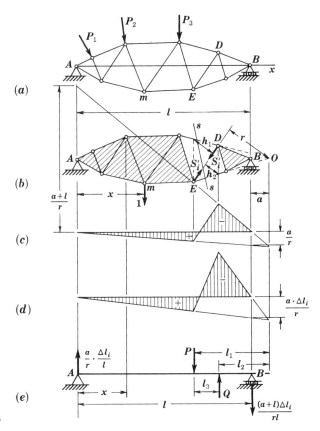

FIG. 6.18

(Fig. 6.18b), we see from geometric similarity that $h_1/r = l_3/l_2$ and $h_2/r = l_3/l_1$. Substituting these values in (e), we obtain

$$P = \frac{\Delta l_i}{h_1} \quad \text{and} \quad Q = \frac{\Delta l_i}{h_2} \tag{f}$$

The directions of these fictitious loads in each particular case are readily obtained from the signs of the ordinates of the influence diagram. We can use, also, the rule stating that the fictitious load at either end of a web member acts downward if, at this end, the chord member and the web member cut by a section such as section ss in Fig. 6.18b have axial forces of the same sign. The load acts upward if the axial forces are of opposite sign.

To illustrate the method, let us consider the truss shown in Fig. 6.19a. The lengths and cross-sectional areas for the bars of this truss are given in

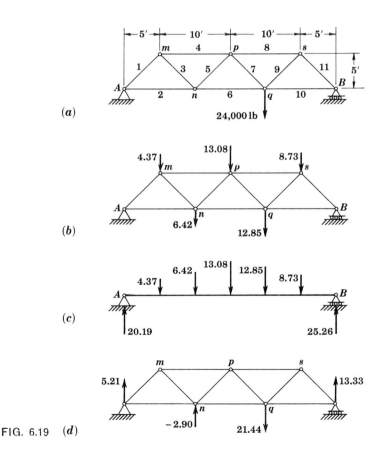

FIG. 6.19

TABLE 6.2

i	l, in.	A, in.^{2}	S	$\dfrac{\Delta l\,E}{1,000}$	Fictitious loads at joints multiplied by $E/1{,}000$				
					m	n	p	q	s
1	84.8	3.66	−11,310	−262	6.18				
2	120	3.66	8,000	262	4.37				
3	84.8	3.66	11,310	262	−6.18	6.18			
4	120	4.98	−16,000	−385		6.42			
5	84.8	2.48	−11,310	−385		−9.08	9.08		
6	120	3.66	24,000	785			13.08		
7	84.8	2.48	11,310	385			−9.08	9.08	
8	120	4.98	−32,000	−771				12.85	
9	84.8	3.66	22,620	524				12.36	−12.36
10	120	3.66	16,000	524					8.73
11	84.8	3.66	−22,620	−524					12.36

Table 6.2. There are given also in this table the axial forces in the bars and the elongations produced by a 24,000-lb load applied at the joint q. To find the deflections due to the corresponding changes in length of the chord members, we calculate fictitious loads from expression (b). Since the chords are parallel, all values of h are equal to 60 in. in this case. The values of these fictitious loads, multiplied by $E/1{,}000$, are shown in Fig. 6.19b and are given also in the table. Assuming that these loads are acting on a simple beam AB (Fig. 6.19c), the bending moments at their points of application, divided by $E/1{,}000$, give the deflections of the corresponding joints of the truss. Considering, for example, the joint p, the corresponding bending moment for the simple beam is

$$M = 20.19 \times 180 - 4.37 \times 120 - 6.42 \times 60 = 2{,}725$$

Hence the deflection of the joint p due to elastic deformation of the chord members is

$$\delta = \frac{1{,}000M}{E} = \frac{1{,}000 \times 2{,}725}{30 \times 10^6} = 0.0908 \text{ in.}$$

To calculate the deflections due to the elastic deformations of the web members, we apply to the ends of each web member the fictitious loads found from Eqs. (f), in which, for this case, the distances h_1 and h_2 are equal to $60/\sqrt{2} = 42.4$ in. The magnitudes of all these loads are given with the proper signs in Table 6.2. After summation, we obtain the fictitious loading of the truss shown in Fig. 6.19d. The bending moment produced by these loads at the cross section of a fictitious beam, corresponding to joint p, is

$$M = 13.33 \times 180 - 21.44 \times 60 = 1,113$$

and the corresponding deflection of the joint p of the truss is

$$\delta_1 = \frac{1,113 \times 1,000}{30 \times 10^6} = 0.0371 \text{ in.}$$

The total deflection of the joint p is obtained by adding δ_1 to the previously found deflection δ, which gives

$$\delta_p = \delta + \delta_1 = 0.128 \text{ in.}$$

In the foregoing discussion of the effect of web members on deflection, we considered a case in which these members were not vertical. To extend the method to the case of vertical web members, we take the truss shown in Fig. 6.20a and consider the vertical member CD. To apply our previous reasoning, we assume, at the beginning, that the member CD is slightly inclined to the vertical as indicated in the figure by the dashed line. Then, our previous reasoning is applicable, and the fictitious loads at the ends of the member are given by Eqs. (e). Assuming, now, that the angle of inclination indefinitely diminishes and approaches zero, the distances r, l_2, and l_1 in Eqs. (e) become equal to the distance c in Fig. 6.20a, while l_3 approaches zero. Thus, both fictitious loads increase indefinitely; but their difference, equal to $\Delta l_i/r$, approaches the value $\Delta l_i/c$, and their moment with respect to joint C approaches the magnitude $(\Delta l_i/l_3)l_3 = \Delta l_i$. The corresponding bending-moment diagram for the fictitious beam is shown in Fig. 6.20b. The discontinuity in this diagram at the point of application of the fictitious couple Δl_i indicates that the deflection of the joint C of the lower chord is larger than the deflection of the joint D of the upper chord by the amount equal to the elongation Δl_i of the vertical member CD.

Considering, now, the vertical member EF (Fig. 6.20a), we readily see that change in length of this bar has no general influence on the deflection of the truss. The deflection of joint F is obtained by completely disregarding the presence of the bar EF, and to obtain the deflection of joint E we have only to add the elongation of the bar EF to the deflection of joint F.

To obtain the deflections produced by a change in length of the middle vertical MN, we consider the influence diagram for this member as shown in Fig. 6.20c.[1] Multiplying the ordinates of this diagram by Δl_i, we obtain, in accordance with Eq. (a), the deflection line of the lower chord of the truss as shown in Fig. 6.20d. This line can be considered as the bending-moment

---

[1] It is assumed that the unit load moves along the lower chord of the truss. Hence, we shall obtain the deflections of that chord.

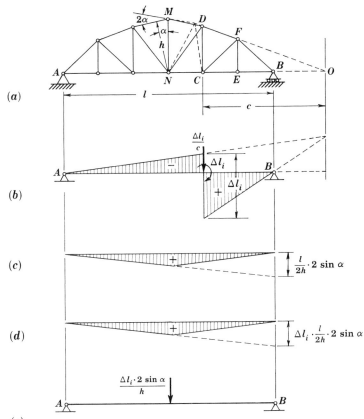

FIG. 6.20   (e)

diagram for the fictitious beam AB loaded as shown in Fig. 6.20e. From this discussion, we see that the deflection of a truss due to changes in length of vertical web members can also be obtained as the bending moment produced by certain fictitious loads, which can be readily obtained in each particular case.

As a specific example dealing with vertical web members, let us consider the truss shown in Fig. 6.21a and assume that the load is symmetrically distributed with respect to the vertical axis of symmetry of the truss. Tension and compression members are indicated in the figure by plus and minus signs, respectively, on the left side of the truss, and the magnitudes of the stresses are so assumed that the unit elongation or contraction of each active member is equal to 1/2,000. Considering first the deflections due to chord members and using expression (b) for fictitious loads, we find that the loading on the fictitious beam is that shown in Fig. 6.21b. For the diagonals we use expres-

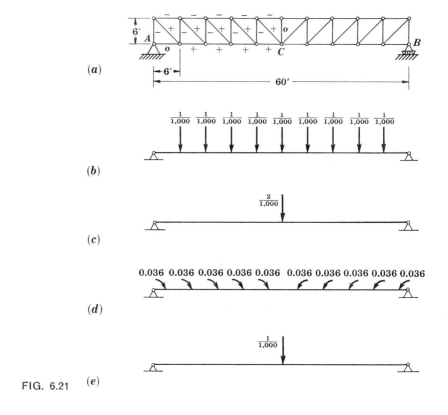

FIG. 6.21   (*e*)

sions (*f*) and find

$$P = Q = \frac{1}{1,000}$$

These fictitious loads act down at the lower ends of the diagonals and up at the upper ends. After summation, we obtain the loading shown in Fig. 6.21*c*.

Coming now to the verticals and using the reasoning illustrated in Fig. 6.20*b*, we find that the corresponding loading on the fictitious beam consists of the fictitious couples shown in Fig. 6.20*d*. At the point of application of each couple we have an abrupt change in the bending moment by the amount 0.036 in. equal to the shortening of the verticals. By calculating the bending moments just to the left of the points of application of the fictitious couples, we obtain the deflections of the joints of the lower chord of the truss. The bending moments just to the right of the same points give the deflections for the joints of the upper chord. Considering the deflections of the lower chord, we see that instead of fictitious couples, we can take the fictitious load shown in Fig. 6.21*e*. This load produces reactions at the ends equal to 1/2,000, and the bending moments at the points corresponding to the joints of the lower chord are the same as those produced by the fictitious couples of Fig. 6.21d. Finally, to get the total deflection of any joint of the lower chord of the truss in Fig. 6.21a, we have to combine the fictitious loadings shown in Fig. 6.21b, c, and e. The deflection at the middle, obtained in this way, is

$$\delta = \frac{4.5}{1,000} \, 360 - \frac{4}{1,000} \, 180 + \frac{1}{1,000} \, 360 + \frac{1}{2,000} \, 360$$

$$= 0.9 + 0.36 + 0.18 = 1.44 \text{ in.}$$

It consists of three parts, a deflection of 0.9 in. due to chord members, a deflection of 0.36 in. due to diagonals, and a deflection of 0.18 in. due to verticals.

PROBLEMS

1   Referring to the truss in Fig. 6.19, calculate the deflection of joint p if the 24-kip load acts at this joint instead of at q. Use all numerical data for the truss as given in Table 6.2.

     Ans. $\delta_p = 0.175$ in.

2   Referring to the truss in Fig. 6.21, calculate the deflection of each lower-chord joint due to a vertical load $P = 10$ kips acting at C. Assume that each bar has a cross-sectional area of 1 in.^{2} and $E = 30(10^6)$ psi.

     Ans. $\delta_c = 1.25$ in.

6.5   ALTERNATIVE METHOD OF FICTITIOUS LOADS

The problem of finding the deflections of the joints of one chord of a truss can be solved by considering only the members of that chord. This solution is especially simple if the chord is a horizontal straight line. Take, for example, the truss shown in Fig. 6.22a, and let it be required to find the vertical deflections of the upper-chord joints. It is evident that such displacements will be completely defined if we know the changes in the lengths of the bars of the upper chord together with their angles of rotation during deflection of the truss. Since the chord is a horizontal straight line, changes in the lengths of its bars result only in horizontal displacements of the upper-chord joints. Thus, vertical displacements of these joints depend only on rotations of the upper-chord members. In calculating these rotations, we assume that the changes in the lengths of all bars of the truss are known. Then, the corresponding changes in the angles of each triangle can be calculated without difficulty, as will be shown later. Assuming for the moment that such changes in the angles ϕ_1, ϕ_2, and ϕ_3 at an upper joint (Fig. 6.22a) have been found, we obtain by their sum a small angle $\Delta\theta_m$ representing the angle between the two chord members at the joint m after deflection. The corresponding deflection of the

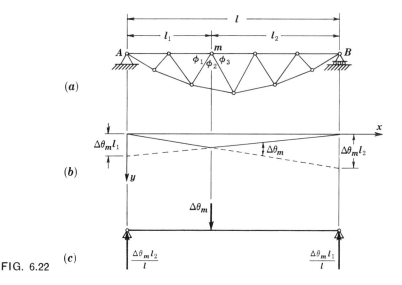

FIG. 6.22

upper chord, assuming that $\Delta\theta_m$ is positive, is shown in Fig. 6.22b. The deflection for any point of the chord to the left of joint m is equal to $\Delta\theta_m\, l_2 x/l$, while, for any point to the right of m, it is $\Delta\theta_m\, l_1(l-x)/l$. We see now that these expressions for deflections are identical with those for bending moments produced in a simply supported beam by the fictitious load $\Delta\theta_m$ acting as shown in Fig. 6.22c. Thus we conclude that by calculating the values of $\Delta\theta_j$ for each joint j of the upper chord and using the method of superposition, the required deflections will be obtained as the bending moments for a simply supported beam subjected to fictitious loads $\Delta\theta_j$.*

We have now to develop a method of calculating the changes in the angles of a triangle if the changes in the lengths of its three sides are known. Since we are dealing with very small elongations, the Williot diagram discussed in Art. 6.3 will be useful for this purpose. Consider, for example, a triangle ABC (Fig. 6.23a) with sides of lengths l_1, l_2, and l_3 and altitude h, and let it be required to find the changes in the angles due to known elongations Δl_1, Δl_2, and Δl_3 of the sides of the triangle. To accomplish this, we assume that the joint A is fixed and that the bar AB retains its horizontal direction. Then, to find the displacement $\overline{CC'}$ of the vertex C, due to the known elongations Δl_1, Δl_2, and Δl_3 of the sides of the triangle, we construct the usual Williot diagram as shown in Fig. 6.23b. If ρ_1 and ρ_2 denote the lengths of the perpendiculars $\overline{C_1C'}$ and $\overline{C_2C'}$ in Fig. 6.23b, the corresponding changes in the angles α_1 and α_2

---

* This method of calculating deflections of trusses was introduced by H. Müller-Breslau, *Z. Architekten-Ingr.-Ver. Hannover*, 1888, p. 605. See also his book "Die graphische Statik der Baukonstructionen," vol. II, pp. 1 and 96, 1904.

at B and A in Fig. 6.23a are[1]

$$\Delta\alpha_1 = \frac{\rho_2}{l_2} = \frac{\rho_2 \sin \alpha_1}{h} \quad \text{and} \quad \Delta\alpha_2 = \frac{\rho_1}{l_1} = \frac{\rho_1 \sin \alpha_2}{h}$$

Remembering, now, that the sum of the angles of a triangle must always be 180°, we conclude that the required change in the angle α_3 at C is

$$\Delta\alpha_3 = -(\Delta\alpha_1 + \Delta\alpha_2) = -\frac{\rho_2 \sin \alpha_1 + \rho_1 \sin \alpha_2}{h} \qquad (a)$$

The numerator on the right side of this expression represents the sum b of the horizontal projections of the perpendiculars ρ_1 and ρ_2 in Fig. 6.23b. Measuring this sum and dividing it by the height h, we obtain the decrease in the angle α_3.

Expression (a) can be represented in a simple analytical form very useful for numerical calculations. We note that the length b is equal to the sum of the horizontal projections of the lengths $\overline{C_2C_3}$ and $\overline{C_1C_3}$ in Fig. 6.23b. The vertical projections of the same lengths are $\overline{D_2D_3}$ and $\overline{D_1D_3}$. Hence,

$$b = \overline{D_2D_3} \cot \alpha_1 + \overline{D_1D_3} \cot \alpha_2 \qquad (b)$$

Observing that the triangle OC_3B in Fig. 6.23b is similar to the traingle ACB in Fig. 6.23a, we conclude that $OD_3 = h\, \Delta l_3 / l_3$. Then,

$$\overline{D_2D_3} = \overline{OD_2} - \overline{OD_3} = \Delta l_2 \sin \alpha_1 - \frac{h\, \Delta l_3}{l_3} = h\left(\frac{\Delta l_2}{l_2} - \frac{\Delta l_3}{l_3}\right)$$

$$\overline{D_1D_3} = \overline{OD_1} - \overline{OD_3} = \Delta l_1 \sin \alpha_2 - \frac{h\, \Delta l_3}{l_3} = h\left(\frac{\Delta l_1}{l_1} - \frac{\Delta l_3}{l_3}\right)$$

[1] The small changes Δl_1 and Δl_2 in the lengths l_1 and l_2 are neglected in these expressions.

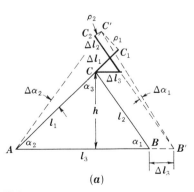

(a)

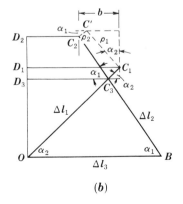

(b)

FIG. 6.23

Substituting these values in expression (b), we obtain

$$b = h \left(\frac{\Delta l_2}{l_2} - \frac{\Delta l_3}{l_3} \right) \cot \alpha_1 + h \left(\frac{\Delta l_1}{l_1} - \frac{\Delta l_3}{l_3} \right) \cot \alpha_2$$

and Eq. (a) becomes

$$\Delta \alpha_3 = - \frac{b}{h} = \left(\frac{\Delta l_3}{l_3} - \frac{\Delta l_2}{l_2} \right) \cot \alpha_1 + \left(\frac{\Delta l_3}{l_3} - \frac{\Delta l_1}{l_1} \right) \cot \alpha_2 \qquad (c)$$

Upon introducing, for the stresses in the bars, the notations

$$\sigma_1 = E \frac{\Delta l_1}{l_1} \qquad \sigma_2 = E \frac{\Delta l_2}{l_2} \qquad \sigma_3 = E \frac{\Delta l_3}{l_3}$$

We can finally represent Eq. (c) in the following simple form:

$$E \, \Delta \alpha_3 = (\sigma_3 - \sigma_2) \cot \alpha_1 + (\sigma_3 - \sigma_1) \cot \alpha_2 \qquad (d)$$

Obviously, this expression for the change in α_3 may be used also for the changes in α_1 and α_2 by a proper change of subscripts. Hence, for further reference, we write

$$E \, \Delta \alpha_1 = (\sigma_1 - \sigma_2) \cot \alpha_3 + (\sigma_1 - \sigma_3) \cot \alpha_2$$

$$E \, \Delta \alpha_2 = (\sigma_2 - \sigma_1) \cot \alpha_3 + (\sigma_2 - \sigma_3) \cot \alpha_1 \qquad (6.4)$$

$$E \, \Delta \alpha_3 = (\sigma_3 - \sigma_2) \cot \alpha_1 + (\sigma_3 - \sigma_1) \cot \alpha_2$$

These three equations furnish a simple way of calculating the changes in the angle of all triangles of a truss if the stresses in the bars are known. In using

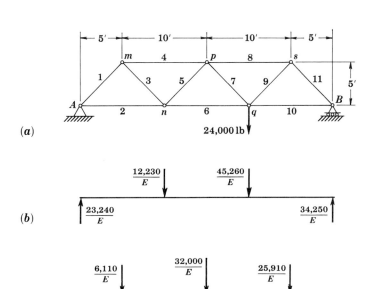

FIG. 6.24

TABLE 6.3

Bar	l_i, in.	A_i, in.^{2}	S_i, lb	σ_i, psi	Fictitious loads multiplied by E				
					n	q	m	p	s
1	84.8	3.66	−11,310	−3,090	−5,276				
2	120.0	3.66	8,000	+2,186			+4,372		
3	84.8	3.66	11,310	+3,090				+6,302	
4	120.0	4.98	−16,000	−3,212	−4,954				
5	84.8	2.48	−11,310	−4,560		−11,120	−1,348		
6	120.0	3.66	24,000	+6,560				+13,120	
7	84.8	2.48	11,310	+4,560	−2,000				+10,985
8	120.0	4.98	−32,000	−6,425		−23,590			
9	84.8	3.66	22,620	+6,180				+12,605	
10	120.0	3.66	16,000	+4,372					+8,744
11	84.8	3.66	−22,620	−6,180		−10,552			
Total					−12,230	−45,262	+3,024	+32,027	+19,729

them, we have only to remember that σ_1, σ_2, and σ_3 denote the stresses in the bars opposite to the angles α_1, α_2, and α_3, respectively.

To illustrate the details in applying this alternative method of fictitious loads, let us consider again the example of the preceding article, repeated in Fig. 6.24a, and calculate the vertical deflections of the lower-chord joints n and q. The lengths l_i of the bars, their cross-sectional areas A_i, and the axial forces S_i due to the loading shown are recorded in the first three columns of Table 6.3. After this, the values of the unit stresses $\sigma_i = S_i/A_i$ are recorded in the fourth column of the table. Now using the first of Eqs. (6.4) and observing that cot $\alpha_2 = 0$ and cot $\alpha_3 = 1$, we obtain

$$E\,\Delta\alpha_1 = (-3,090 - 2,186)1 = -5276$$

which is recorded under n in the table. In a similar way, we find the values of $E\,\Delta\alpha_4$, $E\,\Delta\alpha_7$, $E\,\Delta\alpha_5$, $E\,\Delta\alpha_8$, and $E\,\Delta\alpha_{11}$ as recorded under n and q in the table. Since all these angle changes are negative, the angles decrease, and we obtain deflections downward. Summing up the angle changes at n and at q, we obtain the corresponding fictitious loads for these points on the conjugate beam as shown in Fig. 6.24b. Then, for the deflections of joints n and q, we simply calculate the bending moments at the corresponding points on the conjugate beam. Taking $E = 30(10^6)$ psi, we obtain in this way (see Fig. 6.24b)

$$\delta_n = \frac{23,240}{30(10^6)}\,120 = 0.093 \text{ in.}$$

$$\delta_q = \frac{34,250}{30(10^6)}\,120 = 0.137 \text{ in.}$$

If the chord whose deflection is required is of polygonal form as, for example, the lower chord of the truss in Fig. 6.22a, we have to consider the deflections of the *bar chain* shown in Fig. 6.25a. The deflections due to changes in the angles between the bars of this chain can be calculated in exactly the same manner as in the case of a straight chord. To show this, let us assume that the angle between the two chain members at a joint m diminishes by the amount $\Delta\theta_m$ while the other angles remain unchanged. To find the corresponding deflections, we assume first that the part Am of the chain remains immovable, while the part mB rotates with respect to the hinge m and the end B describes a small arc $r\,\Delta\theta_m$, the vertical projection of which is equal to $l_2\,\Delta\theta_m$. After this rotation, the vertical deflections of the joints to the left of m are zero, while the joints to the right of m have upward deflections,

$$y = -l_2\,\Delta\theta_m\,\frac{x - l_1}{l_2} \tag{e}$$

To satisfy the condition of zero deflection at the right support B, we now rotate the bar chain as a rigid body with respect to joint A by such an amount that the joint B makes a vertical displacement equal to $l_2\,\Delta\theta_m$. The corresponding vertical displacements of other joints are then obtained from the equation

$$y = l_2\,\Delta\theta_m\,\frac{x}{l} \tag{f}$$

Superposing these deflections on the deflections previously found, we conclude that expression (f) gives the total vertical deflections for the part Am of the bar chain, while for the part mB the final deflections are

$$y = -l_2\,\Delta\theta_m\,\frac{x - l_1}{l_2} + l_2\,\Delta\theta_m\,\frac{x}{l} = \Delta\theta_m\,l_1\,\frac{l - x}{l} \tag{g}$$

Expressions (f) and (g) coincide with those previously found for straight line chords (see page 286). Hence, the vertical deflections of the joints of a bar chain, due to changes in the angles between the bars, can be found, as before, by calculating the bending moments produced in a simply supported beam by fictitious loads $\Delta\theta_m$.

In addition to the deflections produced by the changes $\Delta\theta_m$ in the angles, there will also be deflections due to changes in the lengths of the bars. Referring to Fig. 6.25a, let us consider the bar i and assume that it makes an angle ϕ_i with the horizontal and has an elongation Δl_i. Then, if we consider the left portion of the bar chain as immovable, the right portion, due to the elongation Δl_i, obtains a vertical displacement equal to

$$y = -\Delta l_i \sin \phi_i \tag{h}$$

To bring the joint B back to the level AB, we now rotate the chain as a rigid body with respect to the joint A by an angle $\Delta l_i \sin \phi_i / l$. Then, the final

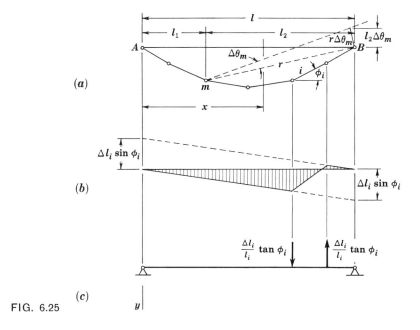

FIG. 6.25

deflection for the left portion of the chain, due to the elongation Δl_i, is

$$y = \Delta l_i \sin \phi_i \frac{x}{l} \qquad (i)$$

For the right portion, combining the displacement (h) with the displacement (i), we find

$$y = \Delta l_i \sin \phi_i \frac{x}{l} - \Delta l_i \sin \phi_i = -\Delta l_i \sin \phi_i \frac{l - x}{l}$$

These deflections are shown in Fig. 6.25b. The shaded area in this figure is identical with the bending-moment diagram for the fictitious loads shown in Fig. 6.25c. Hence, the additional deflections, due to elongations of the chain bars, can be obtained by calculating the bending moments produced in a simply supported beam by the fictitious vertical loads

$$\frac{\Delta l_i \tan \phi_i}{l_i} \qquad \text{and} \qquad -\frac{\Delta l_i \tan \phi_i}{l_i} \qquad (j)$$

applied at the ends of each bar. In these expressions Δl_i is taken positive when it represents an elongation, and ϕ_i is positive if the bar i is rotated in a counterclockwise direction with respect to the axis AB as we pass along the bar chain from A to B.

We may now return to the example in Fig. 6.24 and proceed with the calculation of the vertical deflections of the upper-chord joints. We have to consider here the inclined bars 1 and 11 which, together with the two horizontal bars 4 and 8, form the bar chain attached to the supports A and B. Using the numerical data from Table 6.3 and Eqs. (6.4), we calculate the changes in the angles along the upper chord exactly as was done before for the lower chord. These changes $E \Delta\alpha_2$, $E \Delta\alpha_5$, $E \Delta\alpha_3$, $E \Delta\alpha_6$, $E \Delta\alpha_9$, $E \Delta\alpha_7$, and $E \Delta\alpha_{10}$, computed from Eqs. (6.4), are recorded under m, p, s in the table. The corresponding fictitious loads for the joints m, p, and s are then obtained by summation as shown.

To take care of the changes in the lengths of the chain bars, we use expressions (j) for bars 1 and 11 and obtain, for the magnitudes of additional fictitious loads at m and s,

$$\frac{E \Delta l_1}{l_1} = \sigma_1 = 3{,}090 \quad \text{and} \quad \frac{E \Delta l_{11}}{l_{11}} = \sigma_{11} = 6{,}180 \tag{k}$$

Adding these fictitious loads to those already obtained in Table 6.3, we get the final loading of the conjugate beam as shown in Fig. 6.24c. Then, the required vertical deflections of the joints m, p, and s, obtained as fictitious bending moments in the conjugate beam, are

$$\delta_m = \frac{25{,}410}{30(10^6)} \, 60 = 0.051 \text{ in.}$$

$$\delta_p = \frac{25{,}410}{30(10^6)} \, 180 - \frac{6{,}110}{30(10^6)} \, 120 = 0.128 \text{ in.}$$

$$\delta_s = \frac{38{,}610}{30(10^6)} \, 60 = 0.077 \text{ in.}$$

PROBLEMS

1   Using the method of fictitious loads, find the vertical deflection of joint C of the simple truss supported and loaded as shown in Fig. 6.26. Each bar has cross-sectional area $A_i = 1$ in.^{2} and modulus of elasticity $E = 30(10^6)$ psi.

  Ans. $\delta_C = 0.067$ in.

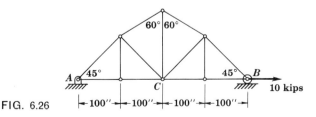

FIG. 6.26

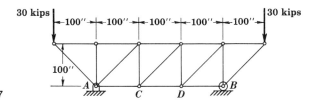

FIG. 6.27

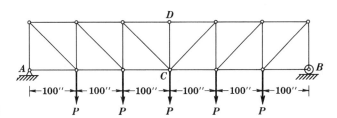

FIG. 6.28

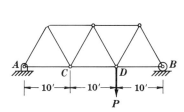

FIG. 6.29

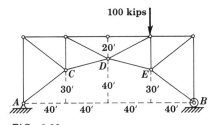

FIG. 6.30

2 Using the method of fictitious loads, find the vertical deflections of joints C and D of the simple truss supported and loaded as shown in Fig. 6.27. Each bar has cross-sectional area $A_i = 1$ in.² and modulus of elasticity $E = 30(10^6)$ psi.

   Ans. $\delta_D = \delta_C = 0.20$ in., up.

3 The truss shown in Fig. 6.28 is symmetrically loaded with respect to the middle vertical CD so that each active member has a unit axial strain of 0.001. Using the method of fictitious loads, calculate the vertical deflection of joint C.

   Ans. $\delta_C = 1.800$ in.

4 Each bar of the simple truss shown in Fig. 6.29 is 10 ft long, 3 in.² in cross section, and has a modulus of elasticity $E = 30(10^6)$ psi. Using the method of fictitious loads, find the vertical deflections of the lower-chord joints C and D if the applied load $P = 30$ kips.

   Ans. $\delta_C = 0.0785$ in., $\delta_D = 0.1215$ in.

5 Each bar of the truss shown in Fig. 6.30 has a cross-sectional area $A_i = 5$ in.² and modulus of elasticity $E = 30(10^6)$ psi. Using the method of fictitious loads, find the vertical deflections of the lower-chord joints C, D, and E.

   Ans. $\delta_C = 1.53$ in., $\delta_D = 3.28$ in., $\delta_E = 2.60$ in.

Chapter 7

Statically indeterminate pin-jointed trusses

7.1 GENERAL CONSIDERATIONS

In Chap. 2 we have already seen that any pin-jointed truss in one plane is generally rigid and *statically determinate* if its j joints are interconnected between themselves and the foundation by $m = 2j$ bars. If the bars exceed this number, the available $2j$ simultaneous equations of statics are insufficient to determine the internal forces, and the truss is said to be *statically indeterminate*. Those bars in excess of the $2j$ which are both necessary and sufficient for the rigidity of a truss are usually called *redundant members*. A simple example of a truss with one redundant member is shown in Fig. 7.1a. Here we have a single joint C attached to a foundation by three bars arranged in one plane as shown. For simplicity, we assume the two inclined bars to be identical so that the system is symmetrical with respect to the vertical axis CD. If a vertical load P is applied at C as shown, some axial force will be induced in each of the three bars; but since, for the joint C, we have only two equations of equilibrium

$$\Sigma X = 0 \quad \text{and} \quad \Sigma Y = 0 \tag{a}$$

there is evidently one redundant element, and the system is statically inde-terminate. That is, so long as we consider the bars to be absolutely rigid, we can assume any value X for the tension in the vertical bar (Fig. 7.1b); and then, using Eqs. (a), we shall find that each inclined bar carries a tensile force

$$S = \tfrac{1}{2}(P - X) \sec \alpha \tag{b}$$

To find the true value of X, we must now consider the elastic deformations of the bars. Denoting by δ the elongation of the middle bar, we see from Fig. 7.1b that the corresponding elongation of each inclined bar must be[1]

$$\delta' = \delta \cos \alpha \tag{c}$$

Now, by using expression (b) for the axial force in an inclined bar and denoting by A and A_0 the cross-sectional areas of the bars as shown in the figure, condition (c) may be written in the following form,

$$\frac{(P - X)l}{2 \cos^3 \alpha A E} = \frac{Xl}{A_0 E}$$

from which

$$X = \frac{P}{1 + 2(A/A_0) \cos^3 \alpha}$$

Using this value of X in Eq. (b), we can now find the corresponding value of S for each inclined bar, and the analysis is completed.

Reviewing the foregoing procedure, we see that to solve the given statically indeterminate problem, we first removed the redundant bar CD and replaced it by the force X which it exerted on the remaining statically determinate system. Then this system (Fig. 7.1b) was analyzed by the ordinary equations of statics

[1] This relation assumes that the elastic elongations of the bars are small compared with the overall dimensions of the structure.

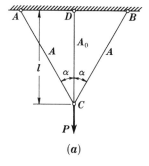

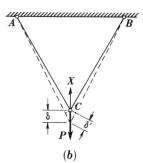

FIG. 7.1   (a)   (b)

and all axial forces expressed in terms of the unknown quantity X. Finally, to find the true value of X, we established an additional equation (c) by taking account of the elastic deformations of the bars.

The same procedure can be applied in more complicated cases. We begin with a proper selection of the members that will be considered as redundants. Removing these bars, we obtain a statically determinate system, called the *primary system*. This primary system can then be analyzed by the methods already discussed in preceding chapters, and we can readily find the forces in all bars and also the displacements of all joints. We shall be especially interested in the changes in distance between those joints corresponding to the removed redundant members; for evidently these changes must be equal to the changes in length of the corresponding redundant bars in the actual truss. In this way we obtain as many equations, similar to Eq. (c), as there are redundant bars; and, from these equations, the forces in the redundant bars are obtained. The forces in the remaining bars are then found from statics.

From the discussion we see that the redundant bars must be so selected that after their removal we obtain a rigid statically determinate truss. Take, for example, the statically indeterminate system shown in Fig. 7.2. The truss proper has 14 bars, and in addition to this we have to consider a vertical supporting bar replacing the movable support at the right end of the truss and two bars replacing the immovable support at the left end. All together, then, we have 17 unknown forces, while the doubled number of joints is 16. Thus, we have a truss with one redundant member. As a redundant member we can select, for example, one of the diagonals in the middle panel of the truss. But we cannot take the diagonal in one of the other panels as a redundant bar, for after removing such a diagonal we obtain a nonrigid system.

In Fig. 7.3 we have another example of a truss with one redundant member. As the redundant member in this case, we can take any one of the supporting bars; but such a bar as DE cannot be selected, for after its removal we obtain a system having a critical form. That is, we have the two rigid shaded portions supported at A and B and joined together by a hinge C like a three-hinged arch; but since the hinge C lies on the straight line AB, it can have considerable vertical movement without appreciable changes in length of any of the bars.

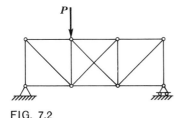

FIG. 7.2

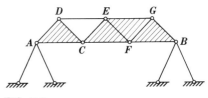

FIG. 7.3

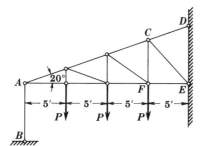

FIG. 7.4

There are, however, other possibilities besides the removal of one of the supporting bars. For example, if we remove the bar CF, we obtain, as our primary system, an ordinary three-hinged arch in which the hinge E does not lie on the straight line AB. Hence, there is no critical form in such case, and the bar CF can be chosen as the redundant bar, if desired.

Figure 7.4 represents another system with one redundant bar. As the redundant in this case, we can take the bar AB or the bar CD; but we cannot select the bar CE, for after its removal we obtain a rigid frame ACF attached to the foundation by three bars AB, CD, and EF that intersect in one point. Such a system, as we already know (see page 58), is not rigid.

7.2 TRUSSES WITH ONE REDUNDANT ELEMENT

As a first example of a system with one redundant element, let us consider the truss on three supports as shown in Fig. 7.5a. As the redundant element, we select the intermediate support C. Removing this support, we obtain a statically determinate simple truss (Fig. 7.5b) that can be readily analyzed. Then the redundant reaction X at the middle support will be determined from the condition that the deflection of joint C due to the combined action of the loads P_1, P_2, P_3 and the reaction X must vanish. Using expression (6.2) for this deflection, we obtain

$$\Sigma \, \Delta l_i \, s_i' = 0 \qquad\qquad (a)$$

in which $\Delta l_i = S_i l_i / A_i E$ denotes the change in length of any bar i due to the loads P_1, P_2, P_3 and the redundant reaction X, and s_i' is obtained by using the unit loading[1] shown in Fig. 7.5c and represents the ratio of the force in any bar i to the unit load at C that produces it. In calculating the values Δl_i in expression (a), we note that the force S_i in a bar i is given by the equation

$$S_i = S_i' + s_i' X \qquad\qquad (b)$$

---

[1] The unit load at C is taken in the upward direction, so we may consider the redundant reaction X as positive in this direction.

in which S_i' is the force in any bar i produced by the known external loads P_1, P_2, P_3, acting on the simple truss shown in Fig. 7.5b, and $s_i'X$ is the force produced in the same bar by the reaction X.   Then the required elongation of any bar i is

$$\Delta l_i = \frac{(S_i' + s_i'X)l_i}{A_iE} = (S_i' + s_i'X)\rho_i \tag{c}$$

where $$\rho_i = \frac{l_i}{A_iE} \tag{d}$$

Substituting expression (c) into Eq. (a), we obtain

$$\Sigma(S_i' + s_i'X)\rho_i s_i' = 0 \tag{e}$$

from which
$$X = -\frac{\Sigma S_i' s_i' \rho_i}{\Sigma (s_i')^2 \rho_i} \tag{7.1}$$

With the value of the redundant reaction X, the forces in the bars of the given statically indeterminate truss (Fig. 7.5a) are obtained from Eq. (b), and the analysis is completed.   It is seen that the statically indeterminate problem (Fig. 7.5a) is reduced to the two statically determinate problems shown in Fig. 7.5b and c.   The values S_i', s_i', and ρ_i for all members of the truss can be

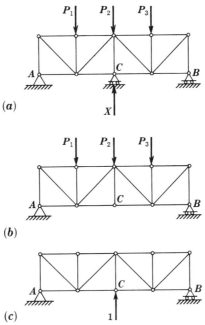

FIG. 7.5 (c)

put in tabular form as was done in Table 6.1, page 259. Then, with the aid of such a table, the values of the sums entering in Eq. (7.1) can be readily calculated.

As a second example, let us consider the statically indeterminate truss shown in Fig. 7.6a. The reactions in this case can be readily calculated from equations of statics, but the forces in the bars cannot be determined by statics alone because the truss contains one redundant member. Let us take the vertical bar BC as the redundant bar. Then, after removal of this bar, we obtain a statically determinate simple truss (Fig. 7.6b) on which, in addition to the known loads P_1, P_2, P_3, there will act the two equal and opposite forces X replacing the removed bar as shown. The magnitude of X is found from the condition that the change in the distance between the joints B and C of the statically determinate truss (Fig. 7.6b) must be equal to the change in length of the vertical bar BC of the actual truss (Fig. 7.6a). This change in the distance BC is $\Sigma \, \Delta l_i \, s_i'$, in which the summation includes all bars of the statically determinate truss (Fig. 7.6b) and the values of Δl_i are given by the equation

$$\Delta l_i = (S_i' + s_i' X)\rho_i \qquad (f)$$

in which S_i' denotes the force produced in any bar i by the given loads P_1, P_2, P_3 and s_i' is found, as before, by using the unit loading shown in Fig. 7.6c.

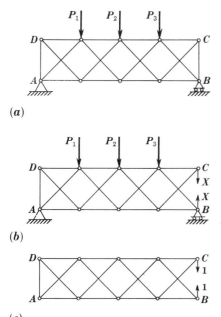

(a)

(b)

FIG. 7.6   (c)

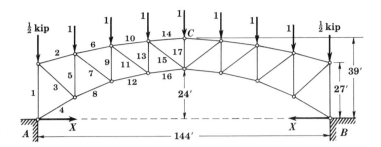

FIG. 7.7

The equation for calculating X then becomes

$$\Sigma(S_i' + s_i'X)\rho_i s_i' = -X\rho_0 \tag{g}$$

where $$\rho_0 = \frac{l_0}{A_0 E} \tag{h}$$

is the quantity defining the extensibility of the redundant bar BC. The minus sign in the right-hand side of Eq. (g) follows from the directions of the unit loads in Fig. 7.6c. With these directions, shortening of the distance BC becomes positive, which corresponds to compression of the vertical bar BC. Solving Eq. (g) for X, we obtain

$$X = -\frac{\Sigma S_i' s_i' \rho_i}{\Sigma(s_i')^2 \rho_i + \rho_0} \tag{7.2}$$

In this example we see again that calculation of the redundant force X is reduced to two statically determinate problems, (1) the calculation of the forces S_i' and (2) the calculation of the forces s_i'. When all these forces are found and the quantities ρ_i and ρ_0 are determined from the given dimensions of the truss, the sums entering into Eq. (7.2) can be readily evaluated.

In each of the foregoing examples, we used expression (6.2) as a basis of evaluation of displacements. However, we can come to the same results by using the theorem of least work as discussed in Art. 5.6. On this basis, for example, the value X for the redundant reaction at C in Fig. 7.5 must be such as to make the total strain energy of the statically indeterminate system a minimum. If we use expression (b) for the forces in the bars, the total strain energy of the truss becomes

$$U = \sum \frac{(S_i' + s_i'X)^2 l_i}{2A_i E}$$

Equating to zero the derivative of this expression with respect to X and using the notation in expression (d), we obtain

$$\Sigma(S_i' + s_i'X)\rho_i s_i' = 0$$

which coincides with our previous expression (e) and leads to Eq. (7.1).   In the same way the total strain energy of the statically indeterminate truss in Fig. 7.6 becomes

$$U = \sum \frac{(S_i' + s_i'X)^2 l_i}{2A_i E} + \frac{X^2 l_0}{2A_0 E}$$

where the summation includes all bars of the primary system (Fig. 7.6b). Equating to zero the derivative of this expression with respect to X and using the notations in expressions (d) and (h), we obtain the previous expression (g), leading to Eq. (7.2).

As a specific example with numerical data and all calculations, let us consider the two-hinged arch loaded as shown in Fig. 7.7 and calculate the magnitude X of the horizontal thrust.   The overall dimensions of the structure are shown in the figure, and the lengths of the individual bars are given in column 2 of Table 7.1.   Here also are given, for each bar, the cross-sectional area A_i, the

TABLE 7.1

i	l_i, in.	A_i, in.^{2}	$\rho_i \times 10^6$, in./lb	S_i', lb	s_i'	$(s_i')^2$	$S_i' s_i' \rho_i \times 10^6$	$(s_i')^2 \rho_i \times 10^6$
(1)	(2)	(3)	(4)	(5)	(6)	(7)	(8)	(9)
1	324	11.5	0.940	−4,000	+0.59	0.35	−2,220	0.329
2	227	11.8	0.641	−3,000	+0.50	0.25	−962	0.160
3	292	9.0	1.081	+3,900	−0.65	0.42	−2,740	0.454
4	259	11.5	0.750	0	−1.16	1.35	0	1.012
5	263	9.0	0.974	−3,800	+0.47	0.22	−1,740	0.214
6	220	11.8	0.621	−6,200	+1.00	1.00	−3,850	0.621
7	277	9.0	1.026	+3,950	−0.64	0.41	−2,600	0.421
8	234	11.5	0.678	+3,150	−1.60	2.56	−3,420	1.735
9	216	9.0	0.800	−2,750	+0.30	0.09	−660	0.072
10	216	11.8	0.610	−8,600	+1.43	2.04	−7,500	1.244
11	270	9.0	1.000	+3,200	−0.55	0.30	−1,760	0.300
12	223	11.5	0.646	+6,200	−2.05	4.20	−8,210	2.712
13	192	9.0	0.711	−1,150	+0.03	0.00	−24	0
14	216	11.8	0.610	−9,700	+1.60	2.56	−9,470	1.560
15	277	9.0	1.026	+1,400	−0.23	0.05	−330	0.051
16	216	11.5	0.626	+8,600	−2.43	5.90	−13,080	3.694
17	180	9.0	0.667	−250	−0.14	0.02	−117,132 / +23	29.158 / 0.013
Σ							−117,109	+29.171

quantity ρ_i, assuming $E = 30(10^6)$ psi, and the axial forces S_i' and s_i'.*
Using the data from the table and forming the sums appearing in Eq. (7.1),
we find

$$X = -\frac{-117,109}{29.171} = 4,015 \text{ lb}$$

PROBLEMS

1   Find the horizontal thrust X for the statically indeterminate truss shown in Fig. 7.8a.
    All dimensions are given in the figure, and the cross-sectional areas of the bars are
    as follows: $A_1 = A_4 = 5$ in.^{2}, $A_2 = A_5 = 3$ in.^{2}, and $A_3 = 2$ in.^{2}
        Ans. $X = (540.9/616.5)P$.
2   Determine the axial force in the redundant horizontal bar of the truss shown in
    Fig. 7.8b if the cross-sectional area of this bar is A_6.   Assume that the other bars
    have the same dimensions as in the preceding problem.
        Ans. $X = 540.9P/(300/A_6 + 616.5)$.
3   Determine the axial forces in all bars of the statically indeterminate system shown
    in Fig. 7.9a, assuming that the cross-sectional areas of all bars are equal.
        Hint   Take the axial force X in the diagonal bar 6 as the redundant
                 element.
        Ans. $X = 0.854P$.

* These axial forces can be found without difficulty by constructing Maxwell diagrams for
the statically determinate primary system obtained by removing the horizontal constraint
at B.

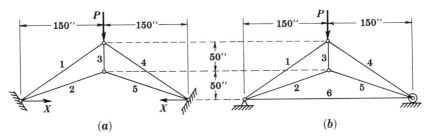

(a)   (b)

FIG. 7.8

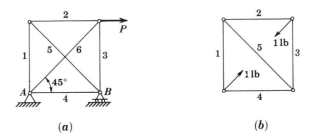

FIG. 7.9   (a)   (b)

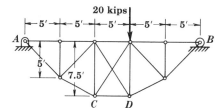

FIG. 7.10

4   Determine the magnitude of the reactive force X in Fig. 7.5a if $P_1 = P_2 = P_3 = 10$
    kips.   The horizontal and vertical members of the truss all have cross-sectional
    areas $A_i = 1$ in.^{2}, while the diagonal members have $A_i = \sqrt{2}$ in.^{2} All bars have
    the same modulus of elasticity, and the panels are square.
            Ans. $X = 19.23$ kips, up.
5   All bars of the statically indeterminate truss shown in Fig. 7.10 have the same
    cross-sectional area $A_i = 1$ in.^{2} and the same modulus of elasticity E.   Find the
    axial force S_x induced in the redundant bar CD due to the 20-kip load acting as
    shown.
            Ans. $S_x = +14,500$ lb.

7.3   TRUSSES WITH SEVERAL REDUNDANT MEMBERS

The method used in the preceding article for the analysis of statically indeterminate trusses with one redundant member can be readily extended to
trusses with two or more redundant members.   As a first example, let us
consider the simple truss with two redundant supports as shown in Fig. 7.11a.
Removing these supports and replacing them by the reactive forces X and Y as
shown in the figure, we obtain a statically determinate system on which, in
addition to the given loads P_1, P_2, P_3, the two redundant reactions X and Y are
acting.   The magnitudes of these reactions will now be found from the conditions that the deflections of the joints C and D must vanish.   For these
deflections, we use Eq. (6.2), which gives in this case the following equations:

$$\Sigma \, \Delta l_i \, s_i' = 0$$
$$\Sigma \, \Delta l_i \, s_i'' = 0$$
(a)

in which the quantities s_i' and s_i'' are obtained by using the unit loadings shown
in Fig. 7.11b and c, respectively.   The quantities Δl_i are the actual elongations
of the bars of the system (Fig. 7.11a) produced by the given loads P_1, P_2, P_3
and the unknown reactions X and Y.   The force in any bar i of the primary
system (Fig. 7.11b) due to the given loads P_1, P_2, P_3 is denoted, as before, by
S_i'.   The forces produced in the same bars by the redundant reactions X and Y
are obtained by using the unit loads shown in Fig. 7.11b and c and are equal to

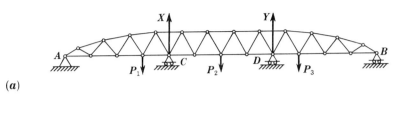

(a)

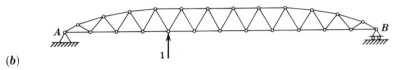

(b)

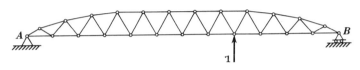

(c)

FIG. 7.11

$s_i'X$ and $s_i''Y$, respectively.   Hence, the total force in any bar i is

$$S_i = S_i' + s_i'X + s_i''Y \qquad (b)$$

and the corresponding elongation is

$$\Delta l_i = (S_i' + s_i'X + s_i''Y)\rho_i$$

Substituting into Eqs. (a), we obtain the following two equations for calculating X and Y:

$$\Sigma(S_i' + s_i'X + s_i''Y)\rho_i s_i' = 0$$
$$\Sigma(S_i' + s_i'X + s_i''Y)\rho_i s_i'' = 0 \qquad (c)$$

or

$$X\Sigma(s_i')^2\rho_i + Y\Sigma s_i's_i''\rho_i = -\Sigma S_i's_i'\rho_i$$
$$X\Sigma s_i's_i''\rho_i + Y\Sigma(s_i'')^2\rho_i = -\Sigma S_i's_i''\rho_i \qquad (d)$$

Having the values of S_i', s_i', s_i'', and ρ_i tabulated, we can readily evaluate the sums that appear in Eqs. (d) and solve the equations for X and Y.   Then upon substituting these values in Eq. (b), we can calculate the forces in all bars of the truss.   It is seen from this discussion that the analysis of a system with two redundant supports reduces to the analysis of three statically determinate problems, i.e., to the evaluation of the forces S_i', s_i', and s_i''.

Equations (c) for calculating the redundant reactions can be obtained also by using the theorem of least work.   The total strain energy of the system shown in Fig. 7.11a is

$$U = \tfrac{1}{2}\Sigma(S_i' + s_i'X + s_i''Y)^2\rho_i$$

.Equating to zero the derivatives of this expression with respect to X and Y, we obtain Eqs. (c).

As a second example let us consider the statically indeterminate truss shown in Fig. 7.12a. This truss has 83 bars. Adding to this number 6 elements of constraint for the system of supports, we have all together 89 unknown forces; twice the number of joints is 86. Hence, there are three redundant members. As these redundants, we select the two horizontal bars ab and cd and the horizontal constraint at the support D. Removing these three redundant elements and replacing their actions by forces X, Y, and Z, we obtain a statically

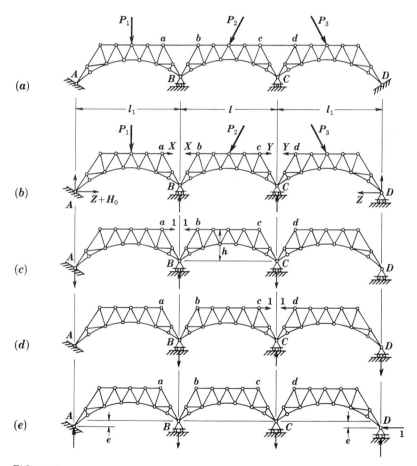

FIG. 7.12

determinate system consisting of the three simple trusses shown in Fig. 7.12b. The forces produced in the members of this statically determinate system by the given loads P_1, P_2, P_3 we denote by S_i'. The forces produced in the members of the same system by the redundant forces X, Y, and Z are found, as before, by using the unit loadings shown in Fig. 7.12c, d, and e. The corresponding axial forces in any bar i we denote, respectively, by s_i', s_i'', and s_i'''. Then, the total force in a bar i of the given system (Fig. 7.12a) is

$$S_i = S_i' + s_i'X + s_i''Y + s_i'''Z \tag{e}$$

The values of the three redundant forces X, Y, and Z are obtained, now, from the conditions that the changes in distance between the joints a and b and the joints c and d (Fig. 7.12b) must be equal to the changes in length of the bars ab and cd (Fig. 7.12a), while the horizontal displacement of the support at D must vanish. Denoting by ρ_x and ρ_y the extensibility factors for the redundant bars ab and cd and using Eq. (6.2) for displacements, we can represent the foregoing conditions in the form of equations as follows:

$$\Sigma(S_i' + s_i'X + s_i''Y + s_i'''Z)\rho_i s_i' = -X\rho_x$$
$$\Sigma(S_i' + s_i'X + s_i''Y + s_i'''Z)\rho_i s_i'' = -Y\rho_y \tag{f}$$
$$\Sigma(S_i' + s_i'X + s_i''Y + s_i'''Z)\rho_i s_i''' = 0$$

The minus signs in the first two equations result from the fact that, for the directions of the unit loads in Fig. 7.12c and d, positive displacements correspond to shortening of the distances ab and cd and hence to compressive forces in the redundant bars ab and cd. If the values ρ_i, s_i', s_i'', s_i''' for all bars of the primary system (Fig. 7.12b) are tabulated, the sums appearing in Eqs. (f) can be evaluated, and we obtain three linear equations, with numerical coefficients, that can be solved for the unknown redundant forces X, Y, and Z.

From the foregoing discussion it may be seen that as the number of redundant forces increases, the number of equations required for their determination increases also, and the problem of analysis becomes more and more involved. Sometimes we find cases where each equation contains only a few of the redundant forces; such equations can be solved without much difficulty even though the total number of unknowns may be large. As an example of this kind, let us consider the truss with five redundant bars as shown in Fig. 7.13a. Selecting one diagonal from each panel as a redundant bar and representing the actions of these bars on the remainder of the truss by redundant forces X, Y, Z, . . . , we obtain as the primary system a statically determinate simple truss loaded as shown in Fig. 7.13b. This system can be readily analyzed, and the force in any bar i will be

$$S_i = S_i' + s_i'X + s_i''Y + s_i'''Z + \cdots$$

The quantity S_i' in this expression denotes the force produced in any bar i of the primary system (Fig. 7.13b) by the given loads P_1, P_2, P_3, while the quantities s_i', s_i'', s_i''', . . . are obtained, as before, by using such unit loadings as those shown in Fig. 7.13c and d. Considering these loadings, we see that in each case the applied unit loads produce axial forces only in those bars which comprise the corresponding panel. Thus, in Fig. 7.13c we conclude that the axial forces s_i' are different from zero only for the bars of the first panel as shown by heavy lines. Likewise, in Fig. 7.13d, the forces s_i'' vanish for all members except those indicated by heavy lines, etc. With the foregoing observations in mind, let us now consider the equations for determining the redundant forces. The first of these equations will be written on the basis of the fact that the change in the distance between joints A and B of the simple truss (Fig. 7.13b) is equal to the change in length of the redundant diagonal AB in the actual truss (Fig. 7.13a). This change in the distance AB obviously depends only on the deformations of the bars within the first panel of the truss,

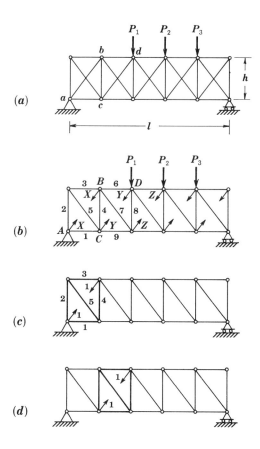

FIG. 7.13

and the forces in these bars depend only on the given loads P_1, P_2, P_3 and the redundant forces X and Y. The remaining redundant forces do not affect the bars of the first panel and need not be considered. Hence, the first equation becomes

$$\sum_{i=1}^{i=5} (S'_i + s'_i X + s''_i Y)\rho_i s'_i = -X\rho_x \qquad (g)$$

This equation contains only two unknowns, X and Y, and the summation includes only the five bars of the first panel. For the remaining bars, as already mentioned, s'_i vanishes.

The second equation is obtained by equating the change in the distance between joints C and D (Fig. 7.13b) to the change in length of the diagonal CD in the complete truss (Fig. 7.13a). This change in the distance CD depends only on the deformations of the bars within the second panel of the truss (Fig. 7.13b), and these deformations in turn depend only on the lateral loads P_1, P_2, P_3 and on the redundant force Y in the second panel, together with the redundant forces X and Z in the adjacent panels. Hence, the second equation becomes

$$\Sigma(S'_i + s'_i X + s''_i Y + s'''_i Z)\rho_i s''_i = -Y\rho_y \qquad (h)$$

where the summation includes all bars of the second panel. This equation contains three unknowns, X, Y, and Z.

Similar equations can be written for the third and fourth panels. The fifth equation will again have only two unknowns, as Eq. (g). Thus, we obtain a system of five equations, two of which have two unknowns each, while the remaining three have three unknowns each. Such a system of equations can be readily solved. They are similar to *three-moment equations* as used in the analysis of continuous beams, and the same methods of solution can be applied.

A method of successive approximations is sometimes useful in the analysis of a statically indeterminate system with many redundant elements. For example, to obtain a first approximation X_1, Y_1, Z_1, . . . for the unknown forces X, Y, Z, . . . in the system above, we assume that the shear in each panel is equally divided between the two diagonals of that panel. Then, coming to Eqs. (g), (h), . . . and noting that the most important terms are those having for coefficients the summations of squares like $\Sigma(s'_i)^2$, $\Sigma(s''_i)^2$, . . . , we replace the unknowns X, Y, Z, . . . in the remaining terms by their first approximations X_1, Y_1, Z_1, . . . and obtain in this way the equations

$$\Sigma S'_i s'_i \rho_i + [\Sigma(s'_i)^2 \rho_i + \rho_x] X + \Sigma s'_i s''_i \rho_i Y_1 = 0$$

$$\Sigma S'_i s''_i \rho_i + \Sigma s'_i s''_i \rho_i X_1 + [\Sigma(s''_i)^2 \rho_i + \rho_y] Y + \Sigma s''_i s'''_i \rho_i Z_1 = 0 \qquad (i)$$

. . . .

Each of these equations contains only one unknown and can be easily solved.

In this manner, we obtain a second approximation X_2, Y_2, Z_2, . . . for the unknown forces. Then, upon putting these new values, instead of X_1, Y_1, Z_1, . . . , in Eqs. (i) and solving again for X, Y, Z, . . . , we can calculate a further approximation for the unknowns. Usually this process converges fairly rapidly so that the third approximation will be satisfactory for all practical purposes.

PROBLEMS

1 Evaluate the redundant reactions at the intermediate supports C and D of the truss shown in Fig. 7.14 if the load $P = 20,000$ lb. All bars of the truss are identical.
    Ans. $X_c = 17,850$ lb, $X_d = 3,600$ lb.
2 Solve the preceding problem if the roller supports at C and D are replaced by vertical bars such as those of which the truss itself is comprised.
    Ans. $X_C = 16,950$ lb, $X_D = 4,200$ lb.
3 Find the magnitude of the vertical reaction X at the support G of the statically indeterminate truss loaded as shown in Fig. 7.15. The dimensions of the truss are shown in the figure, and each bar has cross-sectional area $A_1 = 2$ in.^{2} and modulus of elasticity $E = 30(10^6)$ psi.
    Ans. $X = 35.8$ kips.
4 Solve the preceding problem if the support G settles 0.3 in. during loading of the truss.
    Ans. $X = 21.0$ kips.
5 Make a complete analysis of the statically indeterminate truss shown in Fig. 7.13 if $P_1 = P_2 = P_3 = 20$ kips, $l = 45$ ft, and $h = 12$ ft. Assume that each chord member has a cross-sectional area of 3 in.^{2}, each diagonal 1.5 in.^{2}, and each vertical 1 in.^{2} All bars have the same modulus of elasticity E.
    Ans. $X = -17.7$ kips, $Y = -16.1$ kips, $Z = -6.5$ kips,
        . . . $= +7.1$ kips, . . . $= +16.1$ kips.

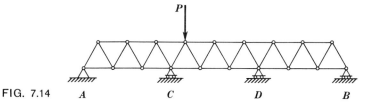

FIG. 7.14 A C D B

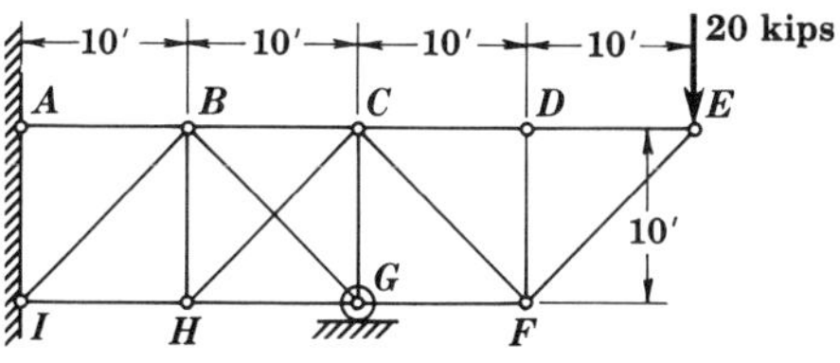

FIG. 7.15

7.4 ASSEMBLY AND THERMAL STRESSES IN STATICALLY INDETERMINATE TRUSSES

From the preliminary discussion of statically indeterminate trusses given in Art. 7.1, it is evident that the lengths of redundant bars must satisfy certain geometrical requirements. The shape of a truss and the mutual distances of all its joints are entirely defined by the lengths of the members of the *primary system*. Hence, a redundant member can be freely placed between two joints only if its length is exactly equal to the distance between these joints. Otherwise the bar will not fit its proper place and can be forced into the primary system only by applying some initial extension or compression. Under such conditions, it is evident that some axial forces, usually called *assembly forces*, will be induced in the bars during the formation of the truss. These internal forces exist even in the absence of external loads and must be superimposed on the axial forces produced by external loading in order to get the total force in each bar.

Take, as a simple example, the statically indeterminate system shown in Fig. 7.1*a*, and assume that in consequence of small errors in the lengths of the inclined bars the distance between the hinges C and D, measured after assembly of the inclined bars, is larger by an amount Δ than the length of the vertical bar. Then, to put this latter bar in place, we must somewhat extend it. Thus, after assembly it will pull up on the joint C and induce compression in the inclined bars while remaining under some tension itself. If X is the magnitude of the tensile force in the vertical bar, after assembly, the compressive forces in the inclined bars will be equal to $X/2 \cos \alpha$, and the corresponding upward displacement of the joint C will be $Xl/2AE \cos^3 \alpha$. The magnitude of the force X is now found from the condition that the vertical displacement of the joint C together with the elongation of the vertical bar must be equal to the initial discrepancy Δ in length. Hence,

$$\frac{Xl}{2AE \cos^3 \alpha} + \frac{Xl}{A_0 E} = \Delta$$

where A_0 is the cross-sectional area of the vertical bar and A the cross-sectional area of an inclined bar. From this equation, we find

$$X = \frac{\Delta AE}{l(\frac{1}{2} \sec^3 \alpha + A/A_0)}$$

Similar reasoning can be applied in more complicated cases of statically indeterminate trusses. Let us consider, for example, the truss in Fig. 7.6*a* and find the assembly forces that will result from inaccuracies in the lengths of the bars. Let Δ_i be the error in length of any bar i, considered positive if the bar is too long, and Δ_0 the error in length of the redundant bar BC. The effect of the errors Δ_i on the distance between the joints B and C of the primary system (Fig. 7.6b) is found by using Eq. (6.3), from which it follows that the above-mentioned distance is shorter than that theoretically designed for by an amount

$$\Sigma \ \Delta_i s_i' \qquad (a)$$

To take care of this error and also of the error Δ_0 in the length of the redundant bar BC, we have to produce some compression in this latter bar before placing it between the joints B and C. After assembly, then, the redundant bar will be pushing on the joints B and C, and assembly forces will be induced throughout the truss. If X denotes the assembly force in the redundant member,[1] the corresponding elongations of the members of the primary system are $s_i' X \rho_i$, and the diminishing of the distance BC, due to these elongations, is $\Sigma (s_i')^2 X \rho_i$. This change in distance, together with the elongation $X\rho_0$ of the redundant bar, must be numerically equal to the initial discrepancy between the distance BC in the primary system and the length of the redundant bar BC. Hence, we obtain

$$\Sigma (s_i')^2 X \rho_i + X \rho_0 = - \ (\Sigma \ \Delta_i s_i' + \Delta_0) \qquad (b)$$

The minus sign on the right follows from the fact that we like to consider positive X as tension, while the expression in parentheses indicates how much the distance BC (Fig. 7.6b) is shorter than the length of the redundant bar. Solving the equation for X, we obtain

$$X = - \ \frac{\Sigma \ \Delta_i s_i' + \Delta_0}{\Sigma (s_i')^2 \rho_i + \rho_0} \qquad (7.3a)$$

If we add this force to that produced by lateral loading of the truss [see Eq. (7.2)], the total force in the redundant bar becomes

$$X = - \ \frac{\Sigma (S_i' \rho_i + \Delta_i) s_i' + \Delta_0}{\Sigma (s_i')^2 \rho_i + \rho_0} \qquad (7.3b)$$

Assembly forces can be calculated in the same way if the redundant force is an external reaction. Take, for example, the truss shown in Fig. 7.5a, and assume that the middle support is too high by an amount Δ_0. Denote also, as before, by Δ_i the error in length of any bar i. Owing to these errors, the joint C of the primary system (Fig. 7.5b) is displaced upward by an amount equal to $\Sigma \ \Delta_i s_i'$, where the values of s_i' are obtained from the unit loading shown in Fig. 7.5c. The required reaction will be found from the condition that the upward deflection of the primary system produced by X is equal to $\Delta_0 - \Sigma \ \Delta_i s_i'$. Hence,

$$\Sigma X (s_i')^2 \rho_i = \Delta_0 - \Sigma \ \Delta_i s_i' \qquad (c)$$

[1] Tension considered positive.

and we obtain

$$X = \frac{-\Sigma \, \Delta_i s_i' + \Delta_0}{\Sigma (s_i')^2 \rho_i} \tag{7.4a}$$

Adding this to the previously found reaction produced by lateral loading of the truss [see Eq. (7.1)], we obtain for the total reaction at the intermediate support

$$X = -\frac{\Sigma (S_i' \rho_i + \Delta_i) s_i' - \Delta_0}{\Sigma (s_i')^2 \rho_i} \tag{7.4b}$$

If the middle support settles by an amount Δ_0, we simply take this quantity with negative sign in these equations.

The equations derived for calculating assembly forces can be used also in calculating forces produced in a statically indeterminate truss by a temperature change. If the temperature of a bar i is increased by an amount t_i above a certain specified uniform temperature of the truss, the length of the bar increases by the amount $\alpha_i t_i l_i$, where α_i is the coefficient of linear thermal expansion for the bar. Treating these thermal elongations of the bars in the same way as the errors in length Δ_i in our preceding discussion, we can readily calculate the thermal stresses in statically indeterminate trusses. Taking, for example, the truss in Fig. 7.6a and using Eq. (7.3a), we find that the force produced in the redundant bar BC by the temperature change is

$$X = -\frac{\Sigma \alpha_i t_i l_i s_i' + \alpha_0 t_0 l_0}{\Sigma (s_i')^2 \rho_i + \rho_0} \tag{7.5}$$

When we deal with statically indeterminate systems having several redundant elements, calculation of the combined effects of applied loads, errors in length of the bars, temperature changes, settlement of supports, etc., become rather involved, and it is desirable to employ a systematic procedure in their analysis. Such an approach will now be described, without reference to any particular system.

Given a statically indeterminate system, we first select the redundant elements and denote the redundant forces by X_a, X_b, X_c, . . . , X_z, and the corresponding generalized displacements by Δ_a, Δ_b, Δ_c, . . . , Δ_z. Then, with these redundant elements all removed, we make a simple statical analysis of the remaining primary system under the action of the external loads and also under the action of a unit force in place of each redundant force. With these data at hand, all the displacements resulting from various causes such as applied loads, errors in length, thermal effects, etc., can be evaluated separately and without difficulty by the methods already discussed in Chap. 6 dealing with the deflection problem. Let Δ_u', Δ_u'', Δ_u''', . . . denote these various displacements corresponding to the redundant force X_u, and let δ_{uv} denote the displacement corresponding to X_u due to a unit force in place of X_v. Finally, let Δ_u denote the net known displacement corresponding to the redundant

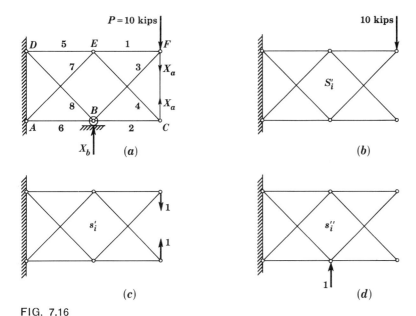

FIG. 7.16

element X_u. Then, by superposition, we must have the algebraic sum of all the displacements corresponding to each redundant force X_u equal to the known final displacement Δ_u. Thus, we may write the following system of equations, analogous to Eqs. (b) and (c):

$$\Delta_a' + \Delta_a'' + \cdots + X_a\delta_{aa} + X_b\delta_{ab} + \cdots + X_z\delta_{az} = \Delta_a$$

$$\Delta_b' + \Delta_b'' + \cdots + X_a\delta_{ba} + X_b\delta_{bb} + \cdots + X_z\delta_{bz} = \Delta_b \tag{7.6}$$

$$\cdots \cdots \cdots \cdots \cdots \cdots \cdots \cdots \cdots \cdots \cdots$$

$$\Delta_z' + \Delta_z'' + \cdots + X_a\delta_{za} + X_b\delta_{zb} + \cdots + X_z\delta_{zz} = \Delta_z$$

This system of linear algebraic equations represents the so-called "superposition equations" for a statically indeterminate system, and their solution gives the magnitudes of the z redundant elements involved.

To illustrate the application of Eqs. (7.6), let us consider the truss with two redundant elements as shown in Fig. 7.16a. Choosing the bar CF and the support at B as the redundant elements, we denote the force in the bar CF by X_a (tension positive) and the reaction at the support by X_b (positive upward). Positive displacement corresponding to X_a will then be a decrease in the distance CF, and positive displacement corresponding to X_b will be an upward deflection of joint B. Three statical analyses of the primary system under the action of the P loading and unit forces in place of each redundant

TABLE 7.2

Bar	l_i, in.	S_i', kips	s_i'	s_i''	$S_i's_i'l_i$	$S_i's_i''l_i$	$s_i'l_i$	$s_i''l_i$	$(s_i')^2l_i$	$(s_i'')^2l_i$	$s_i's_i''l_i$
(1)	(2)	(3)	(4)	(5)	(6)	(7)	(8)	(9)	(10)	(11)	(12)
1	100.0	+10.00	+1.000	0.000	+1,000	0	+100	0	+100	0	0
2	100.0	0	+1.000	0.000	0	0	+100	0	+100	0	0
3	141.4	−14.14	−1.414	0.000	+2,828	0	−200	0	+283	0	0
4	141.4	0	−1.414	0.000	0	0	−200	0	+283	0	0
5	100.0	+10.00	−1.000	0.000	−1,000	0	−100	0	+100	0	0
6	100.0	−20.00	−1.000	+1.000	+2,000	−2,000	−100	+100	+100	+100	−100
7	141.4	0	+1.414	0.000	0	0	+200	0	+283	0	0
8	141.4	+14.14	+1.414	−1.414	+2,828	−2,828	+200	−200	+283	+283	−283
Σ					+7,656	−4,828	0	−100	+1,532	+383	−383

element are now made as indicated in Fig. 7.16b, c, and d. The results of these analyses are recorded in columns 3 to 5 of Table 7.2. The lengths of the bars are given in column 2 of the table. Each bar has cross-sectional area $A = 3.33$ in.^{2} and modulus of elasticity $E = 30(10^6)$ psi; so $AE = 10^8$ lb. The coefficient of thermal expansion for each bar is $\alpha = 6.5(10^6)$ (in./in.)/°F. It is required to find the magnitudes of X_a and X_b due to the combined effects of the given P loading, a uniform rise in temperature of $\Delta t = 50°F$, an error in length of the redundant bar CF of $\Delta l_a = -0.10$ in. (that is, the bar is too short), and a settlement of the support B by the amount $\Delta_b = -0.05$ in.

We begin with a calculation of the displacements corresponding to X_a and X_b due to various causes. Using Eq. (6.3) from Art. 6.2 and the data from Table 7.2, we have

$$\Delta_a' = \sum \frac{S_i's_i'l_i}{AE} = +76,560 \qquad \Delta_b' = \sum \frac{S_i's_i''l_i}{AE} = -48,280$$

$$\Delta_a'' = \Sigma\alpha\,\Delta t\,l_i s_i' = 0 \qquad \Delta_b'' = \Sigma\alpha\,\Delta t\,l_i s_i'' = -32,500$$

$$\delta_{aa} = \sum \frac{(s_i')^2l_i}{AE} = +15.32 \qquad \delta_{ba} = \sum \frac{s_i''s_i'l_i}{AE} = -3.83$$

$$\delta_{ab} = \sum \frac{s_i's_i''l_i}{AE} = -3.83 \qquad \delta_{bb} = \sum \frac{(s_i'')^2l_i}{AE} = +3.83$$

All numerical values are in microinches.

From the statement of the problem, we conclude that the net decrease in length of the redundant bar CF is

$$\Delta_a = -\frac{X_a l_a}{AE} - \alpha\,\Delta t\,l_a - \Delta l_a$$

or, with the given numerical data,

$$\Delta_a = - X_a - 32,500 + 100,000$$

and for the final displacement of the support B,

$$\Delta_b = - 50,000$$

Thus, Eqs. (7.6) become

$$76,560 + 15.32X_a - 3.83X_b = -X_a - 32,500 + 100,000$$

$$-48,280 - 32,500 - 3.83X_a + 3.83X_b = - 50,000$$

which reduce to

$$16.32X_a - 3.83X_b = -9,060$$

$$-3.83X_a + 3.83X_b = +30,780$$

From these simultaneous equations, we find

$$X_a = +1,740 \text{ lb} \qquad X_b = +9,780 \text{ lb}$$

PROBLEMS

1 Referring to the truss in Fig. 7.16 and using Eqs. (7.6) together with the data in Table 7.2, find the magnitudes of the redundant forces X_a and X_b due to the load $P = 10$ kips if there are no errors in length, no change in temperature, and no settlement of the support at B.
    Ans. $X_a = -2,260$ lb, $X_b = +10,340$ lb.
2 Repeat the solution to the preceding problem if the temperature drops by the amount $\Delta t = -50°F$, the redundant bar is too short by the amount $\Delta l_a = -0.05$ in., and the settlement of the support B is zero.
    Ans. $X_a = +1,740$ lb, $X_b = +5,860$ lb.
3 Referring to Fig. 7.17, find the axial force X in the redundant bar x due to the action of the vertical load $P = 10$ kips, a uniform rise in temperature of $\Delta t = 60°F$,

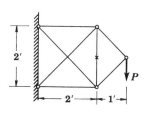

FIG. 7.17

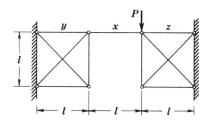

FIG. 7.18

and an error in length of the redundant bar x by the amount $\Delta l_x = -0.05$ in. (too short). Each bar has cross-sectional area $A_i = 1$ in.^{2}, modulus of elasticity $E = 30(10^6)$ psi, and coefficient of thermal expansion $\alpha = 6.5(10^{-6})$ (in./in.)/°F.

Ans. $X = 8,575$ lb, tension.

4   Referring to the truss shown in Fig. 7.18, the following data are given: $P = 10$ kips, $l = 100$ in.   All bars are aluminum, for which $E = 10(10^6)$ psi and $\alpha = 10(10^{-6})$ (in./in.)/°F.   Each horizontal and vertical bar has a cross-sectional area of 1 in.^{2}, and each diagonal bar $\sqrt{2}$ in.^{2} Calculate the magnitudes X, Y, Z of axial force in the three redundant bars x, y, z due to the applied load P.

Ans. $X = -2,100$ lb, $Y = -1,800$ lb, $Z = +3,910$ lb.

5   Repeat the solution to the previous problem if, in addition to the applied load P, there is a uniform rise in temperature of the truss by the amount $\Delta t = +50$°F and an error in length of the redundant bar x of the amount $\Delta l_x = +0.10$ in., that is, the bar is too long.

Ans. $X = -11,840$ lb, $Y = -9,440$ lb, $Z = -3,720$ lb.

7.5 INFLUENCE LINES FOR STATICALLY INDETERMINATE TRUSSES

In preceding articles, we have discussed the analysis of statically indeterminate trusses under the action of stationary loads.   If, as in the case of bridges, we are dealing with moving loads and must consider various positions of these loads, influence lines can be used to advantage.   In general, the construction of influence lines for statically indeterminate trusses can be greatly simplified by using the reciprocal theorem, discussed in Art. 5.7, together with deflection curves for trusses.   The general statement of the reciprocal theorem is represented by Eq. (5.10) (see page 249), and its application in the construction of influence lines will now be illustrated by several examples.

As a first example, let us consider the truss in Fig. 7.19a having one redundant support, assuming that the moving loads are transmitted to the joints of the lower chord.   Taking the reaction X at the intermediate support as the redundant force, we construct the influence line for this force by applying the reciprocal theorem to the two loading conditions shown in Fig. 7.19a and b. In the first case a unit load acts at the joint m of the given truss and produces a reaction X at the intermediate support C.   In the second case the intermediate support is removed, and a unit load is applied at the joint C.   This second case is statically determinate, and we can readily calculate the axial forces and elongations of all bars.   Having such elongations, we calculate the deflections of the lower-chord joints by using the method of fictitious loads discussed in Art. 6.5.   Let δ_m and δ_c be the deflections of the joints m and C obtained in this manner.   Then, observing that the forces of Fig. 7.19a produce on the displacements calculated for Fig. 7.19b the work equal to $1 \times \delta_m - X\delta_c$, and that the work of the forces of Fig. 7.19b on the corresponding displacements of Fig. 7.19a vanishes, we find that Eq. (5.10) becomes

$$1 \times \delta_m - X\delta_c = 0$$

and we obtain

$$X = 1\frac{\delta_m}{\delta_c} \qquad\qquad (a)$$

Hence, for any position of the moving unit load in Fig. 7.19a, the intermediate reaction X is proportional to the deflection of the corresponding joint of the truss in Fig. 7.19b. Upon dividing these deflections by the deflection δ_c, we obtain the ordinates of the influence line acb for the reaction X as shown in Fig. 7.19c. By use of this influence line, the redundant reaction X for any system of moving loads $P_1, P_2, P_3, \ldots$ can now be obtained from the equation

$$X = \Sigma y_m P_m$$

Having the influence line for the redundant force X, we can readily obtain the influence diagrams for other quantities by using the methods developed in Chap. 3 for statically determinate trusses. Take, for example, the influence diagram for the reaction R_a. For any position of the unit load, this reaction is obtained from the statics equation

$$R_a = 1\frac{l - x_m}{l} - X\frac{l_2}{l} \qquad\qquad (b)$$

The first term on the right side of this equation represents the reaction for a simple beam supported at A and B, whereas the second term takes care of the intermediate reaction X. Thus, the ordinates of the required influence diagram will be obtained by subtracting the ordinates of the influence line acb, diminished in the ratio l_2/l, from the ordinates of the influence line constructed as for a simply supported beam AB. This will be accomplished by drawing the straight line bcd as shown in Fig. 7.19c and then reducing in the ratio l_2/l the ordinates of the shaded portions of the diagram.

The bending moment for a cross section through the joint m is evidently obtained by subtracting the moment Xl_2x_m/l, due to the intermediate reaction, from the moment calculated for a simple beam supported at A and B. Thus, to obtain the influence diagram for bending moment at m, we begin with the influence line acb for X, on which we superimpose the triangle adb as shown in Fig. 7.19d. This triangle represents the influence line for simple-beam bending moment at m except that the straight line bde has the ordinate l/l_2 at a instead of the ordinate x_m as it should have. Hence, to obtain the influence coefficients for simple-beam bending moment at m, the ordinates of the triangle adb must be multiplied by $x_m l_2/l$. This, however, is the same factor by which the ordinates of the X influence line must be multiplied to obtain the bending moment due to X. Hence, the ordinates of the shaded area in Fig. 7.19d,

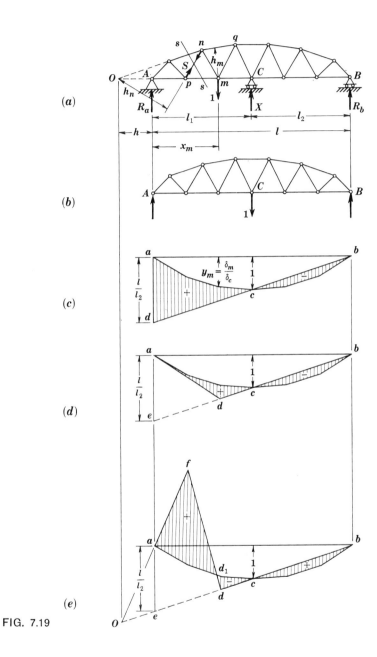

FIG. 7.19

when multiplied by $x_m l_2/l$, represent the required influence coefficients for bending moment at m.

The same diagram can be used also as the influence diagram for axial force in the bar nq of the upper chord of the truss opposite the hinge m. To obtain the force in this bar, we have only to divide the bending moment at m by the distance h_m and change the sign. Hence the influence diagram for the above-mentioned bar is obtained by multiplying the ordinates of the shaded area in Fig. 7.19d by the numerical factor $-x_m l_2/h_m l$. In a similar manner, influence diagrams for the bars of the lower chord can be constructed.

Let us consider now a web member np (Fig. 7.19a). If the unit load is to the right of joint m, we consider the equilibrium of the left portion of the truss. Taking the moments of all forces acting on this portion with respect to point O, we find that the force in the web member np is

$$S = -R_a \frac{h}{h_n} \qquad (c)$$

Hence, for positions of the load to the right of joint m, the influence diagram for S is obtained by using the same shaded areas already used for R_a in Fig. 7.19c, except that in this case the ordinates must be multiplied by $-l_2 h/l h_n$. When the unit load is to the left of panel pm and at the distance x from the support A, we obtain for S, instead of Eq. (c), the following equation:

$$S = -R_a \frac{h}{h_n} + 1 \frac{h + x}{h_n} \qquad (d)$$

All necessary constructions for the required influence diagram are indicated in Fig. 7.19e. For the portion of the span to the right of joint m we use, as already mentioned, the same areas as in Fig. 7.19c, while for the portion to the left of panel pm the second term on the right side of Eq. (d) must be taken into account. We shall accomplish this by drawing the line oaf as previously explained in Chap. 3 (see page 149). The ordinates included between the straight lines oaf and ocb, after multiplication by the factor $l_2 h/l h_n$, give us the second term on the right side of Eq. (d). Hence, the ordinates of the shaded areas in Fig. 7.19e, after multiplication by this factor $l_2 h/l h_n$, give the required influence coefficients for axial force in the bar np. The proper signs of these ordinates are readily determined from Eqs. (c) and (d) and are indicated in Fig. 7.19e.

For a second example, we consider the two-hinged arch shown in Fig. 7.20a and take the horizontal thrust H as the redundant force. Then, to construct the influence line for H, we apply the reciprocal theorem to the two loading conditions shown in Fig. 7.20a and b. In the first case, a unit load, moving along the upper chord, acts at the joint k. In the second case, the redundant constraint is removed, and two equal but opposite unit forces are applied as

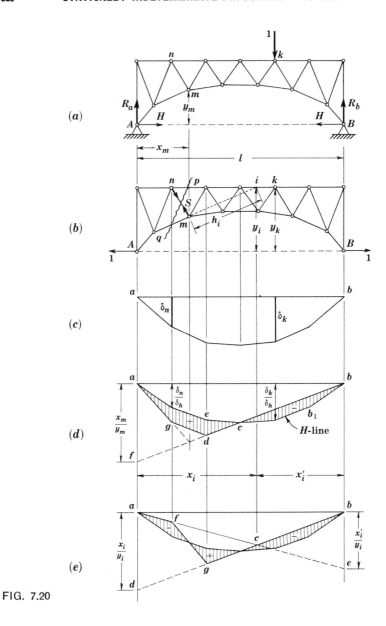

FIG. 7.20

shown.   This second case is statically determinate, and we can calculate the
elongations of all bars.   With these elongations, the increase δ_h in the distance
AB can be found by using Eq. (6.2), and the deflections of the upper-chord
joints can be found by applying the method of fictitious loads discussed in
Art. 6.5.   The deflection curve obtained in this manner is shown in Fig. 7.20c.

Applying, now, the reciprocal theorem, we obtain

$$-H\delta_h + 1 \times \delta_k = 0$$

Hence,
$$H = 1 \frac{\delta_k}{\delta_h}$$

We see that the ordinates of the required influence line for H are obtained by dividing by δ_h the deflections of the upper-chord joints. This line is given by the polygon acb in Fig. 7.20d. The influence line for the redundant force H having been obtained, the influence diagram for any other quantity can be readily constructed by using the methods developed in Chap. 3. In Fig. 7.20d, for example, the influence diagram for bending moment with respect to the joint m is shown. With such influence diagrams for bending moment, the corresponding influence diagrams for axial forces in the chord members can also be obtained without difficulty.

Let us consider now the influence line for the axial force S in a web member mn (Fig. 7.20b). Making a section pq through that member as shown and considering the equilibrium of the left portion of the truss, we obtain

$$S = S_0 - H\frac{y_i}{h_i} = \frac{y_i}{h_i}\left(S_0\frac{h_i}{y_i} - H\right) \qquad (e)$$

where S_0 is the force in the member mn when $H = 0$, and the distances y_i and h_i are as indicated in Fig. 7.20b. Upon drawing the lines ae and bd as shown in Fig. 7.20e, we obtain the influence line $afgb$ for the quantity $S_0 h_i/y_i$. Subtracting from this the ordinates of the influence line for H, we obtain the shaded areas shown in Fig. 7.20e. The ordinates of these areas multiplied by y_i/h_i give us the required influence coefficients for S. Influence diagrams for other web members can be constructed in a similar manner.

As an example of a system with two redundant elements, let us consider the truss on four supports as shown in Fig. 7.21a. It is assumed that the moving loads are transmitted to the joints of the lower chord. For the redundant forces, we select the reactions X and Y at the intermediate supports. In addition to the actual loading condition shown in Fig. 7.21a, we consider the two cases shown in Fig. 7.21b and c in which the intermediate supports are removed and a unit load is applied at joint C and at joint D, respectively. The latter two cases are statically determinate, and we can calculate the deflections of the lower chord for each of these cases by using the method of fictitious loads. Let δ_{cc}, δ_{cd}, and δ_{cm} denote the deflections at C, D, and m, respectively, when the unit load is acting at C, while δ_{dc}, δ_{dd}, and δ_{dm} denote the deflections produced at the same joints by the unit load at D. Assuming that the supports C and D do not displace vertically under the action of the unit load in Fig. 7.21a and applying the reciprocal theorem to Fig. 7.21a and b, we obtain

$$-X\delta_{cc} - Y\delta_{cd} + 1 \times \delta_{cm} = 0 \qquad (f)$$

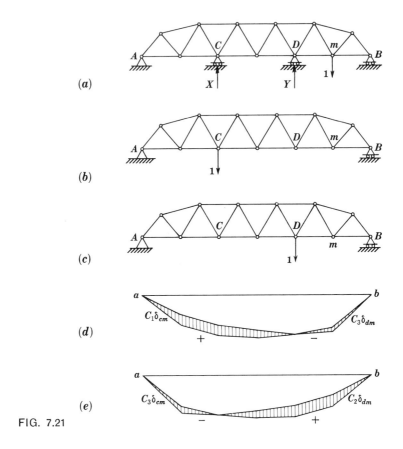

FIG. 7.21

Similarly, considering Fig. 7.21a and c, we obtain

$$-X\delta_{dc} - Y\delta_{dd} + 1 \times \delta_{dm} = 0 \tag{g}$$

Solving Eqs. (f) and (g) for X and Y and observing that $\delta_{cd} = \delta_{dc}$, from the reciprocal theorem, we find the following expressions for the redundant reactions:

$$X = \frac{\delta_{dd}}{\delta_{cc}\delta_{dd} - \delta_{cd}^2}\,\delta_{cm} - \frac{\delta_{cd}}{\delta_{cc}\delta_{dd} - \delta_{cd}^2}\,\delta_{dm} \tag{h}$$

$$Y = \frac{\delta_{cc}}{\delta_{cc}\delta_{dd} - \delta_{cd}^2}\,\delta_{dm} - \frac{\delta_{cd}}{\delta_{cc}\delta_{dd} - \delta_{cd}^2}\,\delta_{cm} \tag{i}$$

It is seen that when the unit load changes position along the truss (Fig. 7.21a), only the quantities δ_{cm} and δ_{dm} in expressions (h) and (i) change in magnitude;

the other quantities remain constant.   Introducing the notations

$$\frac{\delta_{dd}}{\delta_{cc}\delta_{dd} - \delta_{cd}^2} = C_1 \qquad \frac{\delta_{cc}}{\delta_{cc}\delta_{dd} - \delta_{cd}^2} = C_2 \qquad \frac{\delta_{cd}}{\delta_{cc}\delta_{dd} - \delta_{cd}^2} = C_3$$

$$(j)$$

we obtain

$$X = C_1\delta_{cm} - C_3\delta_{dm}$$

$$Y = C_2\delta_{dm} - C_3\delta_{cm}$$

$$(k)$$

The constants C_1, C_2, and C_3 are readily calculated from Eqs. (j) provided that the deflection curves for the loadings in Fig. 7.21b and c have been constructed.   The expressions on the right sides of Eqs. (k) are plotted in Fig. 7.21d and e, and the required influence coefficients for the redundant reactions X and Y are given by the ordinates of the shaded areas.   With these constructions, the influence diagram for axial force in any bar of the truss (Fig. 7.21a) can be easily obtained.   For this purpose, we observe that the force S_i in any member can be represented in the following form:

$$S_i = S_i' - s_i'X - s_i''Y$$

$$(l)$$

where S_i' is the force in that member when the redundant supports are removed, and s_i' and s_i'' are the *influence numbers*[1] for the same member calculated for the unit loads shown in Fig. 7.21b and c, respectively.   Thus, we see that the required influence diagram for axial force in any bar can be obtained by combining the ordinates of the influence diagram, constructed as for a simply supported truss, with those of the $s_i'X$ diagram and the $s_i''Y$ diagram.   These latter diagrams are obtained simply by multiplying the ordinates of the shaded areas in Fig. 7.21d and e by the influence numbers s_i' and s_i''.

PROBLEMS

1   Construct an influence line for the redundant reaction X_c in the truss shown in Fig. 7.22 if live loads are applied to the lower-chord joints.   Each bar has the same cross-sectional area $A_i = 4$ in.^{2} and the same modulus of elasticity E.   Using this influence line, find the maximum value of X_c due to a standard Cooper's E-60 train loading.
  Ans.   Max $X_c = 98.3$ kips.

2   Using the data in the preceding problem, construct an influence diagram for axial force S in the bar EF of the truss shown in Fig. 7.22.   With the aid of this diagram, find the maximum value of S due to a standard Cooper's E-60 loading.
  Ans. $S_{max} = -23.6$ kips.

[1] These influence numbers s_i', s_i'', as defined on page 259, should not be confused with influence coefficients as defined on page 108.

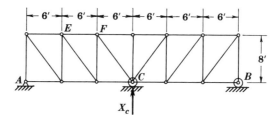

FIG. 7.22

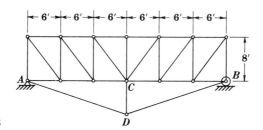

FIG. 7.23

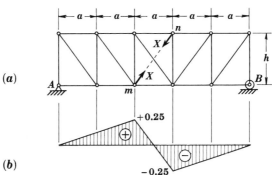

(a)

(b)

FIG. 7.24

3   Repeat the solution to Prob. 1 if, instead of a rigid support at C as shown in Fig. 7.22, there is a vertical steel bar CD (not shown) of cross-sectional area $A_0 = 4$ in.^{2} and length $l_0 = 10$ ft.   All other data remain the same as in Prob. 1.
   Ans. Max $X_c = 85.5$ kips.

4   Construct an influence line for the axial force X in the redundant bar CD of the truss shown in Fig. 7.23 if live load is applied to the lower-chord joints of the truss proper.   Each bar has the same cross-sectional area $A_i = 4$ in.^{2} and the same modulus of elasticity E; the bar CD is 6 ft long.   Using this influence line, find the maximum value of X due to a standard Cooper's E-60 loading.
   Ans. $X_{max} = 40.8$ kips, compression.

5   Construct the influence line for axial force X in the bar mn of the truss shown in Fig. 7.24 if $a = 60$ in., $h = 80$ in., and each bar has the same AE value.   Assume that the moving loads are applied to the lower-chord joints.
   Ans. See Fig. 7.24b.

7.6 STATICALLY INDETERMINATE SPACE STRUCTURES

If a structure in space has n joints and more than $3n$ bars, including supporting bars or their equivalent, the number of equations that can be obtained from statics will be insufficient to determine the unknown axial forces in all members and the system is statically indeterminate.   In analyzing such systems, the elastic deformations of the bars must be considered.   This can be accomplished by using the methods already developed for plane trusses.   To illustrate the application of these methods to space systems, let us consider the simple system consisting of a single joint A attached to the foundation by four bars as shown in Fig. 7.25.   Such a system has one redundant bar.   To define the configuration, we assume that all bars are identical and have the length $l = 5$ ft, that the bars 1 and 3 are in a horizontal plane ABD, and that the bars 2 and 4 are in a vertical plane ACE bisecting the angle BAD.   The force P applied at A acts in a vertical plane parallel to the plane BCD and makes an angle of $45°$ with the vertical bar AE.   We select the bar AE as the redundant bar and denote by X the axial force in it.   Then the forces in the other bars will be found from the equation

$$S_i = S_i' + s_i'X \qquad (a)$$

in which S_i' is the force produced by the load P in any bar i of the primary system, i.e., of the system that remains after removal of the redundant bar AE, and s_i' is the influence number for any bar i.   These influence numbers are obtained by applying at joint A of the primary system a vertical unit load and calculating the corresponding axial forces in the bars.   To obtain the redundant force X by the theorem of least work, we make the expression for strain energy

$$U = \sum \frac{S_i^2 l_i}{2A_i E} + \frac{X^2 l_0}{2A_0 E} = \frac{1}{2}\left(\sum S_i^2 \rho_i + X^2 \rho_0\right) \qquad (b)$$

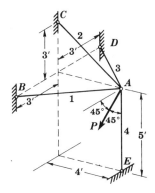

FIG. 7.25

where the summations are understood to include all bars of the primary system. Setting the derivative of this expression with respect to X equal to zero, we obtain

$$\frac{\partial U}{\partial X} = \sum S_i s_i' \rho_i + X \rho_0 = 0 \tag{c}$$

Observing that in this case ρ_i is the same for all members and substituting expression (a) for S_i, we obtain

$$X = -\frac{\Sigma S_i' s_i'}{\Sigma (s_i')^2 + 1} \tag{d}$$

The values of S_i' and s_i' together with all calculations necessary to determine X are shown in Table 7.3. The load P is taken equal to 1 ton, and Eq. (d) then gives

$$X = -\frac{2.95}{5.165} = -0.570 \text{ ton}$$

Finally, using Eq. (a), we obtain the values of S_i as recorded in the last column of the table.

Equation (c) for calculating X can also be obtained by applying the Maxwell-Mohr method as discussed in Art. 6.2. In this case the work done on the actual displacements by the forces corresponding to the unit load must vanish. If it is desired to consider a change in temperature and possible errors Δ_i in the lengths of the bars, we have only to substitute in Eq. (c) the expression $S_i \rho_i + \alpha t_i l_i + \Delta_i$ instead of $S_i \rho_i$ and $X \rho_0 + \alpha t_0 l_0 + \Delta_0$ instead of $X \rho_0$. In this way we obtain the equation

$$\Sigma (S_i \rho_i + \alpha t_i l_i + \Delta_i) s_i' + X \rho_0 + \alpha t_0 l_0 + \Delta_0 = 0$$

from which

$$X = -\frac{\Sigma (S_i' \rho_i + \alpha t_i l_i + \Delta_i) s_i' + \alpha t_0 l_0 + \Delta_0}{\Sigma (s_i')^2 \rho_i + \rho_0} \tag{7.7}$$

This equation can be used to calculate the redundant force in any pin-connected space structure with one redundant member. It is necessary only to extend

TABLE 7.3

i	S_i', tons	s_i'	$S_i' s_i'$, tons	$(s_i')^2$	S_i, tons
1	$-5\sqrt{2}/6$	$-\frac{5}{6}$	0.983	0.694	-0.705
2	$5\sqrt{2}/6$	$\frac{5}{3}$	1.967	2.777	0.230
3	0	$-\frac{5}{6}$	0	0.694	0.475
4					-0.570
Σ			2.95	4.165	

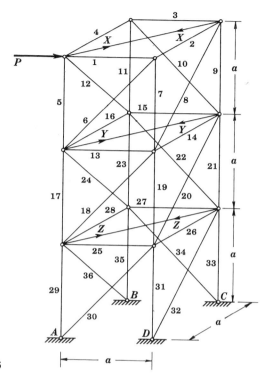

FIG. 7.26

the summations to include all members of the primary system. Omitting terms containing temperature t_i and length errors Δ_i, we see that Eq. (7.7) coincides with Eq. (d).

As a more complicated example, let us consider the space structure shown in Fig. 7.26 to which a horizontal force $P = 1$ ton is applied. This structure has 12 joints and 39 bars. Hence, there are three redundant bars. For these redundants, we choose the three horizontal diagonals and denote their axial forces by X, Y, and Z, as shown. After removal of these bars, we obtain the statically determinate primary system shown in Fig. 7.27. The forces S_i' produced in the bars of this system by the load $P = 1$ ton are given in the second column of Table 7.4, page 328. We consider now the unit loads acting on the primary system as shown in Fig. 7.27a to c and calculate the corresponding influence numbers s_i', s_i'', s_i''', given in columns 3 to 5 of the table. The force in any bar i of the given structure (Fig. 7.26) will now be represented by the expression

$$S_i = S_i' + s_i'X + s_i''Y + s_i'''Z$$

TABLE 7.4

i	S_i'	s_i'	s_i''	s_i'''	$(s_i')^2$	$(s_i'')^2$	$(s_i''')^2$	$S_i' s_i'$	$S_i' s_i''$	$S_i' s_i'''$	$s_i' s_i''$	$s_i' s_i'''$	$s_i'' s_i'''$
(1)	(2)	(3)	(4)	(5)	(6)	(7)	(8)	(9)	(10)	(11)	(12)	(13)	(14)
1	-1	$-1/\sqrt{2}$	0	0	$\tfrac{1}{2}$	0	0	$1/\sqrt{2}$	0	0	0	0	0
2	0	0	0	0	0	0	0	0	0	0	0	0	0
3	0	$-1/\sqrt{2}$	0	0	$\tfrac{1}{2}$	0	0	0	0	0	0	0	0
4	0	0	0	0	0	0	0	0	0	0	0	0	0
5	0	$1/\sqrt{2}$	0	0	$\tfrac{1}{2}$	0	0	0	0	0	0	0	0
6	$\sqrt{2}$	1	0	0	1	0	0	$\sqrt{2}$	0	0	0	0	0
7	-1	$-1/\sqrt{2}$	0	0	$\tfrac{1}{2}$	0	0	$1/\sqrt{2}$	0	0	0	0	0
8	0	-1	0	0	1	0	0	0	0	0	0	0	0
9	0	$1/\sqrt{2}$	0	0	$\tfrac{1}{2}$	0	0	0	0	0	0	0	0
10	0	1	0	0	1	0	0	0	0	0	0	0	0
11	0	$-1/\sqrt{2}$	0	0	$\tfrac{1}{2}$	0	0	0	0	0	0	0	0
12	0	-1	0	0	1	0	0	0	0	0	0	0	0
13	-1	$-1/\sqrt{2}$	$-1/\sqrt{2}$	0	$\tfrac{1}{2}$	$\tfrac{1}{2}$	0	$1/\sqrt{2}$	$1/\sqrt{2}$	0	$\tfrac{1}{2}$	0	0
14	0	$1/\sqrt{2}$	0	0	$\tfrac{1}{2}$	0	0	$1/\sqrt{2}$	$1/\sqrt{2}$	0	0	0	0
15	0	$-1/\sqrt{2}$	$-1/\sqrt{2}$	0	$\tfrac{1}{2}$	$\tfrac{1}{2}$	0	0	0	0	$\tfrac{1}{2}$	0	0
16	0	$1/\sqrt{2}$	0	0	$\tfrac{1}{2}$	0	0	0	0	0	0	0	0
17	1	$3/\sqrt{2}$	$1/\sqrt{2}$	0	$\tfrac{9}{2}$	$\tfrac{1}{2}$	0	$3/\sqrt{2}$	$1/\sqrt{2}$	0	$\tfrac{3}{2}$	0	0
18	$\sqrt{2}$	1	1	0	1	1	0	$\sqrt{2}$	$\sqrt{2}$	0	1	0	0
19	-2	$-3/\sqrt{2}$	$-1/\sqrt{2}$	0	$\tfrac{9}{2}$	$\tfrac{1}{2}$	0	$3\sqrt{2}$	$\sqrt{2}$	0	$\tfrac{3}{2}$	0	0
20	0	-1	-1	0	1	1	0	0	0	0	1	0	0

	C1	C2	C3	C4	C5	C6	C7	C8	C9	C10	C11	C12	C13
21	0	0	$3/2$	0	0	0	0	$1/2$	$9/2$	0	$1/\sqrt{2}$	$3/\sqrt{2}$	0
22	0	0	1	0	0	0	0	1	1	0	1	1	0
23	0	0	$3/2$	0	0	0	0	$1/2$	$9/2$	0	$-1/\sqrt{2}$	$-3/\sqrt{2}$	0
24	0	0	1	0	0	0	0	1	1	0	-1	-1	-1
25	$1/2$	$1/2$	$1/2$	$1/\sqrt{2}$	$1/\sqrt{2}$	$1/\sqrt{2}$	$1/2$	$1/2$	$1/2$	$-1/\sqrt{2}$	$-1/\sqrt{2}$	$-1/\sqrt{2}$	-1
26	0	0	$1/2$	0	0	0	0	$1/2$	$1/2$	0	$-1/\sqrt{2}$	$1/\sqrt{2}$	0
27	$1/2$	$1/2$	$1/2$	0	0	0	$1/2$	1	1	$-1/\sqrt{2}$	$-1/\sqrt{2}$	$-1/\sqrt{2}$	0
28	0	0	$1/2$	0	0	0	0	$1/2$	$1/2$	0	$1/\sqrt{2}$	$1/\sqrt{2}$	0
29	$3/2$	$5/2$	$15/2$	$\sqrt{2}$	$3\sqrt{2}$	$5\sqrt{2}$	$1/2$	$9/2$	$25/2$	$1/\sqrt{2}$	$3/\sqrt{2}$	$5/\sqrt{2}$	$\dfrac{2}{\sqrt{2}}$
30	1	1	1	$\sqrt{2}$	$\sqrt{2}$	$\sqrt{2}$	1	1	1	1	1	1	-3
31	$3/2$	$5/2$	$15/2$	$3/\sqrt{2}$	$9/\sqrt{2}$	$15/\sqrt{2}$	$1/2$	$9/2$	$25/2$	$-1/\sqrt{2}$	$-3/\sqrt{2}$	$-5/\sqrt{2}$	0
32	1	1	1	0	0	0	1	1	1	-1	-1	-1	0
33	$3/2$	$5/2$	$15/2$	0	0	0	$1/2$	$9/2$	$25/2$	$1/\sqrt{2}$	$3/\sqrt{2}$	$5/\sqrt{2}$	0
34	1	1	1	0	0	0	1	1	1	1	1	1	0
35	$3/2$	$5/2$	$15/2$	0	0	0	$1/2$	$9/2$	$25/2$	$-1/\sqrt{2}$	$-3/\sqrt{2}$	$-5/\sqrt{2}$	0
36	1	1	1	0	0	0	1	1	1	-1	-1	-1	0
Σ	11	15	47	$4\sqrt{2}$	$12\sqrt{2}$	$22\sqrt{2}$	7	31	87				

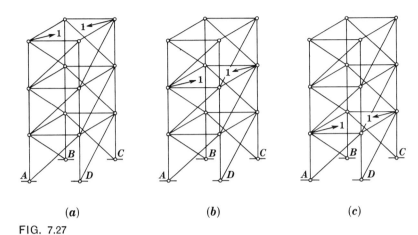

(a) (b) (c)

FIG. 7.27

and Eqs. (7.6) reduce to the following three equations for calculating the redundant forces:

$$\Sigma s_i'(S_i' + s_i'X + s_i''Y + s_i'''Z)\rho_i + X\rho_x = 0$$
$$\Sigma s_i''(S_i' + s_i'X + s_i''Y + s_i'''Z)\rho_i + Y\rho_y = 0 \qquad (e)$$
$$\Sigma s_i'''(S_i' + s_i'X + s_i''Y + s_i'''Z)\rho_i + Z\rho_z = 0$$

In these equations, ρ_x, ρ_y, and ρ_z denote the extensibility factors for the three redundant diagonals. The magnitudes of the redundant forces will, of course, depend on the cross-sectional dimensions of the bars. Assuming, for example, that the extensibilities of all bars are equal, the quantities ρ cancel in Eqs. (e), and the numerical values of all coefficients in these equations are obtained by making summations of columns 6 to 14 of the table. In this way, Eqs. (e) finally become

$$88X + 47Y + 15Z = -22\sqrt{2}$$
$$47X + 32Y + 11Z = -12\sqrt{2} \qquad (f)$$
$$15X + 11Y + 8Z = -4\sqrt{2}$$

from which we find

$$X = -0.2327\sqrt{2} \text{ ton} \qquad Y = -0.0215\sqrt{2} \text{ ton}$$
$$Z = -0.0341\sqrt{2} \text{ ton}$$

PROBLEMS

1   The simple space truss shown in Fig. 7.28 consists of two panels $ABCD$ and $ABEF$ attached to a vertical wall at points C, D, E, F, the panel $ABCD$ being in a horizontal plane. All bars have the same cross-sectional area A and the same modulus

of elasticity E.   Calculate the axial force X produced in the redundant bar x by the vertical load $P = 1$ kip applied at joint A as shown.

   Ans. $X = +56$ lb.

2   What thermal force X_t will be induced in the redundant bar x of the space truss in Fig. 7.28 if there is a uniform rise in temperature of 50°F?   The coefficient of thermal expansion for each bar is $\alpha = 6.5(10^{-6})$ (in./in.)/°F, $A_i = 1$ in.², and $E = 30(10^6)$ psi.

   Ans. $X_t = -1{,}295$ lb.

3   The statically indeterminate ball-jointed space truss shown in Fig. 7.29 has the form of a square pyramid with dimensions $a = 10$ ft and $h = 16$ ft, E, F, G, H being mid-points of the edges AI, BI, CI, DI, respectively.   A horizontal force $P = 10$ kips, acting parallel to AB, is applied at joint I as shown.   Calculate the magnitudes of the axial forces X and Y in the redundant bars x and y, assuming that the redundant bar y has a length error $\Delta_y = -0.01$ ft, that is, the bar is too short.   All bars have the same cross-sectional area $A_i = 4$ in.² and the same modulus of elasticity $E = 30(10^6)$ psi.   The foundation points A, B, C, D are immovable.

   Ans. $X = +14{,}370$ lb, $Y = +18{,}210$ lb.

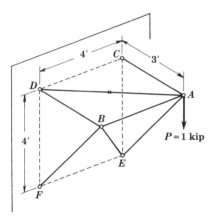

FIG. 7.28

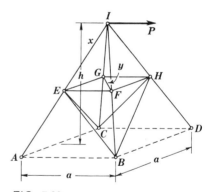

FIG. 7.29

Chapter 8

Arches and frames

8.1 INTRODUCTION

Any plane-curved bar or rib, properly supported at its ends and so loaded that it acts primarily in direct compression, may be called an *arch*. It is assumed that the plane of curvature of the rib is also a plane of symmetry for each cross section and that external forces applied to the arch act only in this plane. Under such conditions, deformation will also take place in the plane of symmetry, and the problem of analysis becomes a two-dimensional one. If the cross sections of the rib are unsymmetrical with respect to the plane of curvature or if loads are applied normal to this plane, there will be twisting of the loaded rib, and under such conditions it is not properly considered to be an arch. Conditions leading to such torsion will be excluded from consideration in all further discussion.

In Chap. 1, a few examples of statically determinate *three-hinged arches* were discussed. Here we shall consider only statically indeterminate arches

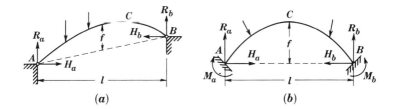

FIG. 8.1 (a) (b)

such as *two-hinged arches* and *hingeless arches* as shown in Fig. 8.1a and b, respectively.   In the case of such statically indeterminate arches, it is essential that the ends A and B, whether hinged or built in, remain immovable when loads are applied to the rib; otherwise, true arch action cannot be developed.[1] The arch in Fig. 8.1a which has one end lower than the other is called an *unsymmetrical arch*, whereas the one in Fig. 8.1b is called a *symmetrical arch*. The highest point C on the arch axis in each case is called the *crown*, and the line AB joining the points of support is called the *springing line*.   The horizontal distance between supports, denoted by l, is called the *span* of the arch, and the maximum vertical distance from springing line to arch axis, denoted by f, is called the rise of the arch.

The two-hinged arch (Fig. 8.1a) represents a structure with one redundant reactive force.   Since the points of support are immovable, applied loads produce, at both ends, not only vertical but also horizontal reactions.   Thus we have four unknown reactive forces, for the calculation of which there are only three equations of statics.   To obtain a fourth equation, deformation of the arch must be considered.   We can take, for instance, the horizontal reaction H_b as the redundant element; then, its magnitude will be determined from the condition that the horizontal displacement of the hinge B vanishes.

In the case of the hingeless arch (Fig. 8.1b), we have six reactive elements, four components of force, and two end moments.   We can take as redundant elements in this case the forces R_a, H_a and the moment M_a.   Then, the magnitudes of these quantities will be determined from the conditions that the corresponding displacements and rotation of the end A of the arch must vanish.

As a general approach to the problem of analysis of statically indeterminate arches, we shall use the second theorem of Castigliano or the theorem of least work, as already developed in Arts. 5.5 and 5.6, respectively.   This requires that we first establish an expression for the total strain energy stored in the arch rib under load.   To do this, we consider an element of the arch rib as shown in Fig. 8.2 and denote by M, V, and N, respectively, the bending

---

[1] Unexpected yielding of the abutments due to poor foundation conditions has led to failure of many arch structures.

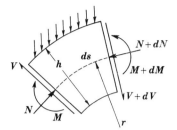

FIG. 8.2

moment, the shearing force, and the normal force at any cross section, positive when directed as shown. Since the depth h of the cross section is usually small compared with the radius of curvature r of the arch axis, we may use for strain energy of bending the expression

$$U_b = \int_0^s \frac{M^2\,ds}{2EI} \tag{a}$$

similar to that used for straight beams, where s is the length of the center line of the arch and I is the moment of inertia of the cross section. Also, the strain energy due to shearing forces V in Fig. 8.2 is usually small compared with that due to bending and can be neglected. Finally, for the strain energy of direct compression, we have

$$U_c = \int_0^s \frac{N^2\,ds}{2AE} \tag{b}$$

where s is the length of the center line of the arch and A is the cross-sectional area. Thus, neglecting the effect of curvature of the arch axis and the effect of shear deformation, we find the total strain energy in the arch rib to be[1]

$$U = \int_0^s \frac{M^2\,ds}{2EI} + \int_0^s \frac{N^2\,ds}{2AE} \tag{8.1}$$

In most practical cases, the cross-sectional area A and the moment of inertia I vary along the length of the arch, and this variation must be taken into account before the indicated integrations can be performed. Particular types of variations will be considered later in examples.

[1] For a more complete expression for strain energy containing the effect of shear deformation and curvature of the arch axis, see S. Timoshenko, "Strength of Materials," 3d ed., vol. I, p. 382, D. Van Nostrand Company, Inc., Princeton, N.J., 1955. Results obtained on the basis of this more exact expression show that for usual proportions of arches, Eq. (8.1) is sufficiently accurate for practical applications.

8.2 SYMMETRICAL TWO-HINGED ARCHES

Let us consider a symmetrical two-hinged arch subjected to any vertical loading as shown in Fig. 8.3. Choosing the thrust H as the redundant reaction and applying the theorem of least work, we obtain

$$\frac{\partial U}{\partial H} = \int_0^s \frac{M}{EI} \frac{\partial M}{\partial H} \, ds + \int_0^s \frac{N}{AE} \frac{\partial N}{\partial H} \, ds = 0 \qquad (a)$$

Let M' and N' denote, respectively, the bending moment and axial compression in the arch when the hinge B is free to move horizontally and H is not acting. Then, the complete expressions for bending moment and axial compression are

$$M = M' - H(f - y) \qquad N = N' + H \cos \phi \qquad (b)$$

where f is the rise of the arch and ϕ is the angle that the tangent to the center line makes with the x axis. When expressions (b) and their derivatives with respect to H are substituted into Eq. (a), it becomes

$$-\int_0^s \frac{M' - H(f - y)}{EI} (f - y) \, ds$$
$$+\int_0^s \frac{N' + H \cos \phi}{AE} \cos \phi \, ds = 0 \qquad (c)$$

Solving for H, we obtain

$$H = \frac{\int_0^s (M'/EI)(f - y) \, ds - \int_0^s (N'/AE) \cos \phi \, ds}{\int_0^s [(f - y)^2/EI] \, ds + \int_0^s [(\cos^2 \phi)/AE] \, ds} \qquad (8.2)$$

This expression holds for a symmetrical two-hinged arch of any shape and under any condition of loading. For ordinary proportions of an arch, the

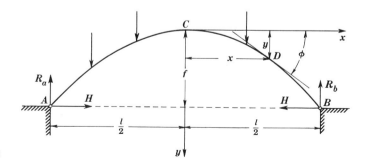

FIG. 8.3

second term in the numerator of Eq. (8.2) is usually small compared with the first and can often be neglected.

As a specific example, let us assume that the arch axis is a parabola defined by the equations

$$y = \frac{4fx^2}{l^2} \qquad \cos \phi = \frac{1}{\sqrt{1 + (8fx/l^2)^2}} \tag{d}$$

and that the cross-sectional area and moment of inertia vary according to the expressions

$$A = \frac{A_0}{\cos \phi} \qquad I = \frac{I_0}{\cos \phi} \tag{e}$$

where A_0 and I_0 denote cross-sectional area and moment of inertia at the crown C. Finally, assuming a uniformly distributed vertical load of intensity q on the arch, we have

$$M' = \frac{ql^2}{8}\left(1 - \frac{4x^2}{l^2}\right) \qquad N' = qx \sin \phi \tag{f}$$

Using expressions (d) to (f), the various integrals appearing in Eq. (8.2) can readily be evaluated, and neglecting the second integral in the numerator, we obtain, as a final result,

$$H = \frac{ql^2}{8f} \frac{1}{1 + \beta} \tag{8.2a}$$

where

$$\beta = \frac{15}{32} \frac{l}{f^3} \frac{I_0}{A_0} \tan^{-1} \frac{4f}{l} \tag{g}$$

The first factor in Eq. (8.2a) represents the thrust for a uniformly loaded three-hinged arch. We see that this must be reduced in the ratio $1/(1 + \beta)$ to obtain the thrust for a two-hinged arch.

Another example of symmetrical deformation of a two-hinged arch (Fig. 8.3) is that produced by a uniform temperature change. Let t be the increase in temperature of the arch above the temperature at which it fits freely between the fixed supports at its ends, and α the coefficient of thermal expansion of the material. Then, in the case of free expansion, the span length would increase by the amount αtl. In the actual case where the ends of the arch are restrained, a thrust H will be developed of such magnitude as to counteract the free expansion αtl. Applying the Castigliano theorem in this case, we obtain

$$\frac{\partial U}{\partial H} = \alpha tl \tag{h}$$

The left-hand side of this equation can be obtained from the previous Eq. (c)

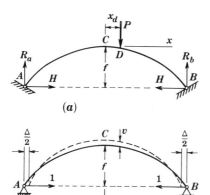

FIG. 8.4   (*b*)

simply by substituting $M' = N' = 0$. Then, solving for H, we obtain

$$H = \frac{\alpha t l}{\int_0^s [(f - y)^2/EI]\ ds + \int_0^s [(\cos^2 \phi)/AE]\ ds} \tag{8.3}$$

For the parabolic arch defined by Eqs. (*d*) and (*e*), this becomes

$$H = \frac{15 E I_0}{8 f^2 l}\ \frac{\alpha t l}{1 + \beta} \tag{8.3a}$$

For an arch of rectangular cross section, the corresponding maximum and minimum thermal stresses at the crown will be

$$\sigma_{\substack{\min \\ \max}} = -\frac{H}{A_0} \mp \frac{6Hf}{A_0 h} = -\frac{15}{8}\ \frac{Eh^2}{12f^2}\ \frac{\alpha t}{1 + \beta}\left(1 \pm \frac{6f}{h}\right) \tag{8.3b}$$

It is seen that these thermal stresses increase rapidly with the ratio h/f and may be very important for thick flat arches.

To obtain an *influence line* for the thrust H of a symmetrical two-hinged arch, we use the reciprocal theorem (see page 249). Comparing the two conditions of loading shown in Fig. 8.4*a* and *b*, we conclude that

$$Pv + H\Delta = 0$$

where v is considered positive downward. This gives

$$H = -P\frac{v}{\Delta} \tag{i}$$

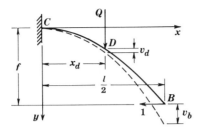

FIG. 8.5

and we see that for the construction of an influence line, we need to calculate the displacements Δ and v produced by the unit loads acting as shown in Fig. 8.4b. The displacement Δ can be obtained from Eq. (8.3) simply by substituting Δ for $\alpha t l$ and taking $H = 1$. Thus,

$$\Delta = \int_0^s \frac{(f - y)^2}{EI}\, ds + \int_0^s \frac{\cos^2 \phi}{AE}\, ds \qquad (j)$$

In calculating deflections v, we consider the right-hand half of the arch as a curved cantilever beam built in at C and acted upon by the horizontal unit force at B as shown in Fig. 8.5. Denoting by v_b and v_d the vertical deflections of points B and D, we obtain the required displacements v from the equation

$$v = v_d - v_b \qquad (k)$$

The deflection v_d will be found by using the Castigliano theorem. Applying an infinitesimal vertical force Q at D, we obtain, by differentiating the strain-energy expression with respect to this force Q,

$$v_d = \int_C^B \frac{M}{EI} \frac{\partial M}{\partial Q}\, ds + \int_C^B \frac{N}{AE} \frac{\partial N}{\partial Q}\, ds \qquad (l)$$

Now, for the portion CD of the bar, the expressions for bending moment and compressive force will be

$$M = -[1(f - y) + Q(x_d - x)] \qquad N = 1 \cos \phi - Q \sin \phi$$

If we put $Q = 0$, these same expressions hold for the portion DB of the bar. Substitution of the appropriate expressions for M and N and their derivatives with respect to Q into Eq. (l) gives, with $Q = 0$,

$$v_d = \int_C^D \frac{(f - y)(x_d - x)}{EI}\, ds - \int_C^D \frac{\cos \phi \sin \phi}{AE}\, ds \qquad (m)$$

Simply by substituting $l/2$ for x_d in this expression, we obtain v_b, and Eq. (k) finally becomes

$$v = -\int_C^B \frac{(f-y)(l/2-x)}{EI}\,ds + \int_C^D \frac{(f-y)(x_d-x)}{EI}\,ds$$
$$+ \int_D^B \frac{\cos\phi\sin\phi}{AE}\,ds \quad (n)$$

Using this equation together with Eq. (j), we can, in each particular case, calculate the ordinates v/Δ of the influence line for thrust H.

As an example, let us consider the parabolic arch defined by Eqs. (d) and (e). Then, from the previous calculations [see Eq. $(8.3a)$], we have

$$\Delta = \frac{8}{15}\frac{lf^2}{EI_0}(1+\beta)$$

Considering the second integral appearing in expression (n), we have

$$\int_C^D \frac{(f-y)(x_d-x)}{EI}\,ds = \frac{f}{EI_0}\int_0^{x_d}\left(1-\frac{4x^2}{l^2}\right)(x_d-x)\,dx$$
$$= \frac{fx_d^2}{EI_0}\left(\frac{1}{2}-\frac{x_d^2}{3l^2}\right)$$

The first integral in expression (n) can be obtained also from this simply by taking $x_d = l/2$. The third integral is usually small and can be neglected. Thus, approximately,

$$v = -\frac{5}{48}\frac{fl^2}{EI_0}+\frac{fx_d^2}{EI_0}\left(\frac{1}{2}-\frac{x_d^2}{3l^2}\right)$$

and the ordinates of the influence line are defined by the expression

$$-\frac{v}{\Delta} = \frac{15}{8(1+\beta)}\left(\frac{5}{48}\frac{l}{f}-\frac{x_d^2}{2fl}+\frac{x_d^4}{3fl^3}\right) \quad (8.4)$$

In Fig. 8.6b, this line is shown by the curve $a_1c_1b_1$. With this line, the influence lines for bending moment and for axial force at any cross section D can be constructed without difficulty. Denoting by M' the bending moment for a simply supported beam AB of span l and defining the position of D by the distances a, b, and c, we find that the bending moment at the cross section D of the arch, for any position of the moving load P, is

$$M = M' - Hc = c\left(\frac{M'}{c} - H\right)$$

It is seen that the moment M is obtained by multiplying by c the ordinates of

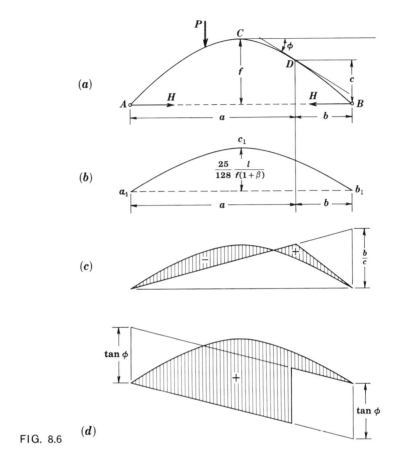

FIG. 8.6   (d)

the shaded area in Fig. 8.6c, which represents the differences of the ordinates of the M'/c influence line and the H influence line.

The axial force for any position of the moving load is

$$N = H \cos \phi - V'_d \sin \phi = \cos \phi \, (H - V'_d \tan \phi)$$

where V'_d is the shearing force at D for a simply supported beam. Hence, N is obtained by multiplying by $\cos \phi$ the ordinates of the shaded area in Fig. 8.6d, which represents the differences of the ordinates of the H influence line and the $V'_d \tan \phi$ influence line.

PROBLEMS

1   The symmetrical two-hinged circular arch shown in Fig. 8.7a has a center line of radius r and subtends a central angle 2α. The cross-sectional area A and moment

of inertia $I = Ak^2$ are both constant along the length of the arch. Using the second Castigliano theorem, develop a general expression for the decrease Δ in the chord distance AB due to thrust H acting as shown.

> *Ans.* $\Delta = (2Hr^3/EI)F(\alpha)[1 + (k^2/r^2)G(\alpha)]$, wherein
> $F(\alpha) = \alpha/2 - \frac{3}{4}\sin 2\alpha + \alpha\cos^2\alpha$,
> $G(\alpha) = (\alpha/2 + \frac{1}{4}\sin 2\alpha)/F(\alpha)$.

2 Referring again to the circular arch shown in Fig. 8.7b, determine the magnitude of the thrust H produced by a uniformly distributed vertical load of intensity q on the arch if the hinged ends A and B are restrained. Use Eq. (8.2), neglecting the second term in the numerator.

> *Ans.* $H = \dfrac{qr}{2}\dfrac{\psi(\alpha)}{F(\alpha)}\dfrac{1}{1 + (k/r)^2 G(\alpha)}$, wherein
> $\psi(\alpha) = \frac{2}{3}\sin^3\alpha + \frac{1}{2}\alpha\cos\alpha\cos 2\alpha - \frac{1}{4}\cos\alpha\sin 2\alpha$.

3 Referring again to the circular arch shown in Fig. 8.7b, determine the thrust H produced by a uniform rise in temperature t if the coefficient of thermal expansion for the arch is α_t and the hinged ends A and B are restrained.

> *Ans.* $H = \dfrac{EI\alpha_t tl}{2r^3 F(\alpha)}\dfrac{1}{1 + (k/r)^2 G(\alpha)}$.

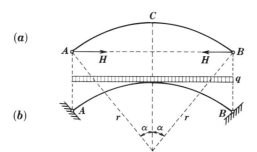

(a)

(b)

FIG. 8.7

8.3 SYMMETRICAL HINGELESS ARCHES

In general, a hingeless arch represents a structure having three redundant elements. We can consider as redundants the bending moment, shearing force, and axial force at some chosen cross section of the arch. In the case of a symmetrical arch, it is advantageous to take this cross section at the crown C. Then, if the loading on the arch is also symmetrically distributed, the shearing force at the crown vanishes, and we have to consider only two redundant quantities: the bending moment M_c and the axial force N_c at the crown as shown in Fig. 8.8a. These redundant elements will be obtained by using the

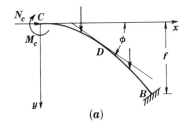
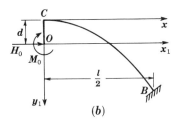

FIG. 8.8

theorem of least work; this gives the equations

$$\frac{\partial U}{\partial M_c} = 2 \int_0^s \frac{M}{EI} \frac{\partial M}{\partial M_c} \, ds = 0$$

$$\frac{\partial U}{\partial N_c} = 2 \int_0^s \frac{M}{EI} \frac{\partial M}{\partial N_c} \, ds + 2 \int_0^s \frac{N}{AE} \frac{\partial N}{\partial N_c} \, ds = 0$$

(a)

where s denotes the length of the arc CB in Fig. 8.8, that is, half the length of the full arch axis.

Denoting by M' and N' the bending moment and axial force at any cross section due to the external loading only, the total bending moment and axial force at any cross section D become

$$M = M_c + N_c y + M' \qquad N = N_c \cos \phi + N' \qquad (b)$$

Substituting these expressions and their derivatives with respect to M_c and N_c into Eqs. (a), we obtain

$$M_c \int_0^s \frac{ds}{EI} + N_c \int_0^s \frac{y \, ds}{EI} = - \int_0^s \frac{M'}{EI} \, ds$$

$$M_c \int_0^s \frac{y \, ds}{EI} + N_c \int_0^s \frac{y^2 \, ds}{EI} + N_c \int_0^s \frac{\cos^2 \phi}{AE} \, ds \qquad (c)$$

$$= - \int_0^s \frac{M'y}{EI} \, ds - \int_0^s \frac{N' \cos \phi}{AE} \, ds$$

When the dimensions of the arch and the type of external loading are known, the magnitudes of the redundant elements M_c and N_c can be calculated from these equations.

Equations (c) can be somewhat simplified if we move the origin of coordinates from the crown C to a point O as shown in Fig. 8.8b and then select the distance d so that the new ordinates $y_1 = y - d$ satisfy the condition

$$\int_0^s \frac{y_1 \, ds}{EI} = \int_0^s \frac{y - d}{EI} \, ds = 0 \qquad (d)$$

from which

$$d = \frac{\int_0^s (y \, ds/EI)}{\int_0^s (ds/EI)} \qquad (8.5)$$

The point O, defined in this way, is called the *elastic center* of the arch. If we use it as the origin, substitute $y_1 + d$ for y into Eqs. (c), and observe that $\int_0^s (y_1/EI) \, ds$ vanishes, we obtain

$$M_0 = M_c + H_0 d = - \frac{\int_0^s (M' \, ds/EI)}{\int_0^s (ds/EI)}$$

$$H_0 = N_c = - \frac{\int_0^s (M'y_1/EI) \, ds + \int_0^s [(N' \cos \phi)/AE] \, ds}{\int_0^s (y_1^2/EI) \, ds + \int_0^s [(\cos^2 \phi)/AE] \, ds} \qquad (8.6)$$

These same results can be obtained also if we imagine a rigid bracket CO attached to the cross section C of the arch and introduce, instead of M_c and N_c, the statically equivalent system of forces M_0 and H_0 acting at the end O of this bracket. Then, choosing M_0 and H_0 as the redundant quantities and proceeding as before with the theorem of least work, Eqs. (8.6) will be obtained directly. In this way, we obtain two independent equations (8.6) for the determination of the magnitudes of the redundant elements M_0 and H_0.

With the aid of the reciprocal theorem, we can see that the use of the elastic center O has a simple physical significance. Namely, the force H_0 applied at O produces no rotation of the cross section at C; conversely, the moment M_0 produces no horizontal displacement of point O.

Let us consider now the case of a symmetrical hingeless arch subjected to a uniform rise in temperature. Taking H_0 and M_0 as the redundant quantities (Fig. 8.8b), we observe that the magnitude of H_0 must be such as to counteract the horizontal displacement $\alpha t l/2$ of point C due to the rise in temperature. Also, from symmetry, it follows that there must be no rotation of the cross section at the crown C. Thus, using the second Castigliano theorem, we have

$$\frac{\partial U}{\partial M_0} = \int_0^s \frac{M}{EI} \frac{\partial M}{\partial M_0} \, ds = 0$$

$$\frac{\partial U}{\partial H_0} = \int_0^s \frac{M}{EI} \frac{\partial M}{\partial H_0} \, ds + \int_0^s \frac{N}{AE} \frac{\partial N}{\partial H_0} \, ds = \frac{\alpha t l}{2} \qquad (e)$$

where $\quad M = M_0 + H_0 y_1 \qquad N = H_0 \cos \phi \qquad (f)$

Substituting expressions (f) and their derivatives into Eqs. (e), we obtain

$M_0 = 0$ and

$$H_0 = \frac{\alpha t l/2}{\displaystyle\int_0^s (y_1{}^2 \, ds/EI) + \int_0^s [(\cos^2 \phi \, ds)/AE]} \tag{8.7}$$

From this equation, the thrust due to a uniform temperature change in any symmetrical hingeless arch can be calculated without difficulty if the dimensions of the arch and the change in temperature are given.

In the development of Eqs. (8.6), we assumed that the arch was symmetrically loaded, in which case the shearing force at the crown cross section vanishes. Let us consider now the case of antimetric loading such as that shown, for example, in Fig. 8.9a. From symmetry of the arch, we conclude that at the crown C the bending moment and the axial compression produced by the force P to the right of C are numerically equal and opposite in sign to those produced by the force P to the left of C. This means that under the simultaneous action of the two forces P, the bending moment and axial compression at the crown both vanish, and we have to consider at the cross section C only the shearing force V_0 as shown in Fig. 8.9b. For the calculation of this redundant quantity, we use the theorem of least work which gives

$$\frac{\partial U}{\partial V_0} = 2 \int_0^s \frac{M}{EI} \frac{\partial M}{\partial V_0} \, ds + 2 \int_0^s \frac{N}{AE} \frac{\partial N}{\partial V_0} \, ds = 0 \tag{g}$$

Since the strain energy is the same for both halves of the arch, we have to make the integration only from C to B and double the result as shown. Observing from Fig. 8.9b that

$$M = V_0 x_1 + M' \qquad N = -V_0 \sin \phi + N' \tag{h}$$

and substituting into Eq. (g), we obtain

$$\int_0^s \frac{V_0 x_1 + M'}{EI} x_1 \, ds - \int_0^s \frac{-V_0 \sin \phi + N'}{AE} \sin \phi \, ds = 0$$

from which

$$V_0 = \frac{-\displaystyle\int_0^s (M' x_1/EI) \, ds + \int_0^s [(N' \sin \phi)/AE] \, ds}{\displaystyle\int_0^s (x_1{}^2/EI) \, ds + \int_0^s [(\sin^2 \phi)/AE] \, ds} \tag{8.8}$$

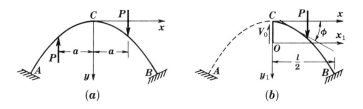

FIG. 8.9   (a)   (b)

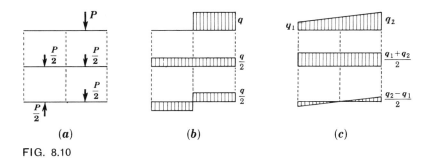

FIG. 8.10

From this equation, the shearing force V_0 can be calculated in each particular case of antimetric loading provided the dimensions of the arch are given.

Having solutions for symmetric and antimetric loadings, the general case of loading can be treated by splitting the load into two parts, symmetric and antimetric, as illustrated in Fig. 8.10 for several particular cases. Some applications of this method of treating the general case of loading will be shown later.

Let us consider now the construction of influence lines for symmetrical hingeless arches, for which purpose we use the reciprocal theorem. To construct the influence line for the thrust H_0, we have to compare the actual condition of loading shown in Fig. 8.11a with the fictitious loading shown in Fig. 8.11b. In the first case, we have the vertical load P at the point D and the unknown redundant forces M_0, H_0, and V_0 at the crown.[1] In the second case, the load P and the redundant quantities M_0 and V_0 are removed, and instead of H_0, two opposite unit forces are applied. Owing to the specific choice of point O [see Eq. (8.5)], the unit forces will not produce any rotation of cross sections C. These cross sections will move apart only by the amount $2u_0$ without any relative rotation or relative sliding. Since the work of the redundant moment M_0 and of the redundant shearing force V_0 on the corresponding displacements produced by the unit forces in Fig. 8.11b vanishes, the reciprocal theorem gives

$$H_0 2u_0 + P v_d = 0$$

and we obtain

$$H_0 = -P \frac{v_d}{2u_0} \qquad (8.9)$$

The displacements u_0 and v_d due to the unit loads acting as shown in Fig. 8.11b

[1] To show these forces more clearly, a small distance between the extension bars OC is shown in Fig. 8.11a.

can be calculated by using Castigliano's second theorem, giving

$$u_0 = \int_C^B \frac{y_1^2}{EI}\, ds + \int_C^B \frac{\cos^2 \phi}{AE}\, ds$$

$$v_d = -\int_D^B \frac{y_1(x_1 - x_d)}{EI}\, ds + \int_D^B \frac{\cos \phi \sin \phi}{AE}\, ds$$

(8.9a)

In any particular case, when the shape and dimensions of the arch are given, the displacements (8.9a) can be evaluated and substituted into Eq. (8.9) to obtain the influence coefficients for the redundant quantity H_0.

In a similar manner, influence lines for the redundant moment M_0 and the redundant shearing force V_0 can be obtained. In the case of M_0, we compare

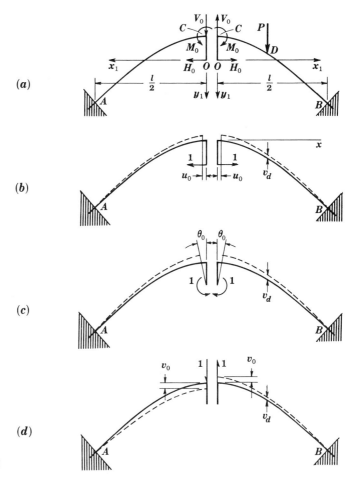

FIG. 8.11

the actual loading condition (Fig. 8.11a) with the fictitious case shown in Fig. 8.11c. In this latter case, the unit moments do not produce any relative displacements of the points O but only rotate the cross sections C, one with respect to the other, by the angle $2\theta_0$ as shown. Owing to this fact the work of actual forces H_0 and V_0 in Fig. 8.11a on the corresponding displacements of the fictitious case in Fig. 8.11c vanishes, whereas the work of M_0 is $M_0(2\theta_0)$. At the same time, in the actual case of a continuous arch, there is no relative displacement corresponding to the unit moments of the fictitious case, and the work of these moments vanishes. The reciprocal theorem then gives

$$M_0 2\theta_0 + P v_d = 0$$

and we obtain

$$M_0 = -P \frac{v_d}{2\theta_0} \tag{8.10}$$

It is seen that the required ordinates of the influence line for M_0 will be obtained as soon as the displacements v_d and θ_0 produced by the fictitious loading in Fig. 8.11c have been calculated. For this purpose, we again use the second Castigliano theorem and obtain

$$\theta_0 = \int_C^B \frac{ds}{EI}$$

$$v_d = -\int_D^B \frac{x_1 - x_d}{EI} \, ds \tag{8.10a}$$

To obtain the influence line for V_0, we have to compare the actual loading condition (Fig. 8.11a) with the fictitious case shown in Fig. 8.11d. Observing that in the later case only relative sliding $2v_0$ of the cross sections at the crown is produced and that no relative rotation or separation occurs, we obtain from the reciprocal theorem the equation

$$- V_0 2v_0 + P v_d = 0$$

from which

$$V_0 = P \frac{v_d}{2v_0} \tag{8.11}$$

For calculating the displacements v_d and v_0 produced by the unit forces in Fig. 8.11d, we again use the Castigliano theorem and obtain

$$v_0 = -\int_C^B \frac{x_1^2}{EI} \, ds - \int_C^B \frac{\sin^2 \phi}{AE} \, ds$$

$$v_d = -\int_D^B \frac{x_1(x_1 - x_d)}{EI} \, ds - \int_D^B \frac{\sin^2 \phi}{AE} \, ds \tag{8.11a}$$

It is seen that, in all three cases, the ordinates of the required influence lines are proportional to the vertical deflections v_d produced in the arch by the unit loads applied as shown in Fig. 8.11b to d.

As a specific example, let us now consider influence lines for a hingeless parabolic arch the central axis of which is defined by the equation

$$y = \frac{4fx^2}{l^2} \tag{i}$$

and the cross-sectional variation by the expressions

$$A = \frac{A_0}{\cos \phi} \qquad I = \frac{I_0}{\cos \phi} \tag{j}$$

Beginning with Eq. (8.5), we find that for such an arch the elastic center is located by the distance

$$d = \frac{\int_0^{l/2} y \, dx}{\int_0^{l/2} dx} = \frac{f}{3} \tag{8.5a}$$

With this elastic center as an origin of coordinates x_1, y_1, we have $x_1 = x$ and $y_1 = y - d$.

For the H_0 influence line, we use Eq. (8.9), in which the values of u_0 and v_d are given by Eqs. (8.9a). For a first approximation to H_0, we may neglect the second terms containing ϕ in Eqs. (8.9a) and, with this simplification, obtain

$$u_0 = \int_0^{l/2} \frac{y_1^2 \, dx_1}{EI_0} = \frac{2f^2l}{45EI_0}$$

$$v_d = - \int_0^{l/2} \frac{y_1(x_1 - x_d) \, dx_1}{EI_0} = - \frac{fl^2}{48EI_0} \left(1 - \frac{4x_d^2}{l^2} \right)^2 \tag{8.9b}$$

Substituting these values into Eq. (8.9), we find

$$H_0 = \frac{15Pl}{64f} \left(1 - \frac{4x_d^2}{l^2} \right)^2 \tag{8.9c}$$

For the M_0 influence line, we use Eqs. (8.10) and (8.10a), the later becoming

$$\theta_0 = \int_0^{l/2} \frac{dx_1}{EI_0} = \frac{l}{2EI_0}$$

$$v_d = - \int_{x_d}^{l/2} \frac{(x_1 - x_d) \, dx_1}{EI_0} = - \frac{1}{2EI_0} \left(\frac{l}{2} - x_d \right)^2 \tag{8.10b}$$

When these values are substituted into Eq. (8.10), we obtain

$$M_0 = \frac{P}{2l} \left(\frac{l}{2} - x_d \right)^2 \tag{8.10c}$$

Having this expression for M_0, we find the bending moment M_c at the crown C from the equation

$$M_c = M_0 - H_0 d \tag{k}$$

For the V_0 influence line, Eqs. (8.11a), neglecting again the second terms containing ϕ, become

$$v_0 = -\int_0^{l/2} \frac{x_1^2 \, dx_1}{EI_0} = -\frac{l^3}{24EI_0}$$

$$v_d = -\int_{x_d}^{l/2} \frac{x_1(x_1 - x_d) \, dx_1}{EI_0} = -\frac{1}{EI_0}\left(\frac{l^3}{24} + \frac{x_d^3}{6} - \frac{l^2 x_d}{8}\right) \tag{8.11b}$$

and Eq. (8.11) then gives

$$V_0 = \frac{P}{2}\left(1 + \frac{4x_d^3}{l^3} - \frac{3x_d}{l}\right) \tag{8.11c}$$

The influence lines for H_0, M_0, V_0, plotted from Eqs. (8.9c), (8.10c), and (8.11c), are shown in Fig. 8.12a, b, and c, respectively. Also shown in Fig. 8.12d is the influence diagram for bending moment M_c at the crown C as defined by Eq. (k).

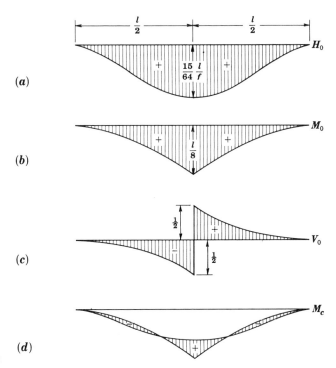

(a)

(b)

(c)

(d)

FIG. 8.12

Comparison of arches of various shapes indicates that considerable deviation from the shape of the arch defined by Eqs. (*i*) and (*j*) produces only a small effect on the ordinates of influence lines.   This means that the influence lines derived for parabolic arches can be used in an approximate analysis of arches of other shapes.   The use of these lines, however, in the calculation of stresses produced by dead load or temperature change may result in errors of considerable magnitude.   The reason for these errors is clearly seen from the influence line in Fig. 8.12*d*.   If we assume, for example, that a dead load ql is uniformly distributed along the span, the bending moment M_c at the crown is obtained by multiplying by q the algebraic sum of the three shaded areas of the influence diagram.   It is evident that the accuracy with which this sum is obtained will be much lower than the accuracy with which the ordinates of the individual H_0 and M_0 influence lines are known.

PROBLEMS

1   Using Eq. (8.7), develop a general formula for thrust H_t in the hingeless parabolic arch defined by Eqs. (*i*) and (*j*) due to a uniform rise t in temperature. The coefficient of thermal expansion for the material is α, and $\sqrt{I_0/A_0} = k_0$ is the radius of gyration of the cross section at the crown.

$$Ans.\quad H_t = \frac{45EI_0\alpha t}{4f^2[1 + \tfrac{4\,5}{1\,6}(l/f)(k^2/f^2)\,\tan^{-1}(4f/l)]}.$$

2   Using the influence lines shown in Fig. 8.12 for the hingeless parabolic arch defined by Eqs. (*i*) and (*j*), calculate the bending moment M_c produced at the crown C by the dead weight of an earth fill extending over the entire span and level with the crown of the arch.   Assume that the earth fill weighs w lb/ft^3 and that the arch rib is 1 ft wide.

$$Ans.\quad M_c = -wl^2f/560.$$

3   Find the distance d defining the position of the elastic center O of the hingeless circular arch shown in Fig. 8.13.   Assume that the cross-sectional area A and moment of inertia I of the rib are constant along its length.

$$Ans.\quad d = (r/\alpha)(\alpha - \sin \alpha).$$

4   Using the first of Eqs. (8.6) and referring to the hingeless circular arch in Fig. 8.13,

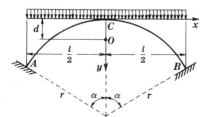

FIG. 8.13

calculate the redundant moment M_0 due to a uniform load of intensity q extending over the full span as shown.

$$Ans. \quad M_0 = \frac{ql^2}{16\alpha \sin^2 \alpha} (\alpha - \sin \alpha \cos \alpha).$$

5 Using Eq. (8.7) and referring to the arch in Fig. 8.13, calculate the magnitude of the thrust H_0 produced by a uniform rise in temperature of $t°$. The coefficient of thermal expansion is α_t, and the radius of gyration of the cross section is $\sqrt{I/A} = k$.

$$Ans. \quad H_0 = F(\alpha)(EI\alpha_t t/r^2), \text{ where } F(\alpha) =$$

$$\frac{2\alpha \sin \alpha}{\alpha^2 + \alpha \sin \alpha \cos \alpha - 2 \sin^2 \alpha + (k^2/r^2)(\alpha^2 + \alpha \sin \alpha \cos \alpha)}.$$

8.4 NUMERICAL CALCULATION OF REDUNDANT ELEMENTS

The calculation of redundant quantities in arches requires, as we have seen, the evaluation of various integrals such as those appearing in Eqs. (8.5), (8.6), (8.7), etc. In the case of parabolic and circular arches like those discussed in the two preceding articles, such integrals can be evaluated in an exact manner. However, we sometimes have more complicated curves, or curves for which no analytic expression exists, and only a set of ordinates is given numerically to define the shape of the arch axis. In all such cases, recourse must be had to numerical methods of evaluating the integrals. For this purpose, the arch axis will be divided into a finite number of segments and the integration replaced by a summation. In using this numerical method of approximate integration, there arises the question regarding the number of subdivisions that must be used in order to obtain the desired accuracy in the result. This question can best be answered and the accuracy of calculations demonstrated with particular examples. To show this, we select an example the rigorous solution of which can be found; then, the error of the approximate calculations can be readily seen.

Let us take a parabolic arch (Fig. 8.8) for which

$$\frac{f}{l} = \frac{1}{8} \qquad A = \frac{A_0}{\cos \phi} \qquad I = \frac{I_0}{\cos^3 \phi} \qquad (a)$$

and calculate the thrust H_0 produced by a uniform rise in temperature. The position of the elastic center is determined from Eq. (8.5), which gives

$$d = \frac{\int_0^{l/2} y \cos^2 \phi \, dx}{\int_0^{l/2} \cos^2 \phi \, dx} = \frac{l[1 - (l/4f) \tan^{-1} (4f/l)]}{4 \tan^{-1} (4f/l)} \qquad (b)$$

The calculation of H_0 now requires the evaluation of the two integrals in the

TABLE 8.1   DATA FOR THE PARABOLIC ARCH
GIVEN BY EQS. (a)

$\dfrac{x}{l}$	$\dfrac{y_1}{l}$	$\dfrac{y_1{}^2}{l^2}$	$\cos^2 \phi$	$\dfrac{y_1{}^2 \cos^2 \phi}{l^2}$	$\sin^2 \phi$
0	-0.03920	0.001537	1	0.001537	0
$\frac{1}{16}$	-0.03725	0.001388	$\frac{256}{257}$	0.001383	$\frac{1}{257}$
$\frac{1}{8}$	-0.03138	0.000984	$\frac{64}{65}$	0.000969	$\frac{1}{65}$
$\frac{3}{16}$	-0.02162	0.000467	$\frac{256}{265}$	0.000452	$\frac{9}{265}$
$\frac{1}{4}$	-0.00795	0.000063	$\frac{16}{17}$	0.000059	$\frac{1}{17}$
$\frac{5}{16}$	$+0.00963$	0.000093	$\frac{256}{281}$	0.000085	$\frac{25}{281}$
$\frac{3}{8}$	$+0.03111$	0.000968	$\frac{64}{73}$	0.000849	$\frac{9}{73}$
$\frac{7}{16}$	$+0.05650$	0.003192	$\frac{256}{305}$	0.002679	$\frac{49}{305}$
$\frac{1}{2}$	$+0.08580$	0.007362	$\frac{4}{5}$	0.005890	$\frac{1}{5}$

denominator of Eq. (8.7).   The first of these integrals is

$$\int_0^s \frac{y_1{}^2 \, ds}{EI} = \frac{1}{EI_0} \int_0^{l/2} y_1{}^2 \cos^2 \phi \, dx$$

$$= \frac{l^3}{32EI_0} \left\{ \frac{1}{3} + \frac{l}{4f} \left[\frac{l}{4f} - \frac{1}{\tan^{-1}(4f/l)} \right] \right\} \quad (c)$$

and the second is

$$\int_0^s \frac{\cos^2 \phi \, ds}{AE} = \frac{1}{A_0 E} \int_0^{l/2} \cos^2 \phi \, dx = \frac{l^2}{8A_0 Ef} \tan^{-1} \frac{4f}{l} \quad (d)$$

With these results, Eq. (8.7) gives

$$H_0 = m \frac{EI_0 \alpha t}{l^2} \quad (e)$$

where

$$m = \cfrac{16}{\dfrac{1}{3} + \dfrac{l}{4f} \left[\dfrac{l}{4f} - \dfrac{1}{\tan^{-1}(4f/l)} \right] + \dfrac{4k^2}{fl} \tan^{-1} \dfrac{4f}{l}} \quad (f)$$

$k = \sqrt{I_0/A_0}$ being the radius of gyration of the cross section.

We shall now repeat the analysis by numerical integration.   For this purpose, we divide the length of the half span into eight equal parts and calculate for each subdivision or segment the quantities given in Table 8.1 by using for a parabola the known equations

$$y_1 = \frac{4fx^2}{l^2} - d \qquad \cos^2 \phi = \frac{1}{1 + 64f^2x^2/l^4}$$

Now applying Simpson's rule to the integral (c), we obtain

$$\frac{1}{EI_0} \int_0^{l/2} y_1^2 \cos^2 \phi \, dx = \frac{l^3}{16EI_0} \times \frac{1}{3} [0.001537 + 4(0.001383$$

$$+ 0.000452 + 0.000085 + 0.002679) + 2(0.000969$$

$$+ 0.000059 + 0.000849) + 0.005890] = 0.004929 \frac{l^3}{8EI_0}$$

Proceeding in the same manner with the integral (d) and assuming a rectangular cross section, we obtain

$$\frac{1}{A_0 E} \int_0^{l/2} \cos^2 \phi \, dx = \frac{l}{2A_0 E} 0.9273 = \frac{l h_0^2}{24EI_0} 0.9273$$

Substituting these calculated values of the integrals into Eq. (8.7), we obtain

$$\frac{H_0 l^3}{8EI_0} \left(0.004929 + \frac{1}{3} \frac{h_0^2}{l^2} 0.9273 \right) = \frac{\alpha t l}{2} \tag{g}$$

The second term in the parentheses represents the influence of the longitudinal force N on the value of H_0. Let us consider the case of a very thick arch and assume $h_0/l = \frac{1}{9}$. Then, Eq. (g) gives

$$\frac{H_0 l^3}{8EI_0} (0.004929 + 0.003816) = \frac{\alpha t l}{2}$$

and we obtain

$$H_0 = 457.4 \frac{\alpha t E I_0}{l^2} \tag{h}$$

Taking $h_0/l = \frac{1}{27}$, we find

$$H_0 = 747.3 \frac{\alpha t E I_0}{l^2} \tag{i}$$

To four significant figures, these results coincide exactly with the values given by Eqs. (e) and (f). This indicates that the subdivision of the half span into eight parts and the use of Simpson's rule give a very high degree of accuracy. If we divide the half span into only four parts, Simpson's rule gives H_0 for the foregoing example with an error of about 0.2 percent. This shows that it is not necessary to divide the arch into many parts to obtain good accuracy by numerical integration.

In applying Simpson's rule, we have to subdivide the center line of an arch into equal parts. Sometimes it is simpler to have unequal subdivisions, and in such case Simpson's rule cannot be used. Then we replace the integrations by simple summations. We calculate the values of the quantities under the integral signs for the center of each segment and sum up these values. To show this kind of calculation, let us determine the thrust produced by a uniform

temperature change in the arch shown in Fig. 8.14a.   We begin with a calculation of the distance d locating the elastic center of the arch.   For this purpose,
we subdivide the arch into eight segments with centers 1, 2, 3, . . . as shown
in Fig. 8.14a.   The designation of these segments, their lengths Δs, and the
cross-sectional dimensions at the mid-points are given in the first four columns
of Table 8.2.   In the fifth column are given the moments of inertia of the

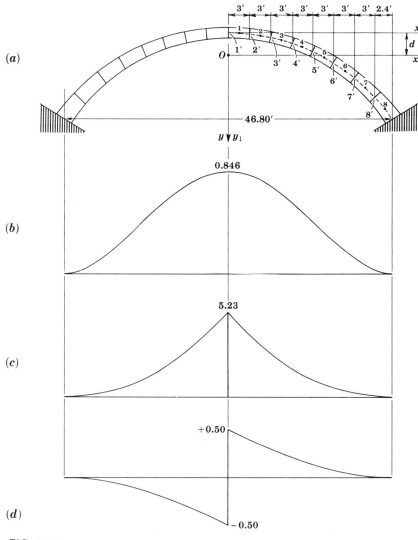

FIG. 8.14

TABLE 8.2   DATA FOR ARCH IN FIG. 8.14

Segment	Δs, ft	b, ft	h, ft	I, ft^4	$\dfrac{\Delta s}{I}$, ft^{-3}	y, ft	$\dfrac{\Delta s\,y}{I}$, ft^{-2}	y_1, ft	$\dfrac{\Delta s\,y_1{}^2}{I}$, ft^{-1}	$\dfrac{\Delta s}{A}$	$\dfrac{\Delta s}{A}\cos^2\phi$
(1)	(2)	(3)	(4)	(5)	(6)	(7)	(8)	(9)	(10)	(11)	(12)
1	3.00	12	1.800	5.832	0.5144	0.045	0.0231	−3.284	5.548	0.139	0.138
2	3.06	12	1.830	6.132	0.4990	0.375	0.1871	−2.954	4.355	0.139	0.131
3	3.15	12	1.860	6.431	0.4898	1.050	0.5142	−2.279	2.544	0.141	0.123
4	3.27	12	1.945	7.241	0.4516	2.130	0.9618	−1.199	0.649	0.141	0.109
5	3.51	12	2.040	8.489	0.4135	3.720	1.5381	+0.391	0.063	0.143	0.097
6	3.93	12	2.190	10.506	0.3741	5.895	2.2052	+2.566	2.463	0.150	0.087
7	4.56	12	2.415	14.086	0.3237	8.835	2.8602	+5.506	9.814	0.157	0.078
8	4.20	12	2.700	19.683	0.2134	12.315	2.6277	+8.986	17.229	0.130	0.055
Σ					3.2795		10.9174		42.665		0.818

middle cross sections, and in the sixth column the quantities $\Delta s/I$ at the centers of the segments. The summation of this column gives the approximate value of the denominator in Eq. (8.5) multiplied by E. The seventh column gives the ordinates of the center points 1, 2, 3, . . . , and the eighth column gives the moments of the quantities $\Delta s/I$ with respect to the x axis. The summation of this column gives the approximate value of the numerator in Eq. (8.5) multiplied by E. The required distance d locating the elastic center then becomes

$$d = \frac{10.9174}{3.2795} = 3.329 \text{ ft} \tag{j}$$

In calculating the required thrust, we now use Eq. (8.7), which gives

$$H_0 = \frac{\alpha t l E/2}{\Sigma(y_1{}^2\,\Delta s/I) + \Sigma(\Delta s\,\cos^2\phi/A)} \tag{k}$$

The summations in the denominator of this equation are given in columns 10 and 12 of Table 8.2. Assuming now, for example, $\alpha = 6(10^{-6})$ (in./in.)/°F, $t = 25$°F, and $E = 432(10^6)$ lb/ft^2, we obtain

$$H_0 = 34,870 \text{ lb}$$

This is the required thrust produced by the temperature change.

The numerical calculation of influence coefficients for redundant quantities in an arch may be made in a manner similar to that used above for the calculation of thrust due to temperature change. Referring to Fig. 8.11 and using Eq. (8.9) together with Eqs. (8.9a), we see that the influence coefficient for

H_0, for example, becomes

$$\xi_0 = \frac{\sum\limits_{D}^{B} (x_1 - x_d)\, y_1 \, \Delta s/I}{2 \sum\limits_{C}^{B} y_1{}^2 \, \Delta s/I} \tag{l}$$

if we neglect the second term in each of Eqs. (8.9a) and replace the integrals by simple summations. We see that the denominator of this expression has already been calculated in Table 8.2. We have now to consider the numerical calculation of the numerator for each point D along the arch axis at which we want an influence coefficient. This numerator is seen to represent the sum of statical moments of the quantities $y_1 \, \Delta s/I$ between D and B, taken with respect to a vertical axis through point D for which the influence coefficient is being calculated. For the subdivisions of the arch axis shown in Fig. 8.14a, values of $y_1 \, \Delta s/I$ are shown in column 3 of Table 8.3, and the cumulative summation of statical moments with respect to the division points $8'$, $7'$, $6'$, . . . are computed and recorded in column 6 of the table. Corresponding values of the influence coefficients computed from Eq. (l) are recorded in column 9, the value of $\Sigma y_1{}^2 \, \Delta s/I$ being taken from Table 8.2.

From Eqs. (8.10) and (8.10a), the influence coefficient for the moment M_0 becomes

$$\zeta_0 = \frac{\sum\limits_{D}^{B} (x_1 - x_d)\, \Delta s/I}{\sum\limits_{C}^{B} \Delta s/I} \tag{m}$$

Likewise, from Eqs. (8.11) and (8.11a), the influence coefficients for shearing force V_0 become

$$\eta_0 = \frac{\sum\limits_{D}^{B} (x_1 - x_d)\, x_1 \, \Delta s/I}{\sum\limits_{C}^{B} x_1{}^2 \, \Delta s/I} \tag{n}$$

if we neglect the second term in each of Eqs. (8.11a) as we did before. Values of the numerators of expressions (m) and (n) for each position of the moving load are recorded in columns 5 and 7 of Table 8.3, and the corresponding influence coefficients in columns 8 and 10. Influence lines for H_0, M_0, and V_0, plotted from the data in Table 8.3, are shown in Fig. 8.14b, c, and d, respectively. If we compare the ordinates of these influence lines with those shown

TABLE 8.3 DATA FOR ARCH IN FIG. 8.14

Point	$\dfrac{\Delta s}{l}$, ft^{-3}	$y_1\dfrac{\Delta s}{l}$, ft^{-2}	$x_1\dfrac{\Delta s}{l}$, ft^{-2}	$\dfrac{\Sigma(x_1-x_d)}{\dfrac{\Delta s}{l}}$	$\dfrac{\Sigma(x_1-x_d)}{y_1\dfrac{\Delta s}{l}}$	$\dfrac{\Sigma(x_1-x_d)}{x_1\dfrac{\Delta s}{l}}$	ζ_0	ξ_0	η_0	$x_1{}^2\dfrac{\Delta s}{l}$
(1)	(2)	(3)	(4)	(5)	(6)	(7)	(8)	(9)	(10)	(11)
8'	0.2134	1.917	4.737	0.26	2.30	5.7	0.039	0.027	0.006	105.2
7'	0.3237	1.782	6.312	1.38	10.72	29.3	0.211	0.126	0.030	123.1
6'	0.3741	0.960	6.173	3.55	23.26	71.8	0.543	0.273	0.073	101.8
5'	0.4135	0.162	5.582	6.91	37.48	131.8	1.055	0.440	0.133	75.4
4'	0.4516	−0.541	4.742	11.56	51.13	207.3	1.765	0.600	0.210	49.8
3'	0.4898	−1.116	3.674	17.62	62.30	295.5	2.691	0.731	0.299	27.5
2'	0.4990	−1.474	2.246	25.17	69.58	392.5	3.843	0.816	0.397	10.1
1'	0.5144	−1.689	0.772	34.24	72.12	494.1	5.228	0.846	0.500	1.2
Σ										494.1

in Fig. 8.12 for a parabolic arch, we see that they agree quite closely. This indicates that the influence lines are not particularly sensitive to small variations in the shape of the arch rib.

PROBLEMS

1   Using the basic differential equation (1.3) (see page 34), develop an analytic expression for the shape of the arch axis CA in Fig. 8.15 which will be the funicular curve for the load diagram $AacC$, q_c and q_a being the intensity of load at the crown C and the abutment A, respectively. The span of the arch is l and the rise is f.

    Ans. $f - y = f(\alpha - \cosh kz)/(\alpha - 1)$, where $\alpha = q_a/q_c$, $k = \cosh^{-1}\alpha = \ln(\alpha + \sqrt{\alpha^2 - 1}$, $z = 2x/l$.

2   A symmetrical earth-filled spandrel arch is to have a span $l = 60$ ft and a rise $f = 10$ ft. Earth weighs 100 lb/ft³, and the depth of fill at the crown is to be 3 ft; so the intensities of load at C and A are $q_c = 300$ lb/ft and $q_a = 1,300$ lb/ft. Using the answer to Prob. 1, calculate the ordinates y of the arch axis for the following values of x (in feet): 2.5, 7.5, 12.5, 17.5, 22.5, 27.5.

    Ans. In feet: 0.048, 0.442, 1.282, 2.674, 4.800, 7.936.

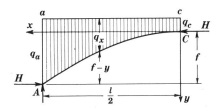

FIG. 8.15

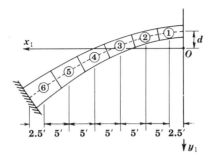

x_1

d

O

2.5' 5' 5' 5' 5' 5' 2.5'

FIG. 8.16

y_1

3   If we divide half the arch described in the preceding problem into six segments as shown in Fig. 8.16, the moments of inertia in units of ft^4 at the mid-points of the segments are as follows: $I_1 = 0.300$, $I_2 = 0.370$, $I_3 = 0.430$, $I_4 = 0.620$, $I_5 = 1.030$, $I_6 = 1.600$. Using these data together with those given in the preceding problem, calculate the distance d defining the location of the elastic center of the arch.

  Ans. $d = 1.69$ ft.

4   Using the data from the preceding problems, calculate the thrust H produced in the symmetrical hingeless arch of Fig. 8.16 due to a rise in temperature $t = 40°F$ if the coefficient of thermal expansion for concrete is $\alpha_t = 6(10^{-6})$ (in./in.)/°F and the modulus of elasticity is $E = 3(10^6)$ psi.

  Ans. $H = 11.1$ kips.

5   Construct influence lines for the redundant quantities H_0, M_0, and V_0 of the symmetrical hingeless arch in Fig. 8.16.

8.5 FUNICULAR CURVE AS THE CENTER LINE OF AN ARCH

It is advantageous, in the case of a three-hinged arch supporting a distributed permanent load, to make the center line of the arch coincide with the funicular curve for that load. If this condition is fulfilled, the resultant force on each cross section of the arch is tangent to the center line, producing only uniformly distributed compressive stresses (see page 30). In the case of a hingeless arch, the internal forces depend on the deformation of the arch, and we cannot entirely eliminate the bending stresses. But their magnitudes can be reduced by a proper selection of the shape of the center line. It is common practice to take as a first approximation for the center line of a hingeless arch the funicular curve constructed as for a three-hinged arch, having hinges at the centroids of the crown and abutment cross sections. Let H denote the thrust at the crown of such a three-hinged arch. Then the thrust in the corresponding hingeless arch will be smaller than H by a certain amount H' that can be readily calculated considering the deformation of the arch. Let CB represent one-half the hingeless arch (Fig. 8.17a), with the given load acting on it.   If the thrust H is applied at the centroid of the cross section C, the resultant force acting on any cross section D produced by H and the load on the portion CD of the arch will be tangent to the center line.   Assuming the load vertical, the magnitude of the axial force will be

$$N = \frac{H}{\cos \phi} \qquad (a)$$

The compression of an element ds of the center line, produced by this force, is

$$\frac{H \, ds}{AE \cos \phi}$$

Summing up the horizontal projections of such compressions, we find that the horizontal displacement at the cross section C is

$$u_c = \int_0^s \frac{H \, ds}{AE} \qquad (b)$$

where s is the length of the arc CB.   In the actual symmetrically loaded hingeless arch, there will be no lateral or rotational displacement of the cross section C.   These conditions will be satisfied if to the forces considered in Fig. 8.17a we add the horizontal force H' (Fig. 8.17b) applied at the elastic center O and of such magnitude as to eliminate the displacement (b).   This

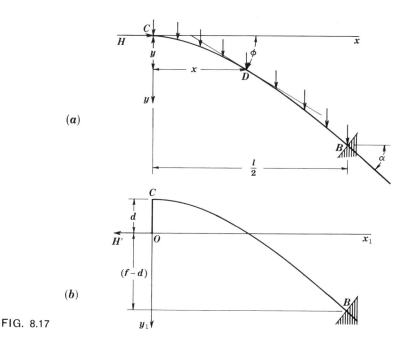

FIG. 8.17

requires [see Eqs. (8.9a)] that

$$H' \left(\int_0^s \frac{y_1^2 \, ds}{EI} + \int_0^s \frac{\cos^2 \phi \, ds}{AE} \right) = \int_0^s \frac{H \, ds}{AE}$$

Hence, $H' = H \dfrac{\displaystyle\int_0^s (ds/AE)}{\displaystyle\int_0^s (y_1^2 \, ds/EI) + \int_0^s (\cos^2 \phi \, ds/AE)}$ (8.12)

Since the combined action of the forces shown in Fig. 8.17a and b satisfies the above-mentioned conditions for the symmetrically loaded hingeless arch, we conclude that the two forces H and H' together represent a system statically equivalent to the internal forces acting on the cross section C of the arch. This system can be reduced to a longitudinal force and a bending moment defined by the equations

$$N_c = H - H' \qquad M_c = H'd \tag{8.13a}$$

The axial force and the bending moment at the support B will then be found from statics by the equations

$$N_b = \frac{H}{\cos \alpha} - H' \cos \alpha \qquad M_b = -H'(f - d) \tag{8.13b}$$

It is seen that an analysis of a symmetrical and symmetrically loaded hingeless arch the center line of which coincides with the funicular curve reduces to calculation of the negative thrust H' defined by Eq. (8.12).

Let us apply this general discussion to a particular case and consider, as an example, a parabolic arch of rectangular cross section having

$$A = \frac{A_0}{\cos \phi} \qquad I = \frac{I_0}{\cos^3 \phi} \tag{c}$$

In this case

$$\int_0^s \frac{ds}{AE} = \frac{1}{A_0 E} \int_0^{l/2} dx = \frac{l}{2A_0 E} \tag{d}$$

The denominator of expression (8.12) has already been calculated [see Eqs. (c) and (d), page 352] and is equal to

$$\frac{l^3}{2EI_0 m} \tag{e}$$

where m, as defined by Eq. (f), page 352, is a numerical factor depending on the proportions of the arch. For various proportions of the arch, values of this factor are given in column 3 of Table 8.4.

TABLE 8.4

$\dfrac{f}{l}$	$\dfrac{h}{l}$	m	(m)	$\%$	$\dfrac{H'}{H}$	$\dfrac{\delta_0}{h_0}$	$\dfrac{\delta_1}{h_1}$
(1)	(2)	(3)	(4)	(5)	(6)	(7)	(8)
$\dfrac{1}{12}$	$\dfrac{1}{6}$	355.0	327.2	8.5	0.7567	0.494	0.729
	$\dfrac{1}{12}$	876.1	832.5	5.2	0.4817	0.296	0.521
	$\dfrac{1}{24}$	1,384.0	1,356.0	2.1	0.1962	0.156	0.292
$\dfrac{1}{10}$	$\dfrac{1}{8}$	484.5	444.1	9.2	0.5778	0.341	0.546
	$\dfrac{1}{16}$	881.2	846.1	4.1	0.2753	0.190	0.342
	$\dfrac{1}{24}$	1,039.0	1,016.0	2.3	0.1470	0.124	0.239
$\dfrac{1}{8}$	$\dfrac{1}{9}$	457.4	415.6	9.9	0.4272	0.254	0.408
	$\dfrac{1}{18}$	679.9	655.4	3.7	0.1686	0.139	0.244
	$\dfrac{1}{27}$	747.3	733.6	1.9	0.0839	0.094	0.169
$\dfrac{1}{6}$	$\dfrac{1}{12}$	395.2	366.4	7.9	0.2118	0.152	0.246
	$\dfrac{1}{24}$	465.8	455.2	2.3	0.0659	0.080	0.137
	$\dfrac{1}{36}$	481.6	476.6	1.0	0.0307	0.054	0.093
$\dfrac{1}{4}$	$\dfrac{1}{16}$	249.3	237.5	5.0	0.0773	0.081	0.122
	$\dfrac{1}{32}$	261.8	258.4	1.3	0.0210	0.042	0.064
	$\dfrac{1}{48}$	264.2	262.7	0.6	0.0095	0.028	0.043

Substituting (d) and (e) into expression (8.12), we obtain

$$H' = mH \frac{I_0}{A_0 l^2} \tag{8.14}$$

Observing that for parabolic three-hinged arches (see page 36)

$$H = \frac{q l^2}{8f}$$

and using for m the values from Table 8.4, we can readily calculate the value of H'. The values of the ratio H'/H for arches of various proportions are given[1] in column 6 of Table 8.4. It is seen that the thrust of a hingeless arch may differ considerably from that of the corresponding three-hinged arch only in the cases of flat and very thick arches.

From Eqs. (8.13a), we see that the internal forces at the crown can be represented by the compressive force $N_c = H - H'$ applied at the distance δ_0 above the centroid where

$$\delta_0 = \frac{M_c}{N_c} = \frac{H'd}{H - H'} \tag{f}$$

---

[1] The values given in the table were obtained by more elaborate calculations, taking into account the effects of curvature of the arch axis and shearing forces. These calculations showed that the simplified Eq. (8.12) is accurate enough in all practical applications.

Using Eqs. (8.13b) in the same manner, we find that at the abutments the point of application of the axial force moves from the centroid downward by the amount

$$\delta_1 = \frac{-M_b}{N_b} = \frac{H'(f - d) \cos \alpha}{H - H' \cos^2 \alpha} \tag{g}$$

In the seventh and eighth columns of Table 8.4 are given the ratios of these displacements to the depths h_0 and h_1 of the corresponding cross sections.

We know that in the case of a rectangular cross section an eccentrically applied compressive force does not produce tensile stresses if the point of application is within the middle third of the depth of the cross section. The ratios δ_0/h_0 and δ_1/h_1 given in Table 8.4 indicate that it is likely that tensile stresses will be produced at the abutments during decentering in the case of flat and thick arches. To eliminate such stresses, thinner arches with larger values of f/l must be used.

Let us consider now a more general case in which the distributed vertical load varies from q_0 to q_1 (Fig. 8.18), following a parabolic law,

$$q = q_0 + (q_1 - q_0) \frac{4x^2}{l^2} \tag{h}$$

The total load on half the span consists, then, of a uniformly distributed load with the resultant

$$Q = \frac{q_0 l}{2}$$

applied at the distance $l/4$ from the crown and of a parabolically distributed load with the resultant

$$Q_1 = \frac{(q_1 - q_0)l}{6}$$

applied at the distance $3l/8$ from the crown.

Assuming that the center line of the arch coincides with the funicular curve for the given load, we find the thrust H from the moment equation with respect to point B, which gives

$$Hf = \frac{q_0 l^2}{8} + \frac{(q_1 - q_0)l^2}{48}$$

Hence, $$H = \frac{5q_0 + q_1}{48} \frac{l^2}{f} \tag{i}$$

The ordinate y for any point D of the center line is obtained by writing the moment equation with respect to point D. The load to the left of that point consists of the uniformly distributed load $q_0 x$ and of the parabolically distributed load

$$(q_1 - q_0) \frac{4x^2}{l^2} \frac{x}{3}$$

the resultants of which are at the distances $x/2$ and $3x/4$ from the crown C, respectively. Hence, the moment equation is

$$Hy = \frac{q_0 x^2}{2} + (q_1 - q_0) \frac{x^4}{3l^2}$$

Substituting for H its value (i), we obtain

$$y = \frac{8f}{5q_0 + q_1} \left[3q_0 + 2(q_1 - q_0) \frac{x^2}{l^2} \right] \frac{x^2}{l^2} \qquad (8.15a)$$

By taking various values for the ratio q_1/q_0, we obtain various shapes of the center line. For $q_1 = q_0$, we obtain the parabolic curve. By taking q_1 larger than q_0 and making the ratio q_1/q_0 larger and larger, we obtain funicular curves located above the parabolic funicular curve and at distances that increase as the ratio q_1/q_0 increases. For arches having the curve $(8.15a)$ as their center line, tables facilitating stress analysis have been calculated.[1] In the preparation of these tables, it was assumed that the cross-sectional moment of inertia varies along the span in accordance with the equation

[1] In our future discussion, we make use of the tables given in F. von Emperger (ed.), "Bogenbrücken, Handbuch für Eisenbetonbau," vol. XI, Wilhelm Ernst & Sohn KG, Berlin, 1927.

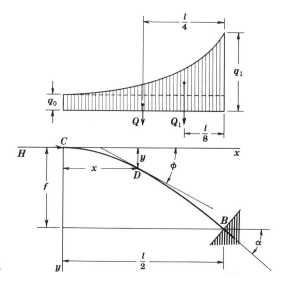

FIG. 8.18

$$I = \frac{I_0}{\cos \phi [1 - \mu(2x/l)]} \qquad (8.15b)$$

in which, as before, ϕ is the angle that the tangent to the center line makes with the x axis (Fig. 8.18), α is the value of ϕ at the abutment, I_0 is the moment of inertia at the crown, and μ is a numerical factor defined by the magnitude I_1 of the moment of inertia at the abutments. Substituting $x = l/2$, $\phi = \alpha$, and $I = I_1$ in Eq. (8.15b), we obtain

$$\mu = 1 - \frac{I_0}{I_1 \cos \alpha} \qquad (j)$$

For any given values of q_1/q_0 and f/l, we calculate the ordinates of the center line and the angles ϕ and α, using Eq. (8.15a). Then, upon taking a definite value for the ratio I_1/I_0, we calculate from Eq. (8.15b) the value of I for each cross section of the arch. In this manner, a variety of arch proportions can be obtained.

Having the shape of the arch completely defined, we calculate now the magnitude of the negative thrust H' from Eq. (8.12). The three integrals entering into this equation we represent in the following form:

$$\int_0^s \frac{y(y - d)\,ds}{EI} = \nu \frac{f^2 l}{2EI_0} \qquad (k)$$

$$\int_0^s \frac{\cos^2 \phi\,ds}{AE} = \frac{l}{2\beta A_0 E} \qquad (l)$$

$$\int_0^s \frac{ds}{AE} = \frac{l}{2\beta_1 A_0 E} \qquad (m)$$

where ν, β, and β_1 are numbers to be taken from Table 8.5. Then the value of the negative thrust is

$$H' = \frac{k_0^2/\nu\beta_1 f^2}{1 + k_0^2/\nu\beta f^2} H \qquad (8.16)$$

In this equation the value of H is given by Eq. (i), $k_0^2 = I_0/A_0$, and the values of the constants ν, β, and β_1 must be taken from Table 8.5.

Take, for example, a parabolic arch with $f/l = 0.25$, $h/l = \frac{1}{32}$, and $I = I_0/\cos^3 \phi$. Then, $\cos \alpha = 1/\sqrt{2}$, and $\mu = 0.5$, from Eq. (j). From the tables we then take $\nu = 0.0588$, $\beta = 1.28$, $\beta_1 = 1.01$. Equation (8.16) then gives $H'/H = 0.0215$, which is in satisfactory agreement with the value given in Table 8.4.

As soon as the value of H' is found from Eq. (8.16), the values of the axial force and of the bending moment at the crown of the given hingeless arch are obtained from Eqs. (8.13a). The distance d of the elastic center occurring

TABLE 8.5

(a) VALUES OF $\nu \times 10^5$

q_1/q_0	$\mu = 0$	0.1	0.2	0.3	0.4	0.5	0.6	0.7	0.8	0.9
1.00	8,889	8,326	7,747	7,149	6,528	5,880	5,198	4,477	3,704	2,866
1.67	8,627	8,069	7,497	6,905	6,292	5,653	4,982	4,272	3,513	2,691
2.50	8,411	7,855	7,291	6,706	6,110	5,469	4,808	4,108	3,363	2,557
3.57	8,196	7,647	7,085	6,505	5,905	5,282	4,629	3,940	3,206	2,415
5.00	7,995	7,460	6,881	6,316	5,723	5,106	4,461	3,781	3,059	2,281
7.00	7,809	7,267	6,712	6,142	5,553	4,942	4,304	3,633	2,921	2,156
10.00	7,639	7,100	6,547	5,980	5,395	4,789	4,157	3,494	2,792	2,039
15.00	7,484	6,946	6,396	5,831	5,250	4,148	4,022	3,366	2,673	1,931

(b) VALUES OF β

μ	$\dfrac{f}{l} = 0.10$	0.14	0.18	0.22	0.26	0.30	0.34	0.38
0.8	1.24	1.27	1.31	1.35	1.39	1.43	1.47	1.52
0.7	1.20	1.24	1.27	1.31	1.35	1.39	1.44	1.48
0.6	1.17	1.20	1.24	1.28	1.32	1.36	1.40	1.45
0.5	1.14	1.18	1.21	1.25	1.29	1.33	1.38	1.42
0.4	1.11	1.14	1.18	1.22	1.26	1.30	1.35	1.39
0.2	1.07	1.10	1.14	1.18	1.22	1.26	1.30	1.35
0	1.03	1.06	1.10	1.14	1.18	1.22	1.26	1.31

(c) VALUES OF β_1

μ	$\dfrac{f}{l} = 0.10$	0.14	0.18	0.22	0.26	0.30	0.34	0.38
0.8	1.19	1.18	1.16	1.13	1.11	1.08	1.06	1.04
0.7	1.15	1.14	1.12	1.09	1.07	1.04	1.02	1.00
0.6	1.12	1.10	1.08	1.06	1.04	1.01	0.99	0.96
0.5	1.09	1.07	1.05	1.03	1.01	0.99	0.96	0.94
0.4	1.06	1.05	1.03	1.01	0.98	0.96	0.94	0.91
0.2	1.02	1.01	0.99	0.96	0.94	0.92	0.90	0.87
0	0.98	0.97	0.95	0.93	0.91	0.89	0.86	0.84

(d) VALUES OF γ

q_1/q_0	$\mu = 0$	0.1	0.2	0.3	0.4	0.5	0.6	0.7	0.8	0.9
1.00	0.333	0.325	0.315	0.304	0.292	0.278	0.262	0.244	0.222	0.197
1.67	0.320	0.311	0.302	0.291	0.279	0.266	0.250	0.232	0.211	0.186
2.50	0.307	0.298	0.289	0.278	0.267	0.253	0.238	0.221	0.200	0.176
3.57	0.294	0.285	0.276	0.266	0.254	0.241	0.226	0.209	0.189	0.165
5.00	0.280	0.272	0.263	0.253	0.242	0.229	0.214	0.197	0.178	0.155
7.00	0.267	0.259	0.250	0.240	0.229	0.217	0.202	0.186	0.167	0.144
10.00	0.253	0.246	0.237	0.227	0.217	0.204	0.190	0.174	0.156	0.133
15.00	0.240	0.232	0.224	0.215	0.204	0.192	0.179	0.163	0.144	0.123

in these equations is calculated by using Eq. (8.5) and is presented in the form

$$d = \gamma f \tag{8.17}$$

in which values of γ for arches of various proportions are to be taken from Table 8.5.

To calculate thermal stresses in an arch defined by Eqs. (8.15a) and (8.15b), we use Eq. (8.7). With the notations (k) and (l), this equation gives

$$H_t = \frac{\alpha t l E I_0}{\nu f^2 l + l I_0 / \beta A_0} \tag{8.18}$$

It is seen that the thrust produced by temperature change can be readily calculated by using Table 8.5 for ν and β. The same equation can be used also in discussing the effect of shrinkage of the concrete, shrinkage being considered as equivalent to a certain lowering of the temperature.

The shortening of the axis of the arch due to dead load [see Eq. (b)], to lowering of the temperature, and to shrinkage of the concrete produces the reduction H' in the thrust H calculated as for a three-hinged arch. As a result of this, the thrust line of a hingeless arch is displaced upward at the crown and downward at the abutments from the assumed center line coinciding with the funicular curve for the dead load. Calculations made for parabolic and circular arches show that the relative displacements δ/h are larger at the abutments and that at these places tensile stresses due to eccentric pressure are likely to occur. From Table 8.4, it may be seen that the displacements are especially large in the case of flat arches and that the values δ_1/h_1 are approximately proportional to h/l. This indicates that in the case of thick and flat arches we must expect tensile stresses at the abutments; if the material is weak in tension, the only way to eliminate cracks is to use a three-hinged arch.

To reduce the above-mentioned displacements of the thrust line in large arch structures, such as bridges, various methods are used. Sometimes temporary hinges are put at the crown and at the abutments that permit free relative rotations at these points during decentering. In this manner, the displacements of the thrust line, which occur as a result of the compression of the center line by dead load, are eliminated. Filling up the gaps at the temporary hinges with concrete after decentering, we obtain a hingeless arch the center line of which coincides with the funicular curve for the dead load. To take care of the thrust-line displacements due to shrinkage and lowering of the temperature, the temporary hinges must be placed with proper eccentricities. The eccentricities must be such that, after decentering and filling up the gaps, bending moments are produced at the crown and the abutments, the signs of which are to be opposite to those we expect later from shrinkage and temperature drop. Sometimes hydraulic jacks are put in the temporary gap at the

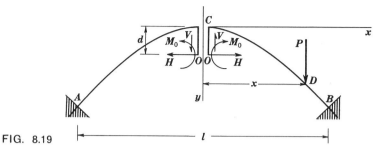

FIG. 8.19

crown between the two halves of the arch.[1]   By using these jacks, we can increase the thrust at the crown, and the arch is raised off the scaffolds.   Later, by a proper distribution of pressures in the jacks, the most favorable position of the thrust line at the crown can be ascertained before filling up the gap with concrete.

The stress conditions in an arch can be improved also by introducing during construction residual stresses in the proper direction.   In the case of concrete arches, this can be accomplished by making the arch in several layers and working on these layers in the proper sequence.[2]

Stresses produced in an arch by live loads are usually calculated by influence lines.   The general method of constructing influence lines for symmetrical arches was described in Art. 8.3.   For arches the shape of which is defined by Eqs. (8.15a) and (8.15b), the ordinates of influence lines for the redundant quantities are calculated for various values of q_1/q_0 and μ and are presented in Tables 8.6 to 8.8.   By using these tables, we can readily calculate the stresses produced by live loads.

If a vertical load P is acting at the distance x from the crown (Fig. 8.19), the thrust produced by this load can be represented by the equation

$$H = \varphi \, \frac{Pl}{4f(1 + I_0/\nu\beta A_0 f^2)} \tag{8.19}$$

The values of the quantities ν and β in this equation have already been given in Table 8.5; the values of φ are given in Table 8.6.

The bending moment at the crown produced by the load P (Fig. 8.19) is

$$M_c = M_0 - Hd = M' - Hd - \varphi_1 \frac{Pl}{4} \tag{8.20}$$

---

[1] Such jacks were used, for example, in the construction of the large arch bridge over the Aar River at Bern, Switzerland.   The description of the construction of that bridge is given in *Schweiz. Bauztg.*, vol. 113, p. 91, 1939.   The idea of using jacks to create a favorable stress distribution in arches belongs to E. Freyssinet.   See his papers in *Génie Civil*, vol. 79, p. 97, 1921; vol. 93, p. 254, 1928.
[2] The question of improving stress conditions by the introduction of residual stresses is discussed in the following papers: E. Baticle, *Compt. Rend.*, vol. 177/II, p. 1006, 1923; A. Paris, *Bauingenieur*, 1928, p. 831.

TABLE 8.6   VALUES OF φ IN EQ. (8.19)

$q_1/q_0 = 1$

$2x/l$	$\mu=0$	0.1	0.2	0.3	0.4	0.5	0.6	0.7	0.8	0.9
0	0.9375	0.9433	0.9505	0.9572	0.9658	0.9760	0.9892	1.0063	1.0299	1.0680
0.1	0.9188	0.9240	0.9300	0.9362	0.9439	0.9529	0.9646	0.9797	1.0008	1.0349
0.2	0.8640	0.8674	0.8716	0.8756	0.8790	0.8867	0.8948	0.9051	0.9195	0.9428
0.3	0.7764	0.7777	0.7792	0.7807	0.7824	0.7845	0.7878	0.7916	0.7972	0.8067
0.4	0.6615	0.6606	0.6596	0.6584	0.6570	0.6552	0.6535	0.6510	0.6471	0.6416
0.5	0.5273	0.5249	0.5223	0.5187	0.5149	0.5100	0.5046	0.4972	0.4867	0.4703
0.6	0.3840	0.3807	0.3773	0.3726	0.3676	0.3616	0.3540	0.3443	0.3304	0.3081
0.7	0.2438	0.2408	0.2375	0.2332	0.2284	0.2190	0.2155	0.2064	0.1930	0.1720
0.8	0.1215	0.1195	0.1173	0.1143	0.1111	0.1070	0.1023	0.0963	0.0872	0.0729
0.9	0.0339	0.0331	0.0326	0.0313	0.0302	0.0285	0.0270	0.0248	0.0216	0.0164

$q_1/q_0 = 1.67$

$2x/l$										
0	0.9418	0.9532	0.9605	0.9690	0.9789	0.9906	1.0056	1.0250	1.0527	1.0978
0.1	0.9233	0.9341	0.9406	0.9483	0.9569	0.9678	0.9811	0.9986	1.0236	1.0642
0.2	0.8694	0.8781	0.8826	0.8881	0.8943	0.9018	0.9114	0.9246	0.9419	0.9714
0.3	0.7826	0.7887	0.7907	0.7937	0.7962	0.7996	0.8041	0.8101	0.8187	0.8331
0.4	0.6688	0.6721	0.6716	0.6711	0.6707	0.6701	0.6694	0.6685	0.6675	0.6663
0.5	0.5352	0.5349	0.5334	0.5308	0.5275	0.5236	0.5189	0.5129	0.5041	0.4901
0.6	0.3914	0.3905	0.3872	0.3830	0.3784	0.3729	0.3650	0.3570	0.3438	0.3233
0.7	0.2498	0.2482	0.2448	0.2410	0.2365	0.2309	0.2240	0.2151	0.2021	0.1814
0.8	0.1247	0.1227	0.1215	0.1190	0.1154	0.1120	0.1072	0.1009	0.0919	0.0777
0.9	0.0350	0.0346	0.0337	0.0327	0.0316	0.0302	0.0285	0.0262	0.0231	0.0178

$q_1/q_0 = 2.5$

$2x/l$										
0	0.9511	0.9585	0.9660	0.9751	0.9841	0.9984	1.0143	1.0357	1.0648	1.1134
0.1	0.9330	0.9396	0.9465	0.9547	0.9623	0.9757	0.9900	1.0009	1.0364	1.0802
0.2	0.8791	0.8844	0.8907	0.8953	0.9001	0.9107	0.9210	0.9353	0.9551	0.9878
0.3	0.7935	0.7962	0.7985	0.8015	0.8038	0.8095	0.8147	0.8220	0.8325	0.8497
0.4	0.6801	0.6802	0.6803	0.6803	0.6803	0.6804	0.6805	0.6809	0.6814	0.6825
0.5	0.5461	0.5445	0.5450	0.5400	0.5363	0.5339	0.5297	0.5271	0.5169	0.5047
0.6	0.4011	0.3989	0.3953	0.3916	0.3869	0.3820	0.3754	0.3670	0.3546	0.3347
0.7	0.2575	0.2547	0.2514	0.2474	0.2429	0.2379	0.2317	0.2225	0.2099	0.1893
0.8	0.1289	0.1278	0.1255	0.1229	0.1196	0.1163	0.1113	0.1051	0.0961	0.0814
0.9	0.0366	0.0365	0.0351	0.0335	0.0325	0.0316	0.0297	0.0276	0.0242	0.0187

$q_1/q_0 = 3.57$

$2x/l$										
0	0.9557	0.9634	0.9719	0.9818	0.9934	1.0072	1.0246	1.0475	1.0805	1.1345
0.1	0.9379	0.9455	0.9526	0.9648	0.9723	0.9849	1.0008	1.0218	1.0520	1.1016
0.2	0.8853	0.8910	0.8967	0.9032	0.9111	0.9206	0.9327	0.9486	0.9747	1.0094
0.3	0.8005	0.8035	0.8083	0.8105	0.8149	0.8203	0.8272	0.8362	0.8493	0.8711
0.4	0.6882	0.6886	0.6900	0.6904	0.6909	0.6919	0.6933	0.6951	0.6980	0.7030
0.5	0.5548	0.5534	0.5517	0.5499	0.5480	0.5453	0.5421	0.5379	0.5320	0.5221
0.6	0.4095	0.4068	0.4038	0.4004	0.3964	0.3916	0.3855	0.3774	0.3656	0.3467
0.7	0.2660	0.2621	0.2591	0.2555	0.2516	0.2465	0.2403	0.2320	0.2199	0.2006
0.8	0.1340	0.1321	0.1298	0.1272	0.1243	0.1205	0.1158	0.1096	0.1004	0.0860
0.9	0.0381	0.0373	0.0364	0.0355	0.0343	0.0330	0.0312	0.0288	0.0252	0.0198

TABLE 8.6   VALUES OF φ IN EQ. (8.19) (continued)

$q_1/q_0 = 5.0$

$2x/l$	$\mu = 0$	0.1	0.2	0.3	0.4	0.5	0.6	0.7	0.8	0.9
0	0.9589	0.9683	0.9779	0.9871	0.9994	1.0145	1.0333	1.0584	1.0942	1.1543
0.1	0.9414	0.9473	0.9590	0.9674	0.9787	0.9925	1.0098	1.0331	1.0661	1.1217
0.2	0.8899	0.8945	0.9036	0.9099	0.9186	0.9293	0.9427	0.9607	0.9865	1.0301
0.3	0.8065	0.8089	0.8152	0.8185	0.8236	0.8302	0.8384	0.8495	0.8643	0.8921
0.4	0.6954	0.6966	0.6983	0.6992	0.7007	0.7028	0.7053	0.7090	0.7140	0.7231
0.5	0.5629	0.5621	0.5615	0.5596	0.5580	0.5562	0.5540	0.5513	0.5471	0.5450
0.6	0.4172	0.4146	0.4132	0.4096	0.4061	0.4019	0.3997	0.3896	0.3796	0.3631
0.7	0.2707	0.2675	0.2656	0.2609	0.2579	0.2531	0.2470	0.2392	0.2275	0.2082
0.8	0.1381	0.1360	0.1343	0.1316	0.1286	0.1250	0.1204	0.1145	0.1056	0.0850
0.9	0.0395	0.0387	0.0381	0.0370	0.0359	0.0345	0.0329	0.0305	0.0270	0.0213

$q_1/q_0 = 7.0$

0	0.9604	0.9691	0.9776	0.9904	1.0037	1.0199	1.0401	1.0670	1.1058	1.1716
0.1	0.9433	0.9515	0.9606	0.9711	0.9834	0.9984	1.0172	1.0421	1.0782	1.1395
0.2	0.8929	0.8993	0.9065	0.9148	0.9245	0.9364	0.9513	0.9711	0.9975	1.0498
0.3	0.8112	0.8152	0.8198	0.8253	0.8313	0.8389	0.8484	0.8612	0.8799	0.9118
0.4	0.7016	0.7032	0.7050	0.7072	0.7091	0.7125	0.7164	0.7215	0.7291	0.7564
0.5	0.5702	0.5697	0.5691	0.5684	0.5676	0.5666	0.5654	0.5639	0.5619	0.5586
0.6	0.4248	0.4229	0.4207	0.4181	0.4151	0.4115	0.4070	0.4010	0.3923	0.3860
0.7	0.2770	0.2746	0.2719	0.2688	0.2651	0.2606	0.2550	0.2475	0.2366	0.2322
0.8	0.1422	0.1404	0.1382	0.1358	0.1329	0.1276	0.1251	0.1192	0.1106	0.0960
0.9	0.0409	0.0402	0.0394	0.0384	0.0373	0.0359	0.0341	0.0318	0.0285	0.0226

$q_1/q_0 = 10.0$

0	0.9600	0.9691	0.9797	0.9917	1.0059	1.0231	1.0471	1.0736	1.1151	1.1864
0.1	0.9434	0.9520	0.9604	0.9730	0.9862	1.0026	1.0223	1.0491	1.0881	1.1548
0.2	0.8944	0.9012	0.9091	0.9181	0.9287	0.9312	0.9579	0.9797	1.0113	1.0658
0.3	0.8145	0.8176	0.8242	0.8342	0.8375	0.8460	0.8569	0.8717	0.8931	0.9303
0.4	0.7069	0.7090	0.7114	0.7141	0.7174	0.7215	0.7266	0.7336	0.7438	0.7618
0.5	0.5768	0.5767	0.5765	0.5764	0.5763	0.5763	0.5726	0.5762	0.5762	0.5762
0.6	0.4318	0.4302	0.4283	0.4262	0.4237	0.4208	0.4170	0.4121	0.4048	0.3926
0.7	0.2831	0.2809	0.2784	0.2755	0.2721	0.2681	0.2628	0.2561	0.2458	0.2283
0.8	0.1462	0.1445	0.1424	0.1402	0.1374	0.1342	0.1299	0.1242	0.1155	0.1015
0.9	0.0423	0.0417	0.0408	0.0399	0.0390	0.0375	0.0356	0.0334	0.0300	0.0241

$q_1/q_0 = 15.0$

0	0.9576	0.9672	0.9783	0.9910	1.0058	1.0239	1.0466	1.0769	1.1210	1.1973
0.1	0.9416	0.9507	0.9609	0.9728	0.9867	1.0037	1.0249	1.0533	1.0977	1.1666
0.2	0.8993	0.9053	0.9097	0.9194	0.9308	0.9448	0.9622	0.9857	1.0200	1.0797
0.3	0.8162	0.8213	0.8271	0.8338	0.8417	0.8514	0.8636	0.8801	0.9043	0.9466
0.4	0.7109	0.7134	0.7164	0.7199	0.7239	0.7290	0.7354	0.7441	0.7531	0.7796
0.5	0.5828	0.5828	0.5832	0.5837	0.5844	0.5855	0.5861	0.5876	0.5897	0.5939
0.6	0.4382	0.4369	0.4354	0.4338	0.4318	0.4296	0.4266	0.4227	0.4170	0.4073
0.7	0.2888	0.2868	0.2846	0.2820	0.2789	0.2753	0.2705	0.2643	0.2549	0.2387
0.8	0.1500	0.1468	0.1464	0.1442	0.1416	0.1385	0.1344	0.1260	0.1208	0.1067
0.9	0.0437	0.0429	0.0423	0.0413	0.0402	0.0389	0.0372	0.0349	0.0315	0.0250

TABLE 8.7   VALUES OF φ_1 IN EQ. (8.20)

$\dfrac{2x}{l}$	$\mu = 0$	0.1	0.2	0.3	0.4	0.5	0.6	0.7	0.8	0.9
0	0.2500	0.2544	0.2593	0.2647	0.2708	0.2778	0.2857	0.2949	0.3056	0.3182
0.1	0.2475	0.2518	0.2565	0.2618	0.2678	0.2745	0.2822	0.2911	0.3015	0.3138
0.2	0.2400	0.2439	0.2483	0.2532	0.2587	0.2649	0.2720	0.2802	0.2898	0.3011
0.3	0.2275	0.2310	0.2348	0.2390	0.2439	0.2493	0.2555	0.2627	0.2711	0.2810
0.4	0.2100	0.2128	0.2160	0.2195	0.2235	0.2280	0.2331	0.2391	0.2460	0.2542
0.5	0.1875	0.1897	0.1921	0.1949	0.1979	0.2014	0.2054	0.2099	0.2153	0.2216
0.6	0.1600	0.1615	0.1633	0.1652	0.1673	0.1698	0.1726	0.1758	0.1796	0.1840
0.7	0.1275	0.1285	0.1295	0.1307	0.1320	0.1335	0.1352	0.1372	0.1395	0.1422
0.8	0.0900	0.0905	0.0910	0.0915	0.0922	0.0929	0.0940	0.0947	0.0958	0.0971
0.9	0.0475	0.0476	0.0478	0.0479	0.0481	0.0483	0.0485	0.0488	0.0491	0.0494

TABLE 8.8   VALUES OF φ_2 IN EQ. (8.21)

$\dfrac{2x}{l}$	$\mu = 0$	0.1	0.2	0.3	0.4	0.5	0.6	0.7	0.8	0.9
0	0	0	0	0	0	0	0	0	0	0
0.1	0.0248	0.0254	0.0262	0.0271	0.0282	0.0296	0.0314	0.0337	0.0369	0.0416
0.2	0.0480	0.0492	0.0506	0.0523	0.0544	0.0570	0.0602	0.0645	0.0704	0.0752
0.3	0.0683	0.0698	0.0717	0.0739	0.0767	0.0800	0.0843	0.0899	0.0977	0.1090
0.4	0.0840	0.0858	0.0878	0.0903	0.0933	0.0970	0.1017	0.1079	0.1164	0.1289
0.5	0.0938	0.0954	0.0974	0.0998	0.1027	0.1063	0.1108	0.1168	0.1260	0.1370
0.6	0.0960	0.0974	0.0991	0.1011	0.1035	0.1066	0.1104	0.1155	0.1224	0.1326
0.7	0.0893	0.0903	0.0915	0.0929	0.0946	0.0968	0.0996	0.1032	0.1081	0.1154
0.8	0.0720	0.0726	0.0732	0.0740	0.0750	0.0762	0.0777	0.0797	0.0824	0.0864
0.9	0.0428	0.0429	0.0431	0.0434	0.0437	0.0440	0.0445	0.0451	0.0459	0.0471

In this equation

$$M' = \frac{Pl}{4}\left(1 - \frac{2x}{l}\right)$$

is the bending moment at the middle of a simply supported beam of length l, and the constant φ_1 is to be taken from Table 8.7. Hence, by using the influence line for bending moment at the middle of a simply supported beam together with the constants φ and φ_1 given in the tables, we can construct the influence line for M_c.

The shearing force V at the crown is obtained from the equation

$$V = V' - \varphi_2 P \tag{8.21}$$

in which

$$V' = \frac{P}{2}\left(1 - \frac{2x}{l}\right)$$

is the shearing force at the middle of a simply supported beam and the constant φ_2 is to be taken from Table 8.8. Equations (8.19) and (8.20) can be used also for negative values of x when the load P is applied to the left of the crown, since the influence lines for M_c and H are symmetrical with respect to the middle of the span. The influence line for V is antimetrical, and the sign of its ordinates must be changed when we take $-x$ instead of x.

By using the tables given in this article, we can readily make the analysis of arches of various proportions defined by Eqs. (8.15a) and (8.15b).

PROBLEMS

1   For what type of load distribution on a symmetrical three-hinged arch will the funicular curve be a circle? Let q_0 denote the intensity of load at the crown, and ϕ the angle that any tangent to the arch axis makes with the horizontal.

   Ans. $q = q_0/\cos^3 \phi$.

2   A symmetrical hingeless arch has a span $l = 60$ ft and rise $f = 15$ ft. The cross section consists of four 4-in. $\times$ 4-in. $\times \frac{1}{2}$-in. angle sections arranged as shown in Fig. 8.20. The dimension h at the crown is $h_0 = 12$ in., and at the abutments

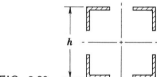

FIG. 8.20

it is $h_1 = 20$ in. The shape of the arch is that given by Eqs. (8.15a) and (8.15b) with the ratio $q_1/q_0 = 1.00$, that is, it is a parabolic arch. Using Eq. (8.18) and the appropriate data from the tables, calculate the thrust due to a uniform rise in temperature of 40°F above the assembly temperature if the coefficient of thermal expansion is $\alpha_t = 6.5(10^{-6})$ (in./in.)/°F and $E = 30(10)^6$ psi.

   Ans. $H_t = 1{,}620$ lb.

3   Calculate the bending moment M_c at the crown of the arch described in the preceding problem due to a uniform distribution of vertical load of intensity $q = 1.0$ kip/ft.

   Ans. $M_c = 19{,}400$ ft-lb.

8.6 UNSYMMETRICAL ARCHES

In the case of an unsymmetrical arch, we take as the redundant quantities the bending moment M_a and the two components R_a and H_a of the reaction at the left support A (Fig. 8.21a). The magnitudes of these three quantities will be found by using Eq. (8.1) and applying the theorem of least work which gives

$$\frac{\partial U}{\partial H_a} = \int_0^s \frac{My}{EI} \, ds + \int_0^s \frac{N \cos \phi}{AE} \, ds = 0$$

$$\frac{\partial U}{\partial R_a} = \int_0^s \frac{Mx}{EI} \, ds - \int_0^s \frac{N \sin \phi}{AE} \, ds = 0 \qquad (a)$$

$$\frac{\partial U}{\partial M_a} = \int_0^s \frac{M \, ds}{EI} = 0$$

where s is the total length of the center line of the arch. In these equations, M and N are bending moment and axial force, and ϕ is the angle that the tangents to the center line make with the x axis. This angle is taken positive if measured clockwise from the horizontal axis, as shown in Fig. 8.21a. Taking the coordinates as shown in the figure and observing the previous sign rule (see page 334) for M and N, we obtain

$$M = M_a + R_a x + H_a y + M'$$

$$N = H_a \cos \phi - R_a \sin \phi + N' \qquad (b)$$

where M' and N' are the moment and axial force contributed by the loads on the arch to the left of the cross section under consideration. If we substitute expressions (b) into Eqs. (a), we obtain, for calculating the redundant quantities, three equations each of which contains all three unknowns. Such equations are not suitable for practical applications.

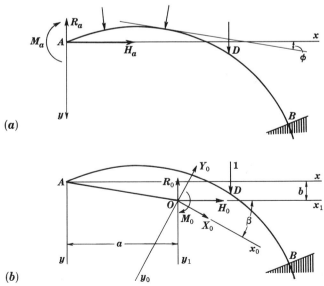

(a)

FIG. 8.21   **(b)**

A considerable simplification can be effected if, by the proper selection of the redundant quantities, we can obtain three equations each containing only one unknown. For this purpose, we select the redundant quantities in such a manner that the displacements corresponding to one of them are not affected by the other two. In Fig. 8.21, the couple M_a acting alone produces not only rotation of the cross section A but also some displacement. The reciprocal theorem then states that forces R_a and H_a will produce not only displacement of point A but also some rotation of that cross section. To make the rotation of the cross section A depend only on the couple and be independent of the forces, we replace the system of redundant forces in Fig. 8.21a by the statically equivalent system H_0, R_0, M_0, as shown in Fig. 8.21b. In this latter case, we assume that an absolutely rigid bracket AO is rigidly attached to the arch at A and that the point O is selected in such a manner that it remains stationary when a couple is applied at O.* Then, from the reciprocal theorem it follows that the forces R_0 and H_0 applied at O will not produce any rotation of the cross section A. To make this new system of redundant forces at O statically equivalent to the previous system at A, we have to satisfy the following equations:

$$R_0 = R_a \qquad H_0 = H_a \qquad M_0 = M_a + R_0 a + H_0 b \qquad (c)$$

To find the proper coordinates a and b of the point O, we assume that a couple M_a alone is applied at the end A of the arch; then, at every cross section $M = M_a$, $N = 0$, and we obtain, by using the Castigliano theorem,

$$u_a = M_a \int_0^s \frac{y\,ds}{EI} \qquad v_a = -M_a \int_0^s \frac{x\,ds}{EI} \qquad \theta_a = M_a \int_0^s \frac{ds}{EI} \quad (d)$$

To obtain the deflections of the end O of the bar AO, we must add to expressions (d) the displacements due to rotation of this bar. Hence,

$$u_0 = u_a - b\theta_a \qquad v_0 = v_a + a\theta_a \qquad (e)$$

These displacements vanish if we take

$$a = -\frac{v_a}{\theta_a} = \frac{\int_0^s (x\,ds/EI)}{\int_0^s (ds/EI)} \qquad b = \frac{u_a}{\theta_a} = \frac{\int_0^s (y\,ds/EI)}{\int_0^s (ds/EI)} \qquad (8.22)$$

The point O, defined by Eqs. (8.22), is the elastic center of the arch. Let us assume fictitious masses of an intensity $1/EI$ distributed along the center line of the arch. Then the point O, as seen from Eqs. (8.22), is the center of gravity of these masses. For constant E, it is completely defined by the geometrical dimensions of the arch and is independent of the applied loads. It is advantageous to take point O for the origin of the new coordinate system

---

* Such reasoning has already been used in the selection of the elastic center for the arch in Fig. 8.8.

$x_1 y_1$ in Fig. 8.21b.   If we substitute $x = x_1 + a$, $y = y_1 + b$, and

$$M = M_0 + R_0 x_1 + H_0 y_1 + M'$$
$$N = H_0 \cos \phi - R_0 \sin \phi + N' \tag{f}$$

into Eqs. (a) and observe that for centroidal axes

$$\int_0^s \frac{x_1 \, ds}{EI} = \int_0^s \frac{y_1 \, ds}{EI} = 0 \tag{g}$$

we obtain equations for calculating the redundant forces in a simpler form. A further simplification of these equations is accomplished in the case of comparatively flat arches carrying vertical loads, since we can then neglect small terms containing $\sin \phi$ or N' as factors.   With these simplifications, Eqs. (a) become

$$R_0 \int_0^s \frac{x_1 y_1 \, ds}{EI} + H_0 \int_0^s \frac{y_1^2 \, ds}{EI} + H_0 \int_0^s \frac{\cos^2 \phi \, ds}{AE}$$
$$+ \int_0^s \frac{M' y_1 \, ds}{EI} = 0$$
$$R_0 \int_0^s \frac{x_1^2 \, ds}{EI} + H_0 \int_0^s \frac{x_1 y_1 \, ds}{EI} + \int_0^s \frac{M' x_1 \, ds}{EI} = 0 \tag{8.23}$$
$$M_0 \int_0^s \frac{ds}{EI} + \int_0^s \frac{M' \, ds}{EI} = 0$$

The third of these equations gives us the redundant moment M_0.   The first two equations each contain the remaining two unknown forces R_0 and H_0.

In the preceding discussion, the reactive forces at the support A were taken as the redundant quantities (Fig. 8.21).   Later on, these redundant elements were replaced by the statically equivalent system of redundant forces H_0, R_0, and M_0, applied at the elastic center.   Instead of this, the arch can be divided into two parts by a cross section at any point D on the arch axis as shown in Fig. 8.22, and the resultants of internal forces acting on this cross section can

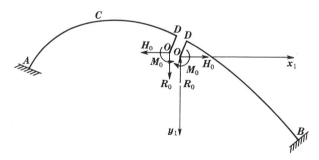

FIG. 8.22

be taken as the redundant quantities. Attaching the cross section D to the elastic center O by the rigid bar DO, we can replace these quantities by the statically equivalent system of forces H_0, R_0, M_0, as shown in the figure.[1] Since in the continuous arch there is no relative displacement between the ends D of the two portions of the arch, the equations for determining the redundant quantities will be

$$\frac{\partial U}{\partial H_0} = 0 \qquad \frac{\partial U}{\partial R_0} = 0 \qquad \frac{\partial U}{\partial M_0} = 0 \qquad (h)$$

Observing now that Eqs. (f) and (g) hold also for this case, we shall find that Eqs. (h) again lead to Eqs. (8.23). Thus, we can use the latter equations for any position of the cross section D, provided the origin of the coordinate axes x_1, y_1 coincide with the elastic center and the integrations are extended over the entire length s of the center line of the arch. The bending moments M' naturally will depend on the choice of the cross section D, and this cross section in each particular case should be selected in such a way as to make the calculation of the integrals containing M' as simple as possible.

If the arch is symmetrical with respect to the vertical axis, the elastic center will lie on that axis and the integral $\int_0^s (x_1 y_1 \, ds/EI)$ vanishes; so each of Eqs. (8.23) will contain only one unknown. The same condition can be realized also for unsymmetrical arches by a proper rotation of the coordinate axes. We observe that the integrals

$$\int_0^s \frac{y_1^2 \, ds}{EI} = I_{x_1} \qquad \int_0^s \frac{x_1^2 \, ds}{EI} = I_{y_1} \qquad \int_0^s \frac{x_1 y_1 \, ds}{EI} = I_{x_1 y_1} \qquad (i)$$

represent the moments of inertia and the product of inertia with respect to the $x_1 y_1$ axes of the previously mentioned fictitious masses distributed along the center line of the arch. If, instead of the $x_1 y_1$ axes, we take the principal axes of inertia $x_0 y_0$, for which the product of inertia of the fictitious masses vanishes, and introduce the forces X_0 and Y_0 instead of H_0 and R_0 (Fig. 8.21b), the equations for calculating the redundant quantities become[2]

$$X_0 \int_0^s \frac{y_0^2 \, ds}{EI} + X_0 \int_0^s \frac{\cos^2(\phi - \beta) \, ds}{AE} + \int_0^s \frac{M' y_0 \, ds}{EI} = 0$$

$$Y_0 \int_0^s \frac{x_0^2 \, ds}{EI} + \int_0^s \frac{M' x_0 \, ds}{EI} = 0 \qquad (j)$$

$$M_0 \int_0^s \frac{ds}{EI} + \int_0^s \frac{M' \, ds}{EI} = 0$$

[1] To show more clearly the forces of interaction at the cross section D, we take some distance between the ends D of the two portions of the arch, and the bar DO appears twice.
[2] Observe that R_0 is taken in the direction opposite to the positive y_1 axis and that Y_0 is opposite to the positive direction of the y_0 axis.

where β (see Fig. 8.21b) is the angle defining the directions of the principal axes. Each of Eqs. (j) contains only one unknown, and we find

$$X_0 = -\frac{\int_0^s (M'y_0 \, ds/EI)}{\int_0^s (y_0^2 \, ds/EI) + \int_0^s [\cos^2 (\phi - \beta) \, ds/AE]}$$

$$Y_0 = -\frac{\int_0^s (M'x_0 \, ds/EI)}{\int_0^s (x_0^2 \, ds/EI)} \qquad (8.24)$$

$$M_0 = -\frac{\int_0^s (M' \, ds/EI)}{\int_0^s (ds/EI)}$$

The calculation of the redundant quantities M_0, X_0, Y_0 reduces to the evaluation of the integrals appearing in Eqs. (8.24).

In each particular case, we begin the analysis of an unsymmetrical arch with the determination of the elastic center from Eqs. (8.22). The next step is the determination of the principal axes, for which purpose we calculate the integrals (i). If the center line of the arch is given in a simple analytical form, the integrals can be calculated exactly. Otherwise, we use the approximate numerical method described in Art. 8.4. Having I_{x_1}, I_{y_1}, and $I_{x_1 y_1}$ and using the known equations for calculation of principal moments of inertia and directions of principal axes,[1] we obtain

$$I_{x_0} + I_{y_0} = I_{x_1} + I_{y_1}$$

$$I_{x_0} - I_{y_0} = (I_{x_1} - I_{y_1}) \cos 2\beta - 2I_{x_1 y_1} \sin 2\beta \qquad (8.25)$$

$$\tan 2\beta = \frac{2I_{x_1 y_1}}{I_{y_1} - I_{x_1}}$$

From these equations, we find I_{x_0} and I_{y_0} entering into the denominators of Eqs. (8.24) and the angle β defining the direction of principal axes. To calculate the other integrals in Eqs. (8.24), we assume that fictitious masses of intensity M'/EI are distributed along the center line of the arch. Then the total fictitious mass and the statical moments of these masses with respect to the principal axes x_0 and y_0 are defined by the integrals

$$\int_0^s \frac{M' \, ds}{EI} \qquad \int_0^s \frac{M'y_0 \, ds}{EI} \qquad \int_0^s \frac{M'x_0 \, ds}{EI} \qquad (k)$$

Finally, the second integral in the denominator of the first of Eqs. (8.24) representing the approximate expression for the displacement due to shortening

[1] See S. P. Timoshenko and D. H. Young, "Engineering Mechanics," 4th ed., p. A-12, McGraw-Hill Book Company, Now York, 1956.

of the arch axis can also be evaluated by numerical integration.[1]   In this way, all the integrals in Eqs. (8.24) can be evaluated, and we obtain the redundant quantities X_0, Y_0, and M_0.*

Equations (8.24) can be used for any kind of loading on the arch.   To obtain expressions for influence coefficients ξ_0, η_0, ζ_0, corresponding to X_0, Y_0, M_0, respectively, we note that for a unit load on the arch at point D (Fig. 8.21b), we have $M' = -1(x_1 - x_d)$, and Eqs. (8.24) become, for constant E,

$$\xi_0 = \frac{\int_D^B [(x_1 - x_d) y_0 \, ds/I]}{\int_A^B (y_0{}^2 \, ds/I) + \int_A^B [\cos^2 (\phi - \beta) \, ds/A]}$$

$$\eta_0 = \frac{\int_D^B [(x_1 - x_d) x_0 \, ds/I]}{\int_A^B (x_0{}^2 \, ds/I)} \qquad (8.26)$$

$$\zeta_0 = \frac{\int_D^B [(x_1 - x_d) \, ds/I]}{\int_A^B (ds/I)}$$

To illustrate some of the details of calculation, let us consider the unsymmetrical arch shown in Fig. 8.23 and construct influence lines for the redundant quantities X_0, Y_0, and M_0.   This arch has a circular center line of radius $r = 100$ ft and subtends a total central angle of 90°.   The rectangular cross section of the rib varies in depth in such a way that

$$A = \frac{A_0}{\cos \phi} \qquad I = \frac{I_0}{\cos^3 \phi} \qquad (l)$$

where $A_0 = 1.50$ ft² and $I_0 = 0.300$ ft⁴ are the cross-sectional area and moment of inertia, respectively, at the crown C.   Although, in this case, the various integrals appearing in Eqs. (8.26) can be evaluated exactly, the analytic expressions are long and cumbersome, and it is actually much simpler to treat the problem numerically as discussed in Art. 8.4.   For this purpose, we divide the center line of the arch into nine segments, each subtending a central angle of 10° as shown in Fig. 8.23.

The first step in calculation is to locate the elastic center O.   Taking coordinate axes x and y through point A as shown in Fig. 8.23b, we compute and record in Table 8.9 the coordinates x and y and the values of A and I at the mid-point of each segment.   Then, noting that $\Delta s = 2\pi r/36 = 17.45$ ft, we calculate and record the quantities appearing in the last four columns of the first portion of Table 8.9.   Using the summations of these quantities in Eqs.

---

[1] This term is usually small, and a rough approximation is sufficient for its calculation.

* The idea of elastic center and fictitious masses was introduced in the theory of structures by C. Culmann; see W. Ritter, "Anwendungen der graphischen Statik," vol. IV, p. 197, Meyer & Zeller, Zurich, 1888–1906.

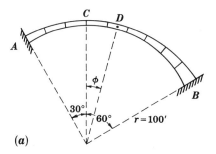

(a)

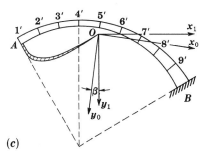

(b)

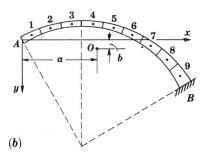

FIG. 8.23   (c)

(8.22), we find

$$a = \frac{22,675}{369.8} = 61.32 \text{ ft} \qquad b = -\frac{2,093.9}{369.80} = -5.66 \text{ ft} \qquad (m)$$

We now take new coordinate axes x_1, y_1 through the elastic center O as shown in Fig. 8.23c and record the new coordinates

$$x_1 = x - a \qquad y_1 = y - b \qquad (n)$$

in the first two columns of the second part of Table 8.9.   After this, the quantities appearing in the integrals (i) are readily computed as shown in the remaining columns of the second portion of the table.   Using the summations

TABLE 8.9 DATA FOR THE ARCH IN FIG. 8.23

Seg.	x	y	A	I	$\Delta s/A$	$\Delta s/I$	$x\,\Delta s/I$	$y\,\Delta s/I$
	(1)	(2)	(3)	(4)	(5)	(6)	(7)	(8)
1	7.74	−4.03	1.655	0.403	10.54	43.31	335	−174.5
2	24.12	−9.99	1.553	0.333	11.24	52.41	1,264	−523.6
3	41.28	−13.02	1.506	0.304	11.59	57.41	2,370	−747.5
4	58.72	−13.02	1.506	0.304	11.59	57.41	3,371	−747.5
5	75.88	−9.99	1.553	0.333	11.24	52.41	3,977	−523.6
6	92.26	−4.03	1.655	0.403	10.54	43.31	3,996	−174.5
7	107.36	+4.68	1.831	0.546	9.53	31.97	3,432	+149.6
8	120.71	15.89	2.121	0.849	8.23	20.56	2,482	326.7
9	131.92	29.24	2.615	1.590	6.67	10.98	1,448	321.0
Σ					91.17	369.77	22,675	−2,093.9

Seg.	x_1	y_1	$x_1{}^2$	$y_1{}^2$	$x_1 y_1$	$x_1{}^2\dfrac{\Delta s}{I}$	$y_1{}^2\dfrac{\Delta s}{I}$	$x_1 y_1\dfrac{\Delta s}{I}$
1	−53.58	1.63	2,871	2.66	−87.33	124,343	115	−3,782
2	−37.20	−4.33	1,384	18.75	+161.08	72,535	983	+8,442
3	−20.04	−7.36	402	54.17	147.49	23,079	3,110	8,467
4	−2.60	−7.36	7	54.17	19.14	402	3,110	1,099
5	+14.56	−4.33	212	18.75	−63.04	11,111	983	−3,304
6	30.94	+1.63	957	2.66	+50.43	41,448	115	+2,184
7	46.04	10.34	2,120	106.92	476.05	67,776	3,418	15,219
8	59.39	21.55	3,527	464.40	1,279.85	72,515	9,548	26,314
9	70.60	34.90	4,984	1,218.01	2,463.94	54,724	13,374	27,054
Σ						467,933	34,756	81,693

Div.	y_0	$y_0\dfrac{\Delta s}{I}$	x	x'	$\Sigma(x-x')$ $y_0\dfrac{\Delta s}{I}$	ξ_0	η_0	ζ_0
9′	21.67	237.9	131.92	126.60	1,266	0.064	0.0092	0.16
8′	10.55	216.9	120.71	114.28	5,592	0.282	0.0474	0.88
7′	1.91	61.1	107.36	100.00	12,537	0.631	0.1329	2.73
6′	−3.95	−171.1	92.26	84.20	19,309	0.972	0.2735	6.39
5′	−6.87	−360.0	75.88	67.36	22,048	1.110	0.4587	12.46
4′	−6.77	−388.7	58.72	50.00	18,395	0.926	0.6582	21.29
3′	−3.65	−209.5	41.28	32.64	9,573	0.482	0.8320	32.80
2′	+2.41	+126.3	24.12	15.80	294	0.015	0.9458	46.46
1′	11.21	485.5	7.74	0	−3,644	−0.183	0.9837	61.32

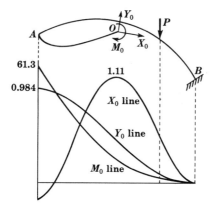

FIG. 8.24

of the last three columns here in Eqs. (8.25), we find

$$I_{x_0} = \int y_0{}^2 \frac{ds}{I} = 19{,}861 \qquad I_{y_0} = \int x_0{}^2 \frac{ds}{I} = 482{,}828$$

$$\beta = 10°20'$$

(o)

Now, having the directions of the principal axes of the arch, we can calculate the new coordinates x_0, y_0 of the mid-point of each segment. Such values of y_0 are shown in the first column of the third portion of Table 8.9. Following this, the summation of statical moments of the quantities $y_0 \, \Delta s/I$ about sucessive division points 9', 8', 7', . . . are computed and recorded in column 5 of the third part of Table 8.9. Using these values as numerators in the first of Eqs. (8.26) and noting that the second term of the denominator is negligible compared with the first, we calculate the influence coefficients ξ_0 for the redundant quantity X_0 as recorded in column 6.

Without showing the calculations, values of the influence coefficients η_0 and ζ_0 for the redundant quantities Y_0 and M_0, respectively, as computed from Eqs. (8.26), are shown in the last two columns of Table 8.9. The corresponding influence lines, plotted from the data in the table, are shown in Fig. 8.24. By way of a check on the numerical calculations, it will be noted that the values of ξ_0 and η_0 for the left end of the arch (point 1') give as their resultant a unit vertical force and that the moment of this force with respect to point A balances the moment ζ_0 as it should be.

PROBLEMS

1   Using the influence coefficients from Table 8.9, calculate the values of the redundant quantities X_0, Y_0, M_0 for the unsymmetrical arch in Fig. 8.24 due to a uniformly distributed load of intensity $q = 1$ kip/ft over the entire arch.

    Ans. $X_0 = 71.9$ kips, $Y_0 = 63.9$ kips, $M_0 = 2{,}545$ kip-ft.

2   Repeat the calculation of X_0, Y_0, M_0 obtained by the use of influence coefficients in the preceding problem by direct application of Eqs. (8.24). Note that the integrals appearing in the denominators of these expressions are already available in Table 8.9. The second term in the denominator of the first equation can be neglected.

3   Calculate the values of X_0, Y_0 that will be produced in the arch in Fig. 8.24 due to a uniform rise in temperature of 40°F. The coefficient of thermal expansion is $\alpha_t = 6(10^{-6})$ (in./in.)/°F. Assume a modulus of elasticity $E = 432(10^6)$ lb/ft². *Ans.* $X_0 = 736$ lb, $Y_0 = -2.47$ lb.

8.7 FRAMES WITHOUT HINGES

Equations (8.23) and (8.24), previously derived for arches, can be used also for calculating redundant forces in frames such as those shown in Figs. 8.25 and 8.26. In such a case, the equations can be somewhat simplified by omitting the terms representing the effect of axial force. Such a simplification is justifiable if we observe that in the case of arches under the action of dead load the center line is usually very close to the line of pressure and the stresses produced by the axial force are of the same order of magnitude as the maximum bending stresses. Hence, the terms representing the action of the axial force may be of practical importance. In the case of frames, the pressure line is usually far from coinciding with the center line, and the effect of axial force is negligible in comparison with that of bending moment. After this simplification, Eqs. (8.23) become

$$R_0 \int_0^s x_1 y_1 \frac{ds}{EI} + H_0 \int_0^s y_1^2 \frac{ds}{EI} = -\int_0^s M'y_1 \frac{ds}{EI}$$

$$R_0 \int_0^s x_1^2 \frac{ds}{EI} + H_0 \int_0^s x_1 y_1 \frac{ds}{EI} = -\int_0^s M'x_1 \frac{ds}{EI} \qquad (8.27)$$

$$M_0 \int_0^s \frac{ds}{EI} = -\int_0^s M' \frac{ds}{EI}$$

In each particular case of a frame analysis, we start with the determination of the coordinates of the elastic center by using Eqs. (8.22). Then, taking the elastic center as the origin of $x_1 y_1$ axes, we calculate the integrals appearing in Eqs. (8.27). Taking fictitious masses ds/EI and $M'\,ds/EI$ distributed along the center line of the frame, we see that each of the above-mentioned integrals has a simple physical meaning. Considering, for example, the first of these equations, we see that the first integral is the product of inertia of the distributed fictitious masses ds/EI. The second integral is the moment of inertia about the x_1 axis of the same masses. The integral on the right-hand side of the equation represents the statical moment about the x_1 axis of the distributed fictitious masses $M'\,ds/EI$, etc. The calculation of these integrals becomes especially simple if the frame consists of prismatic members.

Let us now take, as an example, the case of a frame of uniform cross section as shown in Fig. 8.25a and assume that $l = 2h$ and $c = h$. The redundant reactions R_a, H_a, M_a at the support A we replace by the statically equivalent system of forces R_0, H_0, M_0 applied at the elastic center O as shown in Fig. 8.25b. Then, for calculating the coordinates a and b of the elastic center, we use Eqs. (8.22). Since EI is constant in this case, it can be canceled, and we conclude that the elastic center coincides with the centroid of the center line of the frame. Thus,

$$\int_0^s ds = h + l = 3h \qquad \int_0^s x\,ds = \frac{l^2}{2} = 2h^2$$

$$-\int_0^s y\,ds = lh + \frac{h^2}{2} = \frac{5}{2}h^2$$

and we obtain, from Eqs. (8.22), $a = 2h/3$ and $b = -5h/6$. The integrals on the left-hand side of Eqs. (8.27), after canceling the constant factor $1/EI$, are

$$I_{x_1} = \int_0^s y_1^2\,ds = \frac{lh^2}{36} + \frac{h^3}{12} + \frac{hh^2}{9} = \frac{1}{4}h^3$$

$$I_{y_1} = \int_0^s x_1^2\,ds = \frac{l^3}{12} + \frac{lh^2}{9} + h\frac{4h^2}{9} = \frac{4}{3}h^3 \qquad (a)$$

$$I_{x_1y_1} = \int_0^s x_1y_1\,ds = -l\frac{h}{6}\frac{h}{3} - h\frac{2h^2}{9} = -\frac{1}{3}h^3$$

In calculating the integrals on the right-hand side of Eqs. (8.27), we observe that M' denotes the bending moments in the frame when the redundant quantities M_0, R_0, H_0 are removed. Thus M' is represented by the shaded triangle in Fig. 8.25b, where we consider bending moment to be positive when it produces flexure concave toward the outside of the frame. Accordingly, the resultant and the statical moments of the fictitious distributed masses $M'\,ds$ are

$$\int_0^s M'\,ds = -\tfrac{1}{2}Ph^2 \qquad \int_0^s M'x_1\,ds = -\tfrac{1}{2}Ph^3$$

$$\int_0^s M'y_1\,ds = \frac{Ph^3}{12} \qquad\qquad (b)$$

Substituting the quantities (a) and (b) into Eqs. (8.27), we obtain

$$-4R_0 + 3H_0 = -P$$

$$8R_0 - 2H_0 = 3P$$

$$6M_0 = Ph$$

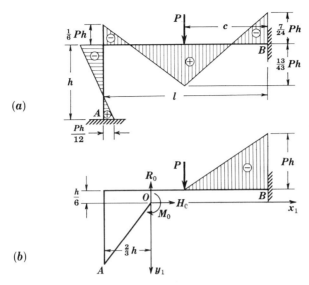

(a)

(b)

FIG. 8.25

from which

$$M_0 = \frac{Ph}{6} \qquad H_0 = \frac{P}{4} \qquad R_0 = \frac{7P}{16}$$

Using these values of the redundant quantities, the complete bending-moment diagram for the frame is easily constructed as shown in Fig. 8.25a. A partial check on this diagram may be obtained by noting that the algebraic sum of the moment areas must vanish since there can be no relative rotation between the fixed ends A and B of the frame.

Equations (8.24), each containing only one unknown, could also be used in the analysis of frames. However, these equations, although useful in calculating influence coefficients for unsymmetrical arches, have no advantage in the analysis of frames under dead load. It is much simpler to solve the system of Eqs. (8.27) for three unknowns than it is to determine the directions of principal axes in the case of an unsymmetrical frame. Therefore, in our further problems only Eqs. (8.27) will be used.

As a second example, let us consider the symmetrically loaded symmetrical frame of uniform cross section shown in Fig. 8.26a. In this case, we conclude at once that the elastic center O will be on the axis of symmetry, and from the second of Eqs. (8.22) we find that its distance from the x axis is $2l/3$. Then, with the elastic center O as origin, the x_1y_1 axes are evidently principal axes, and omitting the constant factor $1/EI$, we obtain

$$I_{x_1y_1} = 0 \qquad I_{x_1} = \int_0^s y_1^2 \, ds = \frac{l^3}{3} \qquad I_{y_1} = \int_0^s x_1^2 \, ds = \frac{7l^3}{12} \qquad (c)$$

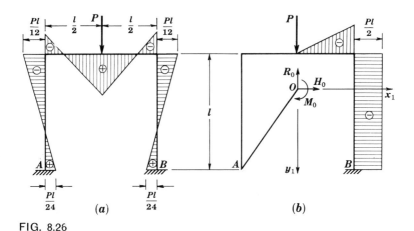

FIG. 8.26

The bending moments M' produced by the external load P are shown by the shaded areas in Fig. 8.26b, and we obtain

$$\int_0^s M' \, ds = -\tfrac{5}{8}Pl^2 \qquad \int_0^s M'y_1 \, ds = \tfrac{1}{24}Pl^3$$

$$\int_0^s M'x_1 \, ds = -\tfrac{7}{24}Pl^3$$

(d)

Substituting the values (c) and (d) into Eqs. (8.27), we find

$$H_0 = \frac{P}{8} \qquad R_0 = \frac{P}{2} \qquad M_0 = \frac{5Pl}{24}$$

(e)

Having these values, we can easily construct the complete bending-moment diagram for the frame as shown in Fig. 8.26a.

In discussing the symmetrical frame in Fig. 8.26, we used Eqs. (8.27) derived for an unsymmetrical frame. To take advantage of the condition of symmetry, it is preferable to use, for symmetric loading, Eqs. (8.6), and for antimetric loading, Eq. (8.8) as derived for symmetrical arches in Art. 8.3. Omitting the influence of the longitudinal force, these equations become

$$M_0 \int_0^s \frac{ds}{EI} = - \int_0^s M' \frac{ds}{EI}$$

$$H_0 \int_0^s y_1{}^2 \frac{ds}{EI} = - \int_0^s M'y_1 \frac{ds}{EI}$$

$$V_0 = 0$$

(8.28)

for the case of symmetrical loading and

$$H_0 = M_0 = 0$$

$$V_0 \int_0^s x_1{}^2 \frac{ds}{EI} = - \int_0^s M'x_1 \frac{ds}{EI} \qquad (8.29)$$

for the case of antimetrical loading. In both cases, the cross section is made at the crown of the arch (see Figs. 8.8 and 8.9) and the integrations are extended over one-half of the arch.

As an example, let us consider an unsymmetrical loading of the previous symmetrical frame as shown in Fig. 8.27a. Resolving this loading into symmetrical and antimetrical parts as shown in Fig. 8.27b and c, we obtain

$$- \int_0^s M' \, ds = \frac{Pc^2}{4} + \frac{Pcl}{2}$$

$$- \int_0^s M'y_1 \, ds = - \frac{Pc^2l}{12} + \frac{Pcl^2}{12}$$

$$- \int_0^s M'x_1 \, ds = \frac{Pc^2}{4}\left(\frac{l}{2} - \frac{c}{3}\right) + \frac{Pcl^2}{4}$$

When these values are substituted into Eqs. (8.28) and (8.29), we find

$$M_0 = \frac{Pc^2}{6l} + \frac{Pc}{3} \qquad H_0 = - \frac{Pc^2}{2l^2} + \frac{Pc}{2l}$$

$$V_0 = \frac{6Pc^2}{7l^2}\left(\frac{1}{2} - \frac{c}{3l}\right) + \frac{6Pc}{7l}$$

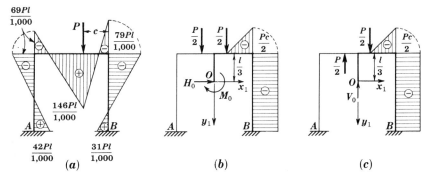

FIG. 8.27

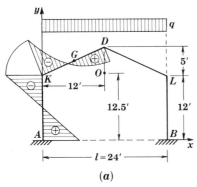

(a)

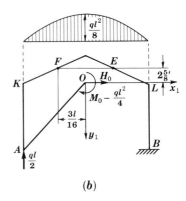

(b)

FIG. 8.28

For $c = l/3$, these results reduce to

$$M_0 = \frac{7Pl}{54} \qquad H_0 = \frac{P}{9} \qquad V_0 = \frac{61P}{189}$$

The corresponding bending-moment diagram is shown in Fig. 8.27a.

In the preceding examples, we have considered only frames of uniform cross section. Frames consisting of prismatic members with different values of I can be treated in a similar manner without much difficulty. To illustrate, we consider the example shown in Fig. 8.28. A symmetrical frame, the ends A and B of which are built in, carries a uniformly distributed load of intensity q as shown. The cross-sectional moment of inertia of the legs is I_1 and that of the rafters is I_0, where $I_1 = 3I_0$. We can reduce the problem to that of a frame of uniform cross section simply by multiplying Eqs. (8.27) by EI_0. In such a way, the difference in the values of I_1 and I_0 will be compensated for by distributing along the legs the fictitious masses $ds\, I_0/I_1$ and $M'\, ds\, I_0/I_1$, instead of ds and $M'\, ds$ as was done before.

To illustrate the actual calculations, we assume the numerical data for the frame as shown in Fig. 8.28a. Then, the summation of fictitious masses $ds\, I_0/I_1$ distributed along the center line becomes

$$2\sqrt{5^2 + 12^2} + \tfrac{1}{3} \times 2 \times 12 = 34 \text{ ft}$$

The statical moment of the same masses with respect to the x axis is

$$2 \times 13 \times 14.5 + \tfrac{1}{3} \times 2 \times 12 \times 6 = 425 \text{ ft}^2$$

Thus, from Eqs. (8.22), the coordinates of the elastic center become

$$a = 12 \text{ ft} \qquad b = \tfrac{425}{34} = 12.5 \text{ ft}$$

Now cutting the frame at A, we have the system of redundant elements acting at the elastic center O as shown in Fig. 8.28b.[1] The moments of inertia of the fictitious masses with respect to the principal axes x_1, y_1 are

$$I_{x_1} = 2\left(\frac{13 \times 5^2}{3} + \frac{4 \times 12^2}{3}\right) - 34(0.5)^2 = 592.2 \text{ ft}^3$$

$$I_{y_1} = 2\left(4 \times 12^2 + \frac{13 \times 12^2}{3}\right) = 2,400 \text{ ft}^3$$

Using for M' the ordinates of the bending-moment diagram shown in Fig. 8.28b, we now consider the fictitious masses $M'\ ds\ I_0/I_1$ distributed along the center line of the inclined members KD and DL. The centers of gravity of these masses will be located at points F and E as shown in Fig. 8.28b. Then the integrals on the right-hand side of Eqs. (8.27), multiplied by EI_0, become

$$-\int_K^L M'y_1\ ds = \frac{2}{3}\frac{ql^2}{8}\ 26 \times 2\tfrac{5}{8} = 3,276q \qquad \text{ft}^4$$

$$-\int_K^L M'x_1\ ds = 0$$

$$-\int_K^L M'\ ds = -\frac{2}{3}\frac{ql^2}{8}\ 26 = -1,248q \qquad \text{ft}^3$$

Substituting the obtained numerical values together with the expression $M_0 - ql^2/4$, instead of M_0, into Eqs. (8.27), we obtain

$$H_0 = \frac{3,276q}{592.2} = 5.532q \qquad \text{ft}$$

$$M_0 - \frac{ql^2}{4} = -\frac{1,248q}{34} = -36.71q \qquad \text{ft}^2$$

With these values of the redundant quantities, the bending moments at the cross sections A, K, G, D (Fig. 8.28a) will be

$$M_a = -36.71 + 5.532 \times 12.5 = +32.44q \qquad \text{ft}^2$$

$$M_k = -36.71 + 5.532 \times 0.5 = -33.94q \qquad \text{ft}^2$$

$$M_g = -36.71 - 5.532 \times 2 + 54 = +6.23q \qquad \text{ft}^2$$

$$M_d = -36.71 - 5.532 \times 4.5 + 72 = +10.40q \qquad \text{ft}^2$$

The corresponding bending-moment diagram for the left-hand half of the frame is shown in Fig. 8.28a.

In the case of frames having nonprismatic members, the problem can be

---

[1] To take advantage of symmetry, we leave the known vertical force $ql/2$ at A and compensate by putting at O the moment $M_0 - ql^2/4$ instead of M_0.

reduced to that of a frame having uniform cross-sectional moment of inertia I_0 by using the modified fictitious loads $ds\ I_0/I$ and $M'\ ds\ I_0/I$, instead of ds and $M'\ ds$ as previously used.

PROBLEMS

1   A rectangular frame $ADFB$ built in at the supports A and B is uniformly loaded along the horizontal member DF as shown in Fig. 8.29. The moment of inertia of the cross section of each leg is I_1 and that of the member DF is I_0. Calculate the bending moment at D and construct the bending-moment diagram for the frame if $h/l = \frac{3}{4}$ and $I_0 = 2I_1$.
   Ans. $M_d = -ql^2/21$.

2   A frame of the same dimensions as that shown in Fig. 8.28a is subjected on the left side to the action of a horizontal load uniformly distributed along the vertical axis as shown in Fig. 8.30a. Calculate the redundant quantities H_0, M_0, V_0 at the elastic center O, and construct the bending-moment diagram for the frame.
   Hint Divide the loading into symmetrical and antimetrical parts as shown in Fig. 8.30b and c and use Eqs. (8.28) and (8.29), derived for symmetrical frames, to make the analysis.
   Ans. $H_0 = 3.743q$ ft, $M_0 = 9.417q$ ft², $V_0 = -1.533q$ ft.

3   An unsymmetrical frame having the dimensions shown in Fig. 8.31 is subjected to the action of horizontal loading uniformly distributed along the vertical axis as shown at the left side. The moment of inertia of the leg on the left is I_0, and for the other members as shown in the figure. Calculate the redundant quantities H_0,

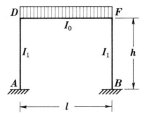

FIG. 8.29

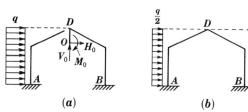
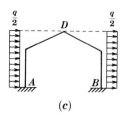

(*a*)   (*b*)   (*c*)

FIG. 8.30

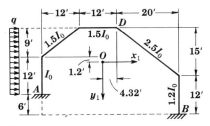

FIG. 8.31

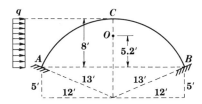

FIG. 8.32

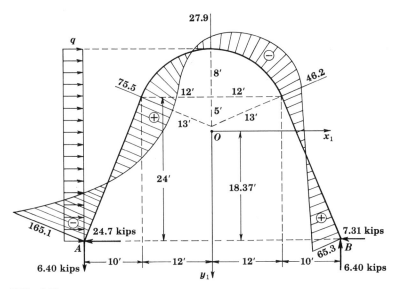

FIG. 8.33

M_0, R_0 acting at the elastic center O, and construct the bending-moment diagram for the frame.

> *Hint* To simplify the calculation of the integrals on the right-hand side of Eqs. (8.27), cut the frame at B rather than at A.

> *Ans.* $H_0 = 4.488q$ ft, $M_0 = 31.14q$ ft^2, $R_0 = 2.659q$ ft.

4 A circular arch of uniform cross section has built-in ends at A and B and is subjected to the action of horizontal loading uniformly distributed with respect to the vertical axis as shown in Fig. 8.32. The dimensions of the arch are shown in the figure. Calculate the redundant quantities H_0, M_0, R_0 at the elastic center O, and construct a bending-moment diagram for the arch.

> *Ans.* $H_0 = 1.730q$ ft, $M_0 = 3.434q$ ft^2, $R_0 = 0.615q$ ft.

5 The frame shown in Fig. 8.33 has built-in ends at A and B and uniform cross section. It is subjected to horizontal loading uniformly distributed with respect to

the vertical axis as shown.   Determine the reactions at the supports A and B and construct a bending-moment diagram for the frame.

   Ans.   For intensity of load $q = 1$ kip/ft, the reactions and the ordinates of the bending-moment diagram are shown in Fig. 8.33.

8.8 FRAMES WITH HINGES

If a frame or arch has one hinge, say at the support A in Fig. 8.34, the bending moment at A vanishes, and we have only two redundant quantities, the components R_a and H_a of the reaction at A.   Assuming that the hinge A is immovable and considering only energy of bending, the equations for calculating R_a and H_a become

$$\frac{\partial U}{\partial R_a} = \int_0^s \frac{M}{EI} \frac{\partial M}{\partial R_a} \, ds = 0$$
$$\frac{\partial U}{\partial H_a} = \int_0^s \frac{M}{EI} \frac{\partial M}{\partial H_a} \, ds = 0 \tag{a}$$

The bending moment at any cross section of the frame is

$$M = R_a x + H_a y + M' \tag{b}$$

where, as before, M' denotes bending moments produced by the loads when R_a and H_a are not acting.   Substituting expression (b) into Eqs. (a), we obtain

$$R_a \int_0^s \frac{xy}{EI} \, ds + H_a \int_0^s \frac{y^2}{EI} \, ds = - \int_0^s \frac{M'y}{EI} \, ds$$
$$R_a \int_0^s \frac{x^2}{EI} \, ds + H_a \int_0^s \frac{xy}{EI} \, ds = - \int_0^s \frac{M'x}{EI} \, ds \tag{8.30a}$$

We see that the integrals on the left-hand side of these equations represent moments of inertia and products of inertia, with respect to the x, y axes, of fictitious masses ds/EI distributed along the center line of the frame.   The integrals on the right-hand side are the statical moments of fictitious masses $M' \, ds/EI$.   For practical applications, we usually multiply Eqs. (8.30a) by a

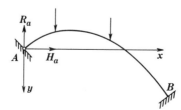

FIG. 8.34

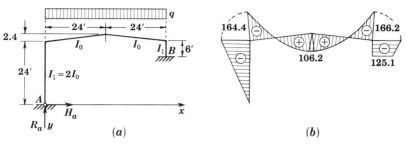

FIG. 8.35

constant factor EI_0 and work with the equations

$$R_a \int_0^s \frac{I_0}{I} xy\, ds + H_a \int_0^s \frac{I_0}{I} y^2\, ds = -\int_0^s \frac{I_0}{I} M'y\, ds$$

$$R_a \int_0^s \frac{I_0}{I} x^2\, ds + H_a \int_0^s \frac{I_0}{I} xy\, ds = -\int_0^s \frac{I_0}{I} M'x\, ds$$

(8.30b)

These equations become especially simple in the case of frames of uniform cross section and frames consisting of prismatic members.

As an example, let us consider the case of a frame having a hinge at the support A and built in at B, the load being uniformly distributed along the horizontal span as shown in Fig. 8.35a. Taking x, y axes as shown in the figure and assuming that $I_1 = 2I_0$, we find the following numerical values for the integrals on the left-hand side of Eqs. (8.30b):

$$I_x = \int_0^s \frac{I_0}{I} y^2\, ds = 34{,}293.5 \text{ ft}^3$$

$$I_y = \int_0^s \frac{I_0}{I} x^2\, ds = 43{,}960.3 \text{ ft}^3$$

$$I_{xy} = \int_0^s \frac{I_0}{I} xy\, ds = -32{,}199.6 \text{ ft}^3$$

In calculating the integrals on the right-hand side of Eqs. (8.30b), we have $M' = -qx^2/2$; so

$$-\int_0^s \frac{I_0}{I} M'y\, ds = -536{,}610q \qquad \text{ft}^4$$

$$-\int_0^s \frac{I_0}{I} M'x\, ds = 832{,}750q \qquad \text{ft}^4$$

Substituting the numerical values of the various integrals into Eqs. (8.30b), we obtain

$$H_a = 6.85q \qquad \text{ft} \qquad R_a = 23.96q \qquad \text{ft}$$

The corresponding bending-moment diagram is shown in Fig. 8.35b for $q = 1$ kip/ft.

In the case of a symmetrically loaded symmetrical frame as shown in Fig. 8.36, we have only one unknown, the thrust H. Taking the origin of coordinates at the hinge D and proceeding as before, the equation for calculating H becomes

$$H \int_D^B \frac{I_0}{I} y^2 \, ds = - \int_D^B \frac{I_0}{I} M'y \, ds \qquad (c)$$

Then, for the dimensions shown in the figure, we obtain

$$\int_D^B \frac{I_0}{I} y^2 \, ds = 4{,}932 \text{ ft}^3$$

The diagram for M' is shown on the right-hand side of the frame in Fig. 8.36, and we obtain

$$- \int_D^B \frac{I_0}{I} M'y \, ds = \tfrac{1}{2} \times 3 \times 18 \times 21P = 567P \qquad \text{ft}^3$$

Substituting these values of the integrals into Eq. (c), we find

$$H = \frac{567P}{4{,}932} = 0.115P$$

The corresponding bending-moment diagram is shown on the left-hand side of the frame in Fig. 8.36, assuming $P = 1$ kip.

In the case of a frame with two hinges, we again have only one redundant quantity and need for its calculation only one equation in addition to equations of statics. As an example, let us consider a symmetrical frame of uniform cross section as shown in Fig. 8.37. It is required to determine the thrust H for the case where a console at E transmits a couple M_0 to the frame as shown.

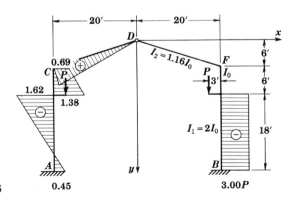

FIG. 8.36

Removing the support at A, we take the thrust H as the redundant quantity. Its magnitude will be calculated from the equation

$$\frac{\partial U}{\partial H} = \int_A^B \frac{M}{EI} \frac{\partial M}{\partial H} \, ds = 0 \tag{d}$$

which states that the distance between the hinges A and B remains unchanged during deformation of the frame. The bending moment at any cross section is

$$M = Hy + M' \tag{e}$$

and, with constant EI, we obtain from Eq. (d)

$$H \int_A^B y^2 \, ds = - \int_A^B M'y \, ds \tag{f}$$

Using the dimensions shown in the figure, we now find, for the integral on the left,

$$\int_A^B y^2 \, ds = 27,529 \text{ ft}^3$$

To calculate the integral on the right, we note that $M' = M_0 x/l$ and obtain

$$-\int_A^B M'y \, ds = \tfrac{1}{2}M_0 26(24 + \tfrac{10}{3}) + \tfrac{1}{8}M_0 26(\tfrac{10}{3})$$
$$= 344.5 M_0 \qquad \text{ft}^2$$

Finally, substituting the numerical values of the two integrals into Eq. (f) and solving for H, we obtain

$$H = \frac{344.5 M_0}{27,529} = 0.01251 M_0 \qquad \text{ft}^{-1}$$

Using this value of H in Eq. (e), we can calculate the bending moment for any cross section of the frame.

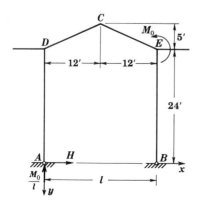

FIG. 8.37

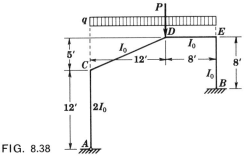

FIG. 8.38

PROBLEMS

1   An unsymmetrical frame, hinged at A and built in at B, has dimensions as shown in Fig. 8.38.   Find the redundant reactions R_a and H_a at A due to the action of a uniformly distributed load of intensity $q = 1$ kip/ft over the horizontal span.

   Ans. $R_a = 11.301$ kips, $H_a = 2.684$ kips.

2   Repeat the solution of the previous problem for the case of a concentrated vertical load $P = 10$ kips applied at D.

   Ans. $R_a = 4.781$ kips, $H_a = 1.822$ kips.

8.9 EFFECTS OF TEMPERATURE CHANGES AND SUPPORT SETTLEMENT

Frames with redundant constraints cannot freely expand or contract with change in temperature, and as a result of this, thermal stresses will ensue. To analyze these stresses in the case of a frame with built-in ends (Fig. 8.39), we assume first that the constraints at the support A are removed so that the frame can expand freely, and then determine the thermal displacements u_t, v_t, and θ_t at the elastic center O.*   The redundant quantities H_0, R_0, and M_0, produced by the temperature change, must evidently be of such magnitudes as to eliminate the thermal displacements, and we obtain, for their calculation,

* The displacements u_t and v_t are taken positive in the positive directions of the x_1, y_1 axes; θ_t is positive if clockwise.

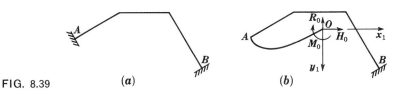

FIG. 8.39   *(a)*   *(b)*

the equations

$$\frac{\partial U}{\partial H_0} = \int_0^s \frac{M}{EI} \frac{\partial M}{\partial H_0} \, ds = - u_t$$

$$\frac{\partial U}{\partial R_0} = \int_0^s \frac{M}{EI} \frac{\partial M}{\partial R_0} \, ds = + v_t \qquad (a)$$

$$\frac{\partial U}{\partial M_0} = \int_0^s \frac{M}{EI} \frac{\partial M}{\partial M_0} \, ds = - \theta_t$$

Observing that there are no loads acting on the frame, in this case, we have

$$M = M_0 + H_0 y_1 + R_0 x_1 \qquad (b)$$

and Eqs. (a) become

$$R_0 \int_0^s \frac{x_1 y_1}{EI} \, ds + H_0 \int_0^s \frac{y_1^2}{EI} \, ds = - u_t$$

$$R_0 \int_0^s \frac{x_1^2}{EI} \, ds + H_0 \int_0^s \frac{x_1 y_1}{EI} \, ds = + v_t \qquad (8.31)$$

$$M_0 \int_0^s \frac{ds}{EI} = - \theta_t$$

where s is the full length of the center line of the frame.

We shall now apply these general equations to the particular case of the symmetrical frame shown in Fig. 8.28. Assuming a uniform rise in temperature of the frame by $t°F$, we obtain[1]

$$u_t = - \alpha t l \qquad v_t = 0 \qquad \theta_t = 0$$

Hence $R_0 = M_0 = 0$, and we have only to find H_0 from the first of Eqs. (8.31). After multiplying this equation by EI_0 and using the numerical value of I_{x_1} from page 387, we obtain

$$H_0 = \frac{\alpha t l E I_0}{592.2}$$

Taking, for example, for concrete

$$\alpha = 6(10^{-6}) \ (\text{in./in.})/°F \qquad E = 2.88(10^5) \ \text{kips/ft}^2$$

and assuming $t = 60°F$, $I_0 = 0.1728 \ \text{ft}^4$, we obtain

$$H_0 = 0.7261 \ \text{kip}$$

Having the thrust H_0, we can readily calculate the bending moments and stresses produced by the assumed change in temperature.

[1] The fictitious bar AO does not change its length, and since for a uniform temperature change there is no rotation, the displacements of points A and O are identical.

In the case of an unsymmetrical frame such as that shown in Fig. 8.31, a uniform temperature change produces both u_t and v_t displacements; so for calculating H_0 and R_0, we must use the first two of Eqs. (8.31). In this case it should be observed that x_1 and y_1 are not principal axes, and the product of inertia does not vanish in Eqs. (8.31).

We have a problem similar to that of thermal stresses when we consider the effect of shrinkage of concrete on the magnitudes of redundant reactions. The amount of shrinkage depends on many factors, but a satisfactory approximation is obtained by considering its effect to be equivalent to that of a uniform temperature drop of 60°F.

Sometimes additional stresses in statically indeterminate frames are produced by settlement of the supports. If the amounts of settlement are known, the magnitudes of the corresponding redundant reactions can also be calculated by using Eqs. (8.31). Let us take again, as an example, the frame shown in Fig. 8.28 and assume that the support A undergoes a vertical settlement Δ. Owing to this, the previously calculated vertical reaction will be diminished by an amount equal to the force R_0 which, if applied at the elastic center O, would produce a downward displacement Δ of this point. The magnitude of this force is obtained from the second of Eqs. (8.31) by substituting Δ for v_t. Multiplying this equation by EI_0, we obtain

$$R_0 = \frac{\Delta EI_0}{I_{y_1}}$$

Taking, for example,

$$\Delta = 0.75 \text{ in.} = 0.0625 \text{ ft} \qquad E = 288,000 \text{ kips/ft}^2$$

$$I_0 = 0.1728 \text{ ft}^4$$

and using the value of I_{y_1} from page 387, we obtain

$$R_0 = \frac{0.0625 \times 288,000 \times 0.1728}{2,400} = 1.296 \text{ kips}$$

acting downward.

As another example of support movement, let us consider the case in which the support A of the previous frame rotates in a counterclockwise direction by a small angle θ as shown in Fig. 8.40. To determine the redundant forces H_0, R_0, M_0 corresponding to this rotation, we observe that the end O of the rigid bar AO undergoes not only rotation θ but also displacements

$$u = -a\theta \qquad v = -\frac{l\theta}{2}$$

in the x_1 and y_1 directions. Substituting these values with the proper signs[1]

[1] In Eqs. (8.31), H_0, R_0, M_0 denote forces required to eliminate displacements produced by a temperature change. Here, the same notations are used for forces producing the known displacements.

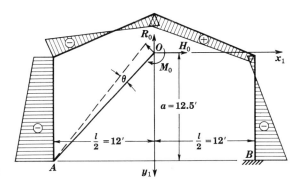

FIG. 8.40

into Eqs. (8.31) and multiplying by EI_0, we obtain

$$H_0 I_{x_1} = - \theta a EI_0 \qquad R_0 I_{y_1} = \frac{\theta l}{2} EI_0 \qquad M_0 A = - \theta EI_0$$

Taking, for example,

$$\theta = 0.005 \qquad E = 288{,}000 \text{ kips/ft}^2 \qquad I_0 = 0.1728 \text{ ft}^4$$

and using the numerical values of I_{x_1} and I_{y_1} from page 387, we obtain

$$H_0 = - \frac{0.005 \times 12.5 \times 49{,}770}{592.2} = - 5.252 \text{ kips}$$

$$R_0 = + \frac{0.005 \times 12 \times 49{,}770}{2{,}400} = 1.244 \text{ kips}$$

$$M_0 = - \frac{0.005 \times 49{,}770}{34} = - 7.318 \text{ kip-ft}$$

Having these quantities, we can readily calculate the bending moment at any cross section of the frame. For example, at the support A we have

$$M_a = -7.318 - 5.252 \times 12.5 - 1.244 \times 12 = -87.89 \text{ kip-ft}$$

The corresponding bending-moment diagram is shown in Fig. 8.40.

PROBLEMS

1   Referring to the unsymmetrical frame shown in Fig. 8.31 and using the numerical data already given for this frame, calculate the magnitudes of the redundant quantities H_0 and R_0 due to a uniform rise in temperature $t = 40°F$. Assume that the coefficient of thermal expansion is $\alpha = 6(10^{-6})$ (in./in.)/°F and that $E = 2.88(10^5)$ kips/ft^2 and $I_0 = 0.1728$ ft^4.

     Ans. $H_0 = 186.4$ lb, $R_0 = -31.8$ lb.

2   Construct a bending-moment diagram for the frame shown in Fig. 8.31 showing the effect of a 1-in. vertical settlement of the support A. Use the same numerical data given in the preceding problem.

8.10 RINGS

The method of analysis developed in preceding articles for arches and frames can be used also in the case of closed rings.   As shown in Fig. 8.41a, a ring on which a system of known self-equilibrating forces $P_1, P_2, P_3, \ldots$ is acting represents a structure with three redundant forces.   We can take, as redundant, the axial force, the shearing force, and the bending moment at any cross section A.   We then assume that the ring is cut at this section and that a rigid bar AO is attached to one side of the section while the other side is fixed as shown in Fig. 8.41b.   Assuming that fictitious masses ds/EI are distributed along the center line of the ring, we determine the position of the elastic center by using Eqs. (8.22).   Then, proceeding as before, we replace the forces acting on the cross section A by the statically equivalent system of forces H_0, R_0, M_0 applied at the elastic center O.   The magnitudes of these redundant forces will be determined by using Eqs. (8.27) derived previously for hingeless frames.

As an example, let us consider the rectangular symmetrical frame shown in Fig. 8.42a.   We first make a cut at A and conclude that the elastic center O

FIG. 8.41   (a)   (b)

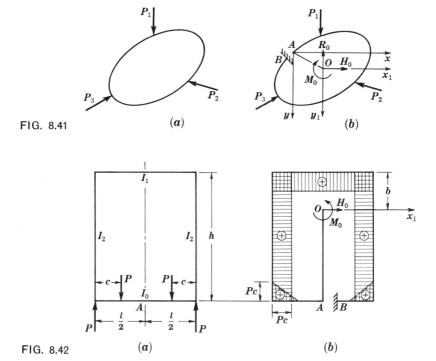

FIG. 8.42   (a)   (b)

is on the axis of symmetry of the frame. Then, with the notations

$$\frac{I_0}{I_1} = \alpha \qquad \frac{I_0}{I_2} = \beta$$

we have

$$\int_0^s \frac{I_0}{I} \, ds = l + 2\beta h + \alpha l \qquad \int_0^s \frac{I_0}{I} y \, ds = \beta h^2 + lh$$

where s denotes the full length of the center line of the ring. Finally, from the second of Eqs. (8.22), the distance of the elastic center from the top of the frame is found to be

$$b = \frac{\beta h^2 + lh}{l(1 + \alpha) + 2\beta h}$$

Having the location of the elastic center, we now find that

$$\int_0^s \frac{I_0}{I} y_1^2 \, ds = l(h - b)^2 + \frac{\beta h^3}{6} + \frac{1}{2}\beta h(h - 2b)^2 + \alpha l b^2$$

The bending moments M' produced by the external forces are shown in Fig. 8.42b, and we obtain

$$\int_0^s \frac{I_0}{I} M' \, ds = Pc^2 + 2\beta Pch + \alpha Pcl$$

$$\int_0^s \frac{I_0}{I} M' y_1 \, ds = \beta Pch(h - 2b) - \alpha Pclb + Pc^2(h - b)$$
$$= Pc[\beta h(h - 2b) - \alpha lb + c(h - b)]$$

Substituting the values of these integrals into Eqs. (8.27), multiplied by EI_0, we find

$$M_0 = -Pc \frac{c + 2\beta h + \alpha l}{l(1 + \alpha) + 2\beta h}$$

$$H_0 = -Pc \frac{\beta h(h - 2b) - \alpha lb + c(h - b)}{l(h - b)^2 + \beta h^3/6 + \frac{1}{2}\beta h(h - 2b)^2 + \alpha l b^2}$$

Having these values of M_0 and H_0, we can readily calculate the bending moment for any cross section of the frame and construct a bending-moment diagram.

As a second example, let us assume that the same rectangular frame discussed above is subjected to the action of lateral forces $\frac{1}{2}P$ as shown in Fig. 8.43a. The external reactions at C and D then will be as shown. Making a cut at the section AB, we find that the external loading produces bending moments M' as shown by the shaded areas in Fig. 8.43b. For this loading, there will be

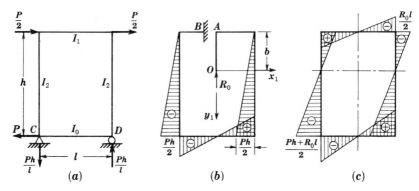

FIG. 8.43

no axial force and no bending moment at A; so we have only one redundant quantity R_0. To calculate its magnitude, we use the second of Eqs. (8.27) multiplied by EI_0. The integrals entering into this equation are

$$\int_0^s \frac{I_0}{I} x_1{}^2\, ds = \frac{l^2}{12}\,[6\beta h + l(1 + \alpha)]$$

$$\int_0^s \frac{I_0}{I} M' x_1\, ds = \frac{Phl}{12}\,(l + 3\beta h)$$

using which we obtain

$$R_0 = -P\,\frac{h(l + 3\beta h)}{l[6\beta h + l(1 + \alpha)]}$$

Having this value of R_0, we can readily construct a bending-moment diagram of the shape shown in Fig. 8.43c for any given dimensions of the frame.

As a last example, we consider the case of an elliptical ring of uniform cross section submitted to uniform internal pressure of intensity p, as shown in Fig. 8.44. Cutting the ring at the section AB, we conclude at once from symmetry that the shearing force at this section vanishes and that the axial force is equal to pa. Thus, there is only one redundant quantity M_0 to be considered. Treating pa as an external force applied at A (see page 387), we

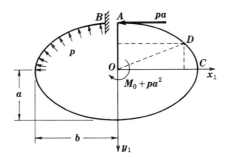

FIG. 8.44

TABLE 8.10   VALUES OF α AND β FOR VARIOUS
             PROPORTIONS OF AN ELLIPSE

		a/b						
	1	0.9	0.8	0.7	0.6	0.5	0.4	0.3
α	2π	5.97	5.67	5.38	5.11	4.85	4.60	4.39
β	2π	6.65	7.18	7.93	9.09	10.94	14.24	21.31

have for the bending moment M' at any cross section D

$$M' = \tfrac{1}{2}p(x_1^2 + y_1^2 - a^2)$$

Then the integrals in the third of Eqs. (8.27) become

$$\int_0^s ds = \alpha b \qquad \int_0^s M' \, ds = -\tfrac{1}{2}pa^2\alpha b + \tfrac{1}{2}p\beta a^2 b$$

in which α and β are constants depending on the proportions of the ellipse and are given in Table 8.10 above.   The value of M_0 is then obtained from the equation

$$M_0 + pa^2 = -\frac{1}{\alpha b}\int_0^s M' \, ds = \frac{1}{2}\,pa^2 - \frac{1}{2}\frac{p}{\alpha b}\,\beta a^2 b$$

PROBLEMS

1   Construct a bending-moment diagram for the frame shown in Fig. 8.42 if $\alpha = \beta = 1$ and $l = h$.
    Ans. $b = 1/2$, $M_0 = -Pc(c + 3l)/4l$, $H_0 = 3Pc(l - c)/4l^2$.
2   A circular ring of uniform cross section is subjected to the action of forces P directed along a vertical diameter DE of the ring as shown in Fig. 8.45.   Calculate the magnitudes of the bending moments at A and at D.
    Ans. $M_a = Pr/\pi - Pr/2$, $M_d = Pr/\pi$.

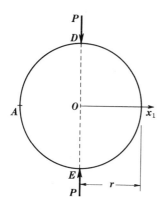

FIG. 8.45

Chapter 9

Continuous beams and frames

9.1 SLOPE-DEFLECTION EQUATIONS

Frame structures like that shown in Fig. 9.1a usually consist of straight prismatic members which can be treated as beams elastically constrained at the ends. Such a member as *ab*, for example, can be isolated as shown in Fig. 9.1b and the elastic constraints at the ends replaced by reactive couples M_a and M_b. In this way, we reduce the problem to that of a simply supported beam acted upon by lateral loads together with end moments. Under such loading, the beam deflects and the end tangents rotate by small angles θ_a and θ_b as shown. For our further discussion, it will be helpful to establish analytical relationships between these angles, the end moments, and the lateral loading. Such relationships are generally known as *slope-deflection equations*, and we shall now consider their derivation.

Assuming that the beam is bent in a principal plane and neglecting shear

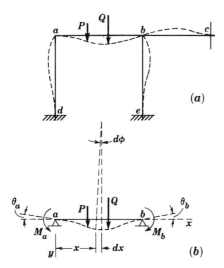

FIG. 9.1

deformation,[1] the curvature of the *elastic line* at any cross section is given by the well-known equation

$$\frac{1}{r} = \frac{M}{EI} \tag{a}$$

in which M is the bending moment and EI the flexural rigidity at the cross section under consideration. In using this equation, we shall take the longitudinal axis of the beam as the x axis and consider the y axis positive downward as shown. We shall also assume that deflections of the beam are small so that the length of an element of the elastic line can be taken equal to the length dx of its projection on the x axis. In such a case, the small angle $d\phi$ between two adjacent cross sections after bending is

$$d\phi = \frac{dx}{r} = \frac{M\,dx}{EI} \tag{b}$$

With this expression, the rotations of the end tangents can be calculated by the method of fictitious loads already used in the analysis of trusses (see page 276). In Fig. 9.2a, for example, let the curve *def* be the bending-moment diagram for a transversely loaded simple beam *AB*. If we assume that only one infinitesimal element dx of this beam is elastic, while the rest of it remains absolutely rigid, the elastic line *acb* will be as shown in Fig. 9.2b. This line consists simply of two straight portions *ac* and *cb* having between them the angle $d\phi$

[1] For frame members of usual proportions, this effect is known to be very small. See S. Timoshenko, "Strength of Materials," 3d ed., vol. I, p. 318, D. Van Nostrand Company Inc., Princeton, N.J., 1955.

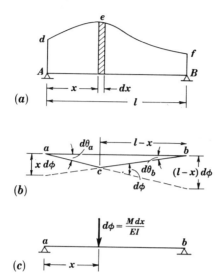

FIG. 9.2

as defined by Eq. (b).   Owing to such deflection, the left end of the beam, as
we see from the figure, rotates by an infinitesimal angle of the magnitude

$$d\theta_a = \frac{l - x}{l}\, d\phi \qquad\qquad (c)$$

Considering clockwise rotations as positive, we take expression (c) with
positive sign.   The end b of the beam rotates counterclockwise, and the corresponding angle of rotation is

$$d\theta_b = -\frac{x}{l}\, d\phi \qquad\qquad (d)$$

Expressions (c) and (d) permit a very simple interpretation.   Imagine a
simply supported beam on which a fictitious load $d\phi = M\, dx/EI$ is acting as
shown in Fig. 9.2c.   Then, expressions (c) and (d) represent the shearing
forces at the ends of this beam due to such a fictitious load.

Having the angles of rotation of the ends resulting from bending of one
element of the beam, we shall obtain the total angles of rotation by summing
up expressions (c) and (d) over the entire length of the beam.   This gives

$$\theta_a = \int_0^l \frac{l - x}{l}\, d\phi = \int_0^l \frac{l - x}{l}\, \frac{M\, dx}{EI}$$

$$\theta_b = -\int_0^l \frac{x}{l}\, d\phi = -\int_0^l \frac{x}{l}\, \frac{M\, dx}{EI} \qquad (e)$$

Observing that $M\,dx$ is the area of an elemental strip of the bending-moment diagram in Fig. 9.2a and that EI is constant for beams of uniform cross section, we conclude that to obtain the angles of rotation of the ends of such beams, we need only consider the bending-moment area $AdefB$ as a fictitious load and then divide by EI the shearing forces produced at the ends of the beam by this load.

Taking, for example, a uniformly loaded beam, we see that the bending-moment area is a parabolic segment (Fig. 9.3a) having the area

$$A = \frac{2l}{3}\frac{ql^2}{8} = \frac{ql^3}{12}$$

If we treat this area as a fictitious load, the corresponding reactions at the supports are $ql^3/24$, and we obtain

$$\theta_a = \frac{ql^3}{24EI} \qquad \theta_b = -\frac{ql^3}{24EI} \qquad\qquad (f)$$

In the case of a concentrated load P applied at a distance c from the right support, the bending-moment area is represented by the triangle in Fig. 9.3b. Treating the area of this triangle as a fictitious load, we obtain for the angles of rotation at the supports

$$\theta_a = \frac{Pc(l^2 - c^2)}{6lEI} \qquad \theta_b = -\frac{Pc(l - c)(2l - c)}{6lEI} \qquad (g)$$

Let us consider now the specific case of bending of a simply supported beam AB by couples applied as shown in Fig. 9.4a. In our further discussion these couples will be called *end moments*, and we shall denote them by the symbols M_{ab} and M_{ba}, the two subscripts indicating the ends of the beam as shown in

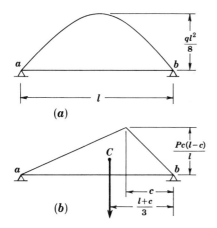

FIG. 9.3

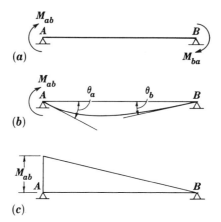

FIG. 9.4   (c)

Fig. 9.4a. Clockwise end moments will be considered as positive. This means that with the conventional rule for sign of bending moment, the end moment M_{ab} is identical with the bending moment at A, while the end moment M_{ba} is equal but opposite in sign to the bending moment at B. Beginning with the case where only the moment M_{ab} is acting (Fig. 9.4b) and observing that the corresponding bending-moment diagram is a triangle (Fig. 9.4c), we obtain

$$\theta_a = \frac{M_{ab}l}{3EI} \qquad \theta_b = -\frac{M_{ab}l}{6EI} \tag{h}$$

We obtain similar formulas for the case where the moment M_{ba} is acting alone. Combining the actions of the two end moments (Fig. 9.4a), we obtain

$$\theta_a = \frac{M_{ab}l}{3EI} - \frac{M_{ba}l}{6EI} \qquad \theta_b = \frac{M_{ba}l}{3EI} - \frac{M_{ab}l}{6EI} \tag{9.1a}$$

Solving these two equations for M_{ab} and M_{ba}, we obtain

$$M_{ab} = \frac{2EI}{l}(2\theta_a + \theta_b) \qquad M_{ba} = \frac{2EI}{l}(2\theta_b + \theta_a) \tag{9.1b}$$

From these two equations the end moments can be calculated if the rotations θ_a and θ_b of the end tangents are known.

Let us consider now a more general case in which there are both end moments and lateral load, acting as shown in Fig. 9.5a. The angles of rotation produced by the end moments alone are given by expressions (9.1a). To obtain the angles of rotation produced by the lateral load, we consider the corresponding bending-moment diagram as shown in Fig. 9.5b. Upon denoting by c and d the distances from the ends of the beam to the vertical through the centroid C of this bending-moment area and by A the magnitude of the area,

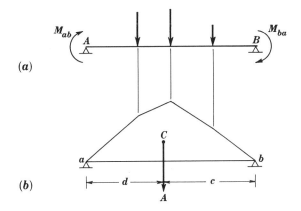

(a)

(b)

FIG. 9.5

the reactions at the ends produced by such fictitious loading are

$$R_a = \frac{Ac}{l} \qquad R_b = \frac{Ad}{l}$$

and the corresponding angles of rotation are

$$\theta_a = \frac{Ac}{EIl} \qquad \theta_b = -\frac{Ad}{EIl} \tag{i}$$

Combining these angles with those produced by the end moments [Eqs. (9.1a)], we obtain the following total angles:

$$\theta_a = \frac{M_{ab}l}{3EI} - \frac{M_{ba}l}{6EI} + \frac{Ac}{EIl}$$

$$\theta_b = \frac{M_{ba}l}{3EI} - \frac{M_{ab}l}{6EI} - \frac{Ad}{EIl} \tag{9.2a}$$

Solving these equations for M_{ab} and M_{ba}, we obtain

$$M_{ab} = \frac{2EI}{l}(2\theta_a + \theta_b) - \frac{2A}{l^2}(2c - d)$$

$$M_{ba} = \frac{2EI}{l}(2\theta_b + \theta_a) + \frac{2A}{l^2}(2d - c) \tag{9.2b}$$

From these equations the end moments can be readily calculated if the rotations of the ends and the bending-moment diagram for the lateral load are known.

Sometimes, as a result of displacements of the supports, a beam, in addition to bending, rotates as a rigid body, and we denote the angle of this rotation by Θ_{ab}, considered positive if the rotation is clockwise. The total angles of rotation of the ends will then be

$$\theta_a = \frac{M_{ab}l}{3EI} - \frac{M_{ba}l}{6EI} + \frac{Ac}{EIl} + \Theta_{ab}$$

$$\theta_b = \frac{M_{ba}l}{3EI} - \frac{M_{ab}l}{6EI} - \frac{Ad.}{EIl} + \Theta_{ab}$$

$$(9.3a)$$

Solving these equations for the end moments, we obtain

$$M_{ab} = \frac{2EI}{l}(2\theta_a + \theta_b) - \frac{2A}{l^2}(2c - d) - \frac{6\Theta_{ab}EI}{l}$$

$$M_{ba} = \frac{2EI}{l}(2\theta_b + \theta_a) + \frac{2A}{l^2}(2d - c) - \frac{6\Theta_{ab}EI}{l}$$

$$(9.3b)$$

Equations (9.1) to (9.3) represent the required slope-deflection equations so widely used in the analysis of frame structures.

9.2 BEAMS WITH FIXED ENDS

Using the slope-deflection equations developed in the preceding article, we can readily analyze various cases of statically indeterminate beams. We shall discuss here only a few particular cases that are of special interest in connection with the analysis of frames. We begin with a beam built in at one end and simply supported at the other, as shown in Fig. 9.6a. Assuming that the magnitude of the active end moment M_{ab} is given, let it be required to find the corresponding magnitude of the reactive end moment M_{ba} produced at the fixed end B and also the relation between the active moment M_{ab} and the angle of rotation θ_a. Observing that the end B of the beam does not rotate and substituting $\theta_b = 0$ in the second of Eqs. (9.1a), we find

$$M_{ba} = \tfrac{1}{2}M_{ab} \qquad\qquad (a)$$

This shows that if an active moment M_{ab} is applied at the end A, a reactive moment M_{ba}, equal to $\tfrac{1}{2}M_{ab}$, is produced at the fixed end B. This latter moment is of particular interest in rigid-frame analysis and is called the *carryover moment*.

Substituting $\theta_b = 0$ in the first of Eqs. (9.1b), we obtain

$$M_{ab} = \frac{4EI}{l}\theta_a \qquad\qquad (b)$$

From this equation, the moment M_{ab} is readily calculated if the angle of rotation θ_a is known.

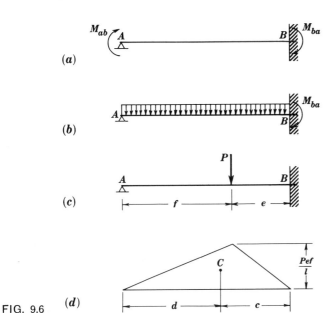

FIG. 9.6   (d)

It is interesting to note that if both ends of the beam are simply supported, the relation between the end moment M_{ab} and the angle θ_{ab} is

$$M_{ab} = \frac{3EI}{l} \theta_a \qquad\qquad (c)$$

This shows that in calculating M_{ab} by using the angle θ_a the placing of a hinge at B is equivalent to reducing the flexural rigidity EI of the beam to the value $3EI/4$.

Considering now lateral loading, we observe that in the case of a uniformly loaded beam (Fig. 9.6b), the reactive end moment M_{ba} is found from the second of Eqs. (9.2a). Substituting into this equation

$$M_{ab} = 0 \qquad \theta_b = 0 \qquad A = \frac{ql^3}{12} \qquad d = \frac{l}{2}$$

we obtain

$$M_{ba} = \frac{ql^2}{8}$$

We note that this end moment has the same value as the bending moment at the middle of a simply supported beam.

If a concentrated force P acts on the beam (Fig. 9.6c), the bending-moment diagram for the corresponding simply supported beam is represented by the triangle shown in Fig. 9.6d, and we obtain

$$A = \frac{Pef}{2} \qquad d = \frac{l+f}{3}$$

The second of Eqs. (9.2b), with $\theta_b = 0$ and $M_{ab} = 0$, then gives

$$M_{ba} = \frac{3Ad}{l^2} = \frac{Pf(l^2 - f^2)}{2l^2}$$

If the built-in end B of the beam suffers a vertical downward displacement Δ without rotation, the end moment M_{ba} produced by such displacement is obtained by using Eqs. (9.3b). Substituting in the first of these equations $M_{ab} = 0$, $\theta_b = 0$, $A = 0$, and $\Theta_{ab} = \Delta/l$, we obtain

$$\theta_a = \frac{3}{2}\frac{\Delta}{l}$$

Substituting this value in the second of Eqs. (9.3b), we find

$$M_{ba} = -\frac{3EI}{l}\frac{\Delta}{l} \qquad\qquad (d)$$

Applications of these results will be shown later in the analysis of frames.

In the case of a beam with both ends built in (Fig. 9.7a) and carrying any lateral load, we use Eqs. (9.2b) to calculate the statically indeterminate end moments. Substituting $\theta_a = \theta_b = 0$ into these equations, we obtain

$$M_{ab} = -\frac{2A}{l^2}(2c - d) \qquad M_{ba} = \frac{2A}{l^2}(2d - c) \qquad (9.4)$$

For any given lateral load, the bending-moment diagram for a corresponding simply supported beam, Fig. 9.7b, can be constructed, and its area A together with the centroidal distances c and d can be calculated. Substituting these quantities into Eqs. (9.4), we obtain the required end moments. These

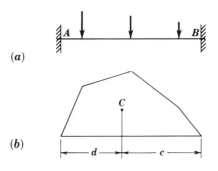

(a)

(b)

FIG. 9.7

moments produced by lateral loads are called the *fixed-end moments* and will be denoted in our further discussion by the symbols $\mathfrak{M}_{ab}$ and $\mathfrak{M}_{ba}$. Observing that they are taken positive when they act clockwise, we conclude that $\mathfrak{M}_{ab}$ is identical with the bending moment at the end A of the beam, while $\mathfrak{M}_{ba}$ is numerically equal but opposite in sign to the bending moment at the end B.

In the case of a load uniformly distributed along the entire length of the beam, $A = ql^3/12$, $c = d = l/2$, and Eqs. (9.4) become

$$\mathfrak{M}_{ab} = -\frac{ql^2}{12} \qquad \mathfrak{M}_{ba} = \frac{ql^2}{12} \tag{9.4a}$$

In the case of a concentrated load P applied at the distance e from the support B, the bending-moment diagram is a triangle (Fig. 9.6d), and we obtain $A = Pfe/2$, $c = (l + e)/3$, $d = (l + f)/3$. Substituting these values into Eqs. (9.4), we find

$$\mathfrak{M}_{ab} = -\frac{Pe^2f}{l^2} \qquad \mathfrak{M}_{ba} = \frac{Pef^2}{l^2} \tag{9.4b}$$

For any value of the distance e, the values of the fixed-end moments can be readily calculated.

Let us consider now the bending of a fixed-end beam produced by nonequal settlements of the supports. Assume, for example, that the support B settles by an amount Δ, while the support A remains stationary. Assume, also, that no rotations of the ends of the beam occur during such displacement. Then, in calculating the end moments produced by such settlement, we use Eqs. (9.3b). Substituting $\theta_a = \theta_b = 0$ and $A = 0$ in these equations and observing that $\Theta_{ab} = \Delta/l$, we obtain

$$M_{ab} = M_{ba} = -\frac{6EI\Delta}{l^2} = -\frac{6EI}{l}\,\Theta_{ab} \tag{9.5}$$

Introducing the notation $k = EI/l$ for the so-called "stiffness factor" of the beam and using the notation $\mathfrak{M}$ for fixed-end moment, we can write the slope-deflection equations (9.3b) in the form

$$M_{ab} = 2k(2\theta_a + \theta_b) + \mathfrak{M}_{ab} - 6k\Theta_{ab}$$
$$M_{ba} = 2k(2\theta_b + \theta_a) + \mathfrak{M}_{ba} - 6k\Theta_{ab} \tag{9.6}$$

These equations will find a wide application in the analysis of frames, as will be shown later. For future reference, expressions for fixed-end moments for various cases of lateral loading of a beam AB are recorded in Table 9.1 below. The first two cases have already been calculated as represented by Eqs. (9.4a) and (9.4b) above. Verification of the remaining cases in the table is left as an exercise for the reader.

TABLE 9.1   FIXED-END MOMENTS FOR PRISMATIC BEAMS

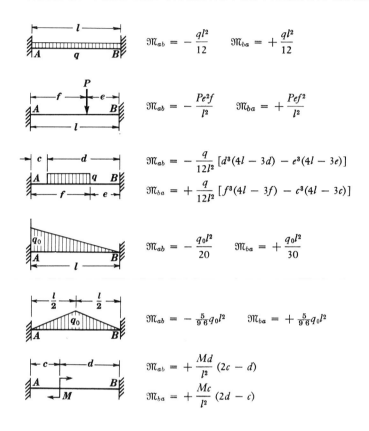

$$\mathfrak{M}_{ab} = -\frac{ql^2}{12} \qquad \mathfrak{M}_{ba} = +\frac{ql^2}{12}$$

$$\mathfrak{M}_{ab} = -\frac{Pe^2f}{l^2} \qquad \mathfrak{M}_{ba} = +\frac{Pef^2}{l^2}$$

$$\mathfrak{M}_{ab} = -\frac{q}{12l^2}\left[d^3(4l-3d) - e^3(4l-3e)\right]$$

$$\mathfrak{M}_{ba} = +\frac{q}{12l^2}\left[f^3(4l-3f) - c^3(4l-3c)\right]$$

$$\mathfrak{M}_{ab} = -\frac{q_0 l^2}{20} \qquad \mathfrak{M}_{ba} = +\frac{q_0 l^2}{30}$$

$$\mathfrak{M}_{ab} = -\tfrac{5}{96}q_0 l^2 \qquad \mathfrak{M}_{ba} = +\tfrac{5}{96}q_0 l^2$$

$$\mathfrak{M}_{ab} = +\frac{Md}{l^2}(2c-d)$$

$$\mathfrak{M}_{ba} = +\frac{Mc}{l^2}(2d-c)$$

9.3 CONTINUOUS BEAMS

Equations (9.2a), derived in Art. 9.1, can be used to advantage in the analysis of continuous beams.   Starting from the left end of the beam, we denote by 0, 1, 2, . . . the consecutive supports, by $l_1, l_2,$ . . . the lengths of the spans, and by $I_1, I_2,$ . . . the cross-sectional moments of inertia, assumed constant along each span.   This done, we consider any two adjacent spans l_n and l_{n+1} as shown in Fig. 9.8a and construct the corresponding simple-beam bending-moment diagrams for the lateral loading as shown in Fig. 9.8b.   The areas of these diagrams are denoted by A_n and A_{n+1} and the positions of their centroids C_n and C_{n+1} by the distances c_n, d_n and c_{n+1}, d_{n+1}, respectively.   Considering bending of each span, we must take into account not only the lateral loading acting on the span but also the end moments representing the action of the adjacent spans on the span under consideration.   The magnitudes of these moments for the span l_n we denote by $M_{n-1,n}$ and $M_{n,n-1}$, and for the span l_{n+1}

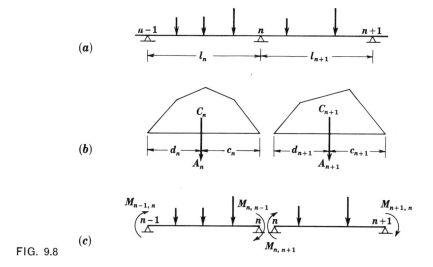

(a)

(b)

(c)

FIG. 9.8

by $M_{n,n+1}$ and $M_{n+1,n}$, as shown in Fig. 9.8c. The equations for calculating these moments can be written on the basis of the continuity of the elastic line. From such continuity, it follows that the angle of rotation $\theta_{n,n-1}$ of the right end of the span l_n must be equal to the angle of rotation $\theta_{n,n+1}$ of the left end of the span l_{n+1}. These angles of rotation will be found from Eqs. (9.2a), which give

$$\theta_{n,n-1} = \frac{M_{n,n-1}l_n}{3EI_n} - \frac{M_{n-1,n}l_n}{6EI_n} - \frac{A_n d_n}{l_n EI_n}$$

$$\theta_{n,n+1} = \frac{M_{n,n+1}l_{n+1}}{3EI_{n+1}} - \frac{M_{n+1,n}l_{n+1}}{6EI_{n+1}} + \frac{A_{n+1}c_{n+1}}{l_{n+1}EI_{n+1}}$$

(a)

Let us introduce now the conventional bending moments M_{n-1}, M_n, M_{n+1} at the supports, instead of the end moments. From the assumed positive directions of the end moments (see page 406) and the conventional rule for sign of bending moment, it follows that

$$M_{n-1,n} = + M_{n-1} \qquad M_{n+1,n} = - M_{n+1}$$

$$M_{n,n+1} = + M_n \qquad M_{n,n-1} = - M_n$$

and expressions (a) become

$$\theta_{n,n-1} = - \frac{M_n l_n}{3EI_n} - \frac{M_{n-1}l_n}{6EI_n} - \frac{A_n d_n}{l_n EI_n}$$

$$\theta_{n,n+1} = \frac{M_n l_{n+1}}{3EI_{n+1}} + \frac{M_{n+1}l_{n+1}}{6EI_{n+1}} + \frac{A_{n+1}c_{n+1}}{l_{n+1}EI_{n+1}}$$

Equating these two angles, we obtain

$$M_{n-1}\frac{l_n}{I_n} - 2M_n\left(\frac{l_n}{I_n} + \frac{l_{n+1}}{I_{n+1}}\right) + M_{n+1}\frac{l_{n+1}}{I_{n+1}}$$

$$= -\frac{6A_n d_n}{I_n l_n} - \frac{6A_{n+1} c_{n+1}}{l_{n+1} I_{n+1}} \qquad (9.7)$$

which is the well-known *equation of three moments*. Such an equation can be written for each intermediate support of a continuous beam; and if the ends of the beam are simply supported, the number of equations is equal to the number of statically indeterminate moments at the supports. Hence, all unknowns can be found from these equations.

If the left end of the beam is built in at the support 0, we have an additional condition stating that the left end of the beam does not rotate. In our previous notations, this means that θ_0 vanishes. Using the first of Eqs. (9.2a), we find that this condition becomes

$$\frac{M_{0,1}l_1}{3EI_1} - \frac{M_{1,0}l_1}{6EI_1} + \frac{A_1 c_1}{l_1 EI_1} = 0$$

Introducing bending moments again, instead of end moments, we obtain

$$2M_0 + M_1 = -\frac{6A_1 c_1}{l_1{}^2} \qquad (9.8)$$

It is seen that a built-in end introduces an additional unknown moment M_0, but at the same time we have an additional equation (9.8). Hence, the number of unknowns is again equal to the number of equations. An equation similar to Eq. (9.8) can be written for the right end of the beam if that end is built in.

Sometimes, instead of the three-moment equation (9.7), an equation containing as unknowns the angles of rotation of the cross sections at three consecutive supports can be used. Considering again two consecutive spans (Fig. 9.8c) and calculating the end moments at the nth support by using Eqs. (9.6), we obtain

$$M_{n,n-1} = 2k_n(2\theta_n + \theta_{n-1}) + \mathfrak{M}_{n,n-1} - 6k_n\Theta_{n,n-1}$$

$$M_{n,n+1} = 2k_{n+1}(2\theta_n + \theta_{n+1}) + \mathfrak{M}_{n,n+1} - 6k_{n+1}\Theta_{n,n+1}$$

Then, observing that $M_{n,n-1} = -M_{n,n+1}$, we find

$$2k_n\theta_{n-1} + 4\theta_n(k_n + k_{n+1}) + 2k_{n+1}\theta_{n+1}$$

$$= -(\mathfrak{M}_{n,n-1} + \mathfrak{M}_{n,n+1}) + 6(k_n\Theta_{n,n-1} + k_{n+1}\Theta_{n,n+1}) \qquad (9.9)$$

This is called the *equation of three angles*.

As a first application of the three-moment equation (9.7), let us consider the case of a beam carrying a uniformly distributed load on each span. If q_n is the intensity of load on the span l_n, we have

$$c_n = d_n = \frac{l_n}{2} \qquad A_n = \frac{q_n l_n^3}{12}$$

We obtain similar expressions for the span l_{n+1}. Equation (9.7) then becomes

$$M_{n-1}\frac{l_n}{I_n} + 2M_n\left(\frac{l_n}{I_n} + \frac{l_{n+1}}{I_{n+1}}\right) + M_{n+1}\frac{l_{n+1}}{I_{n+1}}$$

$$= -\frac{q_n l_n^3}{4I_n} - \frac{q_{n+1} l_{n+1}^3}{4I_{n+1}} \qquad (9.7a)$$

Take, for example, a beam of uniform cross section on five supports and with simply supported ends. In this case $M_0 = M_4 = 0$, and the moments M_1, M_2, M_3 at the intermediate supports will be calculated from Eqs. (9.7a), which become

$$2M_1(l_1 + l_2) + M_2 l_2 = -\frac{q_1 l_1^3}{4} - \frac{q_2 l_2^3}{4}$$

$$M_1 l_2 + 2M_2(l_2 + l_3) + M_3 l_3 = -\frac{q_2 l_2^3}{4} - \frac{q_3 l_3^3}{4}$$

$$M_2 l_3 + 2M_3(l_3 + l_4) = -\frac{q_3 l_3^3}{4} - \frac{q_4 l_4^3}{4}$$

If all spans are equal, $l_1 = l_2 = l_3 = l_4 = l$, and the equations give

$$M_1 = -\frac{l^2}{224}(15q_1 + 11q_2 - 3q_3 + q_4)$$

$$M_2 = -\frac{l^2}{224}(-4q_1 + 12q_2 + 12q_3 - 4q_4) \qquad (b)$$

$$M_3 = -\frac{l^2}{224}(q_1 - 3q_2 + 11q_3 + 15q_4)$$

Taking, for example, $q_2 = q_3 = q_4 = 0$ and only q_1 different from zero, we obtain the case shown in Fig. 9.9a. In such case, the moments at the intermediate supports, from Eqs. (b), are $M_1 = -\frac{15}{224}q_1 l^2$, $M_2 = +\frac{1}{56}q_1 l^2$, $M_3 = -\frac{1}{224}q_1 l^2$. The corresponding bending-moment diagram is shown in Fig. 9.9b.

If a load of constant intensity covers the entire length of the beam (Fig. 9.9c), $q_1 = q_2 = q_3 = q_4 = q$, and Eqs. (b) give

$$M_1 = -\tfrac{3}{28}q l^2 \qquad M_2 = -\tfrac{1}{14}q l^2 \qquad M_3 = -\tfrac{3}{28}q l^2$$

The corresponding bending-moment diagram is shown in Fig. 9.9d.

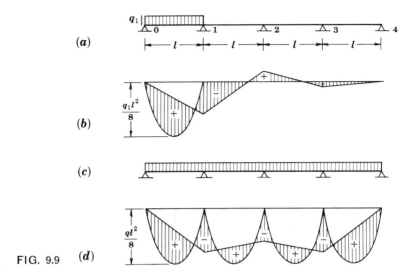

FIG. 9.9   (*d*)

If a concentrated load P_n acts in a span l_n (Fig. 9.10*a*), the area A_n is represented by the triangle shown in Fig. 9.10*b* and we obtain

$$A_n = \frac{P_n e_n f_n}{2} \qquad c_n = \tfrac{1}{3}(l_n + e_n) \qquad d_n = \tfrac{1}{3}(l_n + f_n) \qquad (c)$$

Such expressions for each concentrated force acting on the beam must be used in calculating the right-hand side of Eq. (9.7).

As an example involving concentrated forces, let us consider a beam of uniform cross section on five supports and loaded as shown in Fig. 9.11*a*. From symmetry we conclude that $M_1 = M_3$, and we have to write only two equations. For the loads and distances indicated in the figure, we find

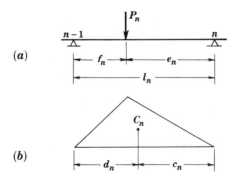

FIG. 9.10

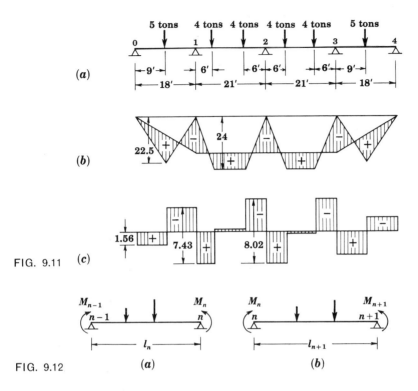

FIG. 9.11

FIG. 9.12

$A_1 = \frac{405}{2}$ ton-ft^2, $c_1 = d_1 = 9$ ft, $A_2 = 360$ ton-ft^2, $c_2 = d_2 = \frac{21}{2}$ ft.   Substituting in Eqs. (9.7), we obtain

$$78M_1 + 21M_2 = -\frac{6 \times 405}{4} - \frac{6 \times 360}{2}$$

$$21M_1 + 84M_2 + 21M_1 = -6 \times 360$$

which give

$$M_1 = -17.0 \text{ ton-ft} \qquad M_2 = -17.2 \text{ ton-ft}$$

Using these values, the bending-moment diagram shown in Fig. 9.11b can be constructed.

When the bending moments at the intermediate supports have been calculated, the reactions at the supports can be found from equations of statics. Considering the support n (Fig. 9.12), we calculate separately the reaction R_n produced by bending of the span l_n and of the span l_{n+1} and then take the sum of these two reactions.   Thus, from Fig. 9.12a, we conclude that the first part of the reaction R_n is

$$R_n' + \frac{M_{n-1} - M_n}{l_n} \tag{d}$$

where R'_n represents the reaction produced by lateral loads. Considering Fig. 9.12b in the same manner, we conclude that the second part of the reaction at the support n is

$$R''_n + \frac{M_{n+1} - M_n}{l_{n+1}} \tag{e}$$

Taking the sum of expressions (d) and (e), we find for the total reaction at the support n

$$R_n = R'_n + R''_n + \frac{M_{n-1} - M_n}{l_n} + \frac{M_{n+1} - M_n}{l_{n+1}} \tag{9.10}$$

where $R'_n + R''_n$ is the magnitude of the reaction at the support n that would be obtained if the continuous beam were cut at all intermediate supports and thus transformed into a system of simply supported beams. It should be noted that if there are loads applied over the supports, they will be transmitted directly to the supports, and reactions equal to these loads must then be added to those calculated from Eq. (9.10).

Using Eq. (9.10) for the case shown in Fig. 9.11, we obtain the following values of the reactions:

$$R_0 = R_4 = 1.56 \text{ tons} \qquad R_1 = R_3 = 7.43 \text{ tons} \qquad R_2 = 8.02 \text{ tons}$$

The corresponding shearing-force diagram is shown in Fig. 9.11c.

In all previous examples, we have assumed a continuous beam of uniform cross section. In such a case, the moments of inertia appearing in Eq. (9.7) cancel, and the magnitudes of moments at the supports do not depend on the cross-sectional dimensions of the beam. If the cross-sectional dimensions of the beam in different spans are different, we multiply Eq. (9.7) by an arbitrary constant moment of inertia I_0* and introduce the notations

$$l_n \frac{I_0}{I_n} = l'_n \qquad l_{n+1} \frac{I_0}{I_{n+1}} = l'_{n+1} \qquad A_n \frac{I_0}{I_n} = A'_n \qquad \frac{A_{n+1} I_0}{I_{n+1}} = A'_{n+1} \tag{f}$$

With these notations, Eq. (9.7) becomes

$$M_{n-1} l'_n + 2M_n(l'_n + l'_{n+1}) + M_{n+1} l'_{n+1}$$
$$= -\frac{6A'_n d_n}{l_n} - \frac{6A'_{n+1} c_{n+1}}{l_{n+1}} \tag{9.11}$$

This equation does not contain moments of inertia explicitly, and the problem is reduced to that of a beam of uniform cross section for which the modified lengths of spans l'_1, l'_2, . . . and the modified moment areas A'_1, A'_2, . . . are calculated from Eqs. (f).

* Usually we take for I_0 the cross-sectional moment of inertia in one of the spans.

Let us consider now the effect of settlement of supports on bending of a continuous beam. Assuming that the vertical displacements of three consecutive supports $n - 1$, n, and $n + 1$ are Δ_{n-1}, Δ_n, and Δ_{n+1} and considering the two consecutive spans shown in Fig. 9.8c as simply supported beams, we conclude that the angle of rotation of the span l_n due to settlement of the supports is $(\Delta_n - \Delta_{n-1})/l_n$. In the same manner for the span l_{n+1}, we obtain $(\Delta_{n+1} - \Delta_n)/l_{n+1}$. Using these angles in Eqs. (9.3a), we obtain, instead of Eqs. (a) above, the following equations:

$$\theta_{n,n-1} = \frac{M_{n,n-1}l_n}{3EI_n} - \frac{M_{n-1,n}l_n}{6EI_n} - \frac{A_nd_n}{l_nEI_n} + \frac{\Delta_n - \Delta_{n-1}}{l_n}$$

$$\theta_{n,n+1} = \frac{M_{n,n+1}l_{n+1}}{3EI_{n+1}} - \frac{M_{n+1,n}l_{n+1}}{6EI_{n+1}} + \frac{A_{n+1}c_{n+1}}{l_{n+1}EI_{n+1}} + \frac{\Delta_{n+1} - \Delta_n}{l_{n+1}}$$

(g)

Again, introducing bending moments, instead of end moments, and equating the angles $\theta_{n,n-1}$ and $\theta_{n,n+1}$, we obtain

$$M_{n-1}\frac{l_n}{I_n} + 2M_n\left(\frac{l_n}{I_n} + \frac{l_{n+1}}{I_{n+1}}\right) + M_{n+1}\frac{l_{n+1}}{I_{n+1}} = -\frac{6A_nd_n}{l_nI_n}$$

$$- \frac{6A_{n+1}c_{n+1}}{l_{n+1}I_{n+1}} + 6E\left(\frac{\Delta_n - \Delta_{n-1}}{l_n} - \frac{\Delta_{n+1} - \Delta_n}{l_{n+1}}\right) \quad (h)$$

If the beam has a constant cross section with moment of inertia I along the entire length, we multiply Eq. (h) by I and obtain

$$M_{n-1}l_n + 2M_n(l_n + l_{n+1}) + M_{n+1}l_{n+1} = -\frac{6A_nd_n}{l_n} - \frac{6A_{n+1}c_{n+1}}{l_{n+1}}$$

$$+ 6EI\left(\frac{\Delta_n - \Delta_{n-1}}{l_n} - \frac{\Delta_{n+1} - \Delta_n}{l_{n+1}}\right) \quad (9.12)$$

If the moments of inertia in different spans are different we multiply Eq. (h) by an assumed constant moment of inertia I_0. Then, using notations (f), we represent the three-moment equation in the following form:

$$M_{n-1}l'_n + 2M_n(l'_n + l'_{n+1}) + M_{n+1}l'_{n+1} = -\frac{6A'_nd_n}{l_n} - \frac{6A'_{n+1}c_{n+1}}{l_{n+1}}$$

$$+ 6EI_0\left(\frac{\Delta_n - \Delta_{n-1}}{l_n} - \frac{\Delta_{n+1} - \Delta_n}{l_{n+1}}\right) \quad (9.13)$$

It is seen that in this case the three-moment equation has the same form as before. Hence, the moments at the supports can be readily calculated if the magnitudes of settlement Δ_{n-1}, Δ_n, and Δ_{n+1} are known.

PROBLEMS

1 Find the bending moment M_1 at the intermediate support of the two-span continuous beam of uniform cross section shown in Fig. 9.13a if a uniformly distributed load acts on the first span and the ratio $l_2:l_1$ is equal to α.

$$Ans. \quad M_1 = -\frac{ql^2}{8}\frac{1}{1+\alpha}.$$

2 Solve the previous problem if the ratio $l_2:l_1$ is equal to γ.

$$Ans. \quad M_1 = -\frac{ql^2}{8}\frac{\gamma}{\alpha+\gamma}.$$

3 Find M_0 and M_1 for the continuous beam shown in Fig. 9.13b. Assume that the cross section is uniform along the entire length and that the intensity of load is q.

$$Ans. \quad M_0 = -\frac{ql^2}{8}\frac{2+4\alpha}{3+4\alpha}, \quad M_1 = -\frac{ql^2}{8}\frac{2}{3+4\alpha}.$$

4 Solve the previous problem if both ends of the beam are built in (Fig. 9.13c) and the cross section is uniform along the entire length.

$$Ans. \quad M_0 = -\frac{ql^2}{8}\frac{2+3\alpha}{3(1+\alpha)}, \quad M_1 = -\frac{ql^2}{8}\frac{2}{3(1+\alpha)},$$

$$M_2 = +\frac{ql^2}{8}\frac{1}{3(1+\alpha)}.$$

5 A beam of uniform cross section rests on four supports and is loaded as shown in Fig. 9.14a. Find the bending moments at the supports if the intensity of load is q.

$$Ans. \quad M_1 = -\frac{ql^2}{8}\frac{4(\alpha+\beta)}{4(1+\alpha)(\alpha+\beta)-\alpha^2},$$

$$M_2 = +\frac{ql^2}{8}\frac{2\alpha}{4(1+\alpha)(\alpha+\beta)-\alpha^2}.$$

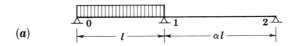

(**a**)

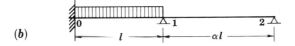

(**b**)

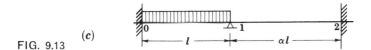

(**c**)

FIG. 9.13

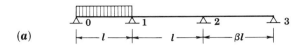

(a)

FIG. 9.14   (b)

6   Solve the previous problem if the middle span is loaded as shown in Fig. 9.14b.

$$Ans. \quad M_1 = -\frac{ql^2}{8} \frac{2\alpha^3(\alpha + 2\beta)}{4(1 + \alpha)(\alpha + \beta) - \alpha^2},$$

$$M_2 = -\frac{ql^2}{8} \frac{2\alpha^3(2 + \alpha)}{4(1 + \alpha)(\alpha + \beta) - \alpha^2}.$$

7   Solve the preceding problem if both ends of the beam are built in and $\beta = 1$.

$$Ans. \quad M_0 = M_3 = \frac{ql^2}{8} \frac{2\alpha^3}{3(1 + 2\alpha)}, \quad M_1 = M_2 = -\frac{ql^2}{8} \frac{4\alpha^3}{3(1 + 2\alpha)}.$$

9.4   BEAMS OF VARIABLE CROSS SECTION

Often, especially in reinforced-concrete structures, beams are deepened near their supports in order to avoid the sharp reentrant corner that otherwise occurs at the junction of a beam with a column. In such a case there arises the question of how the haunches affect the angles of rotation of the ends of the beam under applied loads. To calculate these angles, we use Eqs. (e) of Art. 9.1. Multiplying and dividing these equations by the constant moment of inertia I_0 of the uniform portion of the beam, we obtain

$$\theta_a = \int_0^l \frac{l - x}{l} \frac{M}{EI_0} \frac{I_0}{I} dx$$

$$\theta_b = -\int_0^l \frac{x}{l} \frac{M}{EI_0} \frac{I_0}{I} dx$$

(a)

In this manner the problem is reduced to that of a beam of uniform flexural rigidity EI_0. To take care of the cross-sectional variation, we have only to use MI_0/I, instead of M. This means that the fictitious load is given in this case by the modified bending-moment diagram, obtained by multiplying the bending moment at each cross section by the ratio I_0/I.

Take, for example, the case shown in Fig. 9.15a. A beam with reinforced ends is bent by a load P applied at the middle. The modified bending-moment

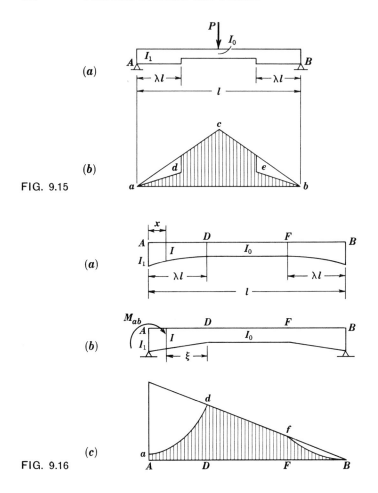

FIG. 9.15

FIG. 9.16

diagram is shown by the shaded area in Fig. 9.15b. Along the reinforced portions of the beam, of length λl, the ordinates of the bending-moment diagram acb are reduced in a constant ratio $I_0:I_1$. The angles of rotation of the ends of the beam are now obtained if we divide by EI_0 the shearing forces produced at the ends of the beam by the fictitious load represented by the shaded area in Fig. 9.15b. It is seen that owing to the reinforcement of the ends of the beam, these angles of rotation will be diminished in the same ratio as the fictitious load is diminished when we replace the bending-moment area acb by the modified bending-moment area. Assume, for example, that $\lambda = \frac{1}{4}$ and $I_0/I_1 = \frac{1}{2}$. Then, the fictitious load is reduced in the ratio $7:8$, and the angles of rotation will be diminished by one-eighth of the values obtained for a beam having uniform flexural rigidity EI_0.

In such cases as shown in Fig. 9.16, the ratio I_0/I varies along the length of the haunches, and instead of the straight lines ad and eb shown in Fig. 9.15b, we shall obtain certain curves. We always can trace these curves with sufficient accuracy by dividing the length λl of a haunch into several parts and calculating the ratio I_0/I for each segment. Naturally, the shape of the modified bending-moment diagram will depend on the form of the haunches. Assume, for example, that a rectangular beam with straight haunches (Fig. 9.16b) is bent by a couple M_{ab} applied at the end A. Then, the bending-moment diagram is the triangle shown in Fig. 9.16c. Since the depth of the beam increases linearly with the distance ξ and since I is proportional to the cube of the depth, we obtain

$$I = I_0 \left[1 + \left(\sqrt[3]{\frac{I_1}{I_0}} - 1 \right) \frac{\xi}{\lambda l} \right]^3 \tag{b}$$

where I_1 is the moment of inertia at the support. Taking, for example, $I_1/I_0 = 10$, $\lambda = 0.3$, we find the values of the ratio I_0/I as given in row 3 of Table 9.2 below. The corresponding modified bending-moment area is shown by the shaded portion of the triangle in Fig. 9.16c. Treating this area as a fictitious load and using Eqs. (a), we can calculate the angles of rotation at the ends of the beam.

To illustrate this kind of calculation by using Simpson's rule, we begin with the portion AD of the beam. The corresponding values of the function under the integral sign in the first of Eqs. (a) are given in row 5 of Table 9.2. Thus the contribution θ'_a of the portion AD of the beam to the total angle of rotation at A is

$$\theta'_a = \int_0^{0.3l} \frac{l - x}{l} \frac{M}{EI_0} \frac{I_0}{I} \, dx = \frac{M_{ab}}{EI_0} \int_0^{0.3l} \frac{(l - x)^2}{l^2} \frac{I_0}{I} \, dx$$

$$= \frac{M_{ab}}{EI_0} \frac{0.3l}{4 \times 3} \left[0.4900 + 4(0.2807 + 0.1318) + 2(0.1842) \right.$$
$$\left. + 0.1000 \right]$$

$$= 0.0652 \frac{M_{ab}l}{EI_0}$$

TABLE 9.2

(1)	$\dfrac{\xi}{\lambda l}$	0	$\frac{1}{4}$	$\frac{1}{2}$	$\frac{3}{4}$	1
(2)	$\dfrac{l - x}{l}$	0.7000	0.7750	0.8500	0.9250	1.0000
(3)	$\dfrac{I_0}{I}$	1.0000	0.4673	0.2549	0.1540	0.1000
(4)	$\dfrac{(l - x)^2}{l^2}$	0.4900	0.6006	0.7225	0:8556	1.0000
(5)	$\dfrac{(I_0/I)(l - x)^2}{l^2}$	0.4900	0.2807	0.1842	0.1318	0.1000

Treating the portion FB of the beam in the same manner, we obtain

$$\theta_a'' = \frac{M_{ab}}{EI_0} \int_{0.7l}^{l} \frac{(l-x)^2}{l^2} \frac{I_0}{I} \, dx = 0.0049 \frac{M_{ab}l}{EI_0}$$

Along the middle portion DF, the cross section is constant, and we obtain

$$\theta_a''' = \frac{M_{ab}}{EI_0} \int_{0.3l}^{0.7l} \frac{(l-x)^2}{l^2} \, dx = 0.1053 \frac{M_{ab}l}{EI_0}$$

The total angle of rotation at A then is

$$\theta_a = \theta_a' + \theta_a'' + \theta_a''' = 0.1754 \frac{M_{ab}l}{EI_0}$$

Proceeding in a similar way with the second of Eqs. (a), we find for the angle of rotation at the right end of the beam

$$\theta_b = -0.1266 \frac{M_{ab}l}{EI_0}$$

In the case of beams having straight-line or parabolic haunches, the integrations in Eqs. (a) can be made rigorously. However, the calculations are tedious and time-consuming. To simplify the analysis of beams of variable cross section, special tables have been prepared giving values of the numerical factors in the expressions for θ_a and θ_b for those shapes of haunches that are most often encountered in practice.[1] For example, in the case of a symmetrical beam with straight or parabolic haunches, the angles of rotation at the ends A and B under the action of end moments M_{ab} and M_{ba} can be readily calculated from the equations

$$\begin{aligned}
\theta_a &= C_1 \frac{M_{ab}l}{EI_0} - C_2 \frac{M_{ba}l}{EI_0} \\
\theta_b &= C_1 \frac{M_{ba}l}{EI_0} - C_2 \frac{M_{ab}l}{EI_0}
\end{aligned}$$

(9.14a)

in which the constants C_1 and C_2 can be taken from Table 9.3.

[1] Such tables were calculated by A. Strassner; see his book "Neue Methoden zur Statik der Rahmentragwerke," 4th ed., vol. 1, Berlin, 1937. Following the work of Strassner, W. Ruppel prepared an extensive set of tables for haunched beams; see *Trans. ASCE*, vol. 90, p. 152, 1927. A useful series of charts for beams of variable cross section are given in the book by R. Guldan, "Rahmentragwerke und Durchlaufträger," Vienna, 1940, and also in the book by James M. Gere, "Moment Distribution," D. Van Nostrand Company, Inc., Princeton, N.J., 1963. In our further discussion, tables published by the Portland Cement Association will be used; see "Handbook of Frame Constants" and "Continuous Concrete Bridges." For beams with abrupt changes in cross section, see *Iowa Eng. Exp. Sta. Bull.* 176, 1954.

TABLE 9.3 CONSTANTS C_1 AND C_2 FOR SYMMETRICAL
HAUNCHED BEAMS

λ	$\dfrac{I_0}{I_1}$	0.60	0.30	0.20	0.15	0.12	0.10	0.08	0.06	0.05	0.04	0.03	0.02
(a)	Beams with straight haunches (Fig. 9.16b)												
0.50	C_1	0.251	0.173	0.140	0.121	0.107	0.099	0.089	0.078	0.071	0.064	0.056	0.047
	C_2	0.141	0.106	0.091	0.082	0.076	0.071	0.065	0.059	0.055	0.050	0.045	0.040
0.40	C_1	0.264	0.198	0.171	0.154	0.144	0.136	0.127	0.117	0.112	0.106	0.099	0.091
	C_2	0.147	0.125	0.115	0.108	0.104	0.100	0.096	0.092	0.089	0.086	0.083	0.072
0.35	C_1	0.271	0.212	0.187	0.172	0.162	0.155	0.147	0.138	0.133	0.128	0.122	0.114
	C_2	0.151	0.138	0.126	0.121	0.117	0.114	0.111	0.107	0.105	0.103	0.100	0.096
0.30	C_1	0.278	0.226	0.204	0.191	0.182	0.175	0.168	0.160	0.156	0.151	0.145	0.139
	C_2	0.155	0.142	0.136	0.132	0.129	0.127	0.124	0.121	0.120	0.118	0.116	0.113
0.25	C_1	0.286	0.241	0.222	0.210	0.203	0.197	0.191	0.184	0.180	0.176	0.171	0.165
	C_2	0.158	0.149	0.144	0.142	0.139	0.138	0.136	0.134	0.133	0.132	0.130	0.128
0.20	C_1	0.294	0.257	0.241	0.231	0.225	0.220	0.215	0.209	0.206	0.202	0.198	0.193
	C_2	0.161	0.155	0.152	0.150	0.149	0.148	0.147	0.145	0.144	0.143	0.142	0.141
0.15	C_1	0.303	0.274	0.261	0.254	0.249	0.245	0.241	0.237	0.234	0.231	0.228	0.224
	C_2	0.163	0.160	0.158	0.157	0.156	0.156	0.155	0.154	0.154	0.153	0.153	0.152
(b)	Beams with parabolic haunches (Fig. 9.16a)												
0.50	C_1	0.273	0.213	0.186	0.170	0.159	0.150	0.141	0.130	0.123	0.116	0.108	0.097
	C_2	0.151	0.132	0.122	0.115	0.111	0.107	0.103	0.098	0.094	0.090	0.086	0.080
0.40	C_1	0.283	0.233	0.210	0.196	0.187	0.180	0.172	0.162	0.157	0.151	0.143	0.134
	C_2	0.156	0.143	0.136	0.132	0.129	0.126	0.123	0.120	0.117	0.115	0.112	0.107
0.35	C_1	0.289	0.243	0.223	0.210	0.202	0.195	0.188	0.179	0.175	0.169	0.162	0.154
	C_2	0.158	0.148	0.143	0.139	0.137	0.135	0.133	0.130	0.128	0.126	0.123	0.120
0.30	C_1	0.294	0.254	0.236	0.225	0.218	0.212	0.205	0.198	0.193	0.188	0.182	0.175
	C_2	0.160	0.153	0.149	0.146	0.144	0.143	0.141	0.139	0.137	0.136	0.134	0.131
0.25	C_1	0.300	0.266	0.250	0.241	0.234	0.229	0.224	0.217	0.213	0.209	0.204	0.197
	C_2	0.162	0.157	0.154	0.152	0.151	0.149	0.148	0.147	0.146	0.144	0.143	0.141
0.20	C_1	0.306	0.278	0.265	0.257	0.252	0.248	0.243	0.237	0.234	0.231	0.226	0.221
	C_2	0.164	0.160	0.158	0.157	0.156	0.155	0.154	0.153	0.153	0.152	0.151	0.150
0.15	C_1	0.312	0.291	0.281	0.274	0.270	0.267	0.263	0.259	0.257	0.254	0.250	0.246
	C_2	0.167	0.163	0.162	0.161	0.161	0.160	0.159	0.159	0.159	0.158	0.158	0.157

If there are no ready tables for the shape of the beam under consideration, the constants C_1 and C_2 have to be calculated as explained above. These two constants completely define the stiffness of a symmetrical beam and are called its *angular coefficients*.

If, in addition to end moments, there are lateral load on the beam and also some displacements of the supports, the general expressions for the angles of rotation at the ends of the beam become

$$\theta_a = C_1 \frac{M_{ab}l}{EI_0} - C_2 \frac{M_{ba}l}{EI_0} + \frac{Ac}{EI_0 l} + \Theta_{ab}$$

$$\theta_b = C_1 \frac{M_{ba}l}{EI_0} - C_2 \frac{M_{ab}l}{EI_0} - \frac{Ad}{EI_0 l} + \Theta_{ab}$$

(9.14b)

in which Ac/l and $-Ad/l$ are shearing forces at the ends produced by the modified bending-moment area A, such as that shown in Fig. 9.15b, and Θ_{ab} is the rotation of the beam due to displacements of the supports.

Solving Eqs. (9.14b) for the end moments M_{ab} and M_{ba}, we obtain

$$M_{ab} = \frac{EI_0}{l} \left(\frac{C_1 \theta_a}{C_1{}^2 - C_2{}^2} + \frac{C_2 \theta_b}{C_1{}^2 - C_2{}^2} - \frac{C_1 + C_2}{C_1{}^2 - C_2{}^2} \Theta_{ab} \right)$$
$$- \frac{A}{l^2} \frac{cC_1 - dC_2}{C_1{}^2 - C_2{}^2}$$

(c)

$$M_{ba} = \frac{EI_0}{l} \left(\frac{C_2 \theta_a}{C_1{}^2 - C_2{}^2} + \frac{C_1 \theta_b}{C_1{}^2 - C_2{}^2} - \frac{C_1 + C_2}{C_1{}^2 - C_2{}^2} \Theta_{ab} \right)$$
$$- \frac{A}{l^2} \frac{cC_2 - dC_1}{C_1{}^2 - C_2{}^2}$$

Then, introducing the notations

$$\frac{EI_0}{l} = k \qquad \frac{C_1}{C_1{}^2 - C_2{}^2} = k_{bb} \qquad \frac{C_2}{C_1{}^2 - C_2{}^2} = k_{ab}$$

(d)

and observing that the last terms in Eqs. (c) represent the end moments for the case in which $\theta_a = \theta_b = \Theta_{ab} = 0$, that is, the *fixed-end moments*, we can rewrite these equations in the following simplified form:

$$M_{ab} = k[k_{bb}\theta_a + k_{ab}\theta_b - (k_{bb} + k_{ab})\Theta_{ab}] + \mathfrak{M}_{ab}$$

$$M_{ba} = k[k_{ab}\theta_a + k_{bb}\theta_b - (k_{bb} + k_{ab})\Theta_{ab}] + \mathfrak{M}_{ba}$$

(9.15)

These are the *slope-deflection equations* for symmetrical beams of variable cross section. In the case of prismatic beams, we have $C_1 = \frac{1}{3}$, $C_2 = \frac{1}{6}$, $k_{bb} = 4$, $k_{ab} = 2$, and Eqs. (9.15) coincide with Eqs. (9.6) obtained before.

To simplify the calculation of end moments from Eqs. (9.15), tables or charts for the constants k_{bb} and k_{ab} have been prepared, examples of which are shown in Figs. 9.17 and 9.18. The values of fixed-end moments for both concentrated and uniformly distributed lateral loads have also been tabulated for various types of haunches.[1]

In all of the foregoing discussion, it has been assumed that the beam is symmetrical. In the case of a nonsymmetrical beam, three constants C_1, C_2, and C_3 are required to define its elastic properties. In such case, the angles

[1] See "Handbook of Frame Constants."

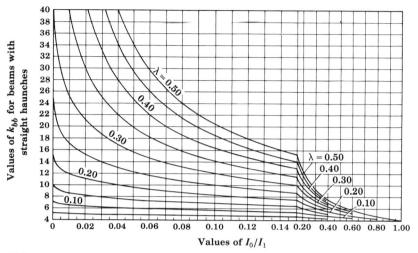

FIG. 9.17

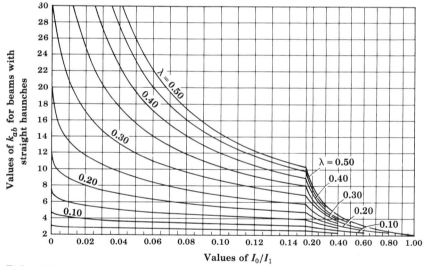

FIG. 9.18

of rotation at A and B in the general case of loading are

$$\theta_a = C_1 \frac{M_{ab}l}{EI_0} - C_2 \frac{M_{ba}l}{EI_0} + \frac{Ac}{EI_0 l} + \Theta_{ab}$$

$$\theta_b = C_3 \frac{M_{ba}l}{EI_0} - C_2 \frac{M_{ab}l}{EI_0} - \frac{Ad}{EI_0 l} + \Theta_{ab}$$

(9.16)

Solving these equations for M_{ab} and M_{ba} and introducing the notations

$$\frac{C_1}{C_1 C_3 - C_2{}^2} = k_{bb} \qquad \frac{C_2}{C_1 C_3 - C_2{}^2} = k_{ab} \qquad \frac{C_3}{C_1 C_3 - C_2{}^2} = k_{aa} \quad (e)$$

we obtain

$$
\begin{aligned}
M_{ab} &= k[k_{aa}\theta_a + k_{ab}\theta_b - (k_{ab} + k_{aa})\Theta_{ab}] + \mathfrak{M}_{ab} \\
M_{ba} &= k[k_{ab}\theta_a + k_{bb}\theta_b - (k_{bb} + k_{ab})\Theta_{ab}] + \mathfrak{M}_{ba}
\end{aligned}
\qquad (9.17)
$$

These are the *slope-deflection equations* for nonsymmetrical beams of variable cross section. For symmetrical beams, we have $C_3 = C_1$, $k_{aa} = k_{bb}$, and Eqs. (9.17) coincide with Eqs. (9.15) obtained previously.

To illustrate the application of Eqs. (9.16) and (9.17), let us consider the unsymmetrical beam with parabolic haunches which is built in at B and simply supported at A as shown in Fig. 9.19a. Assuming that an active end moment M_{ab} is applied at A, the corresponding reactive moment at B can be calculated from the second of Eqs. (9.16). Setting $\theta_b = 0$ in this equation and noting that there are no lateral loads or settlement of the supports in this case, we obtain

$$M_{ba} = \frac{C_2}{C_3} M_{ab}$$

In a similar manner, by using Eqs. (9.17), we obtain

$$M_{ba} = \frac{k_{ab}}{k_{aa}} M_{ab}$$

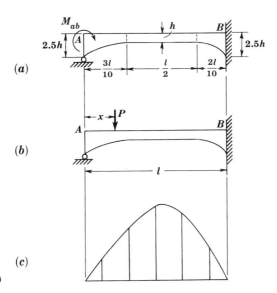

FIG. 9.19

The factor

$$C_{ab} = \frac{C_2}{C_3} = \frac{k_{ab}}{k_{aa}} \qquad (f)$$

showing the fraction of the applied moment that is transmitted from A to B is called the *carry-over factor*. In the same way, it can be shown that the carry-over factor from a pinned end B to a fixed end A is

$$C_{ba} = \frac{C_2}{C_1} = \frac{k_{ab}}{k_{bb}} \qquad (g)$$

These carry-over factors are very useful in the analysis of haunched beams and have been tabulated for various shapes of haunches.

The angle of rotation of the end A of the beam loaded as shown in Fig. 9.19a can be calculated from Eqs. (9.16). Noting in this case that there is no lateral load and no support settlement and that $\theta_b = 0$, we obtain

$$\theta_a = \frac{C_1 C_3 - C_2{}^2}{C_3} \frac{l}{EI_0} M_{ab}$$

We see that the angle of rotation θ_a is inversely proportional to the factor

$$s_{ab} = \frac{C_3}{C_1 C_3 - C_2{}^2} = k_{aa} \qquad (h)$$

which is called the *stiffness factor* for the end A of the beam. Similarly, we find that the stiffness factor for the end B is

$$s_{ba} = \frac{C_1}{C_1 C_3 - C_2{}^2} = k_{bb} \qquad (i)$$

If the beam carries lateral loads (Fig. 9.19b), the reactive moment M_{ba} at the built-in end can be obtained by using Eqs. (9.17). If we substitute $\theta_b = M_{ab} = \Theta_{ab} = 0$ in these equations, they reduce to

$$kk_{aa}\theta_a = -\mathfrak{M}_{ab}$$

$$M_{ba} = kk_{ab}\theta_a + \mathfrak{M}_{ba}$$

Then, eliminating θ_a and using notation (f), we have

$$M_{ba} = -\frac{k_{ab}}{k_{aa}} \mathfrak{M}_{ab} + \mathfrak{M}_{ba} = -C_{ab}\mathfrak{M}_{ab} + \mathfrak{M}_{ba} \qquad (9.18)$$

We see that for each particular case of loading, the reactive moment M_{ba} can be calculated very easily by using the tabulated values of the fixed-end moments and carry-over factor.[1]

As an illustration of the numerical details, let us construct an influence line for M_{ba} in the case of the beam in Fig. 9.19b. For several values of the ratio x/l defining the position of the load P on the beam, values of the fixed-end

[1] See *ibid.*

TABLE 9.4

	x/l					
	0.1	0.3	0.5	0.7	0.9	
$\mathfrak{M}_{ab}$	−0.0958	−0.2148	−0.1752	−0.0665	−0.0032	× Pl
$\mathfrak{M}_{ba}$	0.0025	0.0443	0.1370	0.1881	0.0954	× Pl
M_{ba}	0.062	0.177	0.245	0.229	0.097	× Pl

moments $\mathfrak{M}_{ab}$ and $\mathfrak{M}_{ba}$ taken from the tables are shown in lines 1 and 2 of Table 9.4 above. Also from the tables the carry-over factor for the beam is found to be $C_{ab} = 0.618$. The values of M_{ba}, calculated from Eq. (9.18), are shown in line 3 of Table 9.4. The influence line for M_{ba}, plotted from these data, is shown in Fig. 9.19c.

In conclusion, let us recapitulate the relations between the various constants that have arisen throughout the preceding discussion of haunched beams. First, the *angular coefficients* C_1, C_2, C_3 were introduced, and it was shown how these quantities can be calculated for any particular shape of haunches. Following this came the factors k_{bb}, k_{ab}, k_{aa}, which appear in the slope-deflection equations and which are defined by notations (e).

In discussing a beam built in at one end and simply supported at the other, the notion of *carry-over factor*, as defined by notations (f) and (g), was encountered. Also, in connection with the same problem, we met the idea of *stiffness factors* as defined by notations (h) and (i).

It is seen that all of the derived constants can be expressed in terms of the angular coefficients C_1, C_2, C_3. However, in the tables of the Portland Cement Association, the values of carry-over factors and stiffness factors are given instead of the angular coefficients. In such a case, by using the tabulated values, the angular coefficients can be readily calculated from the following equations:

$$C_1 = \frac{1}{s_{ab}} \frac{1}{1 - C_{ab}C_{ba}} \qquad C_3 = \frac{1}{s_{ba}} \frac{1}{1 - C_{ab}C_{ba}}$$
$$C_2 = \frac{1}{s_{ab}} \frac{C_{ba}}{1 - C_{ab}C_{ba}} = \frac{1}{s_{ba}} \frac{C_{ab}}{1 - C_{ab}C_{ba}}$$

(9.19)

PROBLEMS

1 A symmetrical beam with straight haunches (Fig. 9.20) has $I_0/I_1 = 0.20$ and the haunches have the lengths $\lambda l = l/4$. If the beam is fixed at both ends, calculate the fixed-end moments (a) due to a uniform lateral load of intensity q, (b) due to a concentrated load P at mid-span.

Ans. (a) $\mathfrak{M}_{ab} = -\mathfrak{M}_{ba} = -0.1138ql^2$.
(b) $\mathfrak{M}_{ab} = -\mathfrak{M}_{ba} = -0.1708Pl$.

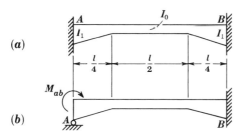

(a)

M_{ab}

(b)

FIG. 9.20

2   What end moments will be produced in the haunched beam described in the preceding problem if the right-hand support B settles by an amount $\Delta = 1$ in. relative
to the support A?   Assume that the span $l = 16$ ft.
        Ans. $M_{ab} = M_{ba} = -0.0668EI_0/l$.
3   Assuming that the symmetrical beam in Fig. 9.20b is built in at B and simply supported at A, calculate the reactive end moment M_{ba} if an active moment M_{ab} is
applied at A.
        Ans. $M_{ba} = \dfrac{C_2}{C_1} M_{ab}.$
4   If the beam in Fig. 9.20b carries a uniform load of intensity q and $M_{ab} = 0$, calculate the reactive moment M_{ba} at B.   The following numerical data are given:
$\lambda = 0.3$, $I_0/I_1 = 0.1$.
        Ans. $M_{ba} = 0.238ql^2$.
5   Assuming that the unsymmetrical beam in Fig. 9.19b carries a uniformly distributed load of intensity q, calculate the magnitude of the reactive end moment
M_{ba} at the built-in end of the beam.   Values of the angular coefficients for this
beam are $C_1 = 0.201$, $C_2 = 0.146$, $C_3 = 0.237$.
        Ans. $M_{ba} = 0.159ql^2$.

9.5 CONTINUOUS BEAMS OF VARIABLE CROSS SECTION

In discussing continuous beams of variable cross section, we consider two
consecutive spans (Fig. 9.21) and denote by θ_0, θ_1, θ_2, . . . the angles of rotation
of the cross sections at the supports.   Considering the span to the left and
applying the second of Eqs. (9.17), we obtain[1]

$$M_{n,n-1} = k_n[k_{n-1,n}\theta_{n-1} + k_{n,n}^n\theta_n$$

$$- (k_{n,n}^n + k_{n-1,n})\theta_{n-1,n}] + \mathfrak{M}_{n,n-1} \quad (a)$$

Similarly, the first of Eqs. (9.17) applied to the right-hand span gives

$$M_{n,n+1} = k_{n+1}[k_{n,n}^{n+1}\theta_n + k_{n,n+1}\theta_{n+i}$$

$$- (k_{n,n+1} + k_{n,n}^{n+1})\theta_{n,n+1}] + \mathfrak{M}_{n,n+1} \quad (b)$$

[1] Since the support n belongs to both spans n and $n + 1$, we use the notations $k_{n,n}^u$ and
$k_{n,n}^{n+1}$ to distinguish the two values of $k_{n,n}$.

Observing now that at the support n we must have

$$M_{n,n-1} = -M_{n,n+1}$$

we obtain the three-angle equation

$$k_n k_{n-1,n} \theta_{n-1} + (k_n k^n_{n,n} + k_{n+1} k^{n+1}_{n,n}) \theta_n + k_{n+1} k_{n,n+1} \theta_{n+1}$$
$$= k_n (k^n_{n,n} + k_{n-1,n}) \Theta_{n-1,n} + k_{n+1}(k_{n,n+1} + k^{n+1}_{n,n}) \Theta_{n,n+1}$$
$$- \mathfrak{M}_{n,n-1} - \mathfrak{M}_{n,n+1} \quad (9.20a)$$

which can be written for each intermediate support. If the ends 0 and m of the beam are built in, we have $\theta_0 = \theta_m = 0$, and Eqs. (9.20a) are sufficient to determine all of the unknowns. If the end 0 of the beam is simply supported, the end moment M_{01} vanishes and the first of Eqs. (9.17) gives

$$0 = k_1[k_{00}\theta_0 + k_{01}\theta_1 - (k_{01} + k_{00})\Theta_{01}] + \mathfrak{M}_{01} \quad (9.20b)$$

Similarly, if the end m of the beam is simply supported, the second of Eqs. (9.17) gives

$$0 = k_m[k_{m-1,m}\theta_{m-1} + k_{mm}\theta_m - (k_{mm} + k_{m-1,m})\Theta_{m,m-1}]$$
$$+ \mathfrak{M}_{m,m-1} \quad (9.20c)$$

Thus, in any case, from all of Eqs. (9.20), the angles of rotation θ_0, θ_1, θ_2, . . . can be calculated. Having these angles, all end moments can then be calculated from the slope-deflection equations (9.17) and the analysis is completed.

Instead of the three-angle equations, the three-moment equations can also be derived. For that purpose, we use Eqs. (9.16), which we rewrite in the following form:

$$\theta_a = C_1 \frac{M_{ab}l}{EI_0} - C_2 \frac{M_{ba}l}{EI_0} + \gamma_a + \Theta_{ab}$$

$$\theta_b = C_3 \frac{M_{ba}l}{EI_0} - C_2 \frac{M_{ab}l}{EI_0} - \gamma_b + \Theta_{ab}$$

$$\quad (c)$$

wherein $\quad \gamma_a = \dfrac{Ac}{EI_0 l} \qquad \gamma_b = \dfrac{Ad}{EI_0 l} \qquad (d)$

These quantities γ_a and $-\gamma_b$ represent the angles of rotation of the ends of the beam produced by lateral loads alone. From Eqs. (9.17), we find that their

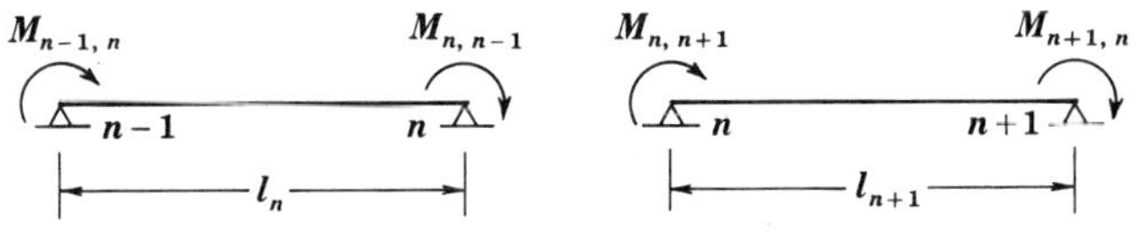

FIG. 9.21

magnitudes in terms of fixed-end moments are

$$\gamma_a = \frac{l}{EI_0}(-C_1\mathfrak{M}_{ab} + C_2\mathfrak{M}_{ba})$$

$$\gamma_b = \frac{l}{EI_0}(C_3\mathfrak{M}_{ba} - C_2\mathfrak{M}_{ab})$$

(9.21)

Since the fixed-end moments are tabulated for many particular cases and the constants C_1, C_2, C_3 are given by Eqs. (9.19), the angles γ_a and γ_b can be readily calculated from the above equations.

Considering now two adjacent spans n and $n+1$ and writing the expressions for the angle of rotation θ_n, we obtain

$$C_3{}^n \frac{M_{n,n-1}l_n}{EI_0{}^n} - C_2{}^n \frac{M_{n-1,n}l_n}{EI_0{}^n} - \gamma_n{}^n + \Theta_{n,n-1}$$

$$= C_1{}^{n+1} \frac{M_{n,n+1}l_{n+1}}{EI_0{}^{n+1}} - C_2{}^{n+1} \frac{M_{n+1,n}l_{n+1}}{EI_0{}^{n+1}} + \gamma_n{}^{n+1} + \Theta_{n,n+1}$$

Introducing the notations

$$\frac{EI_0{}^n}{l_n} = k_n \qquad \frac{EI_0{}^{n+1}}{l_{n+1}} = k_{n+1}$$

and observing that $M_{n,n-1} = -M_{n,n+1}$, we obtain finally

$$-\frac{C_2{}^n}{k_n}M_{n-1,n} + \left(\frac{C_3{}^n}{k_n} + \frac{C_1{}^{n+1}}{k_{n+1}}\right)M_{n,n-1} + \frac{C_2{}^{n+1}}{k_{n+1}}M_{n+1,n}$$

$$= \gamma_n{}^n + \gamma_n{}^{n+1} - \Theta_{n,n-1} + \Theta_{n,n+1} \quad (9.22a)$$

This represents the three-moment equation for the case of a continuous beam of variable cross section. It can be written for each intermediate support; so in the case of a beam with simply supported ends, we have as many equations as there are unknown moments. If the ends of the beam are built in, there will be two additional unknown moments M_{01} and $M_{m,m-1}$, and we have two additional conditions of constraint; namely, the end cross sections 0 and m do not rotate. Using Eqs. (9.16), we express these conditions as follows:

$$C_1{}^1 \frac{M_{01}l_1}{EI_0{}^1} - C_2{}^1 \frac{M_{10}l_1}{EI_0{}^1} + \gamma_0{}^1 + \Theta_{01} = 0$$

$$C_3{}^m \frac{M_{m,m-1}l_m}{EI_0{}^m} - C_2{}^m \frac{M_{m-1,m}l_m}{EI_0{}^m} - \gamma_m{}^m + \Theta_{m-1,m} = 0$$

(9.22b)

Thus, all of Eqs. (9.22) again represent a sufficient number of equations for calculating all statically indeterminate moments.

Application of the three-angle equations (9.20) will now be illustrated with the analysis of a three-span bridge loaded as shown in Fig. 9.22a. In the case

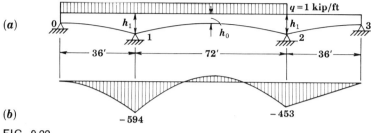

(a)

(b)

FIG. 9.22

of large spans, the bridge usually consists of a deck of constant thickness reinforced by ribs of variable depth so that we have to analyze beams of T section. To use the tables, calculated for rectangular beams, we replace the T-section beams by equivalent rectangular beams the depth of which at the supports is given by the formula (see page 423)

$$h_1 = h_0 \sqrt[3]{\frac{I_1}{I_0}} \qquad (e)$$

in which I_0 and I_1 are the centroidal moments of inertia of the T sections at mid-span and at the supports, respectively. The shapes of the haunches of the equivalent rectangular beam are taken the same as those of the actual ribs. In this case, we have parabolic haunches with $\lambda l = l/2$ and the depths $h_0 = 2.5$ ft, $h_1 = 7.5$ ft. Starting with the first span and using the Portland Cement Association tables[1] we find the following constants:

C_{01}	C_{10}	s_{01}	s_{10}	$\mathfrak{M}_{01}$	$\mathfrak{M}_{10}$
1.260	0.266	6.45	30.58	$-0.0439ql_1^2$	$0.1622ql_1^2$

Then the various constants entering into Eqs. (9.20) become

$$k_{00} = s_{01} = 6.45 \qquad k_{01} = k_{10} = C_{01}k_{00} = 1.26(6.45) = 8.12$$

$$k_{11}{}^{\mathrm{I}} = s_{10} = 30.58 \qquad \mathfrak{M}_{01} = -56.9 \text{ kip-ft} \qquad \mathfrak{M}_{10} = 210.2 \text{ kip-ft}$$

For the second span, we find again from the tables[2]

C_{12}	C_{21}	s_{12}	s_{21}	$\mathfrak{M}_{12}$	$\mathfrak{M}_{21}$
0.784	0.784	22.83	22.83	$-0.1099ql_2^2$	$0.1099ql_2^2$

and the constants entering into Eqs. (9.20) become

$$k_{11}{}^{\mathrm{II}} = s_{12} = 22.83 \qquad k_{12} = C_{12}k_{11}{}^{\mathrm{II}} = 0.784(22.83) = 17.89$$

$$k_{22}{}^{\mathrm{II}} = s_{21} = 22.83 \qquad \mathfrak{M}_{12} = -570 \text{ kip-ft} \qquad \mathfrak{M}_{21} = 570 \text{ kip-ft}$$

[1] See "Handbook of Frame Constants," p. 13, table 26.
[2] See *ibid.*, table 25.

For the third span, the tables give

C_{23}	C_{32}	s_{23}	s_{32}	$\mathfrak{M}_{23}$	$\mathfrak{M}_{32}$
0.266	1.260	30.58	6.45	$-0.1622ql_3^2$	$0.0439ql_3^2$

and the constants entering into Eqs. (9.20) become

$$k_{22}^{III} = s_{23} = 30.58 \qquad k_{23} = k_{32} = C_{23}k_{22}^{III} = 0.266(30.58)$$
$$= 8.13$$
$$k_{33} = s_{32} = 6.45 \qquad \mathfrak{M}_{23} = \mathfrak{M}_{32} = 0$$

Equations (9.20) for the problem are now written as follows:

$$k_1(k_{00}\theta_0 + k_{01}\theta_1) = -\mathfrak{M}_{01}$$
$$k_1k_{01}\theta_0 + (k_1k_{11}^{I} + k_2k_{11}^{II})\theta_1 + k_2k_{12}\theta_2 = -\mathfrak{M}_{10} - \mathfrak{M}_{12}$$
$$k_2k_{12}\theta_1 + (k_2k_{22}^{II} + k_3k_{22}^{III})\theta_2 + k_3k_{23}\theta_3 = -\mathfrak{M}_{21} - \mathfrak{M}_{23} \qquad (f)$$
$$k_3(k_{23}\theta_2 + k_{33}\theta_3) = -\mathfrak{M}_{32}$$

Observing now that

$$k_1 = \frac{EI_0}{l_1} \qquad k_2 = \frac{EI_0}{l_2} = \frac{k_1}{2} \qquad k_3 = \frac{EI_0}{l_3} = k_1$$

we divide Eqs. (f) by k_1 and obtain, after substituting the numerical values for the various constants,

$$6.45\theta_0 + 8.12\theta_1 = \frac{56.9}{k_1}$$
$$8.12\theta_0 + (30.58 + \tfrac{1}{2} \times 22.83)\theta_1 + \tfrac{1}{2} \times 17.89\theta_2 = \frac{-210.2 + 570}{k_1}$$
$$\tfrac{1}{2} \times 17.83\theta_1 + (\tfrac{1}{2} \times 22.83 + 30.58)\theta_2 + 8.13\theta_3 = \frac{-570}{k_1}$$
$$8.13\theta_2 + 6.45\theta_3 = 0$$

Solving these equations, we obtain

$$\theta_0 = -\frac{10.46}{k_1} \qquad \theta_1 = \frac{15.33}{k_1} \qquad \theta_2 = -\frac{22.24}{k_1} \qquad \theta_3 = \frac{27.95}{k_1}$$

Finally, substituting these values of the angles of rotation and the values of the constants into Eqs. (a) and (b) above, we find

$$M_{10} = -M_{12} = -8.12(10.46) + 30.58(15.33) + 210.2$$
$$= 594 \text{ kip-ft}$$
$$M_{21} = -M_{23} = \tfrac{1}{2}[17.89(15.33) - 22.83(22.24)] + 570$$
$$= 453 \text{ kip-ft}$$

The corresponding bending-moment diagram is shown in Fig. 9.22b.

Let us now solve the same problem (Fig. 9.22) by using the three-moment equations (9.22). First, using Eqs. (9.19), we calculate, for each span, the angular coefficients C_1, C_2, C_3 and then, using Eqs. (9.21), the quantities γ_a and γ_b as follows:

Span	C_1	C_2	C_3	γ_a	γ_b
I	0.2330	0.0620	0.0492	$0.0203\,\dfrac{ql^3}{EI_0}$	$0.0107\,\dfrac{ql^3}{EI_0}$
II	0.1140	0.0893	0.1140	$0.0223\,\dfrac{ql^3}{EI_0}$	$0.0223\,\dfrac{ql^3}{EI_0}$
III	0.0492	0.0620	0.2330		

With these numerical data, the three-moment equations (9.22a) become

$$(0.0492 + 2 \times 0.114)M_{10} + 2 \times 0.0893 M_{21}$$
$$= 0.0107 q l_1{}^2 + 2 \times 0.0223 q l_2{}^2$$
$$- 0.0893 M_{12} + (0.114 + \tfrac{1}{2} \times 0.0492)M_{21} = 0.0223 q l_2{}^2$$

Introducing bending moments with conventional signs instead of end moments, we have

$$M_{10} = -M_1 \qquad M_{21} = -M_2 \qquad M_{12} = M_1$$

Then with the given numerical values for l_1 and l_2, we have

$$M_1 = -590 \text{ kip-ft} \qquad M_2 = -450 \text{ kip-ft}$$

Within the limits of accuracy of the calculations, these values coincide with the values previously obtained by using the three-angle equations (see Fig. 9.22b).

As a second example, let us consider the construction of influence lines for the four-span bridge shown in Fig. 9.23a. This beam has symmetrical parabolic haunches with $\lambda l = l/2$. The minimum depth in all spans is $h_0 = 30$ in., and the depths at the intermediate supports are $h_1 = 69$ in., $h_2 = 75$ in., $h_3 = 69$ in. The extreme ends of the bridge are simply supported. Using the same tables and formulas as in the preceding example, we obtain the constants in the slope-deflection equations as shown in Fig. 9.23a.

To construct influence lines for bending moments at the supports, we start with loading the first span. Dividing this span into ten equal parts, we put the concentrated load successively at each division point and calculate the bending moments at the supports. The three-angle equations for any of these

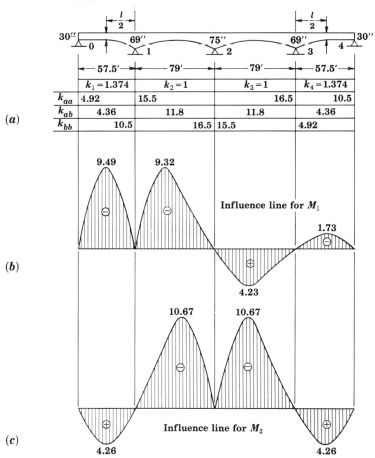

FIG. 9.23

loading conditions will be of the following form:

$$k_1(k_{00}\theta_0 + k_{01}\theta_1) = -\mathfrak{M}_{01}$$

$$k_1 k_{01}\theta_0 + (k_1 k_{11}{}^{\mathrm{I}} + k_2 k_{11}{}^{\mathrm{II}})\theta_1 + k_2 k_{12}\theta_2 = -\mathfrak{M}_{10}$$

$$k_2 k_{12}\theta_1 + (k_2 k_{22}{}^{\mathrm{II}} + k_3 k_{22}{}^{\mathrm{III}})\theta_2 + k_3 k_{23}\theta_3 = 0$$

$$k_3 k_{23}\theta_2 + (k_3 k_{33}{}^{\mathrm{III}} + k_4 k_{33}{}^{\mathrm{IV}})\theta_3 + k_4 k_{34}\theta_4 = 0$$

$$k_4(k_{34}\theta_3 + k_{44}\theta_4) = 0$$

in which

$$k_1 = \frac{EI_0}{l_1} \qquad k_2 = k_3 = \frac{k_1}{1.374} \qquad k_4 = k_1$$

and the other constants are given in Fig. 9.23a.

In solving this system of equations, we begin with the first equation and solve it for θ_0. Then substituting this in the second equation, we obtain

$$\left(-k_1 \frac{k_{01}{}^2}{k_{00}} + k_1 k_{11}{}^{\mathrm{I}} + k_2 k_{11}{}^{\mathrm{II}}\right)\theta_1 + k_2 k_{12}\theta_2 = \frac{k_{01}}{k_{00}} \mathfrak{M}_{01} - \mathfrak{M}_{10}$$

$$k_2 k_{12}\theta_1 + (k_2 k_{22}{}^{\mathrm{II}} + k_3 k_{22}{}^{\mathrm{III}})\theta_2 + k_3 k_{23}\theta_3 = 0 \qquad (g)$$

$$k_3 k_{23}\theta_2 + (k_3 k_{33}{}^{\mathrm{III}} + k_4 k_{33}{}^{\mathrm{IV}})\theta_3 + k_4 k_{34}\theta_4 = 0$$

$$k_4(k_{34}\theta_3 + k_{44}\theta_4) = 0$$

From the last of these equations, we can calculate the ratio θ_3/θ_4. Then, substituting this in the third equation, we find the ratio θ_2/θ_3, and with this value we find from the second equation the ratio θ_1/θ_2. We see that all these ratios are independent of the position of the load in the first span, and can be readily calculated by using the constants given in Fig. 9.23a. Having these values we use the first of Eqs. (g) to calculate the value of θ_1 which evidently will be proportional to the magnitude of the expression on the right-hand side of the equation. This right-hand side of the first of Eqs. (g) can be taken from the ready tables for each position of the load in the first span. Proceeding in the described manner and using the constants as given in Fig. 9.23, we find

$$\frac{\theta_4}{\theta_3} = -0.886 \qquad \frac{\theta_3}{\theta_2} = -0.479 \qquad \frac{\theta_2}{\theta_1} = -0.432$$

The first of Eqs. (g) then gives

$$\theta_1 = \frac{0.0703}{k_1}(0.886\mathfrak{M}_{01} - \mathfrak{M}_{10}) \qquad (h)$$

Values of the fixed-end moments for various positions of the load, obtained by interpolation from the tables, are given in Table 9.5 below, together with the values of the quantity in the parentheses in Eq. (h).

TABLE 9.5

$\dfrac{x}{l_1}$	$\dfrac{\mathfrak{M}_{01}}{Pl_1}$	$\dfrac{\mathfrak{M}_{10}}{Pl_1}$	$\dfrac{0.886\mathfrak{M}_{01} - \mathfrak{M}_{10}}{Pl_1}$	$\dfrac{\theta_1 k_1}{Pl_1}$	$\dfrac{M_1}{Pl_1}$	$\dfrac{M_2}{Pl_1}$	$\dfrac{M_3}{Pl_1}$
0.1	−0.077	0.019	−0.087	−0.0061	−0.047	+0.021	−0.008
0.3	−0.121	0.130	−0.238	−0.0167	−0.128	+0.057	−0.023
0.5	−0.079	0.237	−0.307	−0.0216	−0.165	+0.074	−0.030
0.7	−0.026	0.231	−0.254	−0.0179	−0.136	+0.061	−0.024
0.9	−0.002	0.095	−0.094	−0.0068	−0.052	+0.023	−0.009

TABLE 9.6

Span	C_{ab}	C_{ba}	s_a	s_b	k	C_1	C_2	C_3
I	0.888	0.417	4.92	10.47	1.374	0.323	0.135	0.152
II	0.758	0.717	15.54	16.47	1.0	0.141	0.101	0.133
III	0.717	0.758	16.47	15.54	1.0	0.133	0.101	0.141
IV	0.417	0.888	10.47	4.92	1.374	0.152	0.135	0.323

Having the ratios of the angles of rotation and the value of θ_1, we obtain the values of the bending moments at the supports from Eqs. (*a*) and (*b*), which in this case give

$$M_{12} = k_2(k_{11}{}^{II}\theta_1 + k_{12}\theta_2) = k_2\theta_1\left(k_{11}{}^{II} + k_{12}\frac{\theta_2}{\theta_1}\right) = M_1$$

$$M_{23} = k_3(k_{22}{}^{III}\theta_2 + k_{23}\theta_3) = k_3\theta_2\left(k_{22}{}^{III} + k_{23}\frac{\theta_3}{\theta_2}\right) = M_2$$

$$M_{34} = k_4(k_{33}{}^{IV}\theta_3 + k_{34}\theta_4) = k_4\theta_3\left(k_{33}{}^{IV} + k_{34}\frac{\theta_4}{\theta_3}\right) = M_3$$

where M_1, M_2, M_3 are the bending moments at the supports. From these equations, we obtain

$$M_1 = k_2\theta_1(15.5 - 11.8 \times 0.432) \qquad M_2 = -0.450M_1$$
$$M_3 = +0.181M_1$$

Using now the above calculated value of θ_1, the bending moments at the supports are readily obtained. Their values are given in the last three columns of Table 9.5 above. This finishes all necessary calculations for positions of the load in the first span.

We now consider loads in the second span and, for the purpose of illustration, use the three-moment equations (9.22) instead of the three-angle equations (9.20). We begin with a calculation of the constants C_1, C_2, C_3 by using Eqs. (9.19) and of γ_a, γ_b by using Eqs. (9.21). The values, so obtained, for all four spans are given in Table 9.6.

For span II, the quantities γ_a and γ_b are

$$\gamma_a = \frac{1}{k_2}(-0.141\mathfrak{M}_{12} + 0.101\mathfrak{M}_{21})$$

$$\gamma_b = \frac{1}{k_2}(+0.133\mathfrak{M}_{21} - 0.101\mathfrak{M}_{12})$$

(*i*)

With these values of the constants, the three-moment equations (9.22) become

$$\left(\frac{0.152}{1.374} + 0.141\right) M_{10} + 0.101 M_{21} = -0.141 \mathfrak{M}_{12} + 0.101 \mathfrak{M}_{21}$$

$$-0.101 M_{12} + (0.133 + 0.133) M_{21} + 0.101 M_{32}$$
$$= 0.133 \mathfrak{M}_{21} - 0.101 \mathfrak{M}_{12}$$

$$-0.101 M_{23} + \left(0.141 + \frac{0.152}{1.374}\right) M_{32} = 0$$

Introducing bending moments

$$M_1 = -M_{10} = M_{12} \qquad M_2 = -M_{21} = M_{23} \qquad M_3 = -M_{32}$$

and solving the equations, we obtain, for any position of the load in the second span, the values

$$M_1 = -0.200 \mathfrak{M}_{21} + 0.464 \mathfrak{M}_{12}$$

$$M_2 = -0.500 \mathfrak{M}_{21} + 0.240 \mathfrak{M}_{12}$$

$$M_3 = -0.400 M_2$$

Now, using the available tables for fixed-end moments, the bending moments at the supports can be readily calculated. The values of these bending moments, so obtained, are shown in Table 9.7.

It is seen that use of the three-moment equations resulted in considerable simplification since, in this case with simply supported ends, we have only three redundant quantities to calculate, whereas in using the three-angle equations, we had to calculate five unknown angles of rotation at the supports. In the case of a beam with built-in ends, the three-angle equations would hold a like advantage over the three-moment equations.

We have now considered the concentrated load acting in each of the first two spans. Owing to symmetry of the beam in this case, the results already obtained are sufficient to construct the influence lines for all four spans. Such influence lines for M_1 and M_2 are shown in Fig. 9.23b and c, respectively.

TABLE 9.7

x/l	$\mathfrak{M}_{12}$	$\mathfrak{M}_{21}$	M_1	M_2	M_3
0.1	$-0.092 Pl_2$	$0.006 Pl_2$	$-0.044 Pl_2$	$-0.025 Pl_2$	$+0.010 Pl_2$
0.3	$-0.203 Pl_2$	$0.065 Pl_2$	$-0.107 Pl_2$	$-0.081 Pl_2$	$+0.033 Pl_2$
0.5	$-0.163 Pl_2$	$0.182 Pl_2$	$-0.112 Pl_2$	$-0.130 Pl_2$	$+0.052 Pl_2$
0.7	$-0.055 Pl_2$	$0.214 Pl_2$	$-0.069 Pl_2$	$-0.120 Pl_2$	$+0.048 Pl_2$
0.9	$-0.004 Pl_2$	$0.094 Pl_2$	$-0.021 Pl_2$	$-0.048 Pl_2$	$+0.019 Pl_2$

9.6 SIMPLE FRAMES WITH PRISMATIC MEMBERS

In the analysis of simple frames like those discussed in the preceding chapter, the slope-deflection equations derived in Art. 9.1 can also be used to advantage. In discussing such frames here, we make the same simplification as before and neglect the effect of axial forces on deformation of the frame.

As an example, let us consider the symmetrical frame ABC pinned at A and C and loaded as shown in Fig. 9.24a. Neglecting shortening of the bar BC due to axial compression, there will be no displacement of joint B, and the slope-deflection equations in the form (9.2) will apply. Using Eqs. (9.2a), we obtain, for the member AB,

$$\theta_b = \frac{M_{ba}l}{3EI} - \frac{ql^3}{24EI}$$

and, for the member BC,

$$\theta_b = \frac{M_{bc}l}{3EI}$$

Equating these angles and observing, from the equilibrium of joint B, that $M_{ba} = -M_{bc}$, we obtain

$$\frac{2}{3}\frac{M_{bc}l}{EI} = -\frac{ql^3}{24EI}$$

Since the end moment M_{bc} is identical with the bending moment M_b, we find

$$M_b = -\frac{ql^2}{16}$$

The corresponding bending-moment diagram is shown in Fig. 9.24b.

It should be noted that the continuity condition at joint B is the same as was used in the derivation of the three-moment equation, which suggests the use of this equation in the analysis of frames. Treating the frame ABC as a two-span continuous beam and using the three-moment equation [Eq. (9.7a)], we

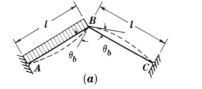

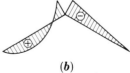

FIG. 9.24 (a) (b)

obtain directly

$$4M_b l = -\frac{q l^3}{4}$$

which gives the same value for M_b as that calculated above.

Having the magnitude of the bending moment M_b, we can find from statics the axial compressive forces in the bars AB and BC and the corresponding small displacement of the rigid joint B, which was neglected in the above analysis. Upon introducing the additional angles of rotation of the two bars, due to this displacement, we can find a correction to the previously calculated value of M_b by using Eqs. (9.3a). This correction is usually small and can be disregarded in most practical calculations.

In the case of a symmetrical frame loaded as shown in Fig. 9.25 there will be no lateral sway, and the three-moment equation can be applied in calculating the bending moments at the rigid joints B and C. Using Eq. (9.7) and observing from symmetry that $M_b = M_c$, we obtain

$$2M_b \left(\frac{h I_2}{I_1} + l \right) + M_b l = -\frac{3 P l^2}{8} \qquad (a)$$

Then with the notations

$$\alpha = \frac{h}{l} \qquad \frac{I_2}{I_1} = \gamma$$

we find

$$M_b = M_c = -\frac{3 P l}{8} \frac{1}{2 \alpha \gamma + 3} \qquad (b)$$

The corresponding bending-moment diagram is shown in Fig. 9.25b.

If there is no symmetry, the top of the loaded frame will move laterally, and this motion must be considered in calculating the bending moments at the rigid joints. Take, as an example, the case shown in Fig. 9.26a, where a load P is applied nonsymmetrically. To solve the problem by using the three-moment equation, we assume first that there is a horizontal force H applied as shown and of such magnitude that the lateral sway of the frame is prevented.

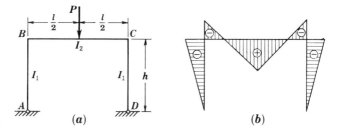

FIG. 9.25   (a)   (b)

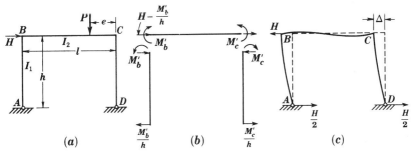

FIG. 9.26

Then, proceeding as before, we obtain the bending moments M'_b and M'_c at the rigid joints B and C from the following three-moment equations:

$$2M'_b\left(\frac{h}{I_1}+\frac{l}{I_2}\right)+M'_c\frac{l}{I_2}=-\frac{Pe(l^2-e^2)}{I_2 l}$$

$$M'_b\frac{l}{I_2}+2M'_c\left(\frac{l}{I_2}+\frac{h}{I_1}\right)=-\frac{Pe(l-e)(2l-e)}{I_2 l} \qquad (c)$$

When the bending moments M'_b and M'_c have been found, the axial forces acting on the horizontal girder BC can be calculated from equations of statics. These forces, assuming positive bending moments M'_b and M'_c, are indicated in Fig. 9.26. The condition of equilibrium then gives

$$H-\frac{M'_b}{h}+\frac{M'_c}{h}=0$$

and the force required to restrain the frame against lateral sway is

$$H=-\frac{M'_c-M'_b}{h} \qquad (d)$$

To find the values M_b and M_c of the bending moments when there is no horizontal restraining force H, we consider the auxiliary problem shown in Fig. 9.26c. The required moments will evidently be obtained by superimposing the solutions for this case and that shown in Fig. 9.26a. Denoting by M''_b and M''_c the bending moments at B and C for the case in Fig. 9.26c, we obtain

$$M_b=M'_b+M''_b$$

$$M_c=M'_c+M''_c \qquad (e)$$

The bending of the frame in this case is of a very simple nature since, from symmetry of the frame, the horizontal reactions of the hinges A and D must each be equal to $H/2$. Hence,

$$M_b'' = -M_c'' = -\frac{hH}{2}$$

Substituting for H its value (d), we obtain

$$M_b'' = -M_c'' = \frac{M_c' - M_d'}{2} \qquad (f)$$

and Eqs. (e) give

$$M_b = M_c = \frac{M_b' + M_c'}{2} \qquad (g)$$

The sum of the moments M_b' and M_c' is obtained by adding together Eqs. (c), which gives

$$M_b' + M_c' = -\frac{3Pe(l - e)}{l[3 + 2(h/l)(I_2/I_1)]}$$

Hence, the required solution is

$$M_b = M_c = -\frac{3Pe(l - e)}{2l[3 + 2(h/l)(I_2/I_1)]} \qquad (h)$$

In the foregoing example, we obtained the required solution by superimposing the solutions of two separate problems as shown in Fig. 9.26a and c. In the first of these two problems, the lateral sway was restrained, and in the second, the effect of lateral sway alone was considered.

However, by using the slope-deflection equations, we can write directly all equations necessary to determine the bending moments at the rigid joints and also the lateral sway of any given frame. Take, for example, the symmetrical frame shown in Fig. 9.27a and assume that, under the action of the load P, the top of the frame undergoes a lateral displacement Δ to the right. Then with the notations

$$k_1 = k_3 = \frac{EI_1}{l_1} \qquad k_2 = \frac{EI_2}{l_2} \qquad \theta = \frac{\Delta}{l_1} \qquad (i)$$

we write the following slope-deflection equations [see Eqs. (9.6)]:

$$
\begin{aligned}
M_{ab} &= 2k_1\theta_b - 6k_1\theta \\
M_{ba} &= 4k_1\theta_b - 6k_1\theta \\
M_{bc} &= 2k_2(2\theta_b + \theta_c) + \mathfrak{M}_{bc} \\
M_{cb} &= 2k_2(2\theta_c + \theta_b) + \mathfrak{M}_{cb} \\
M_{cd} &= 4k_1\theta_c - 6k_1\theta \\
M_{dc} &= 2k_1\theta_c - 6k_1\theta
\end{aligned}
\qquad (j)
$$

We see that all end moments are expressed in terms of the three quantities θ_b, θ_c, and Θ. For their determination, we note first that

$$M_{ba} = -M_{bc} \qquad M_{cb} = -M_{cd}$$

which, after substitution from Eqs. (j), become

$$4(k_1 + k_2)\theta_b + 2k_2\theta_c = 6k_1\Theta - \mathfrak{M}_{bc}$$
$$2k_2\theta_b + 4(k_1 + k_2)\theta_c = 6k_1\Theta - \mathfrak{M}_{cb} \qquad (k)$$

To obtain a third equation, we consider the equilibrium of the beam BC under the action of horizontal forces transmitted to it by the legs of the frame. From the action of the end moments on the vertical member AB (Fig. 9.27b) we conclude that there must act at A and B the horizontal shearing forces

$$H = \frac{M_{ba} + M_{ab}}{l_1} \qquad (l)$$

Similarly, for the member CD, we obtain

$$H_1 = \frac{M_{cd} + M_{dc}}{l_1} \qquad (m)$$

Then from equilibrium considerations of the beam BC, we conclude that

$$H + H_1 = \frac{1}{l_1}(M_{ba} + M_{ab} + M_{cd} + M_{dc}) = 0$$

Substituting for the end moments from Eqs. (j), we obtain

$$\theta_b + \theta_c = 4\Theta \qquad (n)$$

From Eqs. (k) and (n), the quantities θ_b, θ_c, and Θ can be determined. They

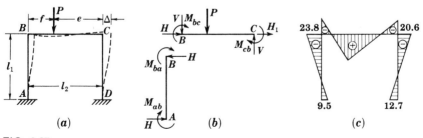

(a)   (b)   (c)

FIG. 9.27

are

$$\theta_b = -\frac{\mathfrak{M}_{bc} + \mathfrak{M}_{cb}}{2(k_1 + 6k_2)} + \frac{\mathfrak{M}_{cb} - \mathfrak{M}_{bc}}{4(2k_1 + k_2)}$$

$$\theta_c = -\frac{\mathfrak{M}_{bc} + \mathfrak{M}_{cb}}{2(k_1 + 6k_2)} - \frac{\mathfrak{M}_{cb} - \mathfrak{M}_{bc}}{4(2k_1 + k_2)} \qquad (o)$$

$$\theta = -\frac{\mathfrak{M}_{bc} + \mathfrak{M}_{cb}}{4(k_1 + 6k_2)}$$

For the indicated loading, we have the fixed-end moments (see page 412)

$$\mathfrak{M}_{bc} = -\frac{Pe^2 f}{l_2^2} \qquad \mathfrak{M}_{cb} = \frac{Pf^2 e}{l_2^2}$$

and Eqs. (o) become

$$\theta_b = \frac{Pef(e - f)}{2l_2^2(k_1 + 6k_2)} + \frac{Pef}{4l_2(2k_1 + k_2)}$$

$$\theta_c = \frac{Pef(e - f)}{2l_2^2(k_1 + 6k_2)} - \frac{Pef}{4l_2(2k_1 + k_2)} \qquad (p)$$

$$\theta = \frac{Pef(e - f)}{4l_2^2(k_1 + 6k_2)}$$

Substituting these values into Eqs. (j), we find

$$M_{ab} = -\frac{Pef(e - f)}{2l_2^2(1 + 6k_2/k_1)} + \frac{Pef}{2l_2(2 + k_2/k_1)}$$

$$M_{bc} = -M_{ba} = -\frac{Pef(e - f)}{2l_2^2(1 + 6k_2/k_1)} - \frac{Pef}{l_2(2 + k_2/k_1)}$$

$$M_{cb} = -M_{cd} = -\frac{Pef(e - f)}{2l_2^2(1 + 6k_2/k_1)} + \frac{Pef}{l_2(2 + k_2/k_1)} \qquad (q)$$

$$M_{dc} = -\frac{Pef(e - f)}{2l_2^2(1 + 6k_2/k_1)} - \frac{Pef}{2l_2(2 + k_2/k_1)}$$

Using these formulas, the end moments can be calculated and the bending-moment diagram constructed for any position of the load P. It is seen that the moments depend only on the ratio k_2/k_1 but not on the values of these quantities. Take, for example, $l_1 = 15$ ft, $l_2 = 30$ ft, $k_1 = k_2$, $f = 10$ ft, $P = 10$ kips. Then from Eqs. (q), we obtain

$$M_{ab} = 9.52 \text{ kip-ft} \qquad M_{bc} = -23.8 \text{ kip-ft}$$

$$M_{cb} = 20.6 \text{ kip-ft} \qquad M_{dc} = -12.7 \text{ kip-ft}$$

and the bending-moment diagram will be as shown in Fig. 9.27c.

To calculate the lateral displacement Δ of the top of the frame, we use the expression for the angle of rotation θ as given by the last of Eqs. (p). Thus,

$$\Delta = l_1\theta = \frac{Pef(e - f)l_1}{4k_1l_2{}^2(1 + 6k_2/k_1)} \tag{r}$$

It is seen that we need not only the ratio k_2/k_1 but also the value of k_1 to get the numerical value of Δ. Assume $E = 288,000$ kips/ft^2, $I_1 = 0.80$ ft^4; then

$$k_1 = \frac{288,000 \times 0.80}{15}$$

and from Eq. (r) we find $\Delta = 0.0093$ in.

In numerical calculation of the deflection of a frame without lateral restraint, the following procedure is frequently used: We calculate first the end moments and shear forces, assuming that there is no lateral displacement. Then we assume a certain lateral displacement, say $\Delta = 1$ in., and calculate the corresponding values of the end moments and shear forces at the joints. Since the value of the lateral displacement was arbitrary, these shear forces will not balance those calculated for the laterally restrained frame. But since the shear forces are proportional to the assumed value of Δ, it is easy to find, in each particular case, a numerical factor by which the assumed Δ must be multiplied in order to attain the required equilibrium of the frame. To illustrate this method of calculation, let us consider the unsymmetrical frame shown in Fig. 9.28a. Considering first that the frame is laterally restrained and assuming that $k_1 = k_2 = \frac{1}{2}k_3 = k$, we obtain, from the slope-deflection equations (9.6), the following expressions for the end moments:

$$
\begin{aligned}
M'_{ab} &= 2k\theta_b + \mathfrak{M}_{ab} \\
M'_{ba} &= 4k\theta_b + \mathfrak{M}_{ba} \\
M'_{bc} &= 2k(2\theta_b + \theta_c) + \mathfrak{M}_{bc} \\
M'_{cb} &= 2k(2\theta_c + \theta_b) + \mathfrak{M}_{cb} \\
M'_{cd} &= 8k\theta_c + 4k\theta_d = 6k\theta_c \\
0 &= 2\theta_d + \theta_c \qquad \theta_d = -\tfrac{1}{2}\theta_c
\end{aligned}
\tag{s}
$$

Then, from the conditions

$$M_{ba} = -M_{bc} \qquad M_{cb} = -M_{cd}$$

we obtain

$$4\theta_b + \theta_c = -\frac{\mathfrak{M}_{ba} + \mathfrak{M}_{bc}}{2k}$$

$$\theta_b + 5\theta_c = -\frac{\mathfrak{M}_{cb}}{2k} \tag{t}$$

Taking $l_1 = l_2 = 2l_3 = 20$ ft, $P = 2Q = 20$ kips, we have

$$\mathfrak{M}_{ab} = -19.2 \text{ kip-ft} \qquad \mathfrak{M}_{ba} = 28.8 \text{ kip-ft}$$
$$\mathfrak{M}_{bc} = -57.6 \text{ kip-ft} \qquad \mathfrak{M}_{cb} = 38.4 \text{ kip-ft}$$

and Eqs. (t) give

$$\theta_b = -\theta_c = \frac{4.8}{k} \qquad \theta_d = \frac{2.4}{k}$$

With these values of the angles of rotation at the joints, we obtain from Eqs. (s)

$$M'_{ab} = -9.6 \text{ kip-ft} \qquad M'_{ba} = -M'_{bc} = 48.0 \text{ kip-ft}$$
$$M'_{cb} = -M'_{cd} = 28.8 \text{ kip-ft} \tag{u}$$

The horizontal forces transmitted from the vertical members to the horizontal beam BC will then be

$$H = \frac{10 \times 12}{20} + \frac{M'_{ab} + M'_{ba}}{l_1} = 7.92 \text{ kips}$$
$$H_1 = \frac{M'_{cd}}{l_3} = -2.88 \text{ kips}$$

These horizontal forces, as shown in Fig. 9.28b, are not in equilibrium, and without lateral restraint, the beam BC would move to the right.

In the second step of calculation, we remove the lateral restraint as well as the loads P and Q and assume that the beam BC is moved to the right by the amount $\Delta = 0.1$ ft. Then the angles of rotation of the members will be

$$\theta_1 = \frac{\Delta}{l_1} = \frac{1}{200} \qquad \theta_2 = 0 \qquad \theta_3 = \frac{\Delta}{l_3} = \frac{1}{100}$$

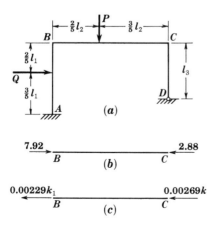

FIG. 9.28

For this case, the slope-deflection equations (9.6) become

$$M''_{ab} = 2k\theta_b - 6k\Theta_1 = 2k\theta_b - 0.03k$$
$$M''_{ba} = 4k\theta_b - 6k\Theta_1 = 4k\theta_b - 0.03k$$
$$M''_{bc} = 2k(2\theta_b + \theta_c)$$
$$M''_{cb} = 2k(2\theta_c + \theta_b)$$
$$M''_{cd} = 4k(2\theta_c + \theta_d) - 12k\Theta_3$$
$$0 = 4k(2\theta_d + \theta_c) - 12k\Theta_3 \qquad \theta_d = -\tfrac{1}{2}\theta_c + \tfrac{3}{2}\Theta_3$$

(v)

Substituting these end moments into the conditions

$$M''_{ba} = -M''_{bc} \qquad M''_{cb} = -M''_{cd}$$

we obtain

$$4\theta_b + \theta_c = 0.015$$
$$\theta_b + 5\theta_c = 0.030$$

from which

$$\theta_b = 0.00237 \qquad \theta_c = 0.00552$$

and Eqs. (v) give

$$M''_{ab} = -0.0253k \qquad M''_{ba} = -M''_{bc} = -0.0205k$$
$$M''_{cd} = -M''_{cb} = -0.0269k$$

(w)

The corresponding axial forces acting on the beam BC are shown in Fig. 9.28c. Since the magnitude of the displacement $\Delta = 0.10$ ft was arbitrary, these forces usually will not balance the previously calculated forces shown in Fig. 9.28b. To attain equilibrium, we multiply the assumed displacement by a factor x. Then the axial forces in Fig. 9.28c will also be multiplied by x, and the condition of equilibrium becomes

$$(0.00229k + 0.00269k)x = 7.92 - 2.88 = 5.04 \text{ kips}$$

from which we find

$$x = \frac{5.04}{0.00498k}$$

The true end moments, corresponding to the actual lateral displacement of the frame, will then be obtained by multiplying the values (w) by x, which gives

$$M'''_{ab} = xM''_{ab} = -25.6 \text{ kip-ft}$$
$$M'''_{ba} = -M'''_{bc} = xM''_{ba} = -20.75 \text{ kip-ft}$$
$$M'''_{cd} = -M'''_{cb} = xM''_{cd} = -27.2 \text{ kip-ft}$$

Superimposing these moments on those given by Eqs. (u), the actual end moments are obtained as follows:

$$M_{ab} = -9.6 - 25.6 = -35.2 \text{ kip-ft}$$

$$M_{ba} = -M_{bc} = 27.25 \text{ kip-ft}$$

$$M_{cd} = -M_{cb} = -56.0 \text{ kip-ft}$$

With these values of the end moments, the bending-moment diagram for the frame can be constructed, if desired.

PROBLEMS

1 Construct the bending-moment diagram for the symmetrically loaded symmetrical frame shown in Fig. 9.29. The following numerical data are given: $P = 150$ kips, $l = 12$ ft, $h = 30$ ft, $c = 3.5$ ft, $I_0/I_2 = 2$, $I_1/I_2 = \frac{1}{2}$.
   Ans. $M_{ad} = -M_{ab} = -94.0$ kip-ft, $M_{ba} = -M_{bc} = +21.4$ kip-ft.

2 A symmetrical frame like that shown in Fig. 9.25 has built-in ends at A and D and carries, instead of the concentrated load P, a uniformly distributed load of intensity q along the beam BC. For the particular case where $I_1 = I_2$, find the bending moments at the ends of the members.
   Ans. $M_b = M_c = -ql^2/6(2 + \alpha)$, $M_a = M_d = -M_b/2$, $\alpha = h/l$.

3 Find the bending moment M_b for the frame shown in Fig. 9.30 if $q_0 = 0$.
   Ans. $M_b = \dfrac{-1}{\alpha\gamma + 1} \dfrac{Pe^2(l - e)}{l^2}$, where $\alpha = h/l$, $\gamma = I_2/I_1$.

4 Find the bending moment M_b for the frame loaded as shown in Fig. 9.30 if $P = 0$.
   Ans. $M_b = -\dfrac{q_0 l^2}{20(1 + \alpha\gamma)}$, where $\alpha = h/l$, $\gamma = I_2/I_1$.

5 Find the bending moments M_b and M_c for the frame shown in Fig. 9.26 if the girder BC is uniformly loaded along the right half of the span and the frame is free to sway.
   Ans. $M_b = M_c = -(ql^2)/8(3 + 2\alpha\gamma)$, where $\alpha = h/l$, $\gamma = I_2/I_1$.

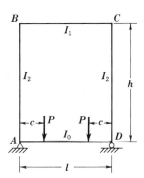

FIG. 9.29

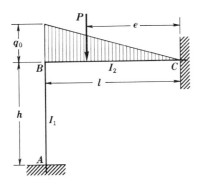

FIG. 9.30

6   Find the bending moments at A, B, C, and D for the frame shown in Fig. 9.26 if lateral sway is restrained and the columns are built in at A and D.

   Ans.   With $\alpha = h/l$ and $\gamma = I_2/I_1$,

$$M_b = -\frac{2Pe(l-e)[\alpha\gamma(l+e)+2e]}{l^2(\alpha\gamma+2)(3\alpha\gamma+2)}$$

$$M_c = -\frac{2Pe(l-e)[\alpha\gamma(2l-e)+2(l-e)]}{l^2(\alpha\gamma+2)(3\alpha\gamma+2)}$$

$$M_a = -\frac{M_b}{2} \qquad M_d = -\frac{M_c}{2}$$

7   Solve the preceding problem if the load is uniformly distributed along the right half of the girder.

   Hint   Substitute qde, instead of P, in the answers of the preceding problem, and integrate with respect to e from 0 to $l/2$.

9.7   CONTINUOUS FRAMES WITH PRISMATIC MEMBERS

In the preceding article, several simple cases of frames were considered in which direct application of the slope-deflection equations gives the required solution.   In practice, such systems as those shown in Fig. 9.31 are often encountered.   These frames are more complicated than those previously considered, and before writing the necessary equations, some preliminary discussion is desirable.[1]   For this purpose, we divide the systems into two groups.   In the first group, we include frames of the type shown in Fig. 9.31a where, owing to the fact that the hinge a is fixed, displacements of all the joints are prevented, and only rotations of these joints need to be considered.   For the case shown in Fig. 9.31b, both ends a and f of the girder are free to move horizontally, so as a result of bending of the members, *lateral sway* can take

[1] The slope-deflection equations and their application in frame analysis were developed by Axel Bendixen; see his book "Die Methode der Alpha-Gleichungen zur Berechnung von Rahmenkonstruktionen," Berlin, 1914.

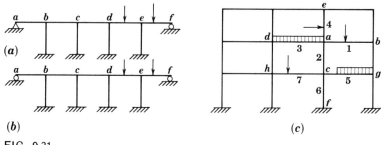

FIG. 9.31

place. The building frame shown in Fig. 9.31c is also subject to lateral sway. In the analysis of frames of the second class, the calculations are usually made in two steps. First, we assume that the lateral sway is prevented by some constraints and consider only rotations of the joints. Afterward, in the second step, the effect of lateral sway can be studied separately.

In deriving equations for the analysis of frames restrained against side sway, we take the structure shown in Fig. 9.31c and consider a typical joint a attached to the adjacent joints b, c, d, and e by the bars 1, 2, 3, and 4. Denoting by k_1, k_2, k_3, and k_4 the stiffness factors for the bars and by θ_a, θ_b, . . . the angles of rotation of the joints, we see that the end moments for the bars that meet at joint a will be [see Eqs. (9.6)]

$$M_{ab} = 2k_1(2\theta_a + \theta_b) + \mathfrak{M}_{ab}$$
$$M_{ac} = 2k_2(2\theta_a + \theta_c) + \mathfrak{M}_{ac}$$
$$M_{ad} = 2k_3(2\theta_a + \theta_d) + \mathfrak{M}_{ad} \tag{a}$$
$$M_{ae} = 2k_4(2\theta_a + \theta_e) + \mathfrak{M}_{ae}$$

where the last terms on the right-hand side of the equations represent the fixed-end moments produced by forces acting on the bars. In each particular case of loading, these fixed-end moments can be easily calculated or taken from existing tables.

The end moments (a) represent actions on the bars; equal moments, but of opposite signs, will represent actions on the joint a, and from the condition of equilibrium of this joint we conclude that

$$M_{ab} + M_{ac} + M_{ad} + M_{ae} = 0 \tag{b}$$

Then substituting from Eqs. (a) for the moments, the following equation of equilibrium for the joint a will be obtained:

$$4(k_1 + k_2 + k_3 + k_4)\theta_a + 2k_1\theta_b + 2k_2\theta_c + 2k_3\theta_d + 2k_4\theta_e$$
$$= -(\mathfrak{M}_{ab} + \mathfrak{M}_{ac} + \mathfrak{M}_{ad} + \mathfrak{M}_{ae}) \tag{9.23a}$$

Such an equation can be written for each joint of the frame, and we shall obtain as many equations as there are unknown angles of rotation. Thus, the problem is reduced to the solution of a system of linear algebraic equations. Solving this system, we find the numerical values of the angles of rotation. Substituting these into Eqs. (a), we then calculate the end moments for all members of the frame.

In the above derivation of Eqs. $(9.23a)$, we considered a joint a at which four members meet and obtained an equation with five unknowns. Considering joint b where only three members meet, we shall have only four unknowns, etc. In the case of joint c, we shall again get only four unknowns since the bar cf is built in at f and the angle θ_f vanishes. If there were a hinge at f, the angle θ_f would not vanish but the end moment M_{fc} would, and we get the equation

$$0 = 2k_6(2\theta_f + \theta_c) + \mathfrak{M}_{fc}$$

Hence, $$\theta_f = -\frac{1}{2}\theta_c - \frac{\mathfrak{M}_{fc}}{4k_6}$$

and we obtain

$$M_{cf} = 2k_6(2\theta_c + \theta_f) + \mathfrak{M}_{cf} = 3k_6\theta_c - \tfrac{1}{2}\mathfrak{M}_{fc} + \mathfrak{M}_{cf}$$

The equilibrium equation for the joint c then becomes

$$4(k_5 + \tfrac{3}{4}k_6 + k_7 + k_2) + 2k_2\theta_a + 2k_5\theta_g + 2k_7\theta_h$$

$$= -(\mathfrak{M}_{ca} + \mathfrak{M}_{cg} + \mathfrak{M}_{ch} + \mathfrak{M}_{cf} - \tfrac{1}{2}\mathfrak{M}_{fc}) \quad (9.23b)$$

Comparing Eq. $(9.23b)$ with the previously developed Eq. $(9.23a)$, it can be seen that if, in considering the equilibrium of a joint like c, we have a member hinged at the far end, a modified stiffness factor $k' = \tfrac{3}{4}k$ should be used instead of k (see page 409). Also, instead of a true fixed-end moment, a modified fixed-end moment

$$\mathfrak{M}'_{cf} = \mathfrak{M}_{cf} - \tfrac{1}{2}\mathfrak{M}_{fc}$$

for a bar with one end fixed and the other simply supported appears on the right-hand side of Eq. $(9.23b)$.

The above equations are sufficient for the treatment of frames without side sway. In the case of frames subject to side sway, we have still to consider a second step in the analysis. For this second step, we disregard the external loads and consider only rotations of the members due to lateral sway of the frame. Then, instead of Eqs. (a), we shall have equations of the type (see page 411)

$$M_{mn} = 2k(2\theta_m + \theta_n) - 6k\Theta_{mn}$$

and in considering the equilibrium of joints, we shall obtain equations similar to Eqs. (9.23). The only difference will be on the right-hand side of the equations where the fixed-end moments such as $\mathfrak{M}_{mn}$ will be replaced by quantities $-6k_i\Theta_{mn}$.

As an example of analysis of a continuous frame without side sway, let us consider the case shown in Fig. 9.32a. Since the ends of the girder are built in at a and e, there can be no lateral movement, and deformation of the frame is completely defined by the three angles of rotation θ_b, θ_c, θ_d. The necessary three equations of the type (9.23a) will be

$$4(k_1 + k_2 + k_5)\theta_b + 2k_2\theta_c = -(\mathfrak{M}_{ba} + \mathfrak{M}_{bc} + \mathfrak{M}_{bf})$$

$$4(k_2 + k_3 + k_6)\theta_c + 2k_2\theta_b + 2k_3\theta_d = -(\mathfrak{M}_{cb} + \mathfrak{M}_{cd} + \mathfrak{M}_{cg}) \quad (c)$$

$$4(k_3 + k_4 + k_7)\theta_d + 2k_3\theta_c = -(\mathfrak{M}_{dc} + \mathfrak{M}_{de} + \mathfrak{M}_{dh})$$

If the dimensions of the structure and the acting loads are given, the values of k_i and $\mathfrak{M}_{mn}$ can be calculated, and we obtain from Eqs. (c) three linear numerical equations of the same kind as in the case of continuous beams. Assume, for example, that

$$k_1 = k_4 \qquad k_2 = k_3 = k_5 = k_6 = k_7 = \tfrac{1}{2}k_1$$
$$l_1 = l_4 = h = l \qquad l_2 = l_3 = 2l \tag{d}$$

Also, for a uniform load of intensity q covering the entire length of the girder ae, we have

$$\mathfrak{M}_{ab} = \mathfrak{M}_{de} = -\mathfrak{M}_{ba} = -\mathfrak{M}_{ed} = -\frac{ql^2}{12}$$

$$\mathfrak{M}_{bc} = \mathfrak{M}_{cd} = -\mathfrak{M}_{cb} = -\mathfrak{M}_{dc} = -\frac{ql^2}{3} \tag{e}$$

There are, of course, no fixed-end moments for the laterally unloaded columns.

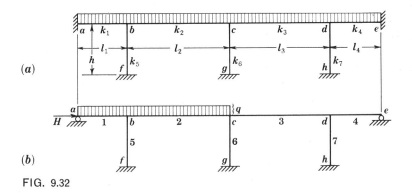

(a)

(b)

FIG. 9.32

Equations (c) then become

$$8k_1\theta_b + k_1\theta_c = \frac{ql^2}{4}$$

$$\theta_b + 6\theta_c + \theta_d = 0 \qquad (f)$$

$$k_1\theta_c + 8k_1\theta_d = -\frac{ql^2}{4}$$

and we obtain

$$\theta_b = -\theta_d = \frac{ql^2}{32k_1} \qquad \theta_c = 0$$

The fact that $\theta_c = 0$ could, of course, have been concluded in advance from symmetry and the solution of Eqs. (f) somewhat simplified. Having the angles of rotation, the end moments are obtained from equations such as Eqs. (a), above, and we find

$$M_{ab} = -M_{ed} = -\frac{ql^2}{48} \qquad M_{ba} = -M_{de} = \frac{5ql^2}{24}$$

$$M_{bc} = -M_{dc} = -\frac{13ql^2}{48} \qquad M_{cb} = -M_{cd} = \frac{35ql^2}{96}$$

$$M_{bf} = -M_{dh} = \frac{ql^2}{16}$$

With these values of the end moments, the bending-moment diagram for the frame can be easily constructed.

If, instead of built-in ends, there are fixed hinges at a and e (Fig. 9.32a), lateral motion is again restrained, but we use Eqs. (9.23b) for joints b and d and Eqs. (9.23a) for joint c. Then, instead of Eqs. (c), we get

$$(3k_1 + 4k_2 + 4k_5)\theta_b + 2k_2\theta_c = -(\mathfrak{M}_{ba} + \mathfrak{M}_{bc} + \mathfrak{M}_{bf} - \tfrac{1}{2}\mathfrak{M}_{ab})$$

$$4(k_2 + k_3 + k_6)\theta_c + 2k_2\theta_b + 2k_3\theta_d = -(\mathfrak{M}_{cb} + \mathfrak{M}_{cd} + \mathfrak{M}_{cg})$$

$$(4k_3 + 3k_4 + 4k_7)\theta_d + 2k_3\theta_c = -(\mathfrak{M}_{dc} + \mathfrak{M}_{de} + \mathfrak{M}_{dh} - \tfrac{1}{2}\mathfrak{M}_{ed})$$

$$(g)$$

These equations again can be readily solved in each particular case.

Let us consider now the case where the frame is free to move laterally. As an example, we take the frame in Fig. 9.32b and assume that it is uniformly loaded only along the first two spans. In this case, the problem will be solved in two steps. Assuming first that there is a lateral constraint at a and using

Eqs. (g) and (d), we obtain the system of equations

$$7k_1\theta_b + k_1\theta_c = \frac{5ql^2}{24}$$

$$k_1\theta_b + 6k_1\theta_c + k_1\theta_d = -\frac{ql^2}{3}$$

$$k_1\theta_c + 7k_1\theta_d = 0$$

from which

$$\theta_b = 0.0388\,\frac{ql^2}{k_1} \qquad \theta_c = -0.0635\,\frac{ql^2}{k_1} \qquad \theta_d = 0.00908\,\frac{ql^2}{k_1}$$

Now using equations similar to Eqs. (a), we can calculate all end moments. For the columns, we get

$$M_{bf} = 2M_{fb} = 2k_1\theta_b \qquad M_{cg} = 2M_{gc} = 2k_1\theta_c$$

$$M_{dh} = 2M_{hd} = 2k_1\theta_d$$

Then, the corresponding shearing forces at the tops of the columns (see Fig. 9.27b for directions) will be

$$H_{bf} = \frac{3k_1\theta_b}{h} \qquad H_{cg} = \frac{3k_1\theta_c}{h} \qquad H_{dh} = \frac{3k_1\theta_d}{h}$$

and the total horizontal force transmitted to the girder, positive in the direction from left to right, becomes

$$\frac{3k_1}{h}(\theta_b + \theta_c + \theta_d) = -0.0156\,\frac{3ql^2}{h} \tag{h}$$

The minus sign indicates that this force has the direction from right to left, and to prevent lateral movement, the force H must act at a as shown in Fig. 9.32b.

In the second step of calculation, we disregard the external forces and consider the effect of lateral sway. Assuming that the girder ae moves to the left by an amount Δ, we find the following angles of rotation for the members 1, 2, 3, . . . of the frame:

$$\theta_1 = \theta_2 = \theta_3 = \theta_4 = 0$$

$$\theta_5 = \theta_6 = \theta_7 = \theta = -\frac{\Delta}{h}$$

The slope-deflection equations for the girder members will have the form

$$M_{mn} = 2k(2\theta_m + \theta_n) \qquad M_{nm} = 2k(2\theta_n + \theta_m)$$

and, for the columns, the form of the equations will be

$$M_{mn} = 2k(2\theta_m + \theta_n) - 6k\Theta$$
$$M_{nm} = 2k(2\theta_n + \theta_m) - 6k\Theta$$
$$(i)$$

Proceeding then as already explained and writing equations of equilibrium for the joints b, c, d, we obtain the equations

$$(3k_1 + 4k_2 + 4k_5)\theta_b + 2k_2\theta_c = 6k_5\Theta$$

$$4(k_2 + k_3 + k_6)\theta_c + 2k_2\theta_b + 2k_3\theta_d = 6k_6\Theta$$

$$(4k_3 + 3k_4 + 4k_7)\theta_d + 2k_3\theta_c = 6k_7\Theta$$

With the previously taken geometrical proportions (d), these equations become

$$7\theta_b + \theta_c = 3\Theta$$
$$\theta_b + 6\theta_c + \theta_d = 3\Theta$$
$$\theta_c + 7\theta_d = 3\Theta$$
$$(j)$$

from which the three angles θ_b, θ_c, θ_d could be found. The end moments for the columns will then be determined from equations of the form (i), and we find

$$M_{bf} = 2k_1\theta_b - 3k_1\Theta \qquad M_{fb} = k_1\theta_b - 3k_1\Theta$$

$$M_{cg} = 2k_1\theta_c - 3k_1\Theta \qquad M_{gc} = k_1\theta_c - 3k_1\Theta$$

$$M_{dh} = 2k_1\theta_d - 3k_1\Theta \qquad M_{hd} = k_1\theta_d - 3k_1\Theta$$

With these values of the end moments for the columns, we calculate the horizontal forces acting on the girder ae. They are as follows:

$$H_{bf} = \frac{M_{bf} + M_{fb}}{h} = \frac{3k_1(\theta_b - 2\Theta)}{h}$$

$$H_{cg} = \frac{3k_1(\theta_c - 2\Theta)}{h} \qquad H_{dh} = \frac{3k_1(\theta_d - 2\Theta)}{h}$$

Then the total horizontal force acting on the girder, positive in the direction from left to right, is

$$H = H_{bf} + H_{cg} + H_{dh} = \frac{3k_1}{h}(\theta_b + \theta_c + \theta_d - 6\Theta) \qquad (k)$$

To get the summation of the angles $\theta_b + \theta_c + \theta_d$, we add together Eqs. ($j$) and obtain

$$\theta_b + \theta_c + \theta_d = \tfrac{9}{8}\Theta$$

Then from Eq. (k), we find

$$H = -\frac{3k_1}{h}\frac{39}{8}\,\theta = \frac{3k_1}{h^2}\frac{39}{8}\,\Delta$$

Taking this result together with the solution (h) obtained on the assumption of lateral constraint, we obtain the lateral sway Δ from the condition of equilibrium of the girder ae which gives

$$-0.0156\frac{3ql^2}{h} + \frac{3k_1}{h^2}\frac{39}{8}\,\Delta = 0$$

From this equation, we find

$$\frac{\Delta}{h} = -\theta = \frac{ql^2}{312k_1}$$

With this value of θ, we obtain now from Eqs. (j)

$$\theta_b = \theta_c = \theta_d = -\frac{ql^2}{832k_1} \tag{l}$$

With these angles known, the end moments corresponding to the lateral movement of the frame can be readily calculated. This finishes the second step of calculation.

To get the complete values of the end moments, we have to superimpose the moments produced by lateral sway on those previously calculated for the frame with lateral constraint. Assuming, for example, that $q = 1$ kip/ft and $l = 12$ ft, and using the angles of rotation θ_b, θ_c, θ_d, calculated in the first step of the analysis (see page 456),we obtain

$$M'_{ba} = 34.8 \text{ kip-ft} \qquad M'_{bc} = -46.0 \text{ kip-ft}$$

$$M'_{cd} = -17.0 \text{ kip-ft} \qquad M'_{cb} = 35.3 \text{ kip-ft} \tag{m}$$

$$M'_{dc} = -6.57 \text{ kip-ft} \qquad M'_{de} = 3.92 \text{ kip-ft}$$

Using the angles (l), we obtain, as a result of side sway,

$$M''_{ba} = M''_{bc} = M''_{cb} = M''_{cd} = M''_{dc} = M''_{de} = -\frac{3ql^2}{832}$$

$$= -0.519 \text{ kip-ft} \tag{n}$$

Adding the moments (m) and (n), we obtain total moments for the girder. It is seen that in this case lateral sway has only a small effect on the end moments.

PROBLEMS

1 Draw the bending-moment diagram for the uniformly loaded girder *bac* as shown in Fig. 9.33*a*. The ends *b* and *c* are built in, and there is a rigid connection between beam and column at *a*. Assume, for the stiffness factors, $k_2 = k_3 = 0.8k_1$ and, for the load, $q = 1$ kip/ft.

   Ans. See Fig. 9.33*b*.

2 Calculate the end moments produced by the forces P and Q acting on the frame shown in Fig. 9.34. Numerical data are given as follows: $h = l = 16$ ft, $f = 6$ ft, and $k_1 = k_2$.

   Ans. $M_{ab} = \frac{4}{7}(\frac{11}{128}Qe - Pd)$, $M_{ac} = -\frac{11}{128}Qe + \frac{3}{7}(\frac{11}{128}Qe - Pd)$.

3 The two-span building frame shown in Fig. 9.35 is subjected to the action of a horizontal uniformly distributed load of intensity q. Construct a bending-moment diagram if $h = l = 12$ ft and $q = 1$ kip/ft. The stiffness factor k is the same for all members.

   Ans. $M_{ba} = -M_{bc} = -2.25$ kip-ft, $M_{cb} = 3.94$ kip-ft, $M_{ce} = 6.94$ kip-ft, $M_{cd} = -10.88$ kip-ft, $M_{ec} = -M_{ef} = 8.25$ kip-ft, $M_{ab} = -26.44$ kip-ft, $M_{dc} = -12.75$ kip-ft, $M_{fe} = -11.44$ kip-ft.

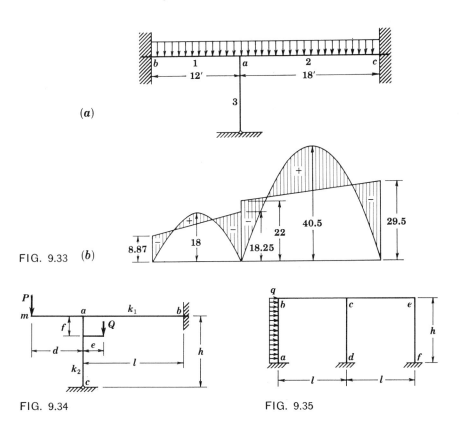

FIG. 9.33 (*b*)

(*a*)

FIG. 9.34   FIG. 9.35

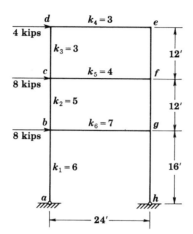

FIG. 9.36

4 Construct a bending-moment diagram for the horizontally loaded symmetrical three-story building frame shown in Fig. 9.36. The stiffness factors for the various members as shown in the figure are given in kip-foot units. Note that the lower ends of the columns are hinged at a and h.

> *Ans.* $M_{ba} = -160.0$ kip-ft, $M_{bc} = -25.3$ kip-ft, $M_{bg} = 185.3$ kip-ft, $M_{cb} = -46.7$ kip-ft, $M_{cd} = -7.86$ kip-ft, $M_{cf} = 54.6$ kip-ft, $M_{dc} = -M_{de} = -16.1$ kip-ft.

9.8 MOMENT-DISTRIBUTION METHOD

We have seen in preceding articles that the analysis of frames with rigid joints requires the solution of a system of linear algebraic equations. Sometimes these equations have the same form as the three-moment equations used in the analysis of continuous beams and can be readily solved. However, in many cases, we obtain more complicated systems of equations, and their solution may be cumbersome. In such cases, a method of successive approximations[1] may be used to advantage. The particular method to be described here is

[1] One such method was developed in connection with calculation of secondary stresses in trusses and is described in the book by O. Mohr, "Abhandlungen aus dem Gebiete der technischen Mechanik," p. 429, 1906. In this country the method was first used by S. Hardesty and is fully explained in the book by J. A. L. Waddell, "Bridge Engineering," 1916. The extension of the method to the analysis of highly statically indeterminate frame structures is due to K. A. Calíšev, who used it in analyzing building frames with and without lateral constraints. See *Tech. List.*, Zagreb, no. 17–21, 1923. A German translation of this paper will be found in *Publ. Intern. Assoc. Bridge Structural Eng.*, vol. 4, pp. 199–215, 1936. The final form of the method of successive approximations for frame structures was obtained by H. Cross; see *Trans. ASCE*, vol. 96, 1932. Solutions of many engineering problems by using methods of successive approximations are discussed in the book by R. V. Southwell, "Relaxation Methods in Engineering Science," Oxford University Press, Fair Lawn, N.J., 1940.

called *moment distribution*. It has a simple physical interpretation and has found a wide application in the analysis of statically indeterminate frame structures.

To describe the procedure, we consider the structure shown in Fig. 9.37. As previously pointed out (see page 452), the deformation of this frame, consisting of four members with built-in ends, is completely defined by the angle of rotation θ_a of the joint a, and for the determination of this angle we need only one equation. To write this equation, we observe that the summation of moments acting on the joint a must vanish. Hence,

$$M_{ab} + M_{ac} + M_{ad} + M_{ae} = 0 \tag{a}$$

Using, now, the slope-deflection equations, we find for the end moments at a

$$M_{ab} = 4k_1\theta_a + \mathfrak{M}_{ab} \qquad M_{ac} = 4k_2\theta_a + \mathfrak{M}_{ac}$$
$$M_{ad} = 4k_3\theta_a + \mathfrak{M}_{ad} \qquad M_{ae} = 4k_4\theta_a + \mathfrak{M}_{ae} \tag{b}$$

With these expressions, Eq. (a) becomes

$$4\theta_a(k_1 + k_2 + k_3 + k_4) = -(\mathfrak{M}_{ab} + \mathfrak{M}_{ac} + \mathfrak{M}_{ad} + \mathfrak{M}_{ae}) = \mathbf{M}_a$$

where we introduce the symbol $\mathbf{M}_a$ for the sum of fixed-end moments at a with reversed sign. From this equation, we find

$$\theta_a = \frac{\mathbf{M}_a}{4(k_1 + k_2 + k_3 + k_4)} \tag{9.24}$$

When this is substituted back into Eqs. (b), they become

$$M_{ab} = \mathfrak{M}_{ab} + \frac{k_1}{k_1 + k_2 + k_3 + k_4} \mathbf{M}_a$$

$$M_{ac} = \mathfrak{M}_{ac} + \frac{k_2}{k_1 + k_2 + k_3 + k_4} \mathbf{M}_a$$

$$M_{ad} = \mathfrak{M}_{ad} + \frac{k_3}{k_1 + k_2 + k_3 + k_4} \mathbf{M}_a \tag{c}$$

$$M_{ae} = \mathfrak{M}_{ae} + \frac{k_4}{k_1 + k_2 + k_3 + k_4} \mathbf{M}_a$$

It is seen that each end moment at joint a consists of two parts: (1) the *fixed-end moment*, which in each particular case of loading can be readily calculated or taken from the tables, and (2) a portion of the moment $\mathbf{M}_a$, obtained as the algebraic sum of all fixed-end moments at joint a, but with opposite sign. This moment, representing the total turning effort exerted on joint a while it is locked, is called the *unbalanced moment* at the joint. We see from Eqs. (c) that owing to rotation of joint a, the unbalanced moment distributes itself among the members meeting there in proportion to their stiffness factors $k_1, k_2, \ldots$.

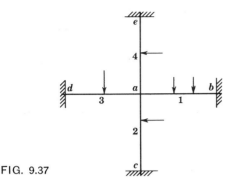

FIG. 9.37

The ratios

$$r_{ab} = \frac{k_1}{k_1 + k_2 + k_3 + k_4} \qquad r_{ac} = \frac{k_2}{k_1 + k_2 + k_3 + k_4} \qquad (d)$$

$$r_{ad} = \frac{k_3}{k_1 + k_2 + k_3 + k_4} \qquad r_{ae} = \frac{k_4}{k_1 + k_2 + k_3 + k_4}$$

by which the unbalanced moment $\mathbf{M}_a$ in Eqs. (c) is multiplied are called *distribution factors*; they will be denoted by $r_{ab}, r_{ac}, \ldots$. We see that their magnitudes are independent of the loading and can be readily calculated when the dimensions of the members are known. It is seen also that only the ratios of the stiffness factors k enter into this calculation. Hence, we can use, instead of the actual values of these factors, any set of numbers proportional to them.

With the introduced notions of *unbalanced moment* and *distribution factors*, we can recapitulate the solution of the problem in Fig. 9.37 in a more condensed form and give it a physical interpretation that will be helpful in further discussion. We start the problem with the assumption that joint a is *locked* against rotation by some constraint and calculate, or take from the ready tables, all fixed-end moments. The sum of these moments at joint a represents the moment that the lock exerts on the joint to keep it from turning. *Unlocking* the joint is equivalent to applying the unbalanced moment, which is equal and opposite to the moment of the constraint. This unbalanced moment will be distributed among the members meeting at joint a in proportion to their distribution factors (d). The final end moments at joint a are then obtained by superimposing the distributed moments on the previously calculated fixed-end moments as shown by Eqs. (c).

Equations (c) give us the end moments at the joint a. Regarding the end moments at the far ends of the members, we observe that when a distributed moment $r_{ab}\mathbf{M}_a$ is applied to the end a of the member 1, a moment $\frac{1}{2}r_{ab}\mathbf{M}_a$ is *carried over* to the far end b of this member (see page 408), and the final value of the end moment at b becomes

$$M_{ba} = \mathfrak{M}_{ba} + \tfrac{1}{2}r_{ab}\mathbf{M}_a$$

The far-end moments for the other members can be calculated similarly.

It was assumed in the foregoing discussion that the far ends of all members meeting at a are built in. If one of them, say member 1, is hinged at b, we take this into account while distributing the unbalanced moment $\mathbf{M}_a$ and introduce the *modified stiffness factor* $3k_1/4$, instead of k_1, in calculating the distribution factors (d) (see page 409). It is also to be noted that a *modified fixed-end moment*

$$\mathfrak{M}'_{ab} = \mathfrak{M}_{ab} - \tfrac{1}{2}\mathfrak{M}_{ba}$$

must be used if the far end b is hinged (see page 453).

The foregoing *moment-distribution procedure* used in the analysis of the frame in Fig. 9.37 was especially simple since there was only one joint a free to rotate. However, the method can be readily extended to the more general case in which the rotations of several joints have to be considered. To illustrate, let us reconsider the example shown in Fig. 9.32a and assume first that the joints b, c, d are all three locked, so that we can calculate the fixed-end moments and the unbalanced moments $\mathbf{M}_b$, $\mathbf{M}_c$, and $\mathbf{M}_d$. Now we unlock the joint c and distribute the unbalanced moment $\mathbf{M}_c$ among the members 2, 3, 6, in accordance with Eqs. (c). Thus, to the initial fixed-end moments at joint c, we now add the corrections

$$M'_{cb} = r_{cb}\mathbf{M}_c \qquad M'_{cd} = r_{cd}\mathbf{M}_c \qquad M'_{cg} = r_{cg}\mathbf{M}_c \qquad (e)$$

During the unlocking of joint c, the adjacent joints b, d, and g are considered as fixed. Hence, moments equal to $M'_{cb}/2$, $M'_{cd}/2$, $M'_{cg}/2$ will be carried over to the far ends of the members 2, 3, and 6, respectively, where they must be added algebraically to the fixed-end moments at these ends. Considering next the joint b, we have to distribute the moment $\mathbf{M}_b - M'_{cb}/2$, where the second term represents the moment that was previously carried over from joint c. Thus, the distributed moments at b are

$$M'_{ba} = r_{ba}(\mathbf{M}_b - \tfrac{1}{2}M'_{cb})$$
$$M'_{bc} = r_{bc}(\mathbf{M}_b - \tfrac{1}{2}M'_{cb}) \qquad (f)$$
$$M'_{bf} = r_{bf}(\mathbf{M}_b - \tfrac{1}{2}M'_{cb})$$

Similar equations for the distributed moments at the joint d can also be written. All these moments represent the first corrections to the initially calculated fixed-end moments. To get a second set of corrections, we start again with joint c.

During unlocking of the joints b and d, the moments $M'_{bc}/2$ and $M'_{dc}/2$ were carried over to the joint c, and an unbalanced moment of the magnitude

$-\frac{1}{2}(M'_{bc} + M'_{dc})$ was created at this joint. Distributing this moment, we obtain the second corrections to the end moments at joint c. Then we can calculate corrections to the end moments at the joints b and d, distributing the unbalanced moments created at these joints during the unlocking of joint c. To calculate the third corrections, we again start with joint c and proceed as before. The calculation of consecutive corrections must be carried far enough to make them negligibly small. The final end moments will then be obtained with sufficient accuracy by adding to the first approximations all of the consecutive corrections.

Recapitulating the described method of successive approximations, we see that the process of calculation consists in repetition of very simple operations of distribution of unbalanced moments and carrying over moments to the adjacent joints. In each particular case, we assume first that all joints, except hinged ends, are locked and calculate on this assumption the fixed-end moments for all members of the structure. The sums of these moments for each joint, taken with reversed signs, give us the unbalanced moments. We calculate also for each joint the distribution factors for the members meeting at that joint. After this preliminary work, we begin preferably with the joint at which the largest unbalanced moment is found. We unlock this joint and distribute the moment between the members meeting at the joint. In our previous example it was joint c, and the distribution of the moment $\mathbf{M}_c$ was accomplished by using Eqs. (e). Now we carry over moments to the adjacent joints and add to the unbalanced moments at these joints the moments equal to the carry-over moments, but with opposite sign. The obtained sums we again distribute, using equations similar to Eqs. (e). When the distribution of moments is accomplished at all joints, we obtain the second approximations for all end moments by adding the distributed moments to the previously found fixed-end moments. To get the second corrections, we repeat the moment-distribution process, but this time we distribute only the carry-over moments remaining after the first cycle of calculation, etc.

Since we always repeat the same simple operations, it is not necessary to write equations which were used in our previous discussion. Instead all calculations can be put in proper order on a sketch of the structure. Take, for example, the continuous beam shown in Fig. 9.38. Assuming that, at the supports a, b, and c, the cross sections of the beam cannot rotate and that at the support d the rotation is free, we obtain the fixed-end moments in kip-feet, as shown in the first line of the table attached to the figure. In calculating the distribution factors, we assume that $k_{ab} = k_{bc} = \frac{9}{8}k_{cd}$. Then,

$$r_{ba} = r_{bc} = \frac{k_{ab}}{k_{ab} + k_{bc}} = 0.5$$

$$r_{cb} = \frac{k_{cb}}{k_{cb} + \frac{3}{4}k_{cd}} = 0.6 \qquad r_{cd} = \frac{\frac{3}{4}k_{cd}}{k_{cb} + \frac{3}{4}k_{cd}} = 0.4$$

In this calculation we observe that the end d of the member cd is free to rotate and introduce $\frac{3}{4}k_{cd}$, instead of k_{cd}, in our formulas. The calculated values of the distribution factors are shown in the figure. We now begin with joint c. The unbalanced moment at this joint is

$$-(24.0 - 48.0) = +24 \text{ kip-ft}$$

Distributing this moment between the members cd and cb in proportion to their distribution factors r_{cd} and r_{cb}, we obtain the distributed moments at c, equal to $+9.6$ kip-ft and $+14.4$ kip-ft. Taking now joint b, we find that the fixed-end moments at this joint balance each other, and we have to consider only the moment -7.2 kip-ft, equal and opposite to the carried-over moment 7.2 kip-ft produced during unlocking of the joint c. This moment will be equally distributed between the members bc and ba, and we obtain the distributed moments at b each equal to -3.6 kip-ft. Considering now joint a and observing that the end a is built in, we conclude that the correction moment -3.6 kip-ft acting at b produces the carry-over moment -1.8 kip-ft at the fixed end. All distributed moments are shown in the second and third lines of the table in Fig. 9.38, and the heavy horizontal lines below these corrections indicate that the first cycle of calculation is concluded. The second cycle we again begin with joint c. Considering the carry-over moment -1.8 kip-ft created during the unlocking of joint b, we have an unbalanced moment $+1.8$ kip-ft at joint c. Distributing this moment between the members cd and cb, we obtain the corrections $+0.72$ kip-ft and $+1.08$ kip-ft. Taking now joint b, we have to distribute the moment -0.54, equal and opposite to the carry-over moment $+0.54$, which gives the corrections -0.27 and -0.27; and finally we obtain the correction -0.14 at the built-in end. We see that the corrections are already small, and we can limit ourselves to two cycles of calculations. The third cycle of calculation is also indicated in the figure, and under the double horizontal lines are given the final values of the end moments equal to the algebraic sums of the initially calculated fixed-end moments and all the corrections.

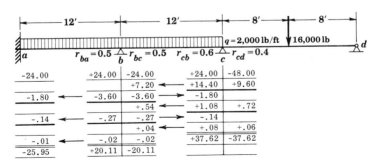

FIG. 9.38

As a second example, let us consider the continuous frame shown in Fig. 9.32*b* and assume first that lateral movement is restrained. We also assume that the proportions of the structure are those defined by Eqs. (*d*), page 454, with $l = 12$ ft and $q = 1$ kip/ft. With these numerical data, we calculate the distribution factors as shown in Fig. 9.39. We start with a calculation of the fixed-end moments, assuming that joints *b*, *c*, and *d* are locked and that there are hinges at the ends *a* and *e*. The calculated values of these moments in kip-feet are given in the first horizontal line of the table above Fig. 9.39. The distribution of the unbalanced moments we begin from joint *c*, at which the unbalanced moment has the largest numerical value. The results of this distribution are given in the second horizontal line above joint *c* and in the second vertical line to the right of column *cg*. Considering, now, joints *b* and *d*, we distribute the moments there as shown in the third horizontal line above joints *b* and *d* and in the vertical lines to the right of columns *bf* and *dh*. This finishes the first cycle of calculation, the results of which are underlined in Fig. 9.39. The second cycle we again begin with joint *c*, at which we have the unbalanced moment $-(5.43 + 1.15)$. The results of the second distribution at this joint and also at the joints *b* and *d* are again underlined in the figure. There is given in the figure also the third cycle of calculation, which gives only very small corrections of end moments; thus, we conclude the calculations with this cycle and put under the double lines the sums of the initially calculated fixed-end moments and of all corrections that give us the required end moments. The same numerical values were obtained previously by the direct solution of the slope-deflection equations (see page 458).

The method of successive approximations can be used also in case the continuous frame is free to move laterally. Let us take again the example shown in Fig. 9.32*b*. The calculated end moments in the columns produce on the girder *ae* the horizontal shear action in the direction from right to left

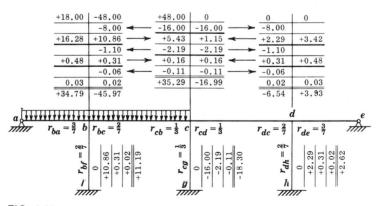

FIG. 9.39

equal to

$$-\frac{3}{2}\frac{M_{bf} + M_{cg} + M_{dh}}{h} = \frac{-11.19 + 18.30 - 2.62}{8} = 561 \text{ lb}$$

$$(g)$$

To prevent any lateral movement, a horizontal external force of the same magnitude but acting from left to right must be applied. If there is no such force and the frame is free to move laterally, it will move to the left by such an amount as to produce shearing forces at the tops of the columns sufficient to balance the above-calculated force (g). In discussing the end moments and shearing forces produced by lateral movement alone, we assume first that the joints b, c, and d do not rotate during this movement. Then, the end moments equal to $-6k_{bf}\Theta_{bf}$, $-6k_{cg}\Theta_{cg}$, $-6k_{dh}\Theta_{dh}$ will be produced at the ends of the columns bf, cg, and dh [see Eqs. (i), page 457]. In our case all these end moments are equal since the stiffness factors and the angles of rotation are the same for all columns. Since we do not know in advance the magnitude of the displacement, we start the calculation by assuming that it is of such magnitude that

$$6k_{bf}\Theta_{bf} = 6k_{cg}\Theta_{cg} = 6k_{dh}\Theta_{dh} = +1.000 \text{ kip-ft}$$

The corresponding end moments are indicated in the first vertical lines to the right of the columns in Fig. 9.40. It is seen that there are unbalanced moments equal to 1.000 kip-ft at joints b, c, and d. Distributing them in the usual way, we finally obtain the values of the end moments written under the double lines. Having these moments, we calculate the shearing forces in the columns and find that the total horizontal force acting on the girder ae in the direction from

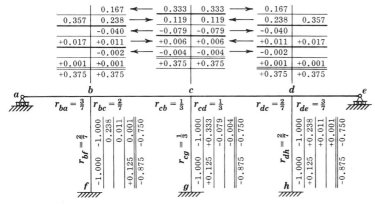

FIG. 9.40

right to left is

$$3 \frac{(0.875 + 0.750) \text{ kip-ft}}{12} = 406 \text{ lb}$$

It is seen that to balance the horizontal force given in Eq. (g) we have to take

$$6k_{bf}\Theta_{bf} = 6k_{cg}\Theta_{cg} = 6k_{dh}\Theta_{dh} = -1.000 \times \tfrac{561}{406} \text{ kip-ft}$$

$$= -1.38 \text{ kip-ft}$$

instead of the previously assumed value of 1 kip-ft.   Hence, the end moments due to lateral sway will be obtained by multiplying the values given in Fig. 9.40 by the factor -1.38.   In this manner, we find

$$M_{ba} = M_{bc} = M_{cb} = M_{cd} = M_{dc} = M_{de} = -0.375(1.38)$$

$$= -0.518 \text{ kip-ft}$$

These same results were obtained before by direct solution of the equations of equilibrium of the joints (see page 458).

PROBLEMS

1   Using the method of moment distribution, construct a bending-moment diagram for the continuous beam shown in Fig. 9.41a.   Assume $P = 40$ kips and stiffness factors as shown in the figure.
      Ans. $M_b = -20.75$ kip-ft, $M_c = -37.6$ kip-ft, $M_d = +18.3$ kip-ft.
2   Using the method of moment distribution, construct a bending-moment diagram for the continuous beam shown in Fig. 9.41b.   Assume $P = 16$ kips, $q = 2$ kips/ft, and moments of inertia $I_1 = I_2 = \tfrac{27}{32}I_3$.
      Ans. $M_a = -25.95$ kip-ft, $M_b = -20.11$ kip-ft, $M_c = -37.62$ kip-ft.
3   Using the moment-distribution method, calculate all end moments for the frame structure shown in Fig. 9.42a if all members have the same flexural rigidity EI.
      Ans. $M_{ab} = -110.5$ kip-ft, $M_{ba} = +78.8$ kip-ft, $M_{bc} = -42.4$ kip-ft, $M_{cb} = -21.2$ kip-ft, $M_{bd} = -37.0$ kip-ft, $M_{db} = -M_{de} = -9.0$ kip-ft.
4   The frame structure shown in Fig. 9.42b is so loaded that the fixed-end moments in the girder are $\mathfrak{M}_{bc} = -20.0$ kip-ft, $\mathfrak{M}_{cb} = +24.0$ kip-ft, and the modified fixed-end moment at b is $\mathfrak{M}'_{ba} = \mathfrak{M}_{ba} - \tfrac{1}{2}\mathfrak{M}_{ab} = +50.0$ kip-ft.   The stiffness factors

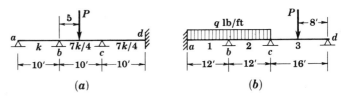

FIG. 9.41   *(a)*   *(b)*

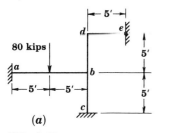

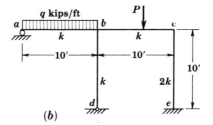

FIG. 9.42

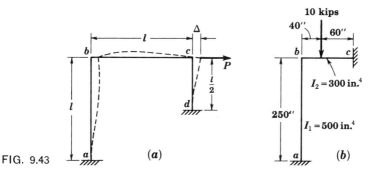

FIG. 9.43

for the various members are as shown in the figure, where $k = 1,000$ kip-ft. Calculate the magnitude of the side sway of the frame.

    Ans. $\Delta = 0.0179$ ft to the left.

5   The simple frame shown in Fig. 9.43a has uniform flexural rigidity $EI = 10(10^6)$ lb-in.^{2} for all three members and $l = 100$ in. The columns are built in at a and d. Calculate the magnitude of the side sway that will be produced by a horizontal force $P = 60.0$ lb acting at joint c as shown.

    Ans. $\Delta = 0.101$ in.

6   The footing at a of the frame shown in Fig. 9.43b is elastically restrained so that it rotates 0.0001 rad per 30 kip-in. of moment M_{ab}. Using the method of moment distribution, find the magnitudes of the end moments produced by a vertical force $P = 10$ kips acting as shown.

    Ans. $M_{ab} = -16.8$ in.-kips, $M_{ba} = -53.6$ in.-kips, $M_{bc} = +53.6$ in.-kips, $M_{cb} = -141.2$ in.-kips.

9.9   ANALYSIS OF BUILDING FRAMES

In the design of building frames we have to analyze complicated structures of the kind shown in Fig. 9.44. The solution of the problem is usually divided into two parts, (1) a calculation of end moments produced by vertical loads, assuming that there are no lateral movements, (2) a calculation of end moments

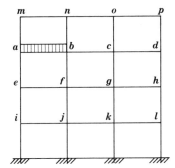

FIG. 9.44

produced by lateral movements, the latter being produced, not only by lateral, but also by vertical loads.

If there are no lateral movements, we apply the method of moment distribution described in the preceding article. Using the known dimensions of the structural elements, we calculate the distribution factors for the members meeting at each joint. We calculate also the fixed-end moments produced by actual loads. When this preliminary work is finished, we start with distribution of unbalanced moments and proceed in exactly the same manner as already described in the preceding article.

If the load is applied in one span only, the end moments produced by it diminish rapidly as we consider joints farther and farther away from the loaded span. Using this fact, we can simplify the calculations by considering, instead of the entire structure, only a portion of the structure adjacent to the loaded member. Assume, for example, that for the case shown in Fig. 9.44, the load covers only one span ab. Then, an approximate solution is obtained if we consider only the portion of the structure shown in Fig. 9.45a and assume that the upper joints m, n, o, the lower joints e, f, g, and joint d are fixed. Assuming that the fixed-end moments and the distribution factors have the numerical values indicated in the figure, the results of the first cycle of calculation will be as underlined by the heavy lines in the second and third lines in the figure. There are shown in the figure, also, the calculations of the second and third cycles, and under the double lines the final values of the end moments are given.

If more accurate values of the end moments at the joints a and b are required, the effect of rotations of the joints m, n, e, and f on these moments can be readily taken into account. This calculation is shown in Fig. 9.45b. We start by writing in the end moments $M_{ab} = -13.14$, $M_{ae} = +7.89$, and $M_{am} = +5.26$, obtained from the previous calculation. The carry-over moments at joints m and e are then $+2.63$ and $+3.95$, respectively, as shown in the first vertical line in the figure. Hence, at joints m and e there are the unbalanced moments -2.63 and -3.95. Unlocking these joints and assuming that $r_{ma} = \frac{1}{3}$ and $r_{ea} = \frac{3}{13}$, we distribute the moments and find the carry-over moments -0.44 and -0.46 at joint a as shown in the second vertical line. Distributing, now, the corresponding unbalanced moment $+(0.46 + 0.44)$ at a, we finally obtain under the double lines the required corrected values of the end moments at joint a. In a similar manner the corrected values of the end moments at joint b can be calculated. When all calculations, made on the assumption that there are no lateral movements of the structure, are finished and the numerical values of all end moments for columns are obtained, we calculate the horizontal forces acting on each floor of the building.

The calculation of the end moments produced by horizontal forces will now be explained by a simple example of a symmetrical three-story frame loaded as shown in Fig. 9.46. We begin with a discussion of the three auxiliary problems shown in Fig. 9.47, in each of which we assume a relative horizontal displacement in one story only. In the case shown in Fig. 9.47a, we assume first that the upper part of the frame is displaced horizontally without any bending. To produce such a displacement, we apply a proper horizontal force at b, and also couples are applied at joints b and f of such magnitude as to

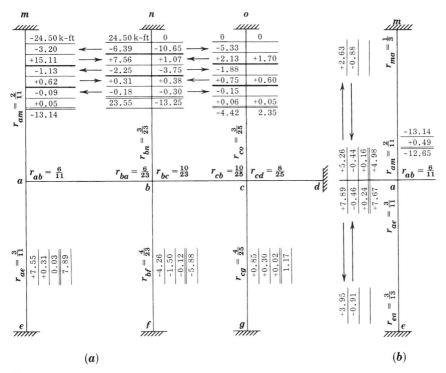

(a) $\qquad\qquad\qquad\qquad\qquad\qquad$ (b)

FIG. 9.45

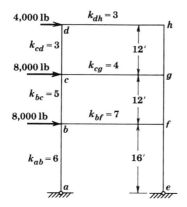

FIG. 9.46

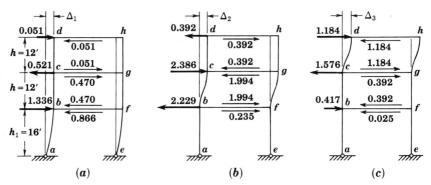

FIG. 9.47

prevent any rotation of these joints.   If Δ_1 is the magnitude of the displacement, the end moments at the tops of the columns of the first story will be

$$M_{ba} = M_{fe} = -3k_{ab}\frac{\Delta_1}{h_1}$$

For our further calculation let us assume some numerical value for these
moments, say $M_{ba} = M_{fe} = -9$ kip-ft.   Now we assume that any further
lateral movements of the joints of the frame are prevented by special constraints, and we unlock the joints b and f.   In calculating the end moments
resulting from rotations of the joints, we observe from symmetry that there
will be inflection points at the middles of the girders.   We can assume hinges
in these points and consider only one-half of the frame as shown in Fig. 9.48a.
The numbers proportional to the stiffness factors of the girders, indicated in
Fig. 9.47, must now be multiplied by 2, and three-quarters of these values
must be used in calculating the distribution factors.   The values of these

factors are indicated in Fig. 9.48a. Starting calculations with joint b, at which we assumed an unbalanced moment of 9 kip-ft, we obtain as usual the values of all end moments. They are written under double lines in Fig. 9.48a. Having these moments, we readily obtain, from equations of statics, the shearing forces in all columns and the horizontal forces acting on the girders. These latter forces in kips are as indicated in Fig. 9.47a. Combining them, we obtain the horizontal forces that must be applied at joints b, c, and d to keep the frame in the assumed displaced position with all joints unlocked. These forces are also indicated in Fig. 9.47a.

Considering the problem in Fig. 9.47b, we assume that, by a proper application of horizontal forces and couples at the joints b, c, g, and f, the upper story of the frame is displaced with respect to the lower story so that only the columns bc and fg are bent. If Δ_2 denotes the amount of horizontal displacement, the end moments for these columns are

$$M_{bc} = M_{cb} = M_{fg} = M_{gf} = -6k_{bc}\frac{\Delta_2}{h}$$

Taking for these moments an arbitrary value, say -10 kip-ft, and assuming that there is no lateral movement of the frame from its displaced position, we unlock the joints and calculate as usual the resulting end moments and horizontal shear forces. These moments are given in Fig. 9.48b, and the shear forces and horizontal forces required to produce the assumed lateral displacement Δ_2 are shown in Fig. 9.47b. The case shown in Fig. 9.47c can be treated in a

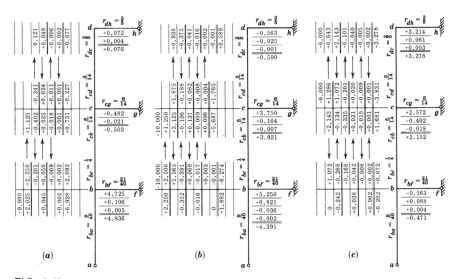

FIG. 9.48

similar manner. Assuming for the end moments in columns cd and gh the value -6 kip-ft, we obtain the values of the end moments and horizontal shear forces as shown in Figs. 9.48c and 9.47c, respectively.

After solving the three auxiliary problems in Fig. 9.47, we can, by a proper combination of these solutions, obtain the required solution for the horizontal forces shown in Fig. 9.46. It is evident that if the displacements Δ_1, Δ_2, and Δ_3, which were assumed in the auxiliary problems, are changed in a certain proportion, the corresponding horizontal forces will change in the same proportion. Assume, now, that the displacements are $\Delta_1 x$, $\Delta_2 y$, $\Delta_3 z$, and select the values of x, y, and z in such a way that the superposition of the horizontal forces corresponding to these displacements will give us the actual horizontal forces. To accomplish this, we have only to multiply the horizontal forces given in Fig. 9.47a, b, and c by x, y, and z, respectively, and after superposing them put the obtained resultant forces equal to the actual horizontal loads in Fig. 9.46. In this manner we obtain the equations

$$0.051x - 0.392y + 1.184z = 4$$
$$-0.521x + 2.386y - 1.576z = 8 \qquad (a)$$
$$1.336x - 2.229y + 0.417z = 8$$

which give

$$x = 26.61 \qquad y = 13.63 \qquad z = 6.75$$

To calculate the actual end moments for the members of the frame in Fig. 9.46, we have to multiply the moments given in Fig. 9.48a, b, and c, respectively, by x, y, and z and then superimpose the obtained results. In this manner we obtain

$$M_{ba} = -6.928 \times 26.61 + 1.882 \times 13.63 - 0.202 \times 6.75$$
$$= -160.1 \text{ kip-ft} \quad (b)$$

To check this result, we observe that in our case the total horizontal load $4 + 8 + 8 = 20$ kip-ft is equally divided between the two supports a and e. Hence, the true value of M_{ba} is $-10 \times 16 = -160$ kip-ft. For the remaining end moments in the columns, we obtain, by using equations similar to Eq. (b), the following values: $M_{bc} = -25.3$ kip-ft, $M_{cb} = -46.7$ kip-ft, $M_{cd} = -7.8$ kip-ft, $M_{dc} = -16.1$ kip-ft.

We have considered here a frame with three stories (Fig. 9.46), but the same method can be used for any number of stories. As the number of stories increases, the number of equations of equilibrium similar to Eqs. (a) naturally increases, and the amount of arithmetical work required may become very great. However, to obtain a satisfactory approximate solution, we do not need to consider all stories of the frame simultaneously. The effect on the end moments of the lateral distortion assumed in one story dies out rapidly as we go farther and farther from the distorted story. Hence, we can get a satisfactory approximation by considering each time only three consecutive stories. In analyzing lateral deflections of a building frame like that shown in Fig. 9.44, we start from the top of the building and consider the three upper stories. Assuming that there are hinges at the mid-points of the columns in the third story from the top, we obtain a problem similar to that in Fig. 9.46, and we can calculate all end moments after solving a system of three equilibrium equations similar to Eqs. (a). The results obtained in this way will not be exact, but they will be accurate enough for the top floor. We can then remove the upper story, replace its action on the remaining portion of the frame by the forces and the moments that have already been calculated, and consider again only three consecutive stories by assuming hinges at the mid-points of the columns of the fourth story from the top, etc.

9.10 FRAMES WITH NONPRISMATIC MEMBERS

The moment-distribution method used in the preceding articles for frames with prismatic members can be extended to the analysis of frames with members of variable cross section. In using the method, we have to perform three operations in which the variation in cross section must be taken into account. They are (1) calculation of fixed-end moments, (2) calculation of distribution factors, and (3) calculation of carry-over factors.

To illustrate the procedure, let us consider the example shown in Fig. 9.49. This three-span highway bridge with span ratios $3:4:3$ consists of a continuous girder with straight-line haunches rigidly attached to vertical columns of constant cross section. It is required to draw the bending-moment diagram for a uniform load $q = 1$ kip/ft distributed along the first two spans as shown. We start, by using the tables,[1] with a determination of the elastic characteristics for each member. The member ab has at the end b a straight haunch of length $0.4l_1$ and a depth of 4.5 ft $= 1.5h_0$. For these proportions, we find from the tables

Carry-over factors		Stiffness factors		Fixed-end moments	
C_{ab}	C_{ba}	s_{ab}	s_{ba}	$\mathfrak{M}_{ab}$	$\mathfrak{M}_{ba}$
0.996	0.403	5.180	12.82	$-0.0541ql^2$	$0.1554ql^2$

Observing that the member ab is hinged at a, we must use, instead of the stiffness factor s_{ba}, a modified stiffness factor s'_{ba} given by the equation

$$s'_{ba} = s_{ba}(1 - C_{ab}C_{ba}) = 12.82(1 - 0.996 \times 0.403) = 7.67$$

[1] See "Handbook of Frame Constants."

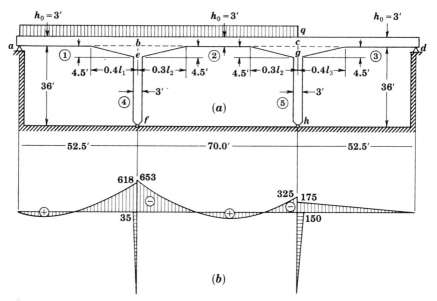

FIG. 9.49

and, from Eq. (9.18), the modified fixed-end moment

$$\mathfrak{M}'_{ba} = \mathfrak{M}_{ba} - C_{ab}\mathfrak{M}_{ab} = (0.1554 + 0.0541 \times 0.996)ql_1^2$$

$$= 576.9 \text{ kip-ft}$$

For the symmetrical middle-span member bc, we find from the tables

C_{bc}	C_{cb}	s_{bc}	s_{cb}	$\mathfrak{M}_{bc}$	$\mathfrak{M}_{cb}$
0.753	0.753	14.27	14.27	$-0.1074ql_2^2$	$+0.1074ql_2^2$

The member cd has the same characteristics as the member ab, except that the fixed-end moments vanish since there is no lateral load on this span. Thus, for this member, we have

C_{cd}	C_{dc}	s_{cd}	s_{dc}	$\mathfrak{M}_{cd}$	$\mathfrak{M}_{dc}$
0.403	0.996	12.82	5.180	0	0

Observing that the end d is hinged, we use for this member the modified stiffness factor $s'_{cd} = s'_{ba} = 7.67$, as already obtained for the member ab.

Regarding the vertical columns, we assume that along the portions be and cg

their flexural rigidities are infinite. Then, from the tables, we have

C_{bf}	C_{fb}	s_{bf}	s_{fb}
0.480	0.715	6.82	4.57

Since the lower ends of the columns are hinged, we use, for each of these members, a modified stiffness factor

$$s'_{ch} = s'_{bf} = s_{bf}(1 - C_{bf}C_{fb}) = 6.82(1 - 0.480 \times 0.715) = 4.48$$

For the rigidity constants k, we take for the first and third spans

$$k_1 = k_3 = \frac{EI_0}{l_1} = 1$$

and for the middle span,

$$k_2 = \frac{EI_0}{l_2} = \frac{3}{4}$$

For the vertical columns, we have

$$k_4 = k_5 = \frac{EI_0}{h} = \frac{52.5}{36} = 1.46$$

To calculate the distribution factors, we observe that in the case of beams of variable cross section the relation between the end moment M_{ab} and the corresponding angle of rotation θ_a is given by the equation (see page 429)

$$M_{ab} = \theta_a \frac{EI_0}{l_n} s_{ab} = \theta_a k_n s_{ab}$$

Hence, the distribution factors will be proportional to the quantities ks. Using now for joint b the numerical values

$$k_1 = 1 \qquad s_{ba} = 7.67 \qquad k_1 s_{ba} = 7.67$$

$$k_2 = 0.75 \qquad s_{bc} = 14.27 \qquad k_2 s_{bc} = 10.70$$

$$k_4 = 1.46 \qquad s_{bf} = 4.48 \qquad k_4 s_{bf} = 6.54$$

we find $\Sigma k_i s_{mn} = 24.91$, and the distribution factors become

$$r_{ba} = \frac{7.67}{24.91} = 0.308 \qquad r_{bc} = \frac{10.70}{24.91} = 0.429$$

$$r_{bf} = \frac{6.54}{24.91} = 0.263$$

From symmetry, we conclude that the same values hold for joint c.

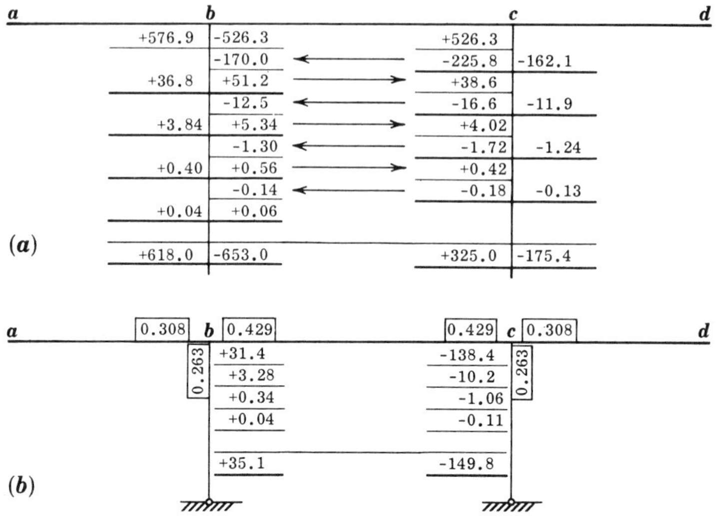

a		b		c		d
	+576.9	−526.3		+526.3		
		−170.0	←	−225.8	−162.1	
	+36.8	+51.2	→	+38.6		
		−12.5	←	−16.6	−11.9	
	+3.84	+5.34	→	+4.02		
		−1.30	←	−1.72	−1.24	
	+0.40	+0.56	→	+0.42		
		−0.14	←	−0.18	−0.13	
	+0.04	+0.06				
(a)	+618.0	−653.0		+325.0	−175.4	

a		0.308	b	0.429		0.429	c	0.308		d
			0.263	+31.4		−138.4	0.263			
				+3.28		−10.2				
				+0.34		−1.06				
				+0.04		−0.11				
				+35.1		−149.8				

(b)

FIG. 9.50

Having the distribution factors, we can now begin the calculation of end moments by the method of moment distribution. These calculations are put in tabular form in Fig. 9.50. We start with the calculation of the fixed-end moments, the values of which are shown in the first horizontal line under the girder *abcd*. The distribution of moments is started with joint *c*, where the unbalanced moment is largest. Using the previously calculated distribution factors, the results of the distribution of the unbalanced moment $\mathbf{M}_c = -526.3$ will be

$$M'_{cb} = -526.3 \times 0.429 = -225.8 \text{ kip-ft}$$

$$M'_{cd} = -526.3 \times 0.308 = -162.1 \text{ kip-ft}$$

$$M'_{cf} = -526.3 \times 0.263 = -138.4 \text{ kip-ft}$$

These distributed moments are shown in the second line under joint *c* in Fig. 9.50*a* and at the top of the column *ch* in Fig. 9.50*b*. The moment $C_{cb}M'_{cb} = -0.753 \times 225.8 = -170.0$ will be carried over to the joint *b* as shown, and there the unbalanced moment, equal to

$$-576.9 + 526.3 + 170.0 = 119.4 \text{ kip-ft}$$

will exist. The results of distribution of this moment are shown in the third line under joint *b* in Fig. 9.50*a* and at the top of the column *bf* in Fig. 9.50*b*. The heavy lines under the distributed moments at the joints *b* and *c* indicate that the first cycle of moment distribution has been completed.

To calculate further corrections, we again start with joint *c*, to which the moment of 38.6 kip-ft has been carried over as indicated. Distributing the corresponding unbalanced moment of −38.6 kip-ft at *c* and the unbalanced moment of $+12.5$ kip-ft created at b, the second cycle of calculation is completed as indicated by the second set of heavy lines under the joints b and c. Further calculations show that the corrections diminish rapidly, and after four cycles, they become negligible. Summing up the initial fixed-end moments and all consecutive corrections, we obtain for the final end moments the values shown in Fig. 9.50. The corresponding bending-moment diagram is shown in Fig. 9.49b.

As another example of application of the moment-distribution method in the analysis of structures having members of variable cross section, let us consider the previously treated symmetrical three-span bridge shown in Fig. 9.22. Using the given elastic constants and observing that there are hinges at the supports 0 and 3, we find, as in the preceding example,

$$s'_{10} = s_{10}(1 - C_{10}C_{01}) = 20.34$$

$$\mathfrak{M}'_{10} = \mathfrak{M}_{10} - C_{01}\mathfrak{M}_{01} = 281.9 \text{ kip-ft}$$

Then, the constants necessary for calculating the distribution factors are

Member	k	s	ks
01	1.0	20.34	20.34
12	0.5	22.83	11.42

and these factors become

$$r_{10} = \frac{20.34}{31.76} = 0.640 \qquad r_{12} = \frac{11.42}{31.76} = 0.360$$

All calculations of consecutive corrections are shown in Fig. 9.51. It is seen that after four cycles, we get results coinciding with those previously obtained on page 435.

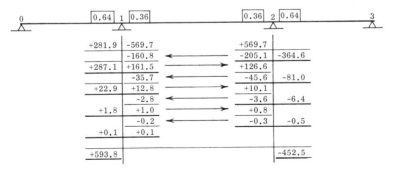

FIG. 9.51

Chapter 10

Matrix methods in structural analysis

10.1 FORCE AND DEFORMATION METHODS

The various methods of analysis of statically indeterminate systems that have been used in preceding chapters fall into two distinct classifications. In the analysis of arches and frames in Chap. 8, for example, the procedure was as follows: First, all redundant constraints were removed and replaced by the corresponding redundant forces (or moments). The magnitudes of these forces were then found by using the theorem of least work based on a consideration of the strain energy in the structure. A similar procedure was used in Chap. 7 in the analysis of statically indeterminate trusses. This general approach is called the *method of forces*.

In the analysis of continuous beams and frames in Chap. 9, a somewhat different procedure was used. In this case, we calculated first the angles of rotation of the joints (deformations) and considered the redundant forces only later. The three-angle equation used in the analysis of continuous beams

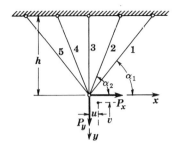

FIG. 10.1

represents again the same kind of approach.   Such procedure is called the *method of deformations.*

To illustrate, on the same example, the distinction between the two methods, let us consider the statically indeterminate plane truss shown in Fig. 10.1.[1] Here, a load P, defined by its components P_x and P_y, is supported by five prismatic members hinged together at A and to a rigid foundation at their upper ends.   Since the number of bars is greater than the number of equations of equilibrium for the joint A, the problem is evidently statically indeterminate. In general, if the hinge A is attached to the foundation by n bars, all in one plane, the number of redundant bars will be $n - 2$.   Then, to determine the corresponding redundant forces $X_1, X_2, X_3, \ldots, X_{n-2}$ by a method of forces, we write the expression for the strain energy of the system as a function of these forces and, by using the theorem of least work, obtain the necessary equations:

$$\frac{\partial U}{\partial X_1} = 0 \qquad \frac{\partial U}{\partial X_2} = 0 \qquad \cdots \qquad \frac{\partial U}{\partial X_{n-2}} = 0 \qquad (a)$$

Each of these equations will contain all of the redundant forces, so with the increase in the number of bars, the solution of Eqs. (a) becomes more and more cumbersome.

To solve the same problem, Navier suggested the use of a method of displacements.   The deformation of the system in Fig. 10.1 is completely determined if we know the horizontal and vertical components u and v, respectively, of the displacement of the hinge A produced by the load P.   Assuming that these displacements are small, the elongation of any bar i will then be

$$\Delta l_i = v \sin \alpha_i - u \cos \alpha_i$$

and the corresponding axial force in the bar becomes

$$S_i = \frac{EA_i}{l_i} (v \sin \alpha_i - u \cos \alpha_i)$$

$$= \frac{EA_i}{h} (v \sin \alpha_i - u \cos \alpha_i) \sin \alpha_i \qquad (b)$$

[1] This is sometimes called Navier's problem.   See his book "Résumé des leçons . . . ," 2d ed., p. 345, Paris, 1833.

Writing now the two equations of equilibrium for the hinge A, we obtain

$$
v \sum_{i=1}^{i=n} A_i \sin^2 \alpha_i \cos \alpha_i - u \sum_{i=1}^{i=n} A_i \cos^2 \alpha_i \sin \alpha_i = \frac{P_x h}{E}
$$

$$
v \sum_{i=1}^{i=n} A_i \sin^3 \alpha_i - u \sum_{i=1}^{i=n} A_i \sin^2 \alpha_i \cos \alpha_i = \frac{P_y h}{E}
$$
(c)

From these two equations, the unknowns u and v can be readily calculated in each particular case. After this, substitution of u and v into expression (b) gives us the force S_i in any bar of the system. It is seen that for this problem, direct consideration of the deformation of the system results in a substantial simplification of the solution, especially if there are a large number of bars since, independently of that number, we have to solve only two equations [Eqs. (c)].

In a similar way, direct consideration of the deformations simplifies the analysis of a continuous beam on many supports. If we remove all intermediate supports and consider the corresponding reactions X_1, X_2, X_3, . . . as the redundant quantities, the theorem of least work yields a system of equations (a), each of which contains all of the unknowns. Thus, the solution of the problem becomes very cumbersome if the number of spans is large. A great improvement in the solution of this problem is attained by considering each span of the continuous beam as a simple beam on two supports and calculating the angles of rotation of the ends of such beams. Then, from the condition that at each intermediate support these angles for two adjacent spans must be equal, the known three-angle equations (or three-moment equations) are obtained (see page 414). Such equations are much simpler than Eqs. (a) because no one of them contains more than three unknowns.

Another example in which the method of deformations resulted in a great simplification is represented by the system shown in Fig. 9.37, where four members are rigidly joined together at a and built in at their far ends. Neglecting the effect of axial forces in the bars, this system has seven redundant reactive elements, and for their determination, the theorem of least work would give seven equations. Again, the problem was greatly simplified by considering the deformation of the structure. This deformation is completely defined by the angle of rotation θ_a of the joint a produced by the applied loads. When the magnitude of this angle is found [see Eq. (9.24)], the end moments for all the members can be readily calculated from the slope-deflection equations. Thus, by considering deformations first, we need only one equation which was written on the basis of the equilibrium of the end moments at joint a.

It is not to be concluded from the foregoing discussion that, in the analysis of a statically indeterminate system, a method of deformations is always superior to a method of forces. For example, in the case of a simple truss having one redundant reaction and ten joints (see Fig. 7.5), the method of deformations described above would become very cumbersome, whereas the method of forces used in Chap. 7 is extremely simple.

In dealing with highly statically indeterminate systems, we usually find that regardless of whether we use a method of forces or a method of deformations, it becomes necessary to solve a large number of simultaneous linear algebraic equations with as many unknowns. Without regard to any particular problem of structural analysis, let us now consider a system of such equations:

$$
\begin{aligned}
a_{11}x_1 + a_{12}x_2 + \cdots + a_{1n}x_n &= c_1 \\
a_{21}x_1 + a_{22}x_2 + \cdots + a_{2n}x_n &= c_2 \\
\cdots \cdots \cdots \cdots \cdots \cdots \cdots \cdots \cdots \\
a_{m1}x_1 + a_{m2}x_2 + \cdots + a_{mn}x_n &= c_m
\end{aligned}
\tag{10.1}
$$

Theoretically, such a system of linear algebraic equations can always be solved, but the process of solution becomes cumbersome as the number of equations increases, and to simplify the technique of this solution, the notation of *matrix algebra*[1] will now be introduced. Thus, in matrix notation, Eqs. (10.1) may be written in the condensed form

$$
\begin{bmatrix}
a_{11} & a_{12} & \cdots & a_{1n} \\
a_{21} & a_{22} & \cdots & a_{2n} \\
\cdots & \cdots & \cdots & \cdots \\
a_{m1} & a_{m2} & \cdots & a_{mn}
\end{bmatrix}
\begin{bmatrix}
x_1 \\ x_2 \\ \cdots \\ x_n
\end{bmatrix}
=
\begin{bmatrix}
c_1 \\ c_2 \\ \cdots \\ c_m
\end{bmatrix}
\tag{10.1a}
$$

or, still more briefly,

$$
[a_{ij}][x_j] = [c_i]
\tag{10.1b}
$$

or simply

$$
Ax = c
\tag{10.1c}
$$

Each array of numbers (or symbols) in the brackets of expression (10.1a) is called a *matrix*. The numbers (or symbols) themselves are called *elements*, and when there are *m rows* and *n columns*, the matrix is said to be of *order m × n*. When there is only one column or one row of elements in the matrix, it is called a *column vector* or a *row vector*. It is understood that the matrix $[a_{ij}]$ in (10.1a) operates on the column vector $[x_j]$ in such a way as to produce the left-hand side of the system of equations (10.1) above. This brings us to

[1] For a discussion of the fundamentals of matrix algebra, see A. C. Aitken, "Determinants and Matrices," Interscience Publishers, Inc., New York, 1958.

the necessity to learn some of the rules of matrix algebra which will be discussed briefly in the next article before proper attention can be given to the treatment of structural problems by matrix methods.

Before proceeding with this, however, the reader should understand that the use of matrix methods in structural analysis holds no particular magic, nor does it represent any great advantage over the methods discussed in preceding chapters so long as numerical calculations are to be made by hand. Its real advantage lies in the fact that it lends itself particularly well to the use of the electronic digital computer and thereby opens the door to the analysis of structural problems that would otherwise be too involved and complex to cope with by desk-calculator techniques. In the limited space available here, we shall be unable to disclose the full power of the matrix approach, but it is hoped that the simple examples to be discussed will give the reader enough familiarity with the method to enable him to study the literature on the subject[1] to better advantage.

10.2 ELEMENTS OF MATRIX ALGEBRA

As pointed out in the preceding article, a matrix is any rectangular array of numbers, symbols, or *elements*. It is not reducible to anything simpler and must be regarded as an entity in itself. Then, like numbers or algebraic symbols, matrices, under certain conditions, may be added, subtracted, multiplied together, or one divided by another. The rules for performing these operations constitute *matrix algebra*.

To add two matrices, we simply add corresponding elements to obtain the elements of the matrix sum. This is possible only if the two matrices to be added are of the same order $m \times n$. This rule of addition is stated symbolically as follows:

$$[a_{ij}] + [b_{ij}] = [a_{ij} + b_{ij}] \qquad (a)$$

Specifically, if $[a_{ij}]$ and $[b_{ij}]$ are both of 2×2 order,

$$\begin{bmatrix} a_{11} & a_{12} \\ a_{21} & a_{22} \end{bmatrix} + \begin{bmatrix} b_{11} & b_{12} \\ b_{21} & b_{22} \end{bmatrix} = \begin{bmatrix} a_{11} + b_{11} & a_{12} + b_{12} \\ a_{21} + b_{21} & a_{22} + b_{22} \end{bmatrix}$$

Similarly, the rule of matrix subtraction is

$$[a_{ij}] - [b_{ij}] = [a_{ij} - b_{ij}] \qquad (b)$$

---

[1] For a general discussion of matrix methods in structural analysis and a bibliography on the subject, see J. H. Argyris, On the Analysis of Complex Elastic Structures, *Appl. Mech. Rev.*, vol. 11, no. 7, 1958.

We see from this that two matrices can be said to be equal only if they are equal element by element.

From the rule of matrix addition, there follows at once a rule of scalar multiplication: namely, to multiply a given matrix by a scalar number, we simply multiply each element of the matrix by this scalar number. In symbolic form, this rule of scalar multiplication becomes

$$\lambda[a_{ij}] = [\lambda a_{ij}] \qquad\qquad (c)$$

where λ is the scalar factor.

To obtain the product AB of two matrices A and B, we have the following rule: The element of the ith row and the jth column of the *product matrix* is obtained by multiplying the ith row of A into the jth column of B, element by element, and summing the products so obtained. If A is of the order $m \times n$ and B is of the order $n \times q$, the product matrix C will be of the order $m \times q$. Stated in symbolic form, the element c_{ij} of the product matrix $C = AB$ will be

$$c_{ij} = \sum_{k=1}^{k=n} a_{ik}b_{kj} \qquad\qquad (d)$$

As a specific example,

$$\begin{bmatrix} a_{11} & a_{12} & a_{13} \\ a_{21} & a_{22} & a_{23} \end{bmatrix} \begin{bmatrix} b_{11} & b_{12} \\ b_{21} & b_{22} \\ b_{31} & b_{32} \end{bmatrix}$$
$$= \begin{bmatrix} a_{11}b_{11} + a_{12}b_{21} + a_{13}b_{31} & a_{11}b_{12} + a_{12}b_{22} + a_{13}b_{32} \\ a_{21}b_{11} + a_{22}b_{21} + a_{23}b_{31} & a_{21}b_{12} + a_{22}b_{22} + a_{23}b_{32} \end{bmatrix}$$

It must be noted that such multiplication is possible only if the number of columns of A is equal to the number of rows of B. It is also necessary to observe that matrix multiplication is not commutative, that is, $AB \neq BA$. For instance, in the above example where the matrix product AB was of order 2×2, the matrix product BA would be of order 3×3. When both AB and BA exist, BA is called the *reversed product* of AB. This makes it necessary to distinguish between *premultiplication* and *postmultiplication*. In the above example, it is said that B is premultiplied by A, or A is postmultiplied by B.

Returning now to the matrix expression (10.1a), let us apply the multiplication rule to the left-hand side of this expression, i.e., we premultiply the column vector $[x_j]$ by the matrix $[a_{ij}]$. When we do this, we see that we obtain the left-hand side of Eqs. (10.1). This explains the reason for the multiplication rule as stated above.

For the present, we defer any discussion of the question of division of one matrix by another, but there is one more useful operation in matrix algebra known as *transposition*.   The *transpose* of a matrix A, denoted by A', is obtained by rewriting the matrix A so that its rows become columns, taken in the same sequence, and vice versa.   Thus, symbolically,

$$[a_{ij}]' = [a_{ji}] \tag{e}$$

Specifically, if

$$A = \begin{bmatrix} a_{11} & a_{12} & a_{13} \\ a_{21} & a_{22} & a_{23} \end{bmatrix} \quad \text{then } A' = \begin{bmatrix} a_{11} & a_{21} \\ a_{12} & a_{22} \\ a_{13} & a_{23} \end{bmatrix}$$

Consideration of the rule of multiplication together with that of transposition shows that the transpose of a matrix product must be the *reversed product* of the individual transposes.   That is,

$$(AB)' = B'A' \tag{f}$$

This is known as the *reversal rule*.

Before proceeding further, we shall mention a few particular types of matrices that will be commonly met with in applications.   The matrix[1]

$$I = \begin{bmatrix} 1 & \cdot & \cdot \\ \cdot & 1 & \cdot \\ \cdot & \cdot & 1 \end{bmatrix} \tag{g}$$

is called a *unit matrix* of 3×3 order.   In general, it is a square matrix of order $n \times n$ having all elements zero except those on the *principal diagonal*, which runs from top left to bottom right.   In matrix algebra, the unit matrix I corresponds in every way with the idea of unity in ordinary algebra.

If a unit matrix I is multiplied by a scalar number λ, we obtain

$$\lambda I = \begin{bmatrix} \lambda & \cdot & \cdot \\ \cdot & \lambda & \cdot \\ \cdot & \cdot & \lambda \end{bmatrix} \tag{h}$$

which is known as a *scalar matrix*.

A matrix of the form

$$A = \begin{bmatrix} a_1 & \cdot & \cdot \\ \cdot & a_2 & \cdot \\ \cdot & \cdot & a_3 \end{bmatrix} \tag{i}$$

is called a *diagonal matrix*.   The unit matrix and the scalar matrix are, of course, special cases of a diagonal matrix.

[1] The dots indicate zero elements.

There are various other special matrices, but the ones introduced so far will suffice for our present purposes. In summary, we have the *rectangular matrix* of order $m \times n$, the *square matrix* of order $n \times n$, the *row vector* and the *column vector*, the *unit matrix*, the *scalar matrix*, and the *diagonal matrix*.

Returning, again, to the system of equations (10.1) and writing them in the matrix form $Ax = c$, we state by definition that the solution can be expressed in the following form:

$$x = \frac{c}{A} = A^{-1}c = Rc \tag{j}$$

This brings us to the idea of dividing one matrix by another, or, more properly, of finding the *reciprocal* R of a given matrix A. This process is called *inversion*. To accomplish it, we look for a matrix R such that $RA = I$, where I is the unit matrix. It is to be noted at this point that since a system of simultaneous equations will have a unique solution only if the number of equations is equal to the number of unknowns, A will always be a square matrix. Otherwise, the idea of inversion has no meaning.

Various procedures have been devised for the inversion of a given square matrix. One such method will now be briefly described.[1] First, it is necessary to introduce the notion of the *adjugate*, or *adjoint*, of a given matrix A which is written *adj A*. This adjugate is defined as the transpose of another matrix C formed out of the *cofactors* of the elements a_{ij} of the given matrix A. This formation of the adjugate of a given matrix is illustrated by the following example.

Let the given matrix be

$$A = \begin{bmatrix} a_1 & b_1 & c_1 \\ a_2 & b_2 & c_2 \\ a_3 & b_3 & c_3 \end{bmatrix} \tag{k}$$

Then the matrix C, formed out of the cofactors of A, will be

$$C = \begin{bmatrix} |b_2c_3| & -|a_2c_3| & |a_2b_3| \\ -|b_1c_3| & |a_1c_3| & -|a_1b_3| \\ |b_1c_2| & -|a_1c_2| & |a_1b_2| \end{bmatrix}$$

where the *determinant*

$$|b_2c_3| \equiv \begin{vmatrix} b_2 & c_2 \\ b_3 & c_3 \end{vmatrix} = b_2c_3 - c_2b_3$$

[1] See Aitken, *op. cit.*, p. 51.

is called the *cofactor* for the element a_1,

$$-|b_1c_3| \equiv - \begin{vmatrix} b_1 & c_1 \\ b_3 & c_3 \end{vmatrix} = -(b_1c_3 - c_1b_3)$$

the *cofactor* for the element a_2, etc.   In general, to find the cofactor for any element a_{ij} of the given matrix, we cross out the row i and the column j, for example, with $i = 2, j = 1$,

$$\begin{bmatrix} a_1 & b_1 & c_1 \\ a_2 & b_2 & c_2 \\ a_3 & b_3 & c_3 \end{bmatrix}$$

and write the determinant of the remaining elements taking the sign plus or minus according to the following rule: If the row number i and the column number j are both *odd* or *even*, the sign of the cofactor is plus; if the row number is *odd* and the column number is *even*, or *vice versa*, the sign of the cofactor is minus.

Having obtained the cofactor matrix C above in accordance with this rule, the adjugate of A, defined as the transpose of C, becomes

$$\text{adj } A = \begin{bmatrix} |b_2c_3| & -|b_1c_3| & |b_1c_2| \\ -|a_2c_3| & |a_1c_3| & -|a_1c_2| \\ |a_2b_3| & -|a_1b_3| & |a_1b_2| \end{bmatrix} \qquad (k')$$

When the adjugate of a given square matrix A has been formed, it can be demonstrated[1] that

$$A(\text{adj } A) = (\text{adj } A)A = |A|I \qquad (l)$$

where $|A|$ is the *determinant* of A and I is the unit matrix.   Dividing expression (l) through by $|A| \neq 0$,

$$\frac{A(\text{adj } A)}{|A|} = \frac{(\text{adj } A)A}{|A|} = I = RA$$

Thus, $$R = \frac{\text{adj } A}{|A|} = |A|^{-1} \text{adj } A \qquad (m)$$

is the required *inverse* of A.

Following the rules for inverting any given square matrix, it can be easily demonstrated that the inverse of any diagonal matrix will be obtained simply

[1] See *ibid.*, p. 53.

by inverting each individual element along the principal diagonal. Thus, if

$$[A] = \begin{bmatrix} 5 & \cdot & \cdot & \cdot \\ \cdot & 3 & \cdot & \cdot \\ \cdot & \cdot & 2 & \cdot \\ \cdot & \cdot & \cdot & 1 \end{bmatrix} \quad \text{then } [A]^{-1} = \begin{bmatrix} \frac{1}{5} & \cdot & \cdot & \cdot \\ \cdot & \frac{1}{3} & \cdot & \cdot \\ \cdot & \cdot & \frac{1}{2} & \cdot \\ \cdot & \cdot & \cdot & 1 \end{bmatrix}$$

Having now the method of inversion of a square matrix, we may illustrate the matrix solution of a system of simultaneous equations like Eqs. (10.1). Consider, as a simple example, the equations

$$3x + 2y - z = 4$$

$$x - y + 2z = 5$$

$$-2x + y - z = -3$$

In matrix notation, these equations will be written in the form

$$\begin{bmatrix} 3 & 2 & -1 \\ 1 & -1 & 2 \\ -2 & 1 & -1 \end{bmatrix} \begin{bmatrix} x \\ y \\ z \end{bmatrix} = \begin{bmatrix} 4 \\ 5 \\ -3 \end{bmatrix}$$

Following the rules outlined above, we find the adjugate of the square coefficient matrix A to be

$$\text{adj } A = \begin{bmatrix} -1 & 1 & 3 \\ -3 & -5 & -7 \\ -1 & -7 & -5 \end{bmatrix}$$

To find the determinant of A, we expand it by cofactors of the elements of the first row[1] and obtain

$$|A| = 3(-1) - 2(3) - 1(-1) = -3 - 6 + 1 = -8$$

Finally, using Eq. (j), we obtain

$$\begin{bmatrix} x \\ y \\ z \end{bmatrix} = -\frac{1}{8} \begin{bmatrix} -1 & 1 & 3 \\ -3 & -5 & -7 \\ -1 & -7 & -5 \end{bmatrix} \begin{bmatrix} 4 \\ 5 \\ -3 \end{bmatrix} = -\frac{1}{8} \begin{bmatrix} -8 \\ -16 \\ -24 \end{bmatrix} = \begin{bmatrix} 1 \\ 2 \\ 3 \end{bmatrix}$$

That is, $x = 1$, $y = 2$, $z = 3$ represents the required solution. This simple example embodies many of the operations of matrix algebra discussed above, and the reader should be sure that all steps are clear to him before proceeding further.

Before proceeding to some applications of matrix methods in the analysis of structures, we shall mention a few examples of writing algebraic expressions

[1] See *ibid.*, p. 38.

in matrix notation. Take, for example,

$$c = a_1b_1 + a_2b_2 + \cdots + a_nb_n \tag{n}$$

To write this in matrix form, let us define two column vectors A and B as

$$A = \begin{bmatrix} a_1 \\ a_2 \\ a_3 \\ \cdot \\ \cdot \\ \cdot \\ a_n \end{bmatrix} \quad \text{and} \quad B = \begin{bmatrix} b_1 \\ b_2 \\ b_3 \\ \cdot \\ \cdot \\ \cdot \\ b_n \end{bmatrix}$$

Then, transposing the column vector A into a row vector A' and performing the multiplication $A'B$, we obtain

$$\begin{bmatrix} a_1 & a_2 & \cdots & a_n \end{bmatrix} \begin{bmatrix} b_1 \\ b_2 \\ \cdot \\ \cdot \\ \cdot \\ b_n \end{bmatrix} = a_1b_1 + a_2b_2 + \cdots + a_nb_n$$

which is the right-hand side of Eq. (n). Thus, in matrix notation, Eq. (n) can be written

$$c = A'B \tag{n'}$$

Again, let us take

$$c = a_{11}x_1y_1 + a_{22}x_2y_2 + a_{33}x_3y_3 \tag{o}$$

in connection with which we define the following matrices:

$$x = \begin{bmatrix} x_1 \\ x_2 \\ x_3 \end{bmatrix} \quad y = \begin{bmatrix} y_1 \\ y_2 \\ y_3 \end{bmatrix} \quad A = \begin{bmatrix} a_{11} & \cdot & \cdot \\ \cdot & a_{22} & \cdot \\ \cdot & \cdot & a_{33} \end{bmatrix}$$

Then, transposing the column vector x into a row vector x' and performing the multiplication $x'Ay$, we obtain

$$\begin{bmatrix} x_1 & x_2 & x_3 \end{bmatrix} \begin{bmatrix} a_{11} & \cdot & \cdot \\ \cdot & a_{22} & \cdot \\ \cdot & \cdot & a_{33} \end{bmatrix} \begin{bmatrix} y_1 \\ y_2 \\ y_3 \end{bmatrix} = \begin{bmatrix} a_{11}x_1y_1 + a_{22}x_2y_2 + a_{33}x_3y_3 \end{bmatrix}$$

From this, we see that Eq. (o) may be expressed in matrix form as

$$c = x'Ay \tag{o'}$$

PROBLEMS

1   Find the matrix sum $A + B$ if

$$A = \begin{bmatrix} 3 & 2 & 1 \\ 0 & 1 & 4 \\ 2 & 0 & 3 \end{bmatrix} \quad \text{and} \quad B = \begin{bmatrix} 2 & 0 & 0 \\ 1 & -3 & 5 \\ -2 & 1 & 1 \end{bmatrix}$$

2   Find the matrix product AB if A and B are as given in the preceding problem.

$$Ans. \quad AB = \begin{bmatrix} 6 & -5 & 11 \\ -7 & 1 & 9 \\ -2 & 3 & 3 \end{bmatrix}$$

3   Find the matrix product BA of the two matrices given in Prob. 1.

$$Ans. \quad BA = \begin{bmatrix} 6 & 4 & 2 \\ 13 & -1 & 4 \\ -4 & -3 & 5 \end{bmatrix}$$

4   Write the transpose of each of the matrices given in Prob. 1.
5   Given the square matrices

$$A = \begin{bmatrix} 1 & 2 & 3 \\ 1 & 3 & 5 \\ 1 & 5 & 12 \end{bmatrix} \quad B = \begin{bmatrix} 11 & -9 & 1 \\ -7 & 9 & -2 \\ 2 & -3 & 1 \end{bmatrix}$$

show that B is the adjugate of A and find the matrix product AB.
$Ans. \quad AB = 3I.$

10.3   APPLICATION OF MATRIX METHODS TO PLANE TRUSSES

To illustrate the use of matrix methods in the analysis of pin-jointed trusses, let us begin with the deflection problem as previously discussed in Chap. 6. In Fig. 10.2a, a simple truss having m members is subjected to the action of a set of external loads P, and it is required to find the vertical deflection of joint j due to this loading.   To accomplish this, we denote by $\mathcal{S}_i$ the axial force in any

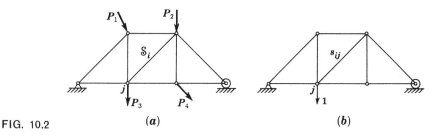

FIG. 10.2   (a)   (b)

bar i due to the P loading (Fig. 10.2a) and by s_{ij} that due to a vertical unit force at joint j (Fig. 10.2b). We have then, for calculating the vertical deflection of joint j, the following expression [see Eq. (6.2), page 258]:

$$\Delta_j = \sum_{i=1}^{i=m} s_{ij}\rho_i \mathcal{S}_i \tag{10.2}$$

where $\rho_i = l_i/A_i E$ is the *flexibility factor* for the bar i.

If we want such a deflection for each of n chosen joints of the truss, we must calculate values of s_{ij} for a vertical unit force at each of these n joints. Let us suppose that this has been done and that we arrange these *influence numbers* in the form of a matrix of order $m \times n$ as follows:

$$[s_{ij}] = \begin{bmatrix} s_{11} & s_{12} & \cdots & s_{1n} \\ s_{21} & s_{22} & \cdots & s_{2n} \\ \cdots\cdots\cdots\cdots\cdots\cdots \\ s_{m1} & s_{m2} & \cdots & s_{mn} \end{bmatrix} \tag{a}$$

This will then be called the *geometry matrix* for the truss or simply the *s matrix*.

Next, let us arrange the flexibility factors ρ_i for the m members in the form of a diagonal matrix,

$$[\rho_i] = \begin{bmatrix} \rho_{11} & \cdot & \cdot & \cdot \\ \cdot & \rho_{22} & \cdot & \cdot \\ \cdot & \cdot & \rho_{33} & \cdot \\ \cdots\cdots\cdots\cdots\cdots\cdots \\ \cdot & \cdot & \cdot & \rho_{mm} \end{bmatrix} \tag{b}$$

which is called the *flexibility matrix* for the truss or simply the ρ *matrix*.

Finally, assuming that the axial forces $\mathcal{S}_i$ produced by the given P loading have been calculated, let these be arranged in the form of a column matrix,

$$[\mathcal{S}_i] = \begin{bmatrix} \mathcal{S}_1 \\ \mathcal{S}_2 \\ \cdot \\ \cdot \\ \cdot \\ \mathcal{S}_m \end{bmatrix} \tag{c}$$

which is called the *load matrix* or simply the $\mathcal{S}$ matrix.

Now recalling the rule of matrix multiplication from the preceding article, we see that Eqs. (10.2) above can be expressed by the matrix formula

$$\Delta = s'\rho\mathcal{S} \tag{10.3}$$

That is, if we transpose the s matrix (a), postmultiply it by the ρ matrix (b), and then postmultiply this product by the $\mathcal{S}$ matrix (c), we obtain the full set of Eqs. (10.2) for the deflections of the n chosen joints of the truss.

To illustrate, let us assume that $m = 3$ and $n = 2$. Then Eq. (10.3) becomes

$$
\begin{bmatrix} \Delta_1 \\ \Delta_2 \end{bmatrix} = \begin{bmatrix} s_{11} & s_{21} & s_{31} \\ s_{12} & s_{22} & s_{32} \end{bmatrix} \begin{bmatrix} \rho_{11} & \cdot & \cdot \\ \cdot & \rho_{22} & \cdot \\ \cdot & \cdot & \rho_{33} \end{bmatrix} \begin{bmatrix} \mathcal{S}_1 \\ \mathcal{S}_2 \\ \mathcal{S}_3 \end{bmatrix}
$$

$$
= \begin{bmatrix} s_{11}\rho_{11} & s_{21}\rho_{22} & s_{31}\rho_{33} \\ s_{12}\rho_{11} & s_{22}\rho_{22} & s_{32}\rho_{33} \end{bmatrix} \begin{bmatrix} \mathcal{S}_1 \\ \mathcal{S}_2 \\ \mathcal{S}_3 \end{bmatrix}
$$

$$
= \begin{bmatrix} s_{11}\rho_{11}\mathcal{S}_1 + s_{21}\rho_{22}\mathcal{S}_2 + s_{31}\rho_{33}\mathcal{S}_3 \\ s_{12}\rho_{11}\mathcal{S}_1 + s_{22}\rho_{22}\mathcal{S}_2 + s_{32}\rho_{33}\mathcal{S}_3 \end{bmatrix}
$$

The matrix product (10.3) is called the Δ *matrix*. We see that it represents a very compact way to express the deflection formulas (10.2) for all of the chosen n joints. In addition to this, as we shall see later, the actual matrix multiplication with numerical values can be made in a systematic manner so that the danger of calculation errors is reduced to a minimum. Also, several different loading conditions can be handled all at once, simply by making a rectangular $\mathcal{S}$ matrix with a column for each different loading condition that it is desired to study.

As an example, let us consider the simple truss shown in Fig. 10.3 which has $m = 9$ members. We assume that it is required to find the vertical deflections of the two upper-chord joints a and b, under the action of two separate loading conditions as shown in Fig. 10.3a and b. The numbering of the members is shown in Fig. 10.3a, whereas the dimensions of the truss are shown in Fig.

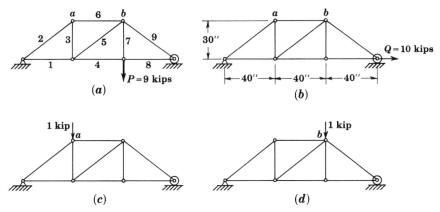

FIG. 10.3

10.3b. Each bar has a cross-sectional area $A_i = 1$ in.^{2} and a modulus of elasticity $E = 30(10^3)$ ksi. We begin with a calculation of the axial forces $\mathcal{S}_i$ in the nine members under the two loading conditions shown in Fig. 10.3a and b. This set of axial forces will constitute the $\mathcal{S}$ matrix for the problem. Similarly, we calculate the axial forces in all bars for each of the unit loads acting at the joints a and b as shown in Fig. 10.3c and d. This set of axial forces will constitute the s matrix for the problem. Finally, we calculate the flexibility coefficient $\rho_i = l_i/AE$ for each member and write down the diagonal flexibility matrix. These three basic matrices for the problem are as follows:

$$
s_{ij} = \tfrac{1}{9}
\begin{bmatrix}
8 & 4 \\
-10 & -5 \\
-3 & 3 \\
4 & 8 \\
5 & -5 \\
-8 & -4 \\
0 & 0 \\
4 & 8 \\
-5 & -10
\end{bmatrix}
$$

$$
\rho_i = \frac{10}{E}
\begin{bmatrix}
4 & \cdot & \cdot & \cdot & \cdot & \cdot & \cdot & \cdot & \cdot \\
\cdot & 5 & \cdot & \cdot & \cdot & \cdot & \cdot & \cdot & \cdot \\
\cdot & \cdot & 3 & \cdot & \cdot & \cdot & \cdot & \cdot & \cdot \\
\cdot & \cdot & \cdot & 4 & \cdot & \cdot & \cdot & \cdot & \cdot \\
\cdot & \cdot & \cdot & \cdot & 5 & \cdot & \cdot & \cdot & \cdot \\
\cdot & \cdot & \cdot & \cdot & \cdot & 4 & \cdot & \cdot & \cdot \\
\cdot & \cdot & \cdot & \cdot & \cdot & \cdot & 3 & \cdot & \cdot \\
\cdot & \cdot & \cdot & \cdot & \cdot & \cdot & \cdot & 4 & \cdot \\
\cdot & \cdot & \cdot & \cdot & \cdot & \cdot & \cdot & \cdot & 5
\end{bmatrix}
\qquad
\mathcal{S}_i =
\begin{bmatrix}
4 & 10 \\
-5 & 0 \\
3 & 0 \\
8 & 10 \\
-5 & 0 \\
-4 & 0 \\
9 & 0 \\
8 & 10 \\
-10 & 0
\end{bmatrix}
$$

Now using Eq. (10.3), the required deflections Δ_j are found by matrix multiplication as follows:

$$
\Delta = \frac{10}{9E}
\begin{bmatrix}
8 & -10 & -3 & 4 & 5 & -8 & 0 & 4 & -5 \\
4 & -5 & 3 & 8 & -5 & -4 & 0 & 8 & -10
\end{bmatrix}
$$

$$
\times
\begin{bmatrix}
4 & \cdot & \cdot & \cdot & \cdot & \cdot & \cdot & \cdot & \cdot \\
\cdot & 5 & \cdot & \cdot & \cdot & \cdot & \cdot & \cdot & \cdot \\
\cdot & \cdot & 3 & \cdot & \cdot & \cdot & \cdot & \cdot & \cdot \\
\cdot & \cdot & \cdot & 4 & \cdot & \cdot & \cdot & \cdot & \cdot \\
\cdot & \cdot & \cdot & \cdot & 5 & \cdot & \cdot & \cdot & \cdot \\
\cdot & \cdot & \cdot & \cdot & \cdot & 4 & \cdot & \cdot & \cdot \\
\cdot & \cdot & \cdot & \cdot & \cdot & \cdot & 3 & \cdot & \cdot \\
\cdot & \cdot & \cdot & \cdot & \cdot & \cdot & \cdot & 4 & \cdot \\
\cdot & \cdot & \cdot & \cdot & \cdot & \cdot & \cdot & \cdot & 5
\end{bmatrix}
\begin{bmatrix}
4 & 10 \\
-5 & 0 \\
3 & 0 \\
8 & 10 \\
-5 & 0 \\
-4 & 0 \\
9 & 0 \\
8 & 10 \\
-10 & 0
\end{bmatrix}
$$

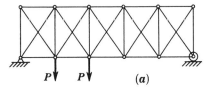 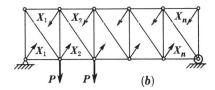

FIG. 10.4

Making the indicated multiplications in two steps, we obtain

$$\Delta = \frac{10}{9E} \begin{bmatrix} 32 & -50 & -9 & 16 & 25 & -32 & 0 & 16 & -25 \\ 16 & -25 & 9 & 32 & -25 & -16 & 0 & 32 & -50 \end{bmatrix}$$

$$\times \begin{bmatrix} 4 & 10 \\ -5 & 0 \\ 3 & 0 \\ 8 & 10 \\ -5 & 0 \\ -4 & 0 \\ 9 & 0 \\ 8 & 10 \\ -10 & 0 \end{bmatrix} = \frac{10}{9E} \begin{bmatrix} 860 & 640 \\ 1{,}417 & 800 \end{bmatrix}$$

Thus, with $E = 30(10^3)$ ksi, the deflections due to the load $P = 9$ kips acting as shown in Fig. 10.3a are

$$\Delta_a' = 0.0318 \text{ in.} \qquad \Delta_b' = 0.0525 \text{ in.}$$

while those due to the load $Q = 10$ kips in Fig. 10.3b are

$$\Delta_a'' = 0.0237 \text{ in.} \qquad \Delta_b'' = 0.0296 \text{ in.}$$

Let us proceed now to a consideration of a statically indeterminate truss having m members, n of which are redundant[1] (Fig. 10.4). For the determination of the axial forces $X_1, X_2, \ldots, X_n$ in the n redundant bars, we can use Eqs. (7.6) on page 313. Assuming that there are no thermal effects or assembly errors, these equations will take the following form:

$$-\Delta_1 = \delta_{11}X_1 + \delta_{12}X_2 + \cdots + \delta_{1n}X_n$$
$$-\Delta_2 = \delta_{21}X_1 + \delta_{22}X_2 + \cdots + \delta_{2n}X_n \qquad (10.4)$$
$$\cdots \cdots \cdots \cdots \cdots \cdots \cdots \cdots \cdots \cdots \cdots$$
$$-\Delta_n = \delta_{n1}X_1 + \delta_{n2}X_2 + \cdots + \delta_{nn}X_n$$

[1] Note that n now refers to the number of redundant bars and not to the number of joints.

where Δ_j is the generalized displacement, corresponding to X_j, caused by the P loading and δ_{ji} is the displacement, corresponding to X_j, caused by unit forces acting in place of X_i.

In matrix form, this set of equations becomes

$$
-\begin{bmatrix} \Delta_1 \\ \Delta_2 \\ \cdots \\ \Delta_n \end{bmatrix} = \begin{bmatrix} \delta_{11} & \delta_{12} & \cdots & \delta_{1n} \\ \delta_{21} & \delta_{22} & \cdots & \delta_{2n} \\ \cdots & \cdots & \cdots & \cdots \\ \delta_{n1} & \delta_{n2} & \cdots & \delta_{nn} \end{bmatrix} \begin{bmatrix} X_1 \\ X_2 \\ \cdots \\ X_n \end{bmatrix}
\tag{10.4a}
$$

or, more simply,

$$ -\Delta = \delta X \tag{10.4b} $$

The solution of Eqs. (10.4b) is

$$ X = -\frac{\Delta}{\delta} = -\delta^{-1}\Delta \tag{d} $$

where $\quad \Delta = [s'\rho\mathcal{S}] \quad$ and $\quad \delta = [s'\rho s] \tag{e}$

from Eq. (10.3). Substituting expressions (e) into Eq. (d), we obtain, for the axial forces in the redundant bars, the matrix formula

$$ X = -[s'\rho s]^{-1}[s'\rho\mathcal{S}] \tag{10.5} $$

When the forces in the redundant bars are known from Eq. (10.5), the forces in the remaining bars can be found from the expression

$$ S_i = \mathcal{S}_i + s_{i1}X_1 + s_{i2}X_2 + \cdots + s_{in}X_n \tag{f} $$

or, in matrix form,

$$ S = \mathcal{S} + sX \tag{g} $$

Substituting for X its expression from (10.5), we obtain

$$ S = \mathcal{S} - s[s'\rho s]^{-1}[s'\rho\mathcal{S}] $$

or, introducing a unit matrix I so as not to have $\mathcal{S}$ appear twice,

$$ S = [I - s(s'\rho s)^{-1}(s'\rho)]\mathcal{S} \tag{10.6} $$

This represents a final matrix formula for the axial forces in all bars of a statically indeterminate plane truss under given loading conditions.

As an example of the application of Eq. (10.6), let us consider the statically

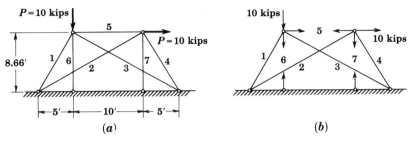

FIG. 10.5

indeterminate truss shown in Fig. 10.5. This plane truss has seven bars, of which three are seen to be redundant. As the redundants, we choose the bars 5, 6, 7, so that the primary system will be as shown in Fig. 10.5b.

As a first step, we make a statical analysis of this primary system under the action of the given P loads and likewise under the action of a pair of unit forces in place of each redundant bar. Then with cross-sectional areas $A_1 = A_4 = A_5 = 5.00$ in.^{2}, $A_2 = A_3 = 8.66$ in.^{2}, and $A_6 = A_7 = 2.89$ in.^{2}, the geometry matrix, the flexibility matrix, and the load matrix become

$$
s = \begin{bmatrix}
+\dfrac{1}{2} & -\dfrac{\sqrt{3}}{2} & 0 \\[2mm]
-\dfrac{\sqrt{3}}{2} & 0 & -\dfrac{1}{2} \\[2mm]
-\dfrac{\sqrt{3}}{2} & -\dfrac{1}{2} & 0 \\[2mm]
+\dfrac{1}{2} & 0 & -\dfrac{\sqrt{3}}{2} \\[2mm]
+1 & 0 & 0 \\
0 & +1 & 0 \\
0 & 0 & +1
\end{bmatrix}
$$

$$
\rho = \begin{bmatrix}
2 & \cdot & \cdot & \cdot & \cdot & \cdot & \cdot \\
\cdot & 2 & \cdot & \cdot & \cdot & \cdot & \cdot \\
\cdot & \cdot & 2 & \cdot & \cdot & \cdot & \cdot \\
\cdot & \cdot & \cdot & 2 & \cdot & \cdot & \cdot \\
\cdot & \cdot & \cdot & \cdot & 2 & \cdot & \cdot \\
\cdot & \cdot & \cdot & \cdot & \cdot & 3 & \cdot \\
\cdot & \cdot & \cdot & \cdot & \cdot & \cdot & 3
\end{bmatrix}
\qquad
\mathbb{S} = \begin{bmatrix}
-5\sqrt{3} \\
+5\sqrt{3} \\
-5 \\
-5 \\
0 \\
0 \\
0
\end{bmatrix}
$$

where, for convenience, we have taken $E = 1$ ksi.

Now transposing s to s' and postmultiplying it by ρ, and then by s, we obtain

$$[s'\rho s] = \begin{bmatrix} 1 & -\sqrt{3} & -\sqrt{3} & 1 & 2 & 0 & 0 \\ -\sqrt{3} & 0 & -1 & 0 & 0 & 3 & 0 \\ 0 & -1 & 0 & -\sqrt{3} & 0 & 0 & 3 \end{bmatrix}$$

$$\times \begin{bmatrix} \dfrac{1}{2} & -\dfrac{\sqrt{3}}{2} & 0 \\ -\dfrac{\sqrt{3}}{2} & 0 & -\dfrac{1}{2} \\ -\dfrac{\sqrt{3}}{2} & -\dfrac{1}{2} & 0 \\ \dfrac{1}{2} & 0 & -\dfrac{\sqrt{3}}{2} \\ 1 & 0 & 0 \\ 0 & 1 & 0 \\ 0 & 0 & 1 \end{bmatrix} = \begin{bmatrix} 6 & \cdot & \cdot \\ \cdot & 5 & \cdot \\ \cdot & \cdot & 5 \end{bmatrix}$$

Since this result is a diagonal matrix, it is easily inverted (see page 489), and we have

$$[s'\rho s]^{-1} = \begin{bmatrix} \frac{1}{6} & \cdot & \cdot \\ \cdot & \frac{1}{5} & \cdot \\ \cdot & \cdot & \frac{1}{5} \end{bmatrix}$$

Premultiplying this by the s matrix, we obtain next

$$s(s'\rho s)^{-1} = \begin{bmatrix} +\dfrac{1}{2} & -\dfrac{\sqrt{3}}{2} & 0 \\ -\dfrac{\sqrt{3}}{2} & 0 & -\dfrac{1}{2} \\ -\dfrac{\sqrt{3}}{2} & -\dfrac{1}{2} & 0 \\ +\dfrac{1}{2} & 0 & -\dfrac{\sqrt{3}}{2} \\ 1 & 0 & 0 \\ 0 & 1 & 0 \\ 0 & 0 & 1 \end{bmatrix} \begin{bmatrix} \frac{1}{6} & \cdot & \cdot \\ \cdot & \frac{1}{5} & \cdot \\ \cdot & \cdot & \frac{1}{5} \end{bmatrix}$$

$$= \frac{1}{120} \begin{bmatrix} 10 & -12\sqrt{3} & 0 \\ -10\sqrt{3} & 0 & -12 \\ -10\sqrt{3} & -12 & 0 \\ 10 & 0 & -12\sqrt{3} \\ 20 & 0 & 0 \\ 0 & 24 & 0 \\ 0 & 0 & 24 \end{bmatrix}$$

Postmultiplication of this by $s'\rho$ gives

$$s(s'\rho s)^{-1}s'\rho$$

$$= \frac{1}{120} \begin{bmatrix} 46 & -\dfrac{30}{\sqrt{3}} & \dfrac{6}{\sqrt{3}} & 10 & 20 & -\dfrac{108}{\sqrt{3}} & 0 \\[2mm] -\dfrac{30}{\sqrt{3}} & 42 & 30 & \dfrac{6}{\sqrt{3}} & -\dfrac{60}{\sqrt{3}} & 0 & -36 \\[2mm] \dfrac{6}{\sqrt{3}} & 30 & 42 & -\dfrac{30}{\sqrt{3}} & -\dfrac{60}{\sqrt{3}} & -36 & 0 \\[2mm] 10 & \dfrac{6}{\sqrt{3}} & -\dfrac{30}{\sqrt{3}} & 46 & 20 & 0 & -\dfrac{108}{\sqrt{3}} \\[2mm] 20 & \dfrac{60}{\sqrt{3}} & -\dfrac{60}{\sqrt{3}} & 20 & 40 & 0 & 0 \\[2mm] -\dfrac{72}{\sqrt{3}} & 0 & -24 & 0 & 0 & 72 & 0 \\[2mm] 0 & -24 & 0 & -\dfrac{72}{\sqrt{3}} & 0 & 0 & 72 \end{bmatrix}$$

Finally, subtracting this from the unit matrix I and completing the operations indicated in Eq. (10.6), we obtain

$$120S = \begin{bmatrix} 74 & \dfrac{30}{\sqrt{3}} & -\dfrac{6}{\sqrt{3}} & -10 & -20 & \dfrac{108}{\sqrt{3}} & 0 \\[2mm] \dfrac{30}{\sqrt{3}} & 78 & -30 & -\dfrac{6}{\sqrt{3}} & \dfrac{60}{\sqrt{3}} & 0 & 36 \\[2mm] -\dfrac{6}{\sqrt{3}} & -30 & 78 & \dfrac{30}{\sqrt{3}} & \dfrac{60}{\sqrt{3}} & 36 & 0 \\[2mm] -10 & -\dfrac{6}{\sqrt{3}} & \dfrac{30}{\sqrt{3}} & 74 & -20 & 0 & \dfrac{108}{\sqrt{3}} \\[2mm] -20 & \dfrac{60}{\sqrt{3}} & \dfrac{60}{\sqrt{3}} & -20 & 80 & 0 & 0 \\[2mm] \dfrac{72}{\sqrt{3}} & 0 & 24 & 0 & 0 & 48 & 0 \\[2mm] 0 & 24 & 0 & \dfrac{72}{\sqrt{3}} & 0 & 0 & 48 \end{bmatrix} \begin{bmatrix} -\dfrac{15}{\sqrt{3}} \\[2mm] \dfrac{15}{\sqrt{3}} \\[2mm] -5 \\[2mm] -5 \\[2mm] 0 \\[2mm] 0 \\[2mm] 0 \end{bmatrix}$$

$$= \begin{bmatrix} -423.5 \\ 692.8 \\ -706.4 \\ -400.0 \\ 400.0 \\ -480.0 \\ 0 \end{bmatrix}$$

Thus, in kip units, the final values of the axial forces in the bars become

Bar	1	2	3	4	5	6	7
S	-3.53	$+5.78$	-5.89	-3.33	$+3.33$	-4.00	0

As a partial check on the calculations, these results can easily be shown to satisfy the conditions of equilibrium at each joint.

PROBLEMS

1 Using a matrix formulation of the problem, find the axial forces that will be induced in the bars of the truss in Fig. 10.5a by a uniform rise in temperature of 50°F. The coefficient of thermal expansion for the bars is $\alpha_t = 6.667(10^{-6})$ (in./in.)/°F, and the modulus of elasticity is $E = 30(10^6)$ psi. The external loads are removed.

   Hint Replace the matrix $[s'\rho\S]$ in Eq. (10.5) by the matrix $\alpha_t\Delta t[s'l]$.
   Ans. $S_1 = S_4 = -6.67$ kips, $S_2 = S_3 = -23.1$ kips, $S_5 = +16.7$ kips, $S_6 = S_7 = +17.3$ kips.

2 Using matrix formulation, find the axial forces induced in the bars of the plane truss shown in Fig. 10.6. All bars have the same modulus of elasticity E, and their

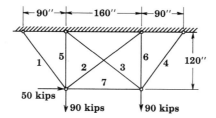

FIG. 10.6

cross-sectional areas are as follows: $A_1 = A_4 = 7.5$ in.², $A_2 = A_3 = 10.0$ in.², $A_7 = 6.4$ in.², $A_6 = A_5 = 8.0$ in.² The dimensions of the truss and the applied loads are shown in the figure.

	Bar	1	2	3	4	5	6	7
Ans.	S	$+51.6$	-4.55	$+35.5$	$+21.6$	$+51.4$	$+51.4$	-15.4

10.4 MATRIX ANALYSIS OF CONTINUOUS BEAMS

The discussion of statically indeterminate trusses in the preceding article represents an illustration of matrix formulation of a *force method* of analysis. As an illustration of matrix formulation of a *deformation method*, we shall discuss the problem of continuous beams. Although a matrix treatment of

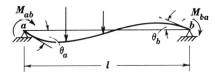

FIG. 10.7

this problem can be made quite general, we shall limit the discussion here to the case of a continuous beam on unyielding supports.   By so doing, attention can be more clearly focused on the essential features of the matrix method.[1]

We begin with the case of a simply supported beam *ab* of uniform cross section subjected to end moments (positive when clockwise) and lateral loads as shown in Fig. 10.7.   For this case, the slope-deflection equations have the form [see Eqs. (9.6), page 411]

$$M_{ab} = k(4\theta_a + 2\theta_b) + \mathfrak{M}_{ab}$$
$$M_{ba} = k(2\theta_a + 4\theta_b) + \mathfrak{M}_{ba}$$

$$(10.7)$$

where $\mathfrak{M}_{ab}$ and $\mathfrak{M}_{ba}$ are the fixed-end moments (see page 411) and $k = EI/l$ is the *stiffness factor* for the beam.   These equations may be written in matrix form as follows:

$$\begin{bmatrix} M_{ab} \\ M_{ba} \end{bmatrix} = \begin{bmatrix} 4k & 2k \\ 2k & 4k \end{bmatrix} \begin{bmatrix} \theta_a \\ \theta_b \end{bmatrix} + \begin{bmatrix} \mathfrak{M}_{ab} \\ \mathfrak{M}_{ba} \end{bmatrix}$$

$$(10.7a)$$

In this expression, the 2 × 2 matrix

$$K = \begin{bmatrix} 4k & 2k \\ 2k & 4k \end{bmatrix}$$

$$(a)$$

is called the *stiffness matrix* for the beam.

This notion of the stiffness matrix for a beam of uniform cross section can readily be extended to the case of a beam of variable cross section.   Referring to the slope-deflection equations (9.17), we conclude that for a nonprismatic beam

$$K = \begin{bmatrix} kk_{aa} & kk_{ab} \\ kk_{ab} & kk_{bb} \end{bmatrix}$$

$$(b)$$

where the values of k_{aa}, k_{ab}, k_{bb} are defined by expressions (*e*) on page 428, and $k = EI_0/l$, I_0 being the moment of inertia of the smallest cross section.   To avoid confusion with subscripts in later discussion, we introduce at this point

[1] See S. U. Benscoter, Matrix Analysis of Continuous Beams, *Trans. ASCE*, vol. 112, p. 1109, 1947.

new notations for the stiffness values in expression (b) and write

$$K = \begin{bmatrix} K_a & R \\ R & K_b \end{bmatrix} \qquad (c)$$

where $\qquad K_a = kk_{aa} \qquad K_b = kk_{bb} \qquad R = kk_{ab} \qquad (d)$

With these notations, the matrix equation (10.7a) becomes

$$\begin{bmatrix} M_{ab} \\ M_{ba} \end{bmatrix} = \begin{bmatrix} K_a & R \\ R & K_b \end{bmatrix} \begin{bmatrix} \theta_a \\ \theta_b \end{bmatrix} + \begin{bmatrix} \mathfrak{M}_{ab} \\ \mathfrak{M}_{ba} \end{bmatrix} \qquad (10.7b)$$

If $M_{ab} = 0$, that is, if we have a beam with only one end moment M_{ba}, Eqs. (10.7b) give

$$0 = K_a\theta_a + R\theta_b + \mathfrak{M}_{ab}$$
$$M_{ba} = R\theta_a + K_b\theta_b + \mathfrak{M}_{ba}$$

Then, upon elimination of θ_a between these two equations, we obtain

$$M_{ba} = \frac{K_aK_b - R^2}{K_a} \theta_b + \left(\mathfrak{M}_{ba} - \frac{R}{K_a} \mathfrak{M}_{ab} \right)$$

Thus, in such a case,

$$M_{ba} = K_b'\theta_b + \mathfrak{M}_{ba}' \qquad (10.7c)$$

where $\qquad K_b' = \dfrac{K_aK_b - R^2}{K_a} \qquad$ and $\qquad \mathfrak{M}_{ba}' = \mathfrak{M}_{ba} - \dfrac{R}{K_a} \mathfrak{M}_{ab} \qquad (e)$

represent a *modified stiffness factor* and a *modified fixed-end moment* for the end b of the beam when there is no end moment at the far end a. In working with continuous beams, these notions of modified stiffness factor and modified fixed-end moment will greatly simplify the treatment of a span having one end simply supported.

Having the basic slope-deflection equations in matrix form (10.7b), we may now proceed to a consideration of continuous beams. The discussion is intended to be perfectly general for a beam having n spans on $n + 1$ unyielding supports and with its two ends either built in or simply supported. However, to avoid cumbersome subscript notations, we take a specific case of four spans, the left end being simply supported and the right end built in as shown in Fig. 10.8. The lateral loads are assumed to be known; so all fixed-end moments can be calculated or taken from the ready tables. Assuming that this has been done, we are ready to write the slope-deflection equations (10.7b) for each of the four spans.

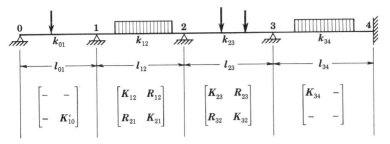

FIG. 10.8

For the left end of each span (except the first where $M_{01} = 0$), the first of these equations gives, with $\theta_4 = 0$,

$$M_{12} = K_{12}\theta_1 + R_{12}\theta_2 + \mathfrak{M}_{12}$$
$$M_{23} = K_{23}\theta_2 + R_{23}\theta_3 + \mathfrak{M}_{23} \qquad\qquad (f)$$
$$M_{34} = K_{34}\theta_3 + \mathfrak{M}_{34}$$

or, in matrix form,

$$\begin{bmatrix} M_{12} \\ M_{23} \\ M_{34} \end{bmatrix} = \begin{bmatrix} K_{12} & R_{12} & 0 \\ 0 & K_{23} & R_{23} \\ 0 & 0 & K_{34} \end{bmatrix} \begin{bmatrix} \theta_1 \\ \theta_2 \\ \theta_3 \end{bmatrix} + \begin{bmatrix} \mathfrak{M}_{12} \\ \mathfrak{M}_{23} \\ \mathfrak{M}_{34} \end{bmatrix} \qquad (f')$$

which is easily verified by performing the indicated matrix multiplication and addition. In the same way, for the right end of each span [except the last, where $\theta_4 = 0$, and the first, for which we use the modified equation (10.7c)], Eqs. (10.7b) give

$$M_{10} = K'_{10}\theta_1 + \mathfrak{M}'_{10}$$
$$M_{21} = R_{21}\theta_1 + K_{21}\theta_2 + \mathfrak{M}_{21} \qquad\qquad (g)$$
$$M_{32} = R_{32}\theta_2 + K_{32}\theta_3 + \mathfrak{M}_{32}$$

or, in matrix form,

$$\begin{bmatrix} M_{10} \\ M_{21} \\ M_{32} \end{bmatrix} = \begin{bmatrix} K'_{10} & 0 & 0 \\ R_{21} & K_{21} & 0 \\ 0 & R_{32} & K_{32} \end{bmatrix} \begin{bmatrix} \theta_1 \\ \theta_2 \\ \theta_3 \end{bmatrix} + \begin{bmatrix} \mathfrak{M}'_{10} \\ \mathfrak{M}_{21} \\ \mathfrak{M}_{32} \end{bmatrix} \qquad (g')$$

In each of expressions (f') and (g'), it should be noted that the first subscript on any of the matrix elements indicates the support number and the second subscript indicates which span is involved. Thus, K_{23} is the stiffness factor for the left end of the third span, $\mathfrak{M}_{21}$ is the fixed-end moment at the right end of the second span, etc.   Since there is only one R value for each span, the order of subscripts in this case is not significant.

The coefficient matrices in Eqs. (f') and (g') can be formed in the following manner: Referring to Fig. 10.8, we write down under each span the stiffness matrix (c) for that span.   Because we have already eliminated one of the slope-deflection equations for each of the end spans, we have only one element in each of the corresponding matrices, as shown in the figure.   In writing these single-element matrices for the end spans, we also take account of the conditions of constraint at the supports 0 and 4.   Thus, for the left-end span, we use the modified stiffness factor K'_{10} as defined in expressions (e), whereas for the right-end span, we use the standard stiffness factor K_{34}. On having these stiffness matrices for the individual spans, the coefficient matrix in Eq. (f') is formed simply by writing the upper rows of the 2×2 single-span matrices as successive rows of the final matrix, each row staggered one place to the right with respect to the preceding row, and filling in the blank spaces with zeros.   The coefficient matrix in Eq. (g') is formed in exactly the same manner, using the lower rows of the 2×2 single-span matrices in Fig. 10.8.

We introduce now the following column-vector notations:

$$M_{ab} = \begin{bmatrix} M_{12} \\ M_{23} \\ M_{34} \end{bmatrix} \qquad M_{ba} = \begin{bmatrix} M_{10} \\ M_{21} \\ M_{32} \end{bmatrix} \qquad \theta = \begin{bmatrix} \theta_1 \\ \theta_2 \\ \theta_3 \end{bmatrix}$$

$$\mathfrak{M}_{ab} = \begin{bmatrix} \mathfrak{M}_{12} \\ \mathfrak{M}_{23} \\ \mathfrak{M}_{34} \end{bmatrix} \qquad \mathfrak{M}_{ba} = \begin{bmatrix} \mathfrak{M}'_{10} \\ \mathfrak{M}_{21} \\ \mathfrak{M}_{32} \end{bmatrix} \tag{h}$$

and the stiffness-matrix notations:

$$K_{ab} = \begin{bmatrix} K_{12} & R_{12} & 0 \\ 0 & K_{23} & R_{23} \\ 0 & 0 & K_{34} \end{bmatrix} \qquad K_{ba} = \begin{bmatrix} K'_{10} & 0 & 0 \\ R_{21} & K_{21} & 0 \\ 0 & R_{32} & K_{32} \end{bmatrix} \tag{i}$$

With these notations, expressions (f') and (g'), representing Eqs. (f) and (g), may be written in the compact form

$$[M_{ab}] = [K_{ab}][\theta] + [\mathfrak{M}_{ab}]$$
$$[M_{ba}] = [K_{ba}][\theta] + [\mathfrak{M}_{ba}] \tag{10.8}$$

These are the slope-deflection equations for any continuous beam, the supports of which are restrained against settlement.   It is to be pointed out that they are exactly the same equations that we would write in following the procedure developed in Chap. 9, the only advantage of the matrix formulation being that of compactness of notation.

In general, we may choose any set of angles of rotation at the intermediate supports, as defined by an arbitrary column vector θ, and then find, from Eqs. (10.8), the corresponding end moments. By so doing, the two end moments found at each intermediate support will not generally be in equilibrium, and some externally applied couple would be required at each support to hold the beam in the assumed configuration. To find the true set of end moments, we must now impose the further condition that, at each intermediate support, the end moments for each pair of adjacent spans must be equal in magnitude but of opposite sign. This condition will be expressed by the matrix equation

$$[M_{ab}] + [M_{ba}] = 0 \tag{10.9}$$

Substituting expressions (10.8) into Eq. (10.9), we obtain

$$[K][\theta] = -[\mathbf{M}] \tag{10.10}$$

where

$$[K] = [K_{ab}] + [K_{ba}] = \begin{bmatrix} K_{12} + K'_{10} & R_{12} & 0 \\ R_{21} & K_{23} + K_{21} & R_{23} \\ 0 & R_{32} & K_{34} + K_{32} \end{bmatrix} \tag{j}$$

and

$$[\mathbf{M}] = \begin{bmatrix} \mathfrak{M}_{12} + \mathfrak{M}'_{10} \\ \mathfrak{M}_{23} + \mathfrak{M}_{21} \\ \mathfrak{M}_{34} + \mathfrak{M}_{32} \end{bmatrix} = \begin{bmatrix} \mathbf{M}_1 \\ \mathbf{M}_2 \\ \mathbf{M}_3 \end{bmatrix} \tag{k}$$

M_i being the summation of fixed-end moments at each intermediate support, similar to the idea of unbalanced moment previously defined in connection with moment distribution (see page 461).

Equation (10.10) represents, in matrix form, the *three-angle equations* for a continuous beam as represented by Eqs. (9.9), page 414, or Eqs. (9.20), page 432, if we ignore the θ terms representing rigid body rotations of the individual spans. The reader may verify this by carrying out the indicated matrix multiplication of Eq. (10.10).

The K matrix defined by expression (j) is called the *stiffness matrix* for the entire continuous beam. For the four-span beam considered here, it is a three-by-three square matrix, but in general, for a beam of n spans on $n + 1$ supports, it will be a square matrix of order $(n - 1) \times (n - 1)$. It always has the same form, consisting of a principal diagonal with a *superdiagonal* directly above and a *subdiagonal* directly below, all other elements being zero. Such a matrix is called a *continuant matrix*.[1] This stiffness matrix for a continuous beam may always be formed by writing the sum of the end stiffness factors at each support as successive elements of the principal diagonal and the R values for each span as successive elements of the super- and subdiagonals.

[1] See Aitken, *op. cit.*, p. 126.

The solution of Eqs. (10.10) will be

$$\theta = -[K]^{-1}[\mathbf{M}] \tag{10.11}$$

where $[K]^{-1}$ is the inverse of $[K]$. Then, upon substituting (10.11) into Eqs. (10.8), the latter become

$$
\begin{aligned}
[M_{ab}] &= [\mathfrak{M}_{ab}] - [K_{ab}][K]^{-1}[\mathbf{M}] \\
[M_{ba}] &= [\mathfrak{M}_{ba}] - [K_{ba}][K]^{-1}[\mathbf{M}]
\end{aligned}
\tag{10.12}
$$

These matrix formulas may be regarded as representing the final solution of the problem; i.e., they define all end moments at the intermediate supports of the beam. Since $[M_{ab}] = -[M_{ba}]$, we need to use only one set of these equations in the analysis of any given continuous beam.

In the case of a continuous beam with built-in ends, we still have to calculate the end moments M_{01} and $M_{n,n-1}$ from the previously unused slope-deflection equations for the end spans. These end moments are given by the equations

$$
\begin{aligned}
M_{01} &= \mathfrak{M}_{01} - \frac{R_{10}}{K_{10}}\left(\mathfrak{M}_{10} - M_{10}\right) \\
M_{n,n-1} &= \mathfrak{M}_{n,n-1} - \frac{R_{n-1,n}}{K_{n-1,n}}\left(\mathfrak{M}_{n-1,n} - M_{n-1,n}\right)
\end{aligned}
\tag{10.13}
$$

As a first example of the application of the matrix formulas (10.12), let us consider the three-span continuous beam shown in Fig. 10.9a. This beam

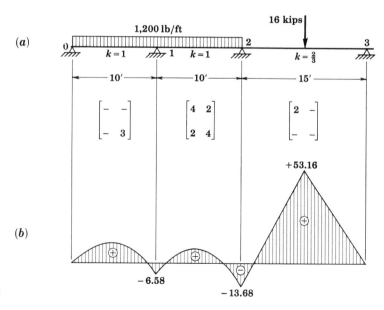

FIG. 10.9

has a uniform cross section, for which we take[1] $EI = 10$ kip-ft^2, and its two ends are simply supported. The dimensions of the beam and the lateral loads together with the values of $k = EI/l$ for each span are as shown in the figure.

We begin the analysis by writing under each span the stiffness matrix for that span. Since the beam is of uniform cross section, expression (*a*) applies, but for the single-element matrices for the end spans, we replace k by $3k/4$ to account for the simply supported ends. With these matrices defined, we next find from expressions (*i*) that

$$K_{ab} = \begin{bmatrix} 4 & 2 \\ 0 & 2 \end{bmatrix} \quad \text{and} \quad K_{ba} = \begin{bmatrix} 3 & 0 \\ 2 & 4 \end{bmatrix} \tag{l}$$

Then, from expression (*j*), the stiffness matrix for the entire beam becomes

$$K = \begin{bmatrix} 7 & 2 \\ 2 & 6 \end{bmatrix} \tag{m}$$

To invert this matrix (see page 488), we first write the adjugate of K:

$$\text{adj } K = \begin{bmatrix} 6 & -2 \\ -2 & 7 \end{bmatrix} \tag{n}$$

and calculate the determinant of K:

$$|K| = \begin{vmatrix} 7 & 2 \\ 2 & 6 \end{vmatrix} = 42 - 4 = 38 \tag{o}$$

Then, the reciprocal of K becomes

$$[K]^{-1} = \frac{\text{adj } K}{|K|} = \frac{1}{38} \begin{bmatrix} 6 & -2 \\ -2 & 7 \end{bmatrix} \tag{p}$$

Using Table 9.1, page 412, the fixed-end moments are found to be

$$\mathfrak{M}'_{10} = +5 \qquad \mathfrak{M}_{12} = -10 \qquad \mathfrak{M}_{21} = +10 \qquad \mathfrak{M}'_{23} = -15$$

all values being in kip-foot units. Then, the several column matrices appearing in Eqs. (10.12) are

$$\mathfrak{M}_{ab} = \begin{bmatrix} -10 \\ -15 \end{bmatrix} \qquad \mathfrak{M}_{ba} = \begin{bmatrix} +5 \\ +10 \end{bmatrix} \qquad \mathbf{M} = \begin{bmatrix} -5 \\ -5 \end{bmatrix}$$

and Eqs. (10.12 become

$$\begin{bmatrix} M_{12} \\ M_{23} \end{bmatrix} = \begin{bmatrix} -10 \\ -15 \end{bmatrix} - \begin{bmatrix} 4 & 2 \\ 0 & 2 \end{bmatrix} \frac{1}{38} \begin{bmatrix} 6 & -2 \\ -2 & 7 \end{bmatrix} \begin{bmatrix} -5 \\ -5 \end{bmatrix}$$

$$\begin{bmatrix} M_{10} \\ M_{21} \end{bmatrix} = \begin{bmatrix} 5 \\ 10 \end{bmatrix} - \begin{bmatrix} 3 & 0 \\ 2 & 4 \end{bmatrix} \frac{1}{38} \begin{bmatrix} 6 & -2 \\ -2 & 7 \end{bmatrix} \begin{bmatrix} -5 \\ -5 \end{bmatrix} \tag{q}$$

[1] Since the results will not depend on the actual value of EI, we choose $EI = 10$ so that the stiffness values will be simple whole numbers, thus simplifying the matrix multiplications.

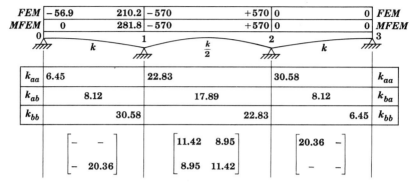

FIG. 10.10

To evaluate these expressions, we first calculate the matrix product:

$$\frac{1}{38}\begin{bmatrix} 6 & -2 \\ -2 & 7 \end{bmatrix}\begin{bmatrix} -5 \\ -5 \end{bmatrix} = \frac{1}{38}\begin{bmatrix} -20 \\ -25 \end{bmatrix} = \frac{5}{38}\begin{bmatrix} -4 \\ -5 \end{bmatrix}$$

Then

$$\begin{bmatrix} 4 & 2 \\ 0 & 2 \end{bmatrix}\frac{5}{38}\begin{bmatrix} -4 \\ -5 \end{bmatrix} = \frac{5}{38}\begin{bmatrix} -26 \\ -10 \end{bmatrix} = \begin{bmatrix} -3.42 \\ -1.32 \end{bmatrix}$$

and

$$\begin{bmatrix} 3 & 0 \\ 2 & 4 \end{bmatrix}\frac{5}{38}\begin{bmatrix} -4 \\ -5 \end{bmatrix} = \frac{5}{38}\begin{bmatrix} -12 \\ -28 \end{bmatrix} = \begin{bmatrix} -1.58 \\ -3.68 \end{bmatrix}$$

so that expressions (q) become

$$\begin{bmatrix} M_{12} \\ M_{23} \end{bmatrix} = \begin{bmatrix} -10 \\ -15 \end{bmatrix} - \begin{bmatrix} -3.42 \\ -1.32 \end{bmatrix} = \begin{bmatrix} -6.58 \\ -13.68 \end{bmatrix}$$

$$\begin{bmatrix} M_{10} \\ M_{21} \end{bmatrix} = \begin{bmatrix} +5 \\ +10 \end{bmatrix} - \begin{bmatrix} -1.58 \\ -3.68 \end{bmatrix} = \begin{bmatrix} 6.58 \\ 13.68 \end{bmatrix}$$

These are the final results for the end moments, and the fact that we obtain identical results, except for signs, from the two sets of equations serves as a partial check on the calculations. The corresponding bending-moment diagram for the beam is shown in Fig. 10.9b.

As a second example, let us consider a matrix analysis of the three-span beam of variable cross section shown in Fig. 9.22, page 434. As a preliminary step, we record, as shown in Fig. 10.10, the fixed-end moments and the stiffness factors k_{aa}, k_{ab}, k_{bb} for each span.[1] We have also recorded, under each span, the value of EI_0/l for that span, using the notation $k = EI_0/36$.

Since the ends of the beam are simply supported in this case, we must next calculate modified fixed-end moments and modified stiffness factors for the two

[1] These data are taken from page 434, where the problem was previously discussed.

end spans. Using Eqs. (*e*) for this purpose, we have

$$\mathfrak{M}'_{10} = \mathfrak{M}_{10} - \frac{k_{01}}{k_{00}}\,\mathfrak{M}_{01} = 210.2 - \frac{8.12}{6.45}\,(-56.9) = +281.8$$

The full set of modified fixed-end moments is recorded in Fig. 10.10 directly above the beam. Similarly, for modified stiffness factors in the first and last spans, we have

$$k'_{10} = k'_{23} = \frac{k_{00}k_{11} - k_{01}{}^2}{k_{00}} = \frac{(6.45)(30.58) - (8.12)^2}{6.45} = 20.36$$

Then using expression (*b*) and suppressing the scalar factor $k = EI_0/36$, the stiffness matrices for the individual spans are formed as shown in Fig. 10.10.

We are now ready to begin the analysis. Using the data from Fig. 10.10 in Eqs. (*i*), we first find

$$K_{ab} = \begin{bmatrix} 11.42 & 8.95 \\ 0 & 20.36 \end{bmatrix} \qquad K_{ba} = \begin{bmatrix} 20.36 & 0 \\ 8.95 & 11.42 \end{bmatrix}$$

Then, using Eq. (*j*) and the rules for inversion (see page 488), we have

$$K = \begin{bmatrix} 31.78 & 8.95 \\ 8.95 & 31.78 \end{bmatrix} \qquad K^{-1} = \frac{1}{929.9}\begin{bmatrix} 31.78 & -8.95 \\ -8.95 & 31.78 \end{bmatrix}$$

Finally, the first set of matrix formulas (10.12) becomes

$$\begin{bmatrix} M_{12} \\ M_{23} \end{bmatrix} = \begin{bmatrix} -570 \\ 0 \end{bmatrix} - \begin{bmatrix} 11.42 & 8.95 \\ 0 & 20.36 \end{bmatrix}$$

$$\times \frac{1}{929.9}\begin{bmatrix} 31.78 & -8.95 \\ -8.95 & 31.78 \end{bmatrix}\begin{bmatrix} -288.2 \\ +570.0 \end{bmatrix} = \begin{bmatrix} -594 \\ -453 \end{bmatrix}$$

These values of the end moments are seen to agree with those obtained on page 435. In the examples discussed above, the number of unknowns is small, and there is no particular advantage in using the matrix method. However, in the case of a continuous beam having many spans, the method may be helpful particularly if the electronic computer is to be used for the numerical solution of the equations.

PROBLEMS

1 Repeat the analysis of the continuous beam of uniform cross section shown in Fig. 10.9 if the ends of the beam are built in instead of simply supported. All other data remain unchanged.

2 Repeat the analysis of the three-span beam shown in Fig. 9.22 if the middle span has a length of 36 ft instead of 72 ft. All other data remain the same.

  Ans. $M_{12} = -115.9$ kip-ft, $M_{23} = -113.8$ kip-ft.

10.5 MATRIX TREATMENT OF ARCHES AND FRAMES

To show some further aspects of matrix methods in structural analysis, let us consider the problem of an unsymmetrical hingeless arch rib AB as shown in Fig. 10.11a. Taking the reactions at A as the redundant quantities and using the theorem of least work, we obtain, for calculating H_a, R_a, M_a, the system of equations (a) and (b) already given on page 372. Substituting expressions (b) into Eqs. (a) and neglecting the terms containing the axial force N, we obtain

$$M_a \int_0^s \frac{y\,ds}{EI} + R_a \int_0^s \frac{xy\,ds}{EI} + H_a \int_0^s \frac{y^2\,ds}{EI} + \int_0^s \frac{M'y\,ds}{EI} = 0$$

$$M_a \int_0^s \frac{x\,ds}{EI} + R_a \int_0^s \frac{x^2\,ds}{EI} + H_a \int_0^s \frac{xy\,ds}{EI} + \int_0^s \frac{M'x\,ds}{EI} = 0$$

$$M_a \int_0^s \frac{ds}{EI} + R_a \int_0^s \frac{x\,ds}{EI} + H_a \int_0^s \frac{y\,ds}{EI} + \int_0^s \frac{M'\,ds}{EI} = 0$$

$$(10.14)$$

This system of equations is not suitable for the practical calculation of the unknowns H_a, R_a, M_a, and, as already pointed out in Art. 8.6, we obtain a great simplification by taking, instead of H_a, R_a, M_a, the statically equivalent system of redundant reactions X_0, Y_0, M_0, acting at the elastic center O of the arch and directed along its principal axes as shown in Fig. 10.11c. By so doing, we obtain, instead of the system of equations (10.14), a system of three independent equations, each of which contains only one unknown. Such a transformation of Eqs. (10.14) can be made by proper manipulation of the associated matrices, and this procedure will now be explained.

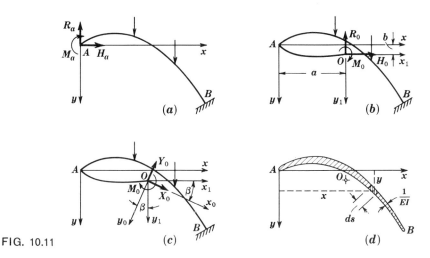

FIG. 10.11

We begin with the following notations:

$$Q_x = \int_0^s \frac{y\,ds}{EI} \qquad Q_y = \int_0^s \frac{x\,ds}{EI} \qquad A = \int_0^s \frac{ds}{EI}$$

$$I_x = \int_0^s \frac{y^2\,ds}{EI} \qquad I_y = \int_0^s \frac{x^2\,ds}{EI} \qquad I_{xy} = \int_0^s \frac{xy\,ds}{EI} \tag{a}$$

If, as shown in Fig. 10.11d, we give the arch axis a fictitious variable thickness $1/EI$, we see that the integrals (a) represent the statical moments, the area, and the moments and product of inertia of this shaded area with respect to the chosen coordinate axes x and y through the end A of the arch axis. Using notations (a), Eqs. (10.14) become

$$I_x H_a + I_{xy} R_a + Q_x M_a = - \int_0^s M'y\,\frac{ds}{EI}$$

$$I_{xy} H_a + I_y R_a + Q_y M_a = - \int_0^s M'x\,\frac{ds}{EI} \tag{10.14a}$$

$$Q_x H_a + Q_y R_a + A M_a = - \int_0^s M'\,\frac{ds}{EI}$$

or, in matrix notation,

$$\begin{bmatrix} I_x & I_{xy} & Q_x \\ I_{xy} & I_y & Q_y \\ Q_x & Q_y & A \end{bmatrix} \begin{bmatrix} H_a \\ R_a \\ M_a \end{bmatrix} = - \begin{bmatrix} \int \dfrac{M'y\,ds}{EI} \\ \int \dfrac{M'x\,ds}{EI} \\ \int \dfrac{M'\,ds}{EI} \end{bmatrix} \tag{10.14b}$$

Now, let us consider, in these equations, the matrix

$$F = \begin{bmatrix} I_x & I_{xy} & Q_x \\ I_{xy} & I_y & Q_y \\ Q_x & Q_y & A \end{bmatrix} \tag{b}$$

which is called the *geometry matrix* for the arch. We see that it is entirely independent of the loading on the arch and depends only on the shape and proportions of the rib, i.e., only on the geometry of the arch. It is called a *symmetric matrix* because its elements are symmetrically arranged with respect to the principal diagonal.

If, instead of axes x and y through point A, we take a parallel set of axes x_1 and y_1 through the elastic center O of the arch, i.e., through the centroid of the fictitious shaded area in Fig. 10.11d, the statical moments Q_{x_1} and Q_{y_1} will vanish, and the corresponding geometry matrix F_1 will have the simpler form

$$F_1 = \begin{bmatrix} I_{x_1} & I_{x_1y_1} & 0 \\ I_{x_1y_1} & I_{y_1} & 0 \\ 0 & 0 & A \end{bmatrix} \tag{c}$$

This new matrix F_1 can be obtained directly from the matrix F by introducing a *transformation matrix* T and its transpose T' as follows:

$$T = \begin{bmatrix} 1 & 0 & -\dfrac{Q_x}{A} \\ 0 & 1 & -\dfrac{Q_y}{A} \\ 0 & 0 & 1 \end{bmatrix} \qquad T' = \begin{bmatrix} 1 & 0 & 0 \\ 0 & 1 & 0 \\ -\dfrac{Q_x}{A} & -\dfrac{Q_y}{A} & 1 \end{bmatrix} \tag{d}$$

Then $\qquad F_1 = TFT'$ $\hspace{4cm}$ (10.15)

To demonstrate this, we note first from the parallel-axis theorem for moments and products of inertia that

$$I_{x_1} = I_x - Ab^2 \qquad I_{y_1} = I_y - Aa^2 \qquad I_{x_1y_1} = I_{xy} - Aab \tag{e}$$

where the coordinates of the elastic center O are

$$a = \frac{Q_y}{A} \qquad b = \frac{Q_x}{A} \tag{f}$$

Substituting these values of a and b into Eqs. (e), we obtain

$$I_{x_1} = I_x - \frac{Q_x{}^2}{A} \qquad I_{y_1} = I_y - \frac{Q_y{}^2}{A} \qquad I_{x_1y_1} = I_{xy} - \frac{Q_xQ_y}{A} \tag{e'}$$

Now, performing the matrix multiplications indicated by Eq. (10.15), we obtain

$$F_1 = \begin{bmatrix} 1 & 0 & -\dfrac{Q_x}{A} \\ 0 & 1 & -\dfrac{Q_y}{A} \\ 0 & 0 & 1 \end{bmatrix} \begin{bmatrix} I_x & I_{xy} & Q_x \\ I_{xy} & I_y & Q_y \\ Q_x & Q_y & A \end{bmatrix} \begin{bmatrix} 1 & 0 & 0 \\ 0 & 1 & 0 \\ -\dfrac{Q_x}{A} & -\dfrac{Q_y}{A} & A \end{bmatrix}$$

$$= \begin{bmatrix} I_x - \dfrac{Q_x{}^2}{A} & I_{xy} - \dfrac{Q_xQ_y}{A} & 0 \\ I_{xy} - \dfrac{Q_xQ_y}{A} & I_y - \dfrac{Q_y}{A} & 0 \\ 0 & 0 & A \end{bmatrix}$$

the elements of which are seen to agree with expressions (e').

Referring now to Fig. 10.11c, let us rotate the axes x_1, y_1 into the positions x_0, y_0 coinciding with principal directions for the fictitious shaded area in Fig. 10.11d. Then, the product of inertia $I_{x_0 y_0}$ will also vanish and the corresponding geometry matrix becomes

$$F_0 = \begin{bmatrix} I_{x_0} & 0 & 0 \\ 0 & I_{y_0} & 0 \\ 0 & 0 & A \end{bmatrix} \tag{g}$$

This matrix again can be obtained from the preceding matrix F_1 by the use of a *transformation matrix* P and its transpose P' as follows:

$$P = \begin{bmatrix} \cos \beta & -\sin \beta & 0 \\ \sin \beta & \cos \beta & 0 \\ 0 & 0 & 1 \end{bmatrix} \qquad P' = \begin{bmatrix} \cos \beta & \sin \beta & 0 \\ -\sin \beta & \cos \beta & 0 \\ 0 & 0 & 1 \end{bmatrix} \tag{h}$$

The elements of this matrix are simply the direction cosines for the new set of axes. Then, as before,

$$F_0 = PF_1P' \tag{10.16}$$

This transformation holds for any value of the angle β, but to make the product of inertia $I_{x_0 y_0}$ vanish, we must take (see page 376)

$$\tan 2\beta = \frac{2I_{x_1 y_1}}{I_{y_1} - I_{x_1}} \tag{i}$$

When both transformations indicated by Eqs. (10.15) and (10.16) have been made, the equations for calculating the redundant reactions X_0, Y_0, M_0 in Fig. 10.11c become

$$\begin{bmatrix} I_{x_0} & 0 & 0 \\ 0 & I_{y_0} & 0 \\ 0 & 0 & A \end{bmatrix} \begin{bmatrix} X_0 \\ Y_0 \\ M_0 \end{bmatrix} = - \begin{bmatrix} \int \dfrac{M' y_0 \, ds}{EI} \\ \int \dfrac{M' x_0 \, ds}{EI} \\ \int \dfrac{M' \, ds}{EI} \end{bmatrix} \tag{10.14c}$$

To illustrate the application of Eq. (10.14c), let us consider the rectangular frame supported and loaded as shown in Fig. 10.12a. The dimensions of this frame and the cross-sectional moments of inertia of its members are shown in the figure, and for simplicity we assume $EI_0 = 1$ kip-ft². Thus, the fictitious area corresponding to the center line of the frame will have the width $1/EI$ as shown in Fig. 10.12b. Taking axes x and y through point A as shown, the

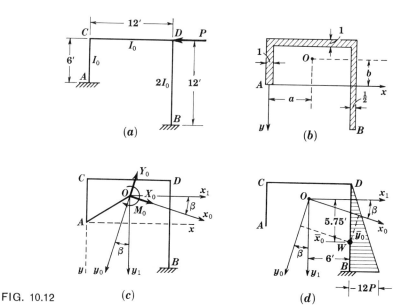

FIG. 10.12   (c)   (d)

geometrical quantities defined by Eqs. (a) become

$$Q_x = -6 \times 3 - 12 \times 6 + 0 = -90$$
$$Q_y = 0 + 12 \times 6 + 6 \times 12 = 144$$
$$A = 6 + 12 + 6 = 24$$

$$I_x = 6 \times \frac{6^2}{3} + 12 \times 6^2 + 6 \times \frac{12^2}{12} = 576 \qquad (j)$$

$$I_y = 0 + 12 \times \frac{12^2}{3} + 6 \times 12^2 = 1440$$

$$I_{xy} = 0 - 12 \times 6 \times 6 + 0 = -432$$

Then, from Eqs. (f), the coordinates of the elastic center O are

$$a = \frac{144}{24} = 6.00 \qquad b = -\frac{90}{24} = -3.75 \qquad (k)$$

Assembling the quantities (j) in accordance with expression (b), the geometry matrix for the frame becomes

$$F = \begin{bmatrix} 576 & -432 & -90 \\ -432 & 1{,}440 & 144 \\ -90 & 144 & 24 \end{bmatrix} \qquad (l)$$

Similarly, using the coordinates a and b from Eqs. (k), the transformation matrix T, as defined by the first of expressions (d), becomes

$$T = \begin{bmatrix} 1 & 0 & 3.75 \\ 0 & 1 & -6 \\ 0 & 0 & 1 \end{bmatrix} \tag{m}$$

Then, for axes x_1, y_1 through the elastic center O in Fig. 10.12c, the geometry matrix F_1 is found from Eq. (10.15) to be

$$F_1$$

$$= \begin{bmatrix} 1 & 0 & 3.75 \\ 0 & 1 & -6 \\ 0 & 0 & 1 \end{bmatrix} \begin{bmatrix} 576 & -432 & -90 \\ -432 & 1,440 & 144 \\ -90 & 144 & 24 \end{bmatrix} \begin{bmatrix} 1 & 0 & 0 \\ 0 & 1 & 0 \\ 3.75 & -6 & 1 \end{bmatrix}$$

$$= \begin{bmatrix} 238.5 & 108 & 0 \\ 108 & 576 & 0 \\ 0 & 0 & 24 \end{bmatrix}$$

Now, from Eq. (i)

$$\tan 2\beta = \frac{2 \times 108}{576 - 238.5} = 0.640$$

and we find

$$\beta = 16°18' \qquad \cos \beta = 0.960 \qquad \sin \beta = 0.281$$

With these values, the second transformation matrix P, as defined by the first of expressions (h), becomes

$$P = \begin{bmatrix} 0.960 & -0.281 & 0 \\ 0.281 & 0.960 & 0 \\ 0 & 0 & 1 \end{bmatrix} \tag{n}$$

Then, from Eq. (10.16) the geometry matrix for the principal axes x_0, y_0 as shown in Fig. 10.12c is found to be

$$F_0$$

$$= \begin{bmatrix} 0.960 & -0.281 & 0 \\ 0.281 & 0.960 & 0 \\ 0 & 0 & 1 \end{bmatrix} \begin{bmatrix} 238.5 & 108 & 0 \\ 108 & 576 & 0 \\ 0 & 0 & 24 \end{bmatrix} \begin{bmatrix} 0.960 & 0.281 & 0 \\ -0.281 & 0.960 & 0 \\ 0 & 0 & 1 \end{bmatrix}$$

$$= \begin{bmatrix} 354.3 & 0 & 0 \\ 0 & 608.0 & 0 \\ 0 & 0 & 24 \end{bmatrix}$$

Having this geometry matrix for the principal axes of the frame, we are now ready to consider the load matrix appearing on the right-hand side of Eq.

(10.14c). To write this matrix, we consider the bending-moment diagram M' as shown in Fig. 10.12d. The area of this diagram, divided by EI, is

$$W = \int_A^B \frac{M' \, ds}{EI} = \int_D^B \frac{M' ds}{2EI_0} = -36P$$

and its centroid is at W having the coordinates

$$x_0 = x_1 \cos \beta + y_1 \sin \beta = 6 \times 0.960 + 5.75 \times 0.281 = 7.38$$

$$y_0 = y_1 \cos \beta - x_1 \sin \beta = 5.75 \times 0.960 - 6 \times 0.281 = 3.84$$

Hence, the load matrix becomes

$$-\begin{bmatrix} \int \dfrac{M' y_0 \, ds}{EI} \\ \int \dfrac{M' x_0 \, ds}{EI} \\ \int \dfrac{M' \, ds}{EI} \end{bmatrix} = 36P \begin{bmatrix} 3.84 \\ 7.38 \\ 1 \end{bmatrix} \tag{o}$$

Now, inverting the above matrix F_0, the solution of Eq. (10.14c) becomes

$$\begin{bmatrix} X_0 \\ Y_0 \\ M_0 \end{bmatrix} = \frac{36P}{1000} \begin{bmatrix} 2.82 & \cdot & \cdot \\ \cdot & 1.64 & \cdot \\ \cdot & \cdot & 41.7 \end{bmatrix} \begin{bmatrix} 3.84 \\ 7.38 \\ 1 \end{bmatrix} = \frac{36P}{1,000} \begin{bmatrix} 10.83 \\ 12.14 \\ 41.70 \end{bmatrix}$$

that is,

$$X_0 = 0.390P \text{ kips} \qquad Y_0 = 0.437P \text{ kips} \qquad M_0 = 1.50P \text{ ft-kips}$$

10.6 MATRIX ANALYSIS OF CONTINUOUS FRAMES

Continuous frame structures such as building frames are likely to be highly statically indeterminate so that in their analysis we have to deal with a large number of unknowns. The only practicable way of solving such problems is to have recourse to the electronic digital computer, and for this purpose a matrix formulation of the problem is the most advantageous. To illustrate a matrix method for such problems, we shall consider here a two-story building frame as shown in Fig. 10.13. On the one hand, this frame will not involve so many unknowns as to make the discussion unwieldy, yet, on the other hand, it will be extensive enough to permit us to illustrate all the steps that would be required in the analysis of a much larger structure.

For simplicity, we assume that each member has the same length l and the same flexural rigidity EI so that the stiffness factors are all equal, that is, $k = EI/l$ is the same for all members. As is usual practice, we also neglect the deforma-

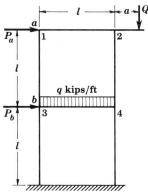

FIG. 10.13

tions caused by axial forces and by shearing forces in the members and consider only bending deformation.   Under these assumptions, the deformation of the frame under load will be completely defined by a set of six displacements: namely, the horizontal displacements δ_a and δ_b of the two floors and the angles of rotation θ_1, θ_2, θ_3, θ_4 of the four rigid joints.   When these six displacements have been found, all end moments can be calculated from the slope-deflection equations (9.6), page 411, and the problem is solved.   We therefore introduce the column vector[1]

$$[\delta_j] = \{\delta_a \quad \delta_b \quad \theta_1 \quad \theta_2 \quad \theta_3 \quad \theta_4\} \tag{a}$$

and select this set of displacements as the unknowns of the problem.

As a preliminary step to the calculation of the displacements (a), we first consider the two simple problems illustrated in Fig. 10.14.   In Fig. 10.14a, we give to the end A of a prismatic beam AB with built-in ends a displacement δ, without allowing any rotation of the tangent at A or any movement at all of the end B.   Then, the reactions at A and B can easily be calculated by using the slope-deflection equations (9.6) on page 411, and we find

$$R_{ab} = \frac{12k}{l^2}\,\delta \qquad M_{ab} = \frac{6k}{l}\,\delta \qquad R_{ba} = \frac{12k}{l^2}\,\delta \qquad M_{ba} = \frac{6k}{l}\,\delta \tag{b}$$

In Fig. 10.14b, the end A of the same beam is given an angle of rotation θ without allowing any lateral deflection of A or any movement at all of the end B.   Then, again using the slope-deflection equations (9.6) on page 411, we find

$$R_{ab} = \frac{6k}{l}\,\theta \qquad M_{ab} = 4k\theta \qquad R_{ba} = \frac{6k}{l}\,\theta \qquad M_{ba} = 2k\theta \tag{b'}$$

---

[1] To save space, a column vector is often written in one horizontal line enclosed by braces instead of brackets to indicate that it is not a row vector.

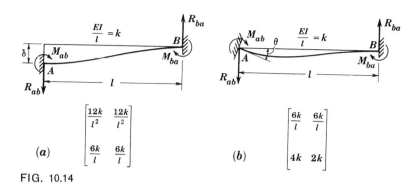

(a)

(b)

FIG. 10.14

The coefficients appearing in front of δ and θ in Eqs. (b) and (b′) are seen to represent the reactions, or forces of constraint, at the ends of the beam when the displacements δ and θ are each equal to unity. These quantities are called the *stiffness influence coefficients* for the beam corresponding to each type of displacement. For convenience of easy reference, these stiffness coefficients are recorded in matrix form under each beam in Fig. 10.14.

Now, let us return to the frame in Fig. 10.13, remove all applied loads, and lock all joints against both translation and rotation. This done, we remove just one constraint corresponding to any one of the six degrees of freedom of the system, say constraint j, and make there a unit displacement $\delta_j = 1$.[*] This will result in some deformation of the structure consistent with the remaining artificial constraints, and we proceed to calculate the reaction corresponding to each of the six degrees of freedom. That is, we calculate the system of external forces and couples necessary to hold the structure in the assumed configuration defined by $\delta_j = 1$. In the generalized sense, we denote such an external reaction at i by S_{ij} regardless of whether it is a force or a couple. Thus, we define the *stiffness influence coefficient* S_{ij} as the external reaction at i due to an imposed unit displacement at j when all other displacements are held equal to zero. In our example there will be 36 of these stiffness influence coefficients, and we now set about their calculation, making use of the single-member stiffness coefficients shown in Fig. 10.14.

Let us begin in Fig. 10.15a with a unit displacement $\delta_a = 1$, that is, a unit lateral displacement of the top floor, all other displacements being held equal to zero. Then, the external forces required to hold the structure in this configuration will act as shown in the figure,[1] and their magnitudes will be as listed beside the structure. In these calculations, we consider linear displacements

---

[*] This may be either a linear displacement or an angular displacement; i.e., we use the symbol δ_j in the sense of a generalized displacement (see page 226).
[1] Since the members of the frame are treated as inextensible, all of the horizontal force of constraint is assumed to act on the left-hand side of the frame.

and forces positive to the right, negative to the left, and angular displacements and couples positive when clockwise, negative when counterclockwise. Consider, for example, the calculation of S_{ba}. From Fig. 10.14a, we see that the reaction at the bottom of each upper-story column in Fig. 10.15a is $12k/l^2$ acting to the left and that there are two such columns; hence, $S_{ba} = -24k/l^2$ as shown. Consider, again, the calculation of S_{4a}. From Fig. 10.14a, we see that the reactive moment at the bottom of the column 42 in Fig. 10.15a is counterclockwise and of magnitude $6k/l$ and that there is only one column;

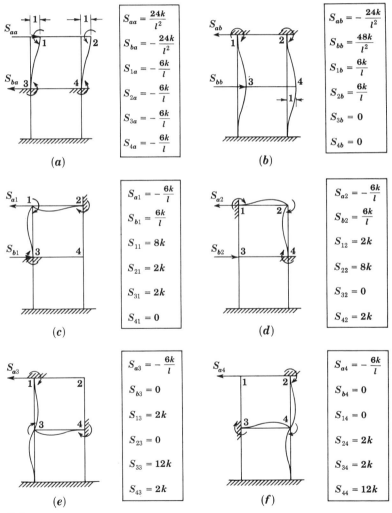

FIG. 10.15

hence, $S_{4a} = -6k/l$. The reader should check the other values of S_{ij} for himself.

Next, in Fig. 10.15b, we make a unit displacement $\delta_b = 1$, that is, a unit horizontal displacement of the middle floor, holding all other displacements equal to zero. Then, as before, using the stiffness coefficients from Fig. 10.14a, we find the external reactions S_{ij} as shown in the figure. Deformation patterns corresponding to $\theta_1 = 1$, $\theta_2 = 1$, $\theta_3 = 1$, $\theta_4 = 1$ and the corresponding induced external forces are shown in Fig. 10.15c, d, e, f. This completes the calculation of the influence coefficients for the frame.

We now assemble these stiffness coefficients in the form of a square matrix, called the *stiffness matrix* for the structure. It is written in the order a, b, 1, 2, 3, 4, both as to rows and as to columns, and becomes

$$
S_{ij} = \begin{bmatrix}
\dfrac{24k}{l^2} & -\dfrac{24k}{l^2} & -\dfrac{6k}{l} & -\dfrac{6k}{l} & -\dfrac{6k}{l} & -\dfrac{6k}{l} \\[2mm]
-\dfrac{24k}{l^2} & \dfrac{48k}{l^2} & \dfrac{6k}{l} & \dfrac{6k}{l} & 0 & 0 \\[2mm]
-\dfrac{6k}{l} & \dfrac{6k}{l} & 8k & 2k & 2k & 0 \\[2mm]
-\dfrac{6k}{l} & \dfrac{6k}{l} & 2k & 8k & 0 & 2k \\[2mm]
-\dfrac{6k}{l} & 0 & 2k & 0 & 12k & 2k \\[2mm]
-\dfrac{6k}{l} & 0 & 0 & 2k & 2k & 12k
\end{bmatrix}
\tag{c}
$$

It will be noted that this is a *symmetric matrix* and that such symmetry is to be expected from the reciprocal theorem.

Having the stiffness influence coefficients as shown in the matrix (c) above, we may now use the principle of superposition to calculate the external forces required to hold the frame in any configuration defined by an arbitrary set of values of the displacements δ_j. For example, the required external force at a would be

$$
F_a = S_{aa}\delta_a + S_{ab}\delta_b + S_{a1}\theta_1 + S_{a2}\theta_2 + S_{a3}\theta_3 + S_{a4}\theta_4
$$

The required external moment at 1 would be

$$
M_1 = S_{1a}\delta_a + S_{1b}\delta_b + S_{11}\theta_1 + S_{12}\theta_2 + S_{13}\theta_3 + S_{14}\theta_4
$$

etc. However, we are looking for a set of values of the displacements that will result from the particular system of external forces shown in Fig. 10.13, i.e., the actual loading on the structure. Thus the true set of displacements is defined by the system of algebraic equations

$$S_{aa}\delta_a + S_{ab}\delta_b + S_{a1}\theta_1 + S_{a2}\theta_2 + S_{a3}\theta_3 + S_{a4}\theta_4 = P_a$$

$$S_{ba}\delta_a + S_{bb}\delta_b + S_{b1}\theta_1 + S_{b2}\theta_2 + S_{b3}\theta_3 + S_{b4}\theta_4 = P_b$$

$$S_{1a}\delta_a + S_{1b}\delta_b + S_{11}\theta_1 + S_{12}\theta_2 + S_{13}\theta_3 + S_{14}\theta_4 = 0$$

$$S_{2a}\delta_a + S_{2b}\delta_b + S_{21}\theta_1 + S_{22}\theta_2 + S_{23}\theta_3 + S_{24}\theta_4 = Qa \qquad (10.17)$$

$$S_{3a}\delta_a + S_{3b}\delta_b + S_{31}\theta_1 + S_{32}\theta_2 + S_{33}\theta_3 + S_{34}\theta_4 = \frac{ql^2}{12}$$

$$S_{4a}\delta_a + S_{4b}\delta_b + S_{41}\theta_1 + S_{42}\theta_2 + S_{43}\theta_3 + S_{44}\theta_4 = -\frac{ql^2}{12}$$

where $ql^2/12$ and $-ql^2/12$ represent, with reversed signs, the fixed-end moments for the girder 34, that is, the *unbalanced moments* at the joints 3 and 4, respectively. Introducing the matrix notation

$$[F_i] = \left\{ P_a \quad P_b \quad 0 \quad Qa \quad \frac{ql^2}{12} \quad -\frac{ql^2}{12} \right\} \qquad (d)$$

which is called the *load matrix*, Eqs. (10.17), in matrix notation, become

$$[S_{ij}][\delta_j] = [F_i] \qquad (10.17a)$$

The three matrices appearing in this equation are defined by expressions (c), (a), and (d), respectively.

Having Eq. (10.17a), the displacements are found from the equation

$$[\delta_j] = [S_{ij}]^{-1}[F_i] \qquad (10.17b)$$

We note that this solution requires the inversion of the stiffness matrix $[S_{ij}]$ [see expression (c)], and it is here that we need the help of the computer.

To illustrate the solution of Eqs. (10.17), let us now introduce the following numerical data:

$$l = 10 \text{ ft} \qquad k = \frac{EI}{l} = 5{,}000 \text{ kip-ft} \qquad a = 2 \text{ ft}$$

$$P_a = 5 \text{ kips} \qquad P_b = 5 \text{ kips} \qquad Q = 2 \text{ kips} \qquad \frac{ql^2}{12} = 8 \text{ kip-ft} \qquad (e)$$

With these data, the stiffness matrix (c) becomes

$$[S_{ij}] = 100 \begin{bmatrix} 12 & -12 & -30 & -30 & -30 & -30 \\ -12 & 24 & 30 & 30 & 0 & 0 \\ -30 & 30 & 400 & 100 & 100 & 0 \\ -30 & 30 & 100 & 400 & 0 & 100 \\ -30 & 0 & 100 & 0 & 600 & 100 \\ -30 & 0 & 0 & 100 & 100 & 600 \end{bmatrix} \qquad (f)$$

and the load matrix (d) becomes

$$[F_i] = \{5 \quad 5 \quad 0 \quad 4 \quad 8 \quad -8\} \tag{g}$$

Then, from Eq. (10.17b), we have[1]

$$
\begin{bmatrix} \delta_a \\ \delta_b \\ \theta_1 \\ \theta_2 \\ \theta_3 \\ \theta_4 \end{bmatrix} = \frac{1}{10,000}
\begin{bmatrix}
34.848 & 15.152 & 0.909 & 0.909 & 1.364 & 1.364 \\
15.152 & 11.515 & 0.091 & 0.091 & 0.636 & 0.636 \\
0.909 & 0.091 & 0.324 & -0.033 & -0.018 & 0.054 \\
0.909 & 0.091 & -0.033 & 0.324 & 0.054 & -0.018 \\
1.364 & 0.636 & -0.018 & 0.054 & 0.234 & 0.020 \\
1.364 & 0.636 & 0.054 & -0.018 & 0.020 & 0.234
\end{bmatrix}
\begin{bmatrix} 5 \\ 5 \\ 0 \\ 4 \\ 8 \\ -8 \end{bmatrix}
$$

$$
= \frac{1}{10,000}
\begin{bmatrix} 253.6 \\ 133.7 \\ 4.296 \\ 6.868 \\ 11.93 \\ 8.216 \end{bmatrix}
$$

The deflections δ_a and δ_b are in feet, whereas the rotations θ_1, θ_2, θ_3, θ_4 are in radians. Thus, $\delta_a = 0.02536$ ft, $\delta_b = 0.01337$ ft, $\theta_1 = 0.0004296$, $\theta_2 = 0.0006868$, $\theta_3 = 0.001193$, $\theta_4 = 0.0008216$.

As already pointed out, once we have these displacements, all end moments in the structure can be readily calculated from the slope-deflection equations (9.6), and the analysis is complete. It will also be noted that the analysis can be made for as many sets of external loads as desired simply by introducing a rectangular load matrix (d) with a column for each set of loads. The stiffness matrix (c) is independent of how the structure is loaded. In this example, we see that the matrix method is superior to any of the methods discussed in Chap. 9, provided that we can have the use of an electronic computer to invert the stiffness matrix (c).

[1] The inversion of the stiffness matrix (f) has been made on the electronic computer.

Chapter 11

Suspension bridges[1]

11.1 PARABOLIC FUNICULAR CURVE

Assume that a uniform and perfectly flexible cable fixed at points A and B (Fig. 11.1) is submitted to the action of distributed vertical load. Then the ordinate y of any point C of the cable is obtained from the equation of moments with respect to C of forces to the left of this point, which gives

$$\mathfrak{M}_x + H \frac{h}{l} x - Hy = 0 \qquad (a)$$

In this equation $\mathfrak{M}_x$ denotes the bending moment at the cross section mn of a simply supported beam of span l and carrying the load acting on the cable. H is the horizontal component of the tensile force in the cable, and h is the difference in elevation of the ends of the cable. In the particular case when

[1] Originally published by S. Timoshenko, *Franklin Inst.*, vol. 235, no. 3, March, and no. 4, April, 1943.

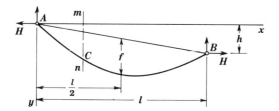

FIG. 11.1

the load of intensity w is uniformly distributed along the horizontal projection of the cable we have

$$\mathfrak{M}_x = \frac{wx}{2}\,(l - x)$$

and Eq. (a) gives

$$y = \frac{wx}{2H}\,(l - x) + \frac{h}{l}\,x \tag{11.1}$$

which shows that the funicular curve in this case is a parabola with vertical axis. If the ends of the cable are on the same level, we obtain

$$y = \frac{wx}{2H}\,(l - x) \tag{11.2}$$

Applying this equation to the mid-point of the cable, where the ordinate of the funicular curve represents the sag f, we obtain

$$f = \frac{wl^2}{8H} \quad \text{or} \quad H = \frac{wl^2}{8f} \tag{11.3}$$

These equations hold also in the more general case shown in Fig. 11.1 if f is measured from the middle of the line AB joining the ends of the cable. In our further discussion the length s of the funicular curve will be required. It is obtained from the equation

$$s = \int_0^l (1 + y'^2)^{\frac{1}{2}}\,dx$$

Developing the expression under the integral sign into a series and substituting expression (11.2) for y, we obtain

$$s = l\left(1 + \frac{8}{3}\frac{f^2}{l^2} - \frac{32}{5}\frac{f^4}{l^4} + \frac{256}{7}\frac{f^6}{l^6} - \cdots\right)$$

In the case of flat parabolic curves, say $f/l \leq \frac{1}{10}$, we can take only the first two terms of the series and use the approximate formula

$$s = l\left(1 + \frac{8}{3}\frac{f^2}{l^2}\right) \tag{11.4}$$

To establish the relation between the change in length of the curve and the change in its sag, we differentiate Eq. (11.4), which gives

$$\Delta s = \frac{16}{3}\frac{f}{l}\,\Delta f \tag{11.5}$$

and

$$\Delta f = \frac{3}{16}\frac{l}{f}\,\Delta s \tag{11.6}$$

To find the change Δf due to a rise in temperature of t^0, we substitute $\Delta s = \epsilon t s$ into Eq. (11.6) and obtain

$$\Delta f = \frac{3}{16}\frac{l^2}{f}\,\epsilon t\left(1 + \frac{8}{3}\frac{f^2}{l^2}\right) \tag{11.7}$$

The elastic elongation of the cable is obtained from the equation

$$\Delta s = \int_0^s \frac{H}{A_c E_c}\frac{ds}{dx}\,ds = \int_0^l \frac{H}{A_c E_c}\,(1 + y'^2)\,dx$$

in which A_c is the cross-sectional area of the cable and E_c its modulus of elasticity. Substituting Eq. (11.2) for y and integrating, we obtain

$$\Delta s = \frac{Hl}{A_c E_c}\left(1 + \frac{16}{3}\frac{f^2}{l^2}\right) \tag{11.8}$$

The corresponding change in sag, from Eq. (11.6), is[1]

$$\Delta f = \frac{3}{16}\frac{Hl^2}{A_c E_c f}\left(1 + \frac{16}{3}\frac{f^2}{l^2}\right) \tag{11.9}$$

11.2 DEFLECTIONS OF UNSTIFFENED SUSPENSION BRIDGES

In the case of a suspension bridge of large span, the dead load uniformly distributed on a horizontal plane is usually many times larger than that uniformly distributed along the cables, and we can assume with sufficient accuracy that the curve of the cable under the action of dead load is a parabola. Let us consider now deflections in the cable produced by live load. As a first example we consider the symmetrical case in which the load of intensity p is uniformly distributed along the distance $2a$ of the span (Fig. 11.2). The solid

[1] In the derivation of Eqs. (11.7) and (11.9) it is assumed that the change Δf in sag is small, and its effect on the horizontal tension H is neglected.

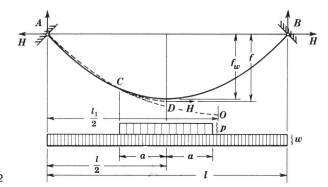

FIG. 11.2

line indicates the shape of the cable under the action of dead load w only. Let f_w and H_w denote the corresponding values of the sag of the cable and of the horizontal component of the tensile force in the cable. The length of the cable then is

$$s = l \left(1 + \frac{8}{3} \frac{f_w^2}{l^2} \right) = l \left(1 + \frac{1}{24} \frac{w^2 l^2}{H_w^2} \right) \tag{a}$$

After application of live load p, the shape of the cable will be as shown by the dashed line ACD. It consists of two parabolic curves AC and CD having a common tangent at C. The curve CD carries the load of intensity $w + p$, and the curve AC carries the load of intensity w. The distance $l_1/2$ of the vertex O of this latter curve from the vertical through A will be found from the condition that the total load along the portion CO of the curve ACO is the same as the total load along the curve CD. Hence,

$$\frac{l_1}{2} = \frac{l}{2} + a \frac{p}{w} \tag{b}$$

We denote by f and H the sag of the cable and the tensile force in the cable at D after application of the live load. One relation between these two quantities is obtained by making the equation of moments with respect to point D, which gives

$$f = \frac{1}{H} \left[\frac{w l^2}{8} + \frac{pa}{2} (l - a) \right] \tag{c}$$

The second equation is obtained from the condition that the length of the cable remains unchanged[1] during application of the live load. Using for the length of the curves AO, CO, and CD the approximate equation (a), the condition of

---

[1] The small influence on the deflection due to elastic elongation of the cable will be discussed later.

inextensibility of the cable is

$$\frac{l}{2}\left(1 + \frac{8}{3}\frac{f_w^2}{l^2}\right) = \frac{l_1}{2}\left(1 + \frac{1}{24}\frac{w^2 l_1^2}{H^2}\right)$$
$$- \frac{a(w+p)}{w}\left[1 + \frac{a^2(w+p)^2}{6H^2}\right] + a\left[1 + \frac{a^2(w+p)^2}{6H^2}\right] \quad (d)$$

Introducing notations

$$\frac{p}{w} = n \qquad\qquad\qquad\qquad\qquad\qquad (e)$$

$$\frac{2a}{l} = z \qquad\qquad\qquad\qquad\qquad\qquad (f)$$

we obtain from Eq. (d)

$$H = H_w \sqrt{1 + 3nz + 3n^2 z^2 - (2n^2 + n)z^3} \qquad (11.10)$$

Substituting this value of H into Eq. (c), we obtain

$$f = f_w \frac{1 + n(2z - z^2)}{\sqrt{1 + 3nz + 3n^2 z^2 - (2n^2 + n)z^3}} \qquad (11.11)$$

To find what portion of the span must be loaded to produce the maximum deflection at the middle of the bridge, we put equal to zero the derivative of expression (11.11) with respect to z, which gives the equation

$$(2n^2 + n)z^4 - 2n(n-1)z^3 - 3(n-1)z^2 - 4z + 1 = 0$$

Solving this equation for several numerical values of n, we obtain for z the values given in Table 11.1. Substituting these values of z into Eq. (11.11), we find the values of the sag f of the cable after application of the live load. The calculated ratios of the change in sag to the initial sag are given in the second line of Table 11.1. In the case of long-span bridges, the ratio p/w is usually

TABLE 11.1

	n				
	0	0.10	0.25	0.50	1.00
z	0.333	0.322	0.306	0.289	0.253
$\dfrac{f - f_w}{f_w}$	0	0.0069	0.0151	0.0281	0.0456
$\dfrac{H}{H_w}$	1	1.047	1.112	1.213	1.379

small,[1] say smaller than 1:4, and it may be seen from Table 11.1 that the deflection at the middle is of the order of one-hundredth of the sag f_w or of one-thousandth of the span l of the bridge. Such deflections can be considered as sufficiently small to make the use of any stiffening truss unnecessary.

To calculate the deflection at the middle due to elastic deformation of the cable produced by live load, we use the approximate formula (11.9) in which $H - H_w$, instead of H, must be substituted. Then, the deflection due to the elongation of the cable is

$$\Delta f = \frac{3}{16} \frac{H_w l}{A_c E_c} \frac{l}{f} \left(\frac{H}{H_w} - 1 \right) \left(1 + \frac{16}{3} \frac{f^2}{l^2} \right) \qquad (g)$$

The values of the ratio H/H_w for various values of n calculated from Eq. (11.10) are given in the last line of Table 11.1. Taking for a numerical example $n = \frac{1}{4}$, $H_w/A_c E_c = 0.002$,* $f/l = 0.1$, we find $H/H_w = 1.112$, and Eq. (g) gives $\Delta f = 0.00044l$. This deflection must be added to the deflection $0.00151l$, calculated from Eq. (11.11), to obtain the total deflection produced by live load.

Let us consider now the deflection of the cable produced by a concentrated force applied at the middle of the span. This force can be considered as a load distributed along a very short distance, and Eq. (11.11) can be used also in this case. From notations (e) and (f) it follows that

$$nz = \frac{2pa}{wl} = \frac{P}{Q} = \psi \qquad (h)$$

where ψ denotes the ratio of the live load P to the dead load Q of the bridge. Substituting ψ for nz and zero for z into Eq. (11.11), we obtain

$$f = f_w \frac{1 + 2\psi}{\sqrt{1 + 3\psi + 3\psi^2}} \qquad (11.12)$$

In the case of long-span bridges, the concentrated load P is small in comparison with the dead load Q of the bridge, and ψ is a small quantity. Developing then the radical in the denominator of expression (11.12) into a series and taking only the first three terms of that series, we obtain

$$\sqrt{1 + 3\psi + 3\psi^2} \approx 1 + \tfrac{3}{2}\psi + \tfrac{3}{8}\psi^2$$

and Eq. (11.12) gives

$$f = f_w(1 + \tfrac{1}{2}\psi - \tfrac{9}{8}\psi^2)$$

Hence, the deflection produced in the cable by a concentrated force applied at

---

[1] In the case of the George Washington Bridge over the Hudson River, this ratio is about 1:6.

* This value depends evidently on the allowable stresses produced by dead load.

the middle is

$$\Delta f = f - f_w = f_w \frac{\psi}{2} (1 - \tfrac{9}{4}\psi) \tag{11.13}$$

Assuming, for example, $\psi = 0.01^*$ and $f_w/l = 0.1$, we obtain

$$\Delta f = 0.000489 l$$

which is a very small deflection. To find the deflection due to elastic elongation of the cable produced by a concentrated force, we calculate first the change $H - H_w$ in the horizontal tensile force. Equation (11.10) in this case gives

$$H = H_w \sqrt{1 + 3\psi + 3\psi^2} \approx H_w(1 + \tfrac{3}{2}\psi + \tfrac{3}{8}\psi^2)$$

and we obtain

$$H - H_w = \tfrac{3}{2}H_w\psi(1 + \tfrac{1}{4}\psi)$$

Substituting this for H in Eq. (11.9), we find

$$\Delta f = \frac{9}{32} \frac{H_w}{A_c E_c} \frac{l}{f} \psi \left(1 + \frac{1}{4}\psi\right)\left(1 + \frac{16}{3}\frac{f_w^2}{l^2}\right) l$$

For a small ψ, which we have in the case of large spans, this deflection is a very small one.

We discussed up to now the symmetrical case of loading (Fig. 11.2). The case of a nonsymmetrical distribution of uniform live load can be treated in a similar manner. Let us consider now a general case of vertical live load acting on a cable with both ends on the same level. The initial ordinates of the funicular curve are obtained from an equation of moments, which gives

$$y = \frac{\mathfrak{M}_w}{H_w} \tag{i}$$

In this equation, $\mathfrak{M}_w$ is the bending moment due to dead load calculated as for a simply supported beam, and H_w is the horizontal component of the tensile force produced in the cable by dead load. If live load is now applied, the bending moment calculated as for a simple beam becomes $\mathfrak{M}_w + \mathfrak{M}_p$, and the horizontal component of cable tension becomes $H_w + H_p$. Denoting by η the vertical deflections of the cable, we obtain, from an equation of moments,

$$y + \eta = \frac{\mathfrak{M}_w + \mathfrak{M}_p}{H_w + H_p} \tag{j}$$

* In the case of the George Washington Bridge, this value of ψ corresponds to a concentrated load of 570 tons.

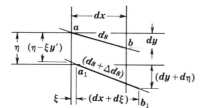

FIG. 11.3

Subtracting Eq. (i) from this equation, we obtain

$$\eta = \frac{\mathfrak{M}_p - H_p y}{H_w + H_p} \tag{11.14}$$

It is seen that the vertical deflections η can be readily calculated, provided that we know the horizontal component H_p of cable tension produced by live load. This latter quantity can be found from geometrical considerations.

Let us consider now an infinitely small element ab of the cable (Fig. 11.3). Under the action of live load this element elongates somewhat and takes a new position $a_1 b_1$. We denote by ξ and η the horizontal and the vertical components of the small displacement of point a. The initial length of the element is obtained from the equation

$$ds^2 = dx^2 + dy^2 \tag{k}$$

The length of the same element after application of live load is found from the equation

$$(ds + \Delta ds)^2 = (dx + d\xi)^2 + (dy + d\eta)^2 \tag{l}$$

in which Δds is the elongation of the element produced by live load. Neglecting the small change in slope of the cable produced by live load,[1] we put

$$\Delta ds = \frac{ds\, H_p}{A_c E_c}\frac{ds}{dx} \tag{m}$$

Since $H_p\, ds/dx$ is that part of the tensile force in the cable which is produced by live load and which is usually much smaller than the part produced by dead load, the unit elongation $\Delta ds/ds$ is usually much smaller than one-thousandth. In such a case $(\Delta ds)^2$ in Eq. (l) can be neglected. For the same reason, and from the observation that the curve of the cable is a flat curve, we neglect also $(d\xi)^2$. Then we obtain, from Eqs. (k) and (l),

$$ds\, \Delta ds = dx\, d\xi + dy\, d\eta + \tfrac{1}{2}(d\eta)^2$$

[1] The error introduced by this omission will be discussed later; see page 535.

which gives

$$d\xi = \frac{ds}{dx} \Delta ds - \frac{dy}{dx} d\eta - \frac{1}{2} \frac{d\eta}{dx} d\eta$$

Substituting expression (*m*) for Δds in this equation and integrating, we obtain

$$\xi = \frac{H_p}{A_c E_c} \int_0^x \left(\frac{ds}{dx}\right)^3 dx - \int_0^x y' \eta' \, dx - \tfrac{1}{2} \int_0^x \eta'^2 \, dx \qquad (11.15)$$

where the primes indicate derivatives with respect to *x*.   With the values of *y'* and *η'* which are encountered in long-span bridges, the value of *ξ* usually does not exceed one-thousandth of *x*.*   At the ends of the cable, *ξ* vanishes, and we obtain from Eq. (11.15)

$$\frac{H_p}{A_c E_c} \int_0^l \left(\frac{ds}{dx}\right)^3 dx = \int_0^l y' \eta' \, dx + \tfrac{1}{2} \int_0^l \eta'^2 \, dx \qquad (n)$$

The integral on the left side of this equation for the assumed parabolic shape of the cable can be readily evaluated, and we obtain

$$\int_0^l \left(\frac{ds}{dx}\right)^3 dx = \int_0^l (1 + y'^2)^{\frac{3}{2}} \, dx = l \left\{ \frac{1}{4} \left(\frac{5}{2} + \frac{16f^2}{l^2} \right) \left(1 + \frac{16f^2}{l^2} \right)^{\frac{1}{2}} \right.$$
$$\left. + \frac{3l}{32f} \ln \left[\frac{4f}{l} + \left(1 + \frac{16f^2}{l^2} \right)^{\frac{1}{2}} \right] \right\} \qquad (o)$$

On the right side of Eq. (*n*), we make integration by parts.   Observing that *η* vanishes at the ends of the cable, and using Eq. (11.2), we obtain

$$\int_0^l y' \eta' \, dx = \left| y' \eta \right|_0^l - \int_0^l y'' \eta \, dx = \frac{w}{H_w} \int_0^l \eta \, dx$$
$$\tfrac{1}{2} \int_0^l \eta'^2 \, dx = \tfrac{1}{2} \left| \eta' \eta \right|_0^l - \tfrac{1}{2} \int_0^l \eta'' \eta \, dx = - \tfrac{1}{2} \int_0^l \eta'' \eta \, dx \qquad (p)$$

Substituting expressions (*o*) and (*p*) into Eq. (*n*) and denoting the integral (*o*) by *L*, we obtain

$$\frac{H_p}{A_c E_c} L = \frac{w}{H_w} \int_0^l \eta \, dx - \tfrac{1}{2} \int_0^l \eta'' \eta \, dx \qquad (11.16)$$

This equation, together with Eq. (11.14), gives the system of equations sufficient for calculation of vertical deflections of the cable.

---

* The maximum value of *ξ/x* occurs near the supports where *η'* and *y'* usually have their largest numerical values.

Let us apply these equations to the above-discussed case shown in Fig. 11.2. In this case

$$\mathfrak{M}_p = pax \qquad x < \frac{l}{2} - a$$

$$\mathfrak{M}_p = pax - \tfrac{1}{2}p\left(x - \frac{l}{2} + a\right)^2 \qquad \frac{l}{2} + a > x > \frac{l}{2} - a$$

$$\eta = \frac{1}{H_w + H_p}\left[pax - \frac{w}{2H_w}x(l - x)H_p\right] \qquad x < \frac{l}{2} - a$$

$$\eta = \frac{1}{H_w + H_p}\left[pax - \tfrac{1}{2}p\left(x - \frac{l}{2} + a\right)^2 - \frac{w}{2H_w}x(l - x)H_p\right]$$

$$\frac{l}{2} + a > x > \frac{l}{2} - a$$

$$\eta'' = \frac{wH_p}{H_w(H_w + H_p)} \qquad x < \frac{l}{2} - a$$

$$\eta'' = \frac{-pH_w + wH_p}{H_w(H_w + H_p)} \qquad \frac{l}{2} + a > x > \frac{l}{2} - a$$

Substituting these expressions into Eq. (11.16), assuming that the cable is inextensible, and introducing our previous notations (e) and (f), we obtain, for calculation of H_p, the following quadratic equation:

$$\left(\frac{H_p}{H_w}\right)^2 + 2\left(\frac{H_p}{H_w}\right) - 3nz - 3n^2z^2 + nz^3 + 2n^2z^3 = 0$$

which gives for $H_p + H_w$ the same value as obtained from the previous Eq. (11.10).

Sometimes Eq. (11.16) is simplified by omitting the second term on the right side and taking

$$\frac{H_p}{A_cE_c} L = \frac{w}{H_w}\int_0^l \eta \, dx \tag{11.17}$$

Considering an inextensible cable and substituting for η its expression (11.14), we obtain, from Eq. (11.17),

$$H_p = \frac{\int_0^l \mathfrak{M}_p \, dx}{\int_0^l y \, dx} = \frac{3}{2fl}\int_0^l \mathfrak{M}_p \, dx \tag{11.18}$$

In the case shown in Fig. 11.2, Eq. (11.18) gives

$$H_p = \frac{nH_w}{2}(3z - z^3) \tag{11.18a}$$

Applying this approximate formula to the numerical examples given in Table 11.1, we find that the results obtained are in good agreement with those given in the last line of the table.

11.3 FUNDAMENTAL EQUATIONS FOR STIFFENED SUSPENSION BRIDGES

It is seen from the preceding discussion that the deflection of the cable produced by live load is small only in the case of heavy long-span bridges. Otherwise, the deflections may be considerable. In order to reduce these deflections, stiffening trusses are usually introduced. A simplest structure of this kind, shown in Fig. 11.4, consists of a single-span cable stiffened by a simply supported truss of constant cross section. It is assumed that by a proper assembly, the dead load of the structure, uniformly distributed along the span, is entirely transmitted to the cable, which takes the parabolic form shown in the figure by a solid line. A live load produces deflection of the cable and of the truss as indicated in the figure by dashed lines. We assume that both these deflections are equal.[1] The spacing of hangers is assumed small as compared with the length of span so that the action of the hangers on the cable and on the truss can be considered as continuously distributed along the span.

Let us consider first the case where the structure is carrying only dead load. The truss does not suffer bending in this case, and the equation of moments for the forces to the left of a cross section mn (Fig. 11.4) then gives

$$\mathfrak{M}_w - H_w y = 0 \qquad\qquad (a)$$

When live load is applied and deflections η are produced, there will be bending

[1] That is, the elongation of the hangers and their small inclination to the vertical during deformation are neglected in this discussion.

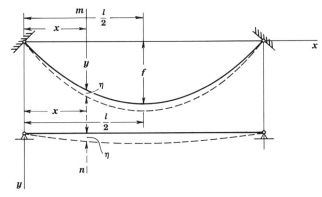

FIG. 11.4

moment M acting in a cross section mn of the truss, and the equation of moments for the forces to the left of this cross section is

$$\mathfrak{M}_w + \mathfrak{M}_p - (H_w + H_p)(y + \eta) - M = 0 \qquad (b)$$

Subtracting Eq. (a) from Eq. (b), we obtain

$$M = \mathfrak{M}_p - (H_w + H_p)\eta - H_p y \qquad (11.19)$$

From this equation, the bending moment at any cross section of the truss can be calculated provided the horizontal component of the tensile force in the cable and deflection η are known.

In the case of very rigid stiffening trusses, the deflections η can be neglected, and we obtain

$$M = \mathfrak{M}_p - H_p y \qquad (11.20)$$

This bending moment is independent of deflections and can be evaluated by the methods used in the analysis of rigid statically indeterminate structures. Investigations show that the stiffening trusses in large-span bridges are usually very flexible; and in calculation of bending moments, recourse must be had to the more complete equation (11.19), which requires the calculation of deflections η* of the truss. Using for the truss the differential equation of the deflection curve of a beam

$$EI \frac{d^2\eta}{dx^2} = -M$$

we obtain, by using expression (11.19), the following equation for calculating η:

$$EI \frac{d^2\eta}{dx^2} - (H_w + H_p)\eta = H_p y - \mathfrak{M}_p \qquad (11.21)$$

The quantity $\mathfrak{M}_p$ in this equation can be readily calculated for any distribution of live load over the span. The quantities y and H_w are given by Eqs. (11.2) and (11.3), and only the quantity H_p is unknown. It depends on the deflections η, and for its determination Eq. (11.16) of the preceding article is used. Equation (11.21), together with Eq. (11.16), completely defined the deflections of the stiffening truss. In the solution of these equations, the trial-and-error method is used. We assume a certain value for H_p, for instance the value obtained for the unstiffened cable, and with this value solve Eq. (11.21). The obtained expression for η we substitute in the integrals on the right side of Eq. (11.16). Since H_p was taken arbitrarily, the result of this substitution usually will not equal the left side of Eq. (11.16), and it will be necessary to

---

* J. Melan was the first who indicated the importance of considering deflections in analysis of suspension bridges; see his book "Theorie der eisernen Bogenbrücken und der Hänge-brücken," Leipzig, 1906; English translation by D. B. Steinman, Chicago, 1913. Melan's theory has been widely used in analysis of large-span suspension bridges in this country.

repeat the calculation with a new assumed value of H_p. These trial calculations are continued far enough to obtain H_p with a sufficient accuracy. The procedure of this calculation with all details will be discussed in the next two articles.

Now we shall discuss how accurate Eqs. (11.16) and (11.21) are and what is the magnitude of errors introduced in these equations by neglecting various small quantities during their derivation. We begin with the discussion of elongation of the cable. In the derivation of Eq. (*m*) of the preceding article, we neglected the change in the deflection of the cable produced by live load. Taking into account this additional deflection, we obtain

$$\Delta ds = \frac{ds\, H_p}{A_c E_c}\,[1 + (y' + \eta')^2]^{\frac{1}{2}} \approx \frac{ds\, H_p}{A_c E_c}\left(\frac{ds}{dx} + y'\eta' + \tfrac{1}{2}\eta'^2\right)$$

Using this more accurate expression for Δds, we obtain, instead of Eq. (*n*) of the preceding article, the following equation:

$$\frac{H_p}{A_c E_c}\int_0^l \left(\frac{ds}{dx}\right)^3 dx = \int_0^l y'\eta'\, dx + \tfrac{1}{2}\int_0^l \eta'^2\, dx$$

$$- \frac{H_p}{A_c E_c}\int_0^l \left(\frac{ds}{dx}\right)^2 (y'\eta' + \tfrac{1}{2}\eta'^2)\, dx$$

The last term on the right side of this equation represents the required correction. Since $H_p/A_c E_c$ is usually smaller than one-thousandth, we conclude that the relative error in the magnitude of the right side of Eq. (*n*) due to the use of the approximate expression (*m*) is of the order of one-thousandth, which can be disregarded in a practical analysis.

Let us consider now the effect on the bending moment in the truss of horizontal displacements ξ in the cable, which were entirely disregarded in our previous derivation. To take these displacements into account, we observe that the vertical distances between the solid-line and dashed-line curves, marked by η in Fig. 11.4, are more accurately equal to $\eta - \xi\, dy/dx$, as shown in Fig. 11.3. We note also that each element of the load transmitted to the cable, and approximately equal to $-dx\,(H_w + H_p)\, d^2y/dx^2$, has a horizontal displacement ξ, which produces the change in moment of this element equal to

$$-\xi\, dx\,(H_w + H_p)\,\frac{d^2y}{dx^2}$$

With these two considerations we obtain, instead of expression (11.19), the following more accurate value of the bending moment:

$$M = \mathfrak{M}_p - (H_w + H_p)\eta - H_p y + (H_w + H_p)\xi\,\frac{dy}{dx}$$

$$- (H_w + H_p)\int_0^x \frac{d^2y}{dx^2}\,\xi\, dx \quad (11.22)$$

The required correction in the bending moment is represented by the last two terms in this expression. To get a clearer idea regarding the magnitude of this correction, let us calculate the intensity of the load acting on the truss. This intensity is obtained as the second derivative with respect to x of the bending moment (11.22), taken with opposite sign, which gives

$$-\frac{d^2M}{dx^2} = p + H_p \frac{d^2y}{dx^2} + (H_w + H_p) \frac{d^2\eta}{dx^2}$$
$$- (H_w + H_p) \frac{d}{dx} \left(\frac{d\xi}{dx} \frac{dy}{dx} \right) \quad (11.23)$$

The last term in this expression represents the correction due to horizontal displacements of the cable.

The same expression for the intensity of the load on the truss is obtained also in another manner by subtracting the intensity of the upward pull of the hangers on the truss from the combined intensity $w + p$ of the downward loading. The intensity of the vertical loading on the cable at a distance x from the left support is

$$q = - (H_w + H_p) \frac{d^2}{dx^2} \left(y + \eta - \xi \frac{dy}{dx} \right) \quad (c)$$

The upward pull transmitted to a length dx of the truss at x is the downward pull on a horizontal length $dx\,(1 + d\xi/dx)$ at $x + \xi$ on the deflected cable. Hence, the required intensity of the load on the truss is

$$w + p - \left(q + \xi \frac{dq}{dx} \right) \left(1 + \frac{d\xi}{dx} \right) = w + p - q - \frac{d}{dx} (q\xi) \quad (d)$$

Substituting for q its expression (c) and neglecting small terms of higher order, we obtain the previous expression (11.23).

Substituting for ξ the first two terms in expression (11.15) into the last term of expression (11.23), we find that the correction in the intensity of the load on the truss, due to horizontal displacements ξ, is

$$- (H_w + H_p) \frac{d}{dx} (\xi'y')$$
$$= - (H_w + H_p) \left[-\frac{w}{H_w} \left(\frac{H_p}{A_cE_c} s'^3 - y'\eta' \right) \right.$$
$$\left. + y' \left(\frac{3H_p}{A_cE_c} s'^2s'' + \frac{w}{H_w} \eta' - y'\eta'' \right) \right]$$

where primes denote the first derivative with respect to x.

For flat curves we can take

$$s' \approx 1 + \tfrac{1}{2}y'^2 \qquad s'' \approx - \frac{w}{H_w} y'$$

which gives

$$- (H_w + H_p) \frac{d}{dx} (\xi' y')$$

$$= \frac{(H_w + H_p)w}{H_w} \left[\frac{H_p}{A_c E_c} (s'^3 + 3s'^2 y'^2) - 2y' \eta' \right]$$

$$+ (H_w + H_p)\eta'' y'^2 \qquad (e)$$

From our previous discussion, we conclude that the first term on the right side of this equation is of the order of one-thousandth of w and can be neglected in practical calculation. The second term, $(H_w + H_p)\eta'' y'^2$, can also be considered as small in comparison with the term $(H_w + H_p)\eta''$ representing the effect on the intensity of the load of vertical deflections of the cable. Hence, the total effect of horizontal displacements of the cable can be considered as small and usually can be neglected in practical calculations.

In a similar manner the effect of extension of hangers on the magnitude of bending moment can be investigated. The calculation shows that this effect is also very small and can be neglected.[1]

Let us consider now the effect of shearing force on deflection of a stiffening truss. For this purpose we take the differential equation of the deflection curve in the following form:

$$EI \frac{d^2\eta}{dx^2} = -M + mEI \frac{d^2 M}{dx^2} \qquad (f)$$

in which the second term on the right side represents the effect of shearing force on deflection. The magnitude of the factor m in this term depends on the kind of structure used for the stiffening truss. In the case of an I beam, we take

$$m = \frac{1}{A_w G} \qquad (g)$$

where A_w is the cross-sectional area of the web of the beam and G is the modulus of elasticity of the material in shear.

In the case of a truss, as shown in Fig. 11.5, we take[2]

$$m = \frac{1}{A_d E \sin \varphi \cos^2 \varphi} \qquad (h)$$

where A_d is the sum of cross-sectional areas of the two diagonals in a panel.

[1] Such calculations were made by F. E. Turneaure; see Johnson, Bryan, and Turneaure, "Modern Framed Structures," 9th ed., vol. 2, p. 299, John Wiley & Sons, Inc., New York, 1917.
[2] See S. P. Timoshenko and J. M. Gere, "Theory of Elastic Stability," 2d ed., p. 137, McGraw-Hill Book Company, New York, 1961.

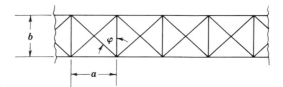

FIG. 11.5

Substituting for M in Eq. (f) its expression (11.19), we obtain

$$EI[1 + m(H_w + H_p)] \frac{d^2\eta}{dx^2} - (H_w + H_p)\eta$$

$$= -\mathfrak{M}_p + H_p y - mEI \left(p - \frac{H_p}{H_w} w \right) \quad (11.24)$$

This equation is of the same form as Eq. (11.21), and we see that the effect of shearing force can be readily taken into account provided the factor m is known.

In the derivation of Eq. (11.16) the elastic elongation of the cable alone was considered. The equation can be readily generalized and extended to those cases in which an elongation of the cable depends also on a change in its temperature. Instead of Eq. (m) of the preceding article, we use in such a case the equation

$$\Delta ds = \frac{ds H_s}{A_c E_c} \frac{ds}{dx} + ds \, \epsilon t \quad (i)$$

where ϵ is the coefficient of thermal expansion, and H_s is the horizontal component of the tensile force produced in the cable by the combined action of live load and temperature change. Using Eq. (i) and introducing the notation

$$\int_0^l \left(\frac{ds}{dx} \right)^2 dx = L_1$$

we obtain

$$\frac{H_s}{A_c E_c} L + \epsilon t L_1 = \frac{w}{H_w} \int_0^l \eta \, dx - \frac{1}{2} \int_0^l \eta'' \eta \, dx \quad (11.25)$$

This equation, instead of Eq. (11.16), must be used if we are considering a simultaneous action of live load and temperature change.

11.4 ANALYSIS OF STIFFENING TRUSSES

Let us begin with the case in which a single concentrated load P is acting on the truss. Making the second derivative of Eq. (11.21), we find that deflections

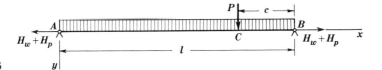

FIG. 11.6

of the truss in this case are the same as those occurring in a simply supported beam subjected to the combined action of an axial tensile force $H_w + H_p$, of a uniformly distributed upward lateral load of intensity $H_p w / H_w$, and a concentrated load P as shown in Fig. 11.6. In such a case, with the notation

$$\frac{H_w + H_p}{EI} = k^2 \tag{11.26}$$

the deflections produced by the load P in the part of the beam to the left of this load $(x < l - c)$ are[1]

$$\eta_1 = -\frac{P}{H_w + H_p} \frac{\sinh kc}{k \sinh kl} \sinh kx + \frac{Pcx}{(H_w + H_p)l} \tag{11.27}$$

For the portion of the beam to the right of the load $(x > l - c)$, the deflections are

$$\eta_1 = -\frac{P}{H_w + H_p} \frac{\sinh k(l - c)}{k \sinh kl} \sinh k(l - x)$$
$$+ \frac{P(l - c)(l - x)}{(H_w + H_p)l} \tag{11.28}$$

The deflections produced by the upward pull are[2]

$$\eta_2 = -\frac{H_p}{H_w} \frac{wl^2}{H_w + H_p} \left[\frac{\cosh (kl/2 - kx)}{k^2 l^2 \cosh (kl/2)} - \frac{1}{k^2 l^2} + \frac{x(l - x)}{2l^2} \right] \tag{11.29}$$

The total deflections η of the truss are obtained by superimposing deflections η_1 on deflections η_2.

To determine the magnitude of tension H_p, entering into Eqs. (11.27) to (11.29), we use Eq. (11.17), which is obtained from Eq. (11.16) by omitting the second term on the right side.[3] Substituting expressions (11.27) to (11.29) into Eq. (11.17) and performing the integration, we obtain, for calculating

[1] See S. Timoshenko, "Strength of Materials," 3d ed., vol. II, p. 42, D. Van Nostrand Company, Inc., Princeton, N.J., 1956.
[2] See *ibid.*, p. 43.
[3] This term usually has only a small effect on the magnitude of H_p. This effect will be discussed in the next article.

H_p, the equation

$$H_p \left[\frac{H_w + H_p}{A_c E_c} \frac{L}{l} + \frac{1}{12} \left(\frac{8f}{l} \right)^2 \left(1 - \frac{12}{k^2 l^2} + \frac{24}{k^3 l^3} \tanh \frac{kl}{2} \right) \right]$$

$$= P \frac{8f}{l} \left\{ \frac{1}{2} \frac{c}{l} \left(1 - \frac{c}{l} \right) - \frac{1}{k^2 l^2 \sinh kl} \right.$$

$$\left. \times [\sinh kl - \sinh kc - \sinh k(l - c)] \right\} \quad (11.30)$$

In the case of long-span bridges the quantity kl is usually a number of considerable magnitude,[1] and all terms in Eq. (11.30) containing k are small and, in a first approximation, can be neglected. The term $(H_w + H_p)/A_c E_c$ can also be neglected as very small, and we obtain

$$H_p = \frac{3}{4} P \frac{l}{f} \frac{c}{l} \left(1 - \frac{c}{l} \right)$$

For $c = l/2$, this gives

$$H_p = \frac{3}{2} P \frac{l}{8f}$$

We obtain the same result for small ψ from Eq. (11.10), which indicates that by omitting all terms containing k, we obtain, from Eq. (11.30), for H_p the same value as in the case of an unstiffened suspension bridge.

Equation (11.30) can be used for calculating the influence line for H_p. In such a case we assume that P is a small load moving along the truss. Then H_p can be neglected in comparison with H_w, $kl \approx l \sqrt{H_w/EI}$, and we obtain

$$H_p = P \frac{8f}{l} \frac{\dfrac{1}{2} \dfrac{c}{l} \left(1 - \dfrac{c}{l} \right) - \dfrac{\sinh kl - \sinh kc - \sinh k(l - c)}{k^2 l^2 \sinh kl}}{\dfrac{H_w}{A_c E_c} \dfrac{L}{l} + \dfrac{1}{12} \left(\dfrac{8f}{l} \right)^2 \left(1 - \dfrac{12}{k^2 l^2} + \dfrac{24}{k^3 l^3} \tanh \dfrac{kl}{2} \right)}$$

The magnitude of H_p depends not only on position of the load P but also on the quantities kl, $H_w/A_c E_c$, and f/l. In Fig. 11.7a is shown the influence line for H_p calculated on the assumption that $kl = 10$, $H_w/A_c E_c = 0.002$, and $f/l = 0.1$. For comparison there are shown in the same figure by dashed line the values of H_p for a nonstiffened cable. It is seen that for the assumed value of kl the stiffening truss has only a small effect on the magnitude of H_p.

Having H_p and using Eqs. (11.27) to (11.29), we can calculate the deflections of the truss. In Fig. 11.7b the deflection curve is constructed for the case where $c = 0.75l$. Since H_p is neglected in comparison with H_w, the deflections

[1] In the case of the Ambassador Bridge (Detroit), $kl = 9.52$. In the case of the George Washington Bridge, after placing the planned stiffening truss, $kl = 35$.

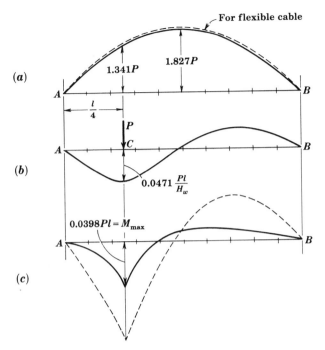

FIG. 11.7

become proportional to P, and the principle of superposition holds. The reciprocal theorem also holds, and the deflection curve in Fig. 11.7b is the influence line for the deflection at the quarter point C. Using this line, we can readily construct the influence line for bending moment at C. Neglecting H_p in comparison with H_w in expression (11.19), we obtain

$$M = \mathfrak{M}_p - H_p y - H_w \eta$$

The first two terms on the right side of this equation give the bending moment if the influence of deflections of the truss is disregarded. The corresponding influence line is given by the dashed line in Fig. 11.7c. The last term on the right side gives the effect of deflection of the truss on the bending moment. Taking this into account, we obtain the full line in Fig. 11.7c. It is seen that. in this case the deflections have a very large effect on the bending moment and cannot be disregarded.

In using the derived influence line for calculation of bending moment, it must be noted that the increase of tension in the cable produced by live load was neglected. Hence, using this influence line will give a satisfactory result only if the live load is very small in comparison with the dead load. If it is not small, the influence line will not give an accurate value of the moment and can be used with sufficient accuracy only for a determination of the limits

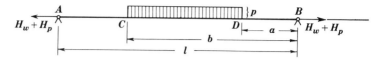

FIG. 11.8

within which the live load must be distributed to produce the maximum value of the moment.[1] Calculations of deflections and moments must then be accomplished by using Eqs. (11.27) to (11.30) in which H_p has been retained.

Assume, for example, that live load is distributed as shown in Fig. 11.8. Then, the equation for calculating H_p is obtained from Eq. (11.30) by substituting $p\,dc$, instead of P, and integrating the right side of the equation from $c = a$ to $c = b$, which gives

$$H_p \left[\frac{H_w + H_p}{A_c E_c} \frac{L}{l} + \frac{1}{12} \left(\frac{8f}{l} \right)^2 \left(1 - \frac{12}{k^2 l^2} + \frac{24}{k^3 l^3} \tanh \frac{kl}{2} \right) \right]$$

$$= 8fp \left\{ \frac{3l(b^2 - a^2) - 2(b^3 - a^3)}{12 l^3} - \frac{1}{k^2 l^2} \left[\frac{b - a}{l} \right. \right.$$

$$\left. \left. - \frac{\cosh kb - \cosh ka + \cosh k(l - a) - \cosh k(l - b)}{kl \sinh kl} \right] \right\}$$

$$(11.31)$$

The value of H_p can now be calculated from this equation by successive approximations. We start by omitting all terms containing k, and we neglect also the term with $(H_w + H_p)/A_c E_c$. In this way, we obtain the first approximation for H_p, which will be close to the true value if kl is of considerable magnitude,[2] say $kl = 10$. To get better accuracy, we use the approximate value of H_p to calculate k from Eq. (11.26) and then substitute this value of k into Eq. (11.31), which gives then the second approximation for H_p, which is usually accurate enough for practical application. If necessary, further approximations can be calculated in the same manner. When H_p has been calculated, the deflection curve will be found by using Eqs. (11.27) to (11.29) together with the method of superposition. To find the deflections for the portion AC of the truss (Fig. 11.8) we substitute $p\,dc$ for P into Eq. (11.27) and integrate from $c = a$ to $c = b$. This gives (for $x < l - b$)

$$\eta_1 = \frac{pl}{H_w + H_p} \int_a^b \left(- \frac{\sinh kc}{kl \sinh kl} \sinh kx + \frac{cx}{l^2} \right) dc$$

$$= \frac{pl^2}{H_w + H_p} \left[\frac{\cosh ka - \cosh kb}{k^2 l^2 \sinh kl} \sinh kx + \frac{(b^2 - a^2)x}{2l^3} \right]$$

[1] The use of influence lines in analysis of suspension bridges was first proposed by T. Godard, *Ann. ponts chaussées*, ser. 7, vol. 8, p. 105, 1894.
[2] An example of such calculation is given in a paper by A. A. Jakkula, *Publ. Intern. Assoc. Bridge Structural Eng.*, vol. 4, p. 333, 1936.

To obtain the complete deflection, we superimpose on this deflection the deflection η_2 produced by the upward pull [Eq. (11.29)], giving, for $x < l - b$,

$$\eta = \eta_1 + \eta_2 = \frac{pl^2}{H_w + H_p}\left[\frac{\cosh ka - \cosh kb}{k^2 l^2 \sinh kl}\sinh kx + \frac{(b^2 - a^2)x}{2l^3}\right]$$
$$- \frac{H_p w l^2}{H_w(H_w + H_p)}\left[\frac{\cosh (kl/2 - kx)}{k^2 l^2 \cosh (kl/2)} - \frac{1}{k^2 l^2} + \frac{x(l - x)}{2l^2}\right]$$

In a similar manner the deflections in the portions CD and DB of the truss can be obtained. A simpler method of calculating deflections is shown in the next article.

If a combined action of live load and temperature change is considered, the equation for calculation of the additional horizontal tension H_s is obtained by substituting into Eq. (11.31) H_s for H_p and $H_s L/A_c E_c + \epsilon t L_1$ for $H_p L/A_c E_c$ (see page 538).

11.5 APPLICATION OF TRIGONOMETRIC SERIES IN CALCULATING DEFLECTIONS

The deflection curve of a stiffening truss can be obtained also by using trigonometric series.[1] In applying this method, not only is the calculation of deflections simplified, but also the calculation of H_p can be made with better accuracy since, without much complication, we can use Eq. (11.16) instead of the simplified Eq. (11.17) used in the preceding article. Let us begin with the case of one concentrated force acting on the stiffening truss (Fig. 11.6). The differential equation (11.21) in this case becomes, for $x < l - c$,

$$EI \frac{d^2\eta}{dx^2} - (H_w + H_p)\eta = H_p \frac{4f}{l^2} x(l - x) - \frac{Pcx}{l} \tag{a}$$

and, for $x > l - c$,

$$EI \frac{d^2\eta}{dx^2} - (H_w + H_p)\eta = H_p \frac{4f}{l^2} x(l - x) - \frac{P(l - c)(l - x)}{l}$$
$$\tag{b}$$

The right sides of these equations can be represented for the entire length l of the truss by the trigonometric series

$$b_1 \sin \frac{\pi x}{l} + b_2 \sin \frac{2\pi x}{l} + b_3 \sin \frac{3\pi x}{l} + \cdots \tag{c}$$

the coefficients $b_1, b_2, b_3, \ldots$ of which must be calculated in the usual way

[1] See S. Timoshenko, *Trans. ASCE*, vol. 94, p. 377, 1930.

from the formula

$$b_m = \frac{2}{l} \left[H_p \frac{4f}{l^2} \int_0^l x(l - x) \sin \frac{m\pi x}{l} \, dx \right.$$

$$\left. - \frac{Pc}{l} \int_0^{l-c} x \sin \frac{m\pi x}{l} \, dx - \frac{P(l - c)}{l} \int_{l-c}^l (l - x) \sin \frac{m\pi x}{l} \, dx \right]$$

which gives

$$b_m = \frac{16 H_p f}{m^3 \pi^3} (1 - \cos m\pi) - \frac{2Pl}{m^2 \pi^2} \sin \frac{m\pi (l - c)}{l} \tag{d}$$

Since the series (c) is applicable for the entire length of the truss, the two equations (a) and (b) can now be replaced by one equation,

$$EI \frac{d^2\eta}{dx^2} - (H_w + H_p)\eta = \sum_{m=1}^{\infty} b_m \sin \frac{m\pi x}{l} \tag{e}$$

The solution of this equation, satisfying the end conditions, will now be taken in the form of the series

$$\eta = \sum_{m=1}^{\infty} a_m \sin \frac{m\pi x}{l} \tag{f}$$

Substituting this series into Eq. (e) and equating, for each value of m, the coefficients of $\sin (m\pi x/l)$, we obtain

$$a_m = - \frac{b_m l^2}{EI m^2 \pi^2 + (H_w + H_p) l^2}$$

and the series (f) becomes

$$\eta = - \sum_{m=1}^{\infty} \frac{b_m l^2 \sin (m\pi x/l)}{EI(m^2 \pi^2 + k^2 l^2)}$$

where k^2, as before, denotes the value of the ratio $(H_w + H_p)/EI$. Substituting expression (d) for b_m, we finally represent the deflection of the truss by the following series:

$$\eta = - \frac{32 H_p f l^2}{\pi^3 EI} \sum_{m=1,3,5,\ldots}^{\infty} \frac{\sin (m\pi x/l)}{m^3 (m^2 \pi^2 + k^2 l^2)}$$

$$+ \frac{2Pl^3}{EI\pi^2} \sum_{m=1,2,3,\ldots}^{\infty} \frac{1}{m^2 (m^2 \pi^2 + k^2 l^2)} \sin \frac{m\pi (l - c)}{l} \frac{\sin m\pi x}{l}$$

$$\tag{11.32}$$

This is a rapidly converging series, and the calculation of deflections requires less time than in the case when we are using Eqs. (11.27) to (11.29). Applying this series to the numerical example of the preceding article (Fig. 11.7b), we have

$$c = 0.75l \qquad H_p = 1.341P \qquad k^2 \approx \frac{H_w}{EI} \qquad kl = 10 \qquad f = 0.1l$$

and the series (11.32) gives the deflection curve

$$
\begin{aligned}
\eta = -0.1384 \frac{Pl}{H_w} \Big(& 0.9102 \sin \frac{\pi x}{l} + 0.0196 \sin \frac{3\pi x}{l} \\
& + 0.0023 \sin \frac{5\pi x}{l} + \cdots \Big) + 0.2026 \frac{Pl}{H_w} \Big(0.6434 \sin \frac{\pi x}{l} \\
& + 0.1793 \sin \frac{2\pi x}{l} + 0.0416 \sin \frac{3\pi x}{l} - 0.0082 \sin \frac{5\pi x}{l} \\
& - 0.0064 \sin \frac{6\pi x}{l} - 0.0024 \sin \frac{7\pi x}{l} - \cdots \Big) \quad (g)
\end{aligned}
$$

The number of terms which are shown in the series (g) is sufficient to get values of the deflections with an error smaller than 1 percent.

The obtained deflection curve is also the influence line for the deflection at the quarter point C in Fig. 11.7b. Using it as explained in the preceding article, we can determine the portion of the truss which must be covered with live load to produce maximum bending moment at C.

The equation of the deflection curve produced by live load uniformly distributed along a portion of the truss (Fig. 11.8) can be readily obtained from Eq. (11.32); it is only necessary to substitute therein $p\,dc$ for P and integrate from $c = a$ to $c = b$. In this manner we obtain

$$
\begin{aligned}
\eta = -&\frac{32 H_p f l^2}{\pi^3 EI} \sum_{m=1,3,5,\ldots}^{\infty} \frac{\sin (m\pi x/l)}{m^3 (m^2 \pi^2 + k^2 l^2)} \\
+ &\frac{2pl^4}{\pi^3 EI} \sum_{m=1,2,3,\ldots}^{\infty} \frac{\cos \dfrac{m\pi (l-b)}{l} - \cos \dfrac{m\pi (l-a)}{l}}{m^3 (m^2 \pi^2 + k^2 l^2)} \sin \frac{m\pi x}{l}
\end{aligned}
$$

Observing that

$$\frac{8 f H_w}{l^2} = w$$

and introducing notations

$$\frac{H_p}{H_w} = \beta \qquad \frac{l - b}{l} = \alpha_1 \qquad \frac{l - a}{l} = \alpha_2 \qquad (11.33)$$

we represent the deflection curve by the series

$$\eta = \sum_{m=1}^{\infty} a_m \sin \frac{m\pi x}{l} \qquad (11.34)$$

in which

$$a_m = \frac{2l^4}{\pi^3 EI} \frac{-\beta w(1 - \cos m\pi) + p(\cos m\pi\alpha_1 - \cos m\pi\alpha_2)}{m^3(m^2\pi^2 + k^2 l^2)} \qquad (11.35)$$

The calculation of these coefficients requires the values of β and of k which depend, as we see from notations (11.26) and (11.33), on the horizontal tension H_p produced by live load p. To get the equation for calculating H_p, we substitute the series (11.34) into Eq. (11.16), which gives

$$\frac{H_p L}{A_c E_c} = \frac{w}{H_w} \frac{2l}{\pi} \left(a_1 + \frac{a_3}{3} + \frac{a_5}{5} + \cdots \right)$$

$$+ \frac{\pi^2}{4l} (a_1^2 + 2^2 a_2^2 + 3^2 a_3^2 + \cdots) \qquad (11.36)$$

This equation can be solved by successive approximations. As a first approximation we can take for H_p the value corresponding to an unstiffened and inextensible cable, as was done in the preceding article. With this approximate value of H_p, we calculate β and k and find the coefficients $a_1, a_2, \ldots$ from Eq. (11.35). Substituting these values into the right side of Eq. (11.36), we shall find that the equation is not satisfied. We then repeat the calculation with a somewhat smaller value for H_p. From two such calculations a sufficiently accurate value of H_p can be obtained by interpolation. Calculations of this kind were made for the Ambassador Bridge in Detroit,[1] and comparison of the obtained values of H_p with those found from the simplified Eq. (11.17) showed that the effect of the second term on the right side of Eq. (11.36) is small. It was of the order of 1 percent for a live load $p = 2,000$ lb/ft covering half of the span. This term takes care of nonuniformity in the distribution of vertical pull transmitted to the cable, and it must become more important in the cases of more concentrated actions of live load. When the tension H_p, from Eq. (11.36), and the deflections η, from the series (11.34), have been found, we calculate the maximum bending moment at C by using Eq. (11.19).

[1] See Jakkula, *op. cit.*

In the case of combined action of live load and temperature change, the method of series can also be used. In such a case it will only be necessary to put on the left side of Eq. (11.36) $H_s L/A_c E_c + \epsilon t L_1$, instead of $H_p L/A_c E_c$, and use the notations $\beta = H_s/H_w$ and $k^2 = (H_w + H_s)/EI$ in formula (11.35).

11.6 THREE-SPAN SUSPENSION BRIDGES WITH SIMPLY SUPPORTED STIFFENING TRUSSES

The methods of analysis of a single-span suspension bridge discussed in the two preceding articles can be readily extended to the case of several spans if each span is stiffened by a separate simply supported truss. Let us consider, for example, a symmetrical three-span bridge as shown in Fig. 11.9. We assume that the cable can slide without friction at the tops of the towers or that the towers are very flexible. Then the horizontal component H_p of the tension produced in the cable by live load is the same for all three spans, and in its calculation we can again use Eq. (11.16). The quantity L (see page 531) in such a case is obtained by extending the integration over all three spans, which gives[1]

$$L = \int_0^l \left(\frac{ds}{dx}\right)^3 dx + 2 \int_0^{l_1} \left(\frac{ds}{dx}\right)^3 dx \qquad (a)$$

Applying the trigonometric series in our analysis and assuming that live load is applied on the middle span, we can use for the deflection of this span the previously obtained series (11.34), the coefficients of which are calculated from formula (11.35). The side spans will be bent by the upward pull of the hangers, and from symmetry it follows that their deflection curves will be identical. Considering the left-hand span and taking the origin of coordinates at the left support, we can represent the deflections η_1 of this span by the following series:

$$\eta_1 = c_1 \sin \frac{\pi x}{l_1} + c_2 \sin \frac{2\pi x}{l_1} + c_3 \sin \frac{3\pi x}{l_1} + \cdots \qquad (11.37)$$

The coefficients in this series are obtained from formula (11.35) by taking

[1] We assume that corresponding truss and cable spans are equal.

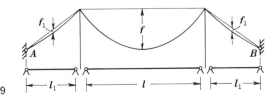

FIG. 11.9

$p = 0$ and substituting the quantities l_1, I_1, w_1, and k_1, instead of l, I, w, and k, for the side span. Then,

$$c_m = - \frac{2l_1{}^4}{\pi^3 EI_1} \frac{\beta w_1 (1 - \cos m\pi)}{m^3 (m^2 \pi^2 + k_1{}^2 l_1{}^2)} \tag{11.38}$$

Substituting the series (11.34) and (11.37) and the quantity L, from Eq. (a), into Eq. (11.16), we obtain the following equation for calculating H_p:

$$\frac{H_p L}{A_c E_c} = \frac{2}{\pi H_w} \left(lw \sum_{1,3,5,\dots} \frac{a_m}{m} + 2l_1 w_1 \sum_{1,3,5,\dots} \frac{c_m}{m} \right)$$
$$+ \frac{\pi^2}{4} \sum_{1,2,3,\dots} \left(\frac{a_m{}^2}{l} + \frac{2c_m{}^2}{l_1} \right) m^2 \tag{11.39}$$

This equation can be solved by the trial-and-error method used in the previous article for the solution of Eq. (11.36). When H_p has been found, the deflections of the trusses are calculated by using series (11.34) and (11.37), and the moments are found from Eq. (11.19).

If, instead of trigonometric series, the expressions (11.27) to (11.29) are used for the deflection curves of the stiffening trusses, we apply the simplified Eq. (11.17) in calculating H_p. Observing that in this case the quantity L is given by Eq. (a) and extending the integration on the right-hand side of Eq. (11.17) over all three spans, we obtain for calculating H_p the following equation:

$$H_p \left\{ \frac{L(H_w + H_p)}{A_c E_c l} + \frac{1}{12} \left(\frac{8f}{l} \right)^2 \left[1 - \frac{12}{k^2 l^2} + \frac{24 \tanh (kl/2)}{k^3 l^3} \right] \right.$$
$$+ \frac{2}{12} \left(\frac{8f_1}{l_1} \right)^2 \frac{l_1}{l} \left[1 - \frac{12}{k_1{}^2 l_1{}^2} + \frac{24 \tanh (k_1 l_1/2)}{k_1{}^3 l_1{}^3} \right] \right\}$$
$$= P \frac{8f}{l} \left\{ \frac{1}{2} \frac{c}{l} \left(1 - \frac{c}{l} \right) - \frac{1}{k^2 l^2 \sinh kl} \right.$$
$$\left. \times \left[\sinh kl - \sinh kc - \sinh k(l - c) \right] \right\} \tag{11.40}$$

Comparing this equation with Eq. (11.30) for a single-span bridge, we see that the difference is represented by the last term on the left-hand side of Eq. (11.40). Because of the presence of this term, the magnitude of H_p becomes smaller than in the case of a single-span bridge having the same dimensions as the middle span in Fig. 11.9.

Substituting $p\, dc$ for P into Eq. (11.40) and integrating with respect to c, an equation for H_p is obtained for the case in which live load is distributed along a portion of the middle span of the bridge.

11.7 THREE-SPAN SUSPENSION BRIDGE WITH CONTINUOUS STIFFENING TRUSS[1]

Let us consider a symmetrical three-span bridge with a uniform continuous stiffening truss as shown in Fig. 11.10a. For the deflection curve of each span, Eq. (11.21) will be used, in which $\mathfrak{M}_p$ will now denote the bending moment in a simply supported beam due to live load and the moments M_1 and M_2 at the supports A and B. We begin with the case in which, in addition to dead load w and w_1, one concentrated force P is applied at a distance c from the support B. The corresponding free-body diagrams for the three spans are shown in Fig. 11.10b, c, and d.

The magnitudes of the bending moments M_1 and M_2 will now be found from the conditions that at the supports A and B the deflection curves of the two adjacent spans have a common tangent. Deflections produced by the concentrated load P and the upward pull of the hangers are given by Eqs. (11.27) to (11.29). To obtain deflections produced by a couple applied at the end of a beam, we use Eq. (11.27) and assume that the distance c indefinitely decreases while the moment Pc remains constant and equal to M. Then, Eq. (11.27) gives

$$\eta = \frac{M}{H_w + H_p}\left(\frac{x}{l} - \frac{\sinh kx}{\sinh kl}\right) \tag{11.41}$$

[1] See the paper by S. Timoshenko and S. Way, *Publ. Intern. Assoc. Bridge Structural Eng.*, vol. 2, p. 452, 1934.

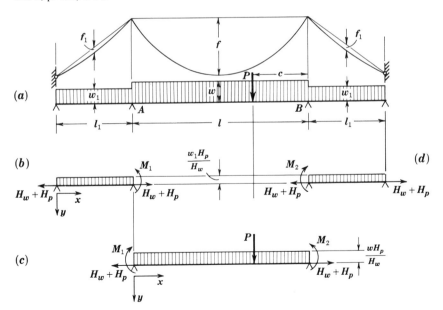

FIG. 11.10

and, by differentiation, we obtain

$$\left(\frac{d\eta}{dx}\right)_{x=0} = \frac{M}{l(H_w + H_p)}\left(1 - \frac{kl}{\sinh kl}\right) = \frac{Ml}{6EI}\frac{6}{k^2l^2}\left(1 - \frac{kl}{\sinh kl}\right)$$

(11.42)

$$\left(\frac{d\eta}{dx}\right)_{x=l} = \frac{M}{l(H_w + H_p)}\left(1 - \frac{kl}{\tanh kl}\right)$$

$$= -\frac{Ml}{3EI}\frac{3}{k^2l^2}\left(\frac{kl}{\tanh kl} - 1\right) \quad (11.43)$$

The slopes produced by the concentrated force P are obtained by differentiation of Eqs. (11.27) and (11.28), which gives

$$\left(\frac{d\eta}{dx}\right)_{x=0} = \frac{P}{H_w + H_p}\left(\frac{c}{l} - \frac{\sinh kc}{\sinh kl}\right)$$

(11.44)

$$\left(\frac{d\eta}{dx}\right)_{x=l} = -\frac{P}{H_w + H_p}\left[\frac{l - c}{l} - \frac{\sinh k(l - c)}{\sinh kl}\right]$$

(11.45)

Finally, the slopes produced by the upward pull are obtained by differentiation of Eq. (11.29), which gives

$$\left(\frac{d\eta}{dx}\right)_{x=0} = -\left(\frac{d\eta}{dx}\right)_{x=l} = -\frac{H_p}{H_w}\frac{wl^3}{24EI}\frac{24}{k^3l^3}\left(\frac{kl}{2} - \tanh\frac{kl}{2}\right)$$

(11.46)

To simplify our writing, we introduce the following notations:

$$\frac{6}{k^2l^2}\left(1 - \frac{kl}{\sinh kl}\right) = \varphi$$

$$\frac{3}{k^2l^2}\left(\frac{kl}{\tanh kl} - 1\right) = \psi$$

(11.47)

$$\frac{24}{k^3l^3}\left(\frac{kl}{2} - \tanh\frac{kl}{2}\right) = \theta$$

With these notations, the slopes at the ends of the middle span produced by all forces shown in Fig. 11.10c are

$$\left(\frac{d\eta}{dx}\right)_{x=0} = \frac{M_2l}{6EI}\varphi + \frac{M_1l}{3EI}\psi - \frac{H_p}{H_w}\frac{wl^3}{24EI}\theta$$

$$+ \frac{P}{H_w + H_p}\left(\frac{c}{l} - \frac{\sinh kc}{\sinh kl}\right)$$

$$\left(\frac{d\eta}{dx}\right)_{x=l} = -\frac{M_1l}{6EI}\varphi - \frac{M_2l}{3EI}\psi + \frac{H_p}{H_w}\frac{wl^3}{24EI}\theta$$

$$- \frac{P}{H_w + H_p}\left[\frac{l - c}{l} - \frac{\sinh k(l - c)}{\sinh kl}\right]$$

Similarly, the slopes at the ends of the two side spans can be obtained.   It is only necessary to substitute l_1 and w_1 for l and w and to denote by φ_1, ψ_1, and θ_1 the corresponding values of the functions (11.47).   The conditions of continuity at the supports A and B give us, then, the following two equations:

$$2M_1(l\psi + l_1\psi_1) + M_2 l\varphi = \frac{H_p}{4H_w}(l_1{}^3w_1\theta_1 + l^3w\theta)$$

$$+ \frac{6P}{k^2}\left(\frac{\sinh kc}{\sinh kl} - \frac{c}{l}\right) \quad (11.48)$$

$$M_1 l\varphi + 2M_2(l\psi + l_1\psi_1) = \frac{H_p}{4H_w}(l_1{}^3w_1\theta_1 + l^3w\theta)$$

$$+ \frac{6P}{k^2}\left[\frac{\sinh k(l-c)}{\sinh kl} - \frac{l-c}{l}\right] \quad (11.49)$$

From these equations, the moments M_1 and M_2 at the supports can be calculated if the additional horizontal tension H_p produced by the live load P is known.

For calculation of H_p, we use the simplified Eq. (11.17).   Then, extending the integration over all three spans and using the notation

$$L = \int_0^l \left(\frac{ds}{dx}\right)^3 dx + 2\int_0^{l_1}\left(\frac{ds}{dx}\right)^3 dx$$

we obtain

$$\frac{H_p L}{A_c E_c} = \frac{w}{H_w}\int_0^l \eta\, dx + \frac{w_1}{H_w}\int_0^{l_1}\eta_1\, dx + \frac{w_1}{H_w}\int_0^{l_1}\eta_2\, dx \quad (11.50)$$

In this equation η, η_1, and η_2 are the deflections of the three spans produced by the loads indicated in Fig. 11.10c, b, and d, respectively.   Using Eqs. (11.27) to (11.29) and (11.41), we obtain for these deflections the following expressions:

For $x < l - c$,

$$\eta = -\frac{P}{H_w + H_p}\frac{\sinh kc}{k\sinh kl}\sinh kx + \frac{Pcx}{l(H_w + H_p)}$$

$$-\frac{H_p}{H_w}\frac{wl^2}{H_w + H_p}\left[\frac{1}{k^2l^2\cosh(kl/2)}\cosh\left(\frac{kl}{2} - kx\right)\right.$$

$$\left. -\frac{1}{k^2l^2} + \frac{x(l-x)}{2l^2}\right] + \frac{M_1}{H_w + H_p}\left[\frac{l-x}{l} - \frac{\sinh k(l-x)}{\sinh kl}\right]$$

$$+\frac{M_2}{H_w + H_p}\left(\frac{x}{l} - \frac{\sinh kx}{\sinh kl}\right) \quad (11.51)$$

For $x > l - c$,

$$
\begin{aligned}
\eta = & -\frac{P}{H_w + H_p} \frac{\sinh k(l - c)}{k \sinh kl} \sinh k(l - x) + \frac{P(l - c)(l - x)}{l(H_w + H_p)} \\
& -\frac{H_p}{H_w} \frac{wl^2}{H_w + H_p} \left[\frac{1}{k^2 l^2 \cosh(kl/2)} \cosh\left(\frac{kl}{2} - kx\right) \right. \\
& \left. -\frac{1}{k^2 l^2} + \frac{x(l - x)}{2l^2} \right] + \frac{M_1}{H_w + H_p} \left[\frac{l - x}{l} - \frac{\sinh k(l - x)}{\sinh kl} \right] \\
& + \frac{M_2}{H_w + H_p} \left(\frac{x}{l} - \frac{\sinh kx}{\sinh kl} \right) \quad (11.52)
\end{aligned}
$$

$$
\begin{aligned}
\eta_1 = & \frac{M_1}{H_w + H_p} \left(\frac{x}{l_1} - \frac{\sinh kx}{\sinh kl_1} \right) \\
& -\frac{H_p}{H_w} \frac{w_1 l_1^2}{H_w + H_p} \left[\frac{1}{k^2 l_1^2 \cosh(kl_1/2)} \cosh\left(\frac{kl_1}{2} - kx\right) \right. \\
& \left. -\frac{1}{k^2 l_1^2} + \frac{x(l_1 - x)}{2l_1^2} \right] \quad (11.53)
\end{aligned}
$$

$$
\begin{aligned}
\eta_2 = & \frac{M_2}{H_w + H_p} \left[\frac{l_1 - x}{l_1} - \frac{\sinh k(l_1 - x)}{\sinh kl_1} \right] \\
& -\frac{H_p}{H_w} \frac{w_1 l_1^2}{H_w + H_p} \left[\frac{1}{k^2 l_1^2 \cosh(kl_1/2)} \cosh\left(\frac{kl_1}{2} - kx\right) \right. \\
& \left. -\frac{1}{k^2 l_1^2} + \frac{x(l_1 - x)}{2l_1^2} \right] \quad (11.54)
\end{aligned}
$$

Substituting these expressions into Eq. (11.50), we obtain

$$
\begin{aligned}
H_p & \left[\frac{(H_w + H_p)L}{A_c E_c} + \left(\frac{w}{H_w}\right)^2 \left(\frac{2}{k^3} \tanh \frac{kl}{2} - \frac{l}{k^2} + \frac{l^3}{12} \right) \right. \\
& \left. + 2 \left(\frac{w_1}{H_w}\right)^2 \left(\frac{2}{k^3} \tanh \frac{kl_1}{2} - \frac{l_1}{k^2} + \frac{l_1^3}{12} \right) \right] \\
& = \frac{w}{H_w} \left\{ \frac{Pc(l - c)}{2} - \frac{P}{k^2 \sinh kl} \left[\sinh kl - \sinh kc \right. \right. \\
& \left. \left. - \sinh k(l - c) \right] + (M_1 + M_2)X \right\} \quad (11.55)
\end{aligned}
$$

where $\quad X = \dfrac{k^2}{24} \left(\theta l^3 + \dfrac{w_1}{w} \theta_1 l_1^3 \right) \quad (11.56)$

Equations (11.48), (11.49), and (11.55) define the three statically indeterminate quantities M_1, M_2, and H_p.

In calculating these quantities, we determine first the value of $M_1 + M_2$ by adding together Eqs. (11.48) and (11.49). Substituting this value into Eq.

(11.55), we obtain

$$
\begin{aligned}
H_p \bigg\{ & \frac{(H_w + H_p)L}{A_c E_c l} + \frac{1}{12}\left(\frac{8f}{l}\right)^2 \left[1 - \frac{12}{k^2 l^2} + \frac{24\,\tanh\,(kl/2)}{k^3 l^3}\right] \\
& + \frac{1}{6}\left(\frac{8f_1}{l_1}\right)^2 \frac{l_1}{l}\left[1 - \frac{12}{k^2 l_1{}^2} + \frac{24\,\tanh\,(kl_1/2)}{k^3 l_1{}^3}\right] \\
& - \frac{1}{2}\left(\frac{8f}{l}\right)^2 \left(\theta + \frac{w_1}{w}\frac{l_1{}^3}{l^3}\theta_1\right)\frac{X}{2(l\psi + l_1\psi_1) + l\varphi}\bigg\} \\
= P\,\frac{8f}{l}\bigg\{ & \frac{1}{2}\frac{c}{l}\left(1 - \frac{c}{l}\right) - \frac{\sinh kl - \sinh kc - \sinh k(l-c)}{k^2 l^2 \sinh kl} \\
& \times \left[1 + \frac{6X}{2(l\psi + l_1\psi_1) + l\varphi}\right]\bigg\} \quad (11.57)
\end{aligned}
$$

From this equation, H_p can be calculated for any position of the live load P. Substituting H_p into Eqs. (11.48) and (11.49), we can find the moments at the supports.

To apply Eq. (11.57) for the construction of influence lines, we neglect H_p in comparison with H_w and assume that $k^2 \approx H_w/EI$. With this value of k^2, the value of H_p can be readily calculated from Eq. (11.57) for any position of the load, and the influence line for H_p can be constructed. Take, as an example, the case in which $l_1 = \frac{1}{2}l$, $w_1 = w$, $kl = 10$, $f/l = 0.1$, $H_w L/A_c E_c l = 0.0043$. Substituting these numerical values into Eq. (11.57), we obtain

$$
0.0753 H_p = 0.8P\bigg\{ \frac{1}{2}\frac{c}{l}\left(1 - \frac{c}{l}\right) - \frac{3.12}{100}\left[1 - \frac{\sinh kc}{\sinh kl} - \frac{\sinh k(l-c)}{\sinh kl}\right]\bigg\}
$$

From this equation, the influence line of H_p for the middle span is obtained as shown in Fig. 11.11. For comparison, there is shown by a dashed line in the same figure the influence line calculated from Eq. (11.40) for the stiffening truss with hinges at the supports (Fig. 11.9). It is seen that by using a continuous truss, we increase the rigidity of the structure somewhat and diminish the values of H_p. Having the influence line for H_p, we can construct the influence lines for M_1 and M_2 by using Eqs. (11.48) and (11.49). The

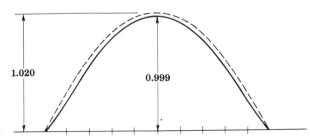

1.020   0.999

FIG. 11.11

influence lines for deflections will then be obtained from Eqs. (11.51) to (11.54), and those for bending moments, from Eq. (11.19). Having all these lines, we can determine the most unfavorable position of live load.

Assume now that the live load is distributed along a portion of the middle span as shown in Fig. 11.8. Then to obtain an equation for calculating H_p, we use Eq. (11.57) and apply the method of superposition. Substituting $p\,dc$ for P in Eq. (11.57) and integrating the right-hand side with respect to c from $c = a$ to $c = b$, we obtain

$$H_p \left\{ \frac{(H_w + H_p)L}{A_c E_c l} + \frac{1}{12} \left(\frac{8f}{l} \right)^2 \left[1 - \frac{12}{k^2 l^2} + \frac{24 \tanh (kl/2)}{k^3 l^3} \right] \right.$$

$$+ \frac{1}{6} \left(\frac{8f_1}{l_1} \right)^2 \frac{l_1}{l} \left[1 - \frac{12}{k^2 l_1^2} + \frac{24 \tanh (kl_1/2)}{k^3 l_1^3} \right]$$

$$\left. - \frac{1}{2} \left(\frac{8f}{l} \right)^2 \left(\theta + \frac{w_1}{w} \frac{l_1^3}{l^3} \theta_1 \right) \frac{X}{2(l\psi + l_1\psi_1) + l\varphi} \right\}$$

$$= 8pf \left\{ \frac{3l(b^2 - a^2) - 2(b^3 - a^3)}{12l^3} - \frac{1}{k^2 l^2} \left[\frac{b - a}{l} \right. \right.$$

$$\left. - \frac{\cosh kl - \cosh ka + \cosh k(l - a) - \cosh k(l - b)}{kl \sinh kl} \right]$$

$$\left. \times \left[1 + \frac{6X}{2(l\psi + l_1\psi_1) + l\varphi} \right] \right\} \quad (11.58)$$

This equation, instead of Eq. (11.57), must be used for calculating H_p if live load is distributed along a portion of the middle span. In a similar manner, equations can be derived if the load is on one of the side spans.

If in addition to live-load action we have to take into account a temperature change, the equation for calculating the change H_s in the horizontal tension in the cable is obtained by substituting (see page 538) $H_s L/A_c E_c + \epsilon t L_1$ instead of $H_p L/A_c E_c$ into Eq. (11.50). This gives

$$H_s \left\{ \frac{(H_w + H_s)L}{A_c E_c l} + \frac{\epsilon t L_1}{l} + \frac{1}{12} \left(\frac{8f}{l} \right)^2 \left[1 - \frac{12}{k^2 l^2} \right. \right.$$

$$+ \frac{24 \tanh (kl/2)}{k^3 l^3} \right] + \frac{1}{6} \left(\frac{8f_1}{l_1} \right)^2 \frac{l_1}{l} \left[1 - \frac{12}{k^2 l_1^2} + \frac{24 \tanh (kl_1/2)}{k^3 l_1^3} \right]$$

$$\left. - \frac{1}{2} \left(\frac{8f}{l} \right)^2 \left(\theta + \frac{w_1}{w} \frac{l_1^3}{l^3} \theta_1 \right) \frac{X}{2(l\psi + l_1\psi_1) + l\varphi} \right\}$$

$$= - \frac{H_w \epsilon t L_1}{l} + 8pf \left\{ \frac{3l(b^2 - a^2) - 2(b^3 - a^3)}{12l^3} - \frac{1}{k^2 l^2} \left[\frac{b - a}{l} \right. \right.$$

$$\left. - \frac{\cosh kl - \cosh ka + \cosh k(l - a) - \cosh k(l - b)}{kl \sinh kl} \right]$$

$$\left. \times \left[1 + \frac{6X}{2(l\psi + l_1\psi_1) + l\varphi} \right] \right\} \quad (11.59)$$

From this equation, H_s can be calculated by trial and error, as has been done in previous cases. Take, as a numerical example, the case in which $l = 800$ ft, $l_1 = 400$ ft, $f/l = 0.105$, $f_1/l_1 = 0.0525$, $H_w = 3.667 \times 10^6$ lb. $EI = 56.84 \times 10^9$ lb-ft², $pl = 0.28361 H_w$, $\epsilon = 65 \times 10^{-7}$, $t = 60°F$, $A_c = 87.8$ in.², $E_c = 29 \times 10^6$ psi, $L/l = 2.5937$, $L_1/l = 2.4975$. For $b = l$ and for various values of the ratio a/l, Eq. (11.59) gives for H_s the values written in the second column of Table 11.2. The values of H_s for small amounts of live load are negative because the temperature rise of 60°, which we have assumed, expands the cable, allowing part of the dead load to be taken by the stiffening truss.

To obtain values of the moments M_1 and M_2 at the supports, we use Eqs. (11.48) and (11.49). Substituting $p\,dc$ for P and integrating from $c = a$ to $c = b$, we obtain

$$2M_1(l\psi + l_1\psi_1) + M_2 l\varphi = \frac{H_p}{4H_w}\,(l_1{}^3 w_1 \theta_1 + l^3 w\theta)$$

$$+ \frac{6pl}{k^2}\left(\frac{\cosh kb - \cosh ka}{kl \sinh kl} - \frac{b^2 - a^2}{2l^2}\right)$$

$$M_1 l\varphi + 2M_2(l\psi + l_1\psi_1) = \frac{H_p}{4H_w}\,(l_1{}^3 w_1\theta_1 + l^3 w\theta) + \frac{6pl}{k^2}$$

$$\times \left[\frac{\cosh k(l - a) - \cosh k(l - b)}{kl \sinh kl} - \frac{2l(b - a) - (b^2 - a^2)}{2l^2}\right]$$

$$(11.60)$$

From these equations, M_1 and M_2 can be calculated provided H_p is found from Eq. (11.58). Similar equations are obtained also when a combined action of live load and temperature change is considered. The values of the moments

TABLE 11.2

$\dfrac{a}{l}$	$\dfrac{H_s}{H_w}$	$\dfrac{M_1 l}{EI}$	$\dfrac{M_2 l}{EI}$
0	0.2430	−0.0160	−0.0160
0.1	0.2386	−0.0188	0.0030
0.2	0.2230	−0.0290	0.0320
0.3	0.1930	−0.0500	0.0500
0.4	0.1535	−0.0742	0.0520
0.5	0.1082	−0.0960	0.0410
0.6	0.0625	−0.1100	0.0180
0.7	0.0222	−0.1085	−0.0070
0.8	−0.0085	−0.0908	−0.0280
0.9	−0.0258	−0.0628	−0.0410
1	−0.0305	−0.0445	−0.0445

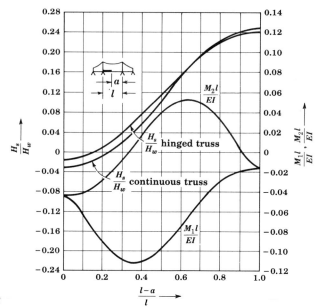

FIG. 11.12

calculated from these equations for our numerical example are given in the third and fourth columns of Table 11.2. The variation of H_s/H_w and of M_1l/EI and M_2l/EI with the length $l - a$ of the loaded portion of the middle span is shown in Fig. 11.12. We see that the moment at the left tower is greatest when the live load extends over 35 percent of the main span.

To show the effect of continuity of the stiffening truss at the support, there is given in Fig. 11.12 also the curve for H_s calculated on the assumption that there are hinges at the supports A and B. In making this later calculation, we have only to omit in Eq. (11.58) the terms containing the function X. It is seen that in the case of hinged spans, the H_s curve is somewhat above the corresponding curve for a continuous stiffening truss.

11.8 STIFFENING TRUSS OF VARIABLE CROSS SECTION

The method of trigonometric series previously applied (see Art. 11.5) to a stiffening truss of uniform cross section can be extended also to cases in which the stiffening truss has a variable cross section.[1] We start with the differential equation for the deflection curve of the stiffening truss [Eq. (e), page 544],

$$EI \frac{d^2\eta}{dx^2} - (H_w + H_p)\eta = \sum b_m \sin \frac{m\pi x}{l} \qquad (a)$$

[1] This extension of the application of trigonometric series was shown by E. Steuerman; see S. Timoshenko, *Trans. ASCE*, vol. 94, p. 377, 1930.

in which

$$b_m = \frac{2}{l} \int_0^l (H_p y - \mathfrak{M}_p) \, dx$$

For the case of one concentrated load P (Fig. 11.6) we have (see page 544)

$$b_m = \frac{16 H_p f}{m^3 \pi^3} (1 - \cos m\pi) - \frac{2Pl}{m^2 \pi^2} \sin \frac{m\pi(l - c)}{l} \tag{b}$$

For the case of distributed load, as in Fig. 11.8, we obtain b_m by substituting $p \, dc$ for P into Eq. (b) and integrating from $c = a$ to $c = b$, which gives

$$b_m = \frac{2l^2}{m^3 \pi^3} \left\{ \frac{8 f H_p}{l^2} (1 - \cos m\pi) \right.$$
$$\left. - p \left[\cos \frac{m\pi(l - b)}{l} - \cos \frac{m\pi(l - a)}{l} \right] \right\} \tag{c}$$

Applying now Eq. (a) to the case of a truss of variable cross section, we assume that the flexural rigidity of the truss is defined by the equation

$$EI = EI_0 \varphi(x) \tag{d}$$

in which $\varphi(x)$ is a known function of x, and take the solution of Eq. (a) in form of the series

$$\eta = \sum_{m=1}^{\infty} a_m \sin \frac{m\pi x}{l} \tag{e}$$

Substituting expressions (d) and (e) into Eq. (a), we obtain

$$-\frac{\pi^2}{l^2} EI_0 \varphi(x) \sum_{m=1}^{\infty} m^2 a_m \sin \frac{m\pi x}{l}$$
$$- (H_w + H_p) \sum_{m=1}^{\infty} a_m \sin \frac{m\pi x}{l} = \sum_{m=1}^{\infty} b_m \sin \frac{m\pi x}{l} \tag{f}$$

To calculate the coefficients $a_1, a_2, a_3, \ldots$ of the series (e), we multiply Eq. (f) by $\sin (i\pi x/l)$, where $i = 1, 2, 3, \ldots$, and integrate from $x = 0$ to $x = l$. In this manner, we obtain

$$-\frac{2\pi^2}{l^3} EI_0 \sum_{m=1}^{\infty} m^2 a_m \int_0^l \varphi(x) \sin \frac{m\pi x}{l} \sin \frac{i\pi x}{l} \, dx$$
$$- a_i (H_w + H_p) = b_i \tag{g}$$

After calculation of the integral on the left side, we obtain a linear equation containing the unknown coefficients $a_1, a_2, a_3, \ldots$. In practical calculations we take only the first few terms of the series (e). Let n denote the number of these terms. Then, taking $i = 1, 2, \ldots, n$, we obtain n linear equations

(g) from which n coefficients $a_1, a_2, \ldots, a_n$ of the series (e) can be calculated for any assumed value of H_p. To determine H_p, we use the previous Eq. (11.36):

$$\frac{H_p L}{A_c E_c} = \frac{16f}{\pi l}\left(a_1 + \frac{a_3}{3} + \cdots + \frac{a_n}{n}\right)$$
$$+ \frac{\pi^2}{4l}\left(a_1{}^2 + 2^2 a_2{}^2 + \cdots + n^2 a_n{}^2\right) \quad (h)$$

This equation, together with n equations (g), is sufficient for the solution of the problem. In each particular case, we start with a calculation of the coefficients b_m for the assumed live-load distribution by using Eq. (b) or (c). Then we calculate the integral on the left side of Eq. (g) for the assumed $\varphi(x)$ and obtain n linear equations for the coefficients $a_1, a_2, \ldots, a_n$. Taking now, as a trial, a certain value for H_p, we calculate these coefficients and substitute them into the right-hand side of Eq. (h). Since the value of H_p was taken arbitrarily, the equation will not be satisfied, and a second trial value of H_p must be taken. After two such trials the correct value of H_p can be obtained with sufficient accuracy by interpolation. Such calculations show that considerable variations of flexural rigidity EI along the span of the truss have only a small effect on the magnitude of H_p and that a very good approximation for H_p is obtained by replacing a variable flexural rigidity by its constant average value.

To illustrate the calculations required in the case of a truss of variable cross section, let us assume that

$$EI = EI_0 \sin\left(\frac{s\pi x}{l} + \alpha\right) \qquad (i)$$

To have a truss symmetrical with respect to the middle, we take

$$s\pi + \alpha = \pi - \alpha$$

Then $$s = 1 - \frac{2\alpha}{\pi} \qquad (j)$$

and Eq. (i) gives

$$(EI)_{x=0, x=l} = EI_0 \sin\alpha \qquad (EI)_{x=l/2} = EI_0 \qquad (k)$$

Taking, for example, $\alpha = \pi/6$, we obtain $s = \frac{2}{3}$, and the flexural rigidity at the ends of the truss is only half of that at the middle. The integral in Eq. (g) for

$$\varphi(x) = \sin\left(\frac{s\pi x}{l} + \alpha\right)$$

is $$\int_0^l \sin\left(\frac{s\pi x}{l} + \alpha\right) \sin\frac{m\pi x}{l} \sin\frac{i\pi x}{l}\, dx$$
$$= \frac{2[(-1)^{m+i+1} - 1]\, slmi \cos\alpha}{\pi[(m-i)^2 - s^2][(m+i)^2 - s^2]} \qquad (l)$$

and Eq. (g) becomes

$$-\frac{4\pi s \cos \alpha}{l^2} EI_0 \sum_{m=1}^{m=n} a_m \frac{im^3[(-1)^{m+i+1} - 1]}{[(m-i)^2 - s^2][(m+i)^2 - s^2]}$$
$$- a_i(H_w + H_p) = b_i$$

Introducing the notations

$$\frac{4\pi s \cos \alpha EI_0}{l^2(H_w + H_p)} = \mu \tag{m}$$

$$\frac{im^3[(-1)^{m+i+1} - 1]}{[(m-i)^2 - s^2][(m+i)^2 - s^2]} = N_{mi} \tag{n}$$

$$\frac{b_i}{H_w + H_p} = c_i \tag{o}$$

we represent Eq. (g) for calculation of the coefficients $a_1, a_2, \ldots, a_n$ in the following form:

$$a_i + \mu \sum_{m=1}^{m=n} a_m N_{mi} + c_i = 0 \qquad i = 1, 2, \ldots, n \tag{p}$$

Assuming, for example, that $\alpha = \pi/6$, $s = \frac{2}{3}$, and taking only four terms of the series (e), we obtain for calculation of the four coefficients the following four equations:

$$a_1 + \mu\left(\frac{81}{64}a_1 - \frac{27 \times 81}{16 \times 140}a_3\right) + c_1 = 0$$

$$a_2 + \mu\left(\frac{162}{35}a_2 - \frac{81}{40}a_4\right) + c_2 = 0$$

$$\tag{q}$$

$$a_3 + \mu\left(-\frac{243}{16 \times 140}a_1 + \frac{81^2}{640}a_3\right) + c_3 = 0$$

$$a_4 + \mu\left(-\frac{81}{160}a_2 + \frac{31 \times 81}{143}a_4\right) + c_4 = 0$$

It is seen that this system of equations is split into two groups, one containing the coefficients a_1, a_3 of odd order, and the other containing the coefficients a_2, a_4 of even order. The solution of these equations for any numerical values of μ, c_1, c_2, c_3, c_4 can be readily accomplished. For a truss of given dimensions and for an assumed value of H_p, we calculate the value of μ from Eq. (m). The quantities $c_1, \ldots, c_4$, for a given load distribution, are calculated from Eq. (o). Then the coefficients $a_1, \ldots, a_4$ will be found from Eqs. (q). Substituting these coefficients into Eq. (h), we check how accurately the assumed value of H_p satisfies this equation. With two trial calculations we find the correct value of H_p and the corresponding values of the coefficients. Equation (e) then gives the deflection curve. The bending moments will be found from Eq. (11.19). Calculations made for a single-span bridge of the

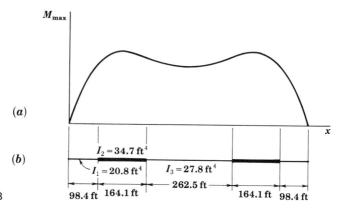

M_max

(a)

x

(b)

$I_2 = 34.7\,\text{ft}^4$

$I_1 = 20.8\,\text{ft}^4$ $I_3 = 27.8\,\text{ft}^4$

$\longleftarrow$ 262.5 ft $\longrightarrow$

FIG. 11.13   98.4 ft   164.1 ft   164.1 ft   98.4 ft

same dimensions as the middle span of the Manhattan Bridge and for live load distributed from $x = 0$ to $x = l/4$ show that the horizontal tension H_p calculated for the constant rigidity EI_0 diminishes only by about 1 percent when the rigidity of the truss, given by Eq. (i), is reduced at the ends to one-half of its value at the middle.

Calculation of M_max for a truss of uniform cross section shows that this quantity varies along the span as shown in Fig. 11.13a.   It is seen that a rational design requires a reinforcement of the cross section of the truss near the quarter points and not at the middle of the span, as was assumed in the preceding example.   A proper variation in flexural rigidity along the span may be represented by the equation

$$EI = \frac{EI_0}{1 - \alpha}\left(1 - \alpha \cos \frac{4\pi x}{l}\right) \tag{r}$$

Substituting

$$\varphi(x) = \frac{1}{1 - \alpha}\left(1 - \alpha \cos \frac{4\pi x}{l}\right)$$

into Eq. (g) and proceeding as in the previous example, we obtain the deflection and the moments for a truss the flexural rigidity of which varies according to Eq. (r).

Practically, the rigidity of a truss is not a continuous function of x but changes abruptly as shown in Fig. 11.13b.   Calculations made for this case[1] show that whereas the moment of inertia of the cross section differs by ± 20

---

[1] Such calculations, made by using a certain generalization of the series method, are given in the book by Hans H. Bleich, "Die Berechnung verankerter Hängebrücken," p. 63, Springer-Verlag OHG, Berlin, 1935.   This book contains several numerical examples completely worked out.   The use of finite-difference equations in handling trusses of variable cross section is shown in the paper by F. Stüssi, *Publ. Intern. Assoc. Bridge Structural Eng.*, vol. 4, p. 531, 1936.

percent of its average value, the values of M_{max} for the middle and for the quarter points differ from the corresponding values, calculated for the truss of constant average cross section, only by 2.5 and 3.5 percent, respectively. We see that a considerable variation in the flexural rigidity along the span of the truss produces only a secondary effect on the bending moments. Hence the usual calculations based on the assumption of a truss of a constant average cross section give satisfactory results.

Chapter 12

Structural dynamics

12.1 FREE VIBRATIONS: ONE DEGREE OF FREEDOM

In previous chapters, the behavior of structures or structural elements under static loads only has been considered. However, there are many cases where the response of a structure to moving or pulsating loads or to suddenly applied loads must be investigated. Examples of such dynamic problems are illustrated by the behavior of buildings subjected to earthquakes, bridges subjected to moving loads, and structures subjected to wind gusts or bomb blasts. Several important problems of this kind will be considered in this chapter.

Since any structure consists of distributed mass interconnected in some manner by elastic constraints, it will perform vibrations if disturbed from its configuration of equilibrium. In dealing with this problem of vibration of a given structure, it is sometimes possible to represent the structure by a single rigid-body mass supported by an elastic massless spring. Such an idealized representation of the structure is called a *model*. Consider, for example, the case

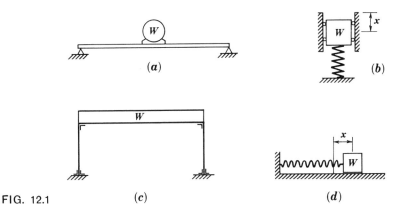

FIG. 12.1   (*c*)

of a simply supported prismatic beam that carries a heavy generator at mid-span as shown in Fig. 12.1*a*. Treating the elastic beam as a *spring* which supports the *mass* of the generator, we obtain the model of the system as shown in Fig. 12.1*b*. Assuming that motion of the mass is restricted to the vertical direction, we have a system with *one degree of freedom;* i.e., a single coordinate *x* defines the configuration of the system. As a second example, we consider the portal frame structure shown in Fig. 12.1*c*, consisting of a very stiff heavy beam supported by flexible vertical columns. Assuming that the beam is completely rigid and that the columns are massless, we see that for horizontal motion of the beam, the structure behaves like the spring-supported mass shown in Fig. 12.1*d*, and again we have a model with one degree of freedom.

Let us now consider, in detail, the dynamic behavior of a spring-suspended mass with one degree of freedom as shown in Fig. 12.2. Under the action of the gravity force *W*, the spring will be extended by the amount

$$\delta_{st} = \frac{W}{k} \tag{a}$$

where *k*, called the *spring constant*, denotes the load required to produce a unit extension of the spring. If the weight *W* is measured in pounds and extension of the spring in inches, the spring constant *k* will have the dimension of pounds per inch. The quantity δ_{st} determines the equilibrium position of the load as shown in the figure.

By means of an impulse or sudden application and removal of a vertical force, vibrations of the system can be produced. Such vibrations which are maintained by the elastic force in the spring alone are called *free* or *natural* vibrations. In studying these vibrations, we shall use Newton's second law of motion stating that the product of the mass of a particle and its acceleration is equal to the force acting in the direction of the acceleration. In this case, the mass of the vibrating body is W/g, where *g* is the acceleration due to gravity.

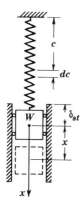

FIG. 12.2

The acceleration of the body is given by the second derivative of the displacement x, from the equilibrium position, with respect to time and will be denoted by $\ddot{x}$. The forces acting on the vibrating body are the gravity force W, acting downward, and the force in the spring, which, for the position of the weight indicated in Fig. 12.2, acts upward and is equal to $W + kx$. Thus, the differential equation of motion, in the case under consideration, becomes

$$\frac{W}{g} \ddot{x} = W - (W + kx) = -kx \tag{b}$$

Introducing the notation

$$p^2 = \frac{kg}{W} = \frac{g}{\delta_{st}} \tag{c}$$

Eq. (b) can be represented in the following form:

$$\ddot{x} + p^2 x = 0 \tag{12.1}$$

This equation will be satisfied if we take either

$$x = C_1 \cos pt \qquad \text{or} \qquad x = C_2 \sin pt$$

where C_1 and C_2 are arbitrary constants. By adding these two solutions, we obtain the general solution of Eq. (12.1). Thus,

$$x = C_1 \cos pt + C_2 \sin pt \tag{12.2}$$

It is seen that the vertical motion of the weight W has a vibratory character since $\cos pt$ and $\sin pt$ repeat themselves after intervals of time τ such that

$$p(t + \tau) - pt = 2\pi \tag{d}$$

This interval of time is called the *period of vibration*. Its magnitude, from

Eqs. (d) and (c), is

$$\tau = \frac{2\pi}{p} = 2\pi \sqrt{\frac{W}{kg}} = 2\pi \sqrt{\frac{\delta_{st}}{g}} \tag{12.3a}$$

It is seen that the period of oscillation of the suspended weight W is the same as that of a simple pendulum the length of which is equal to δ_{st} and is independent of the magnitude of oscillations. To determine the period τ, we have only to calculate, or to obtain experimentally, the static deflection δ_{st}. The number of oscillations per unit time, say per second, is called the *frequency of vibration* and will be denoted by f. Thus, from Eq. (12.3a), we obtain

$$f = \frac{1}{\tau} = \frac{1}{2\pi} \sqrt{\frac{g}{\delta_{st}}} \tag{12.3b}$$

The vibratory motion represented by Eq. (12.2) is called *simple harmonic motion*. To determine the constants C_1 and C_2 in this equation, we must consider the initial conditions of motion. Assume, for instance, that at the initial moment $(t = 0)$ the weight W has *initial displacement* x_0 from the equilibrium position and *initial velocity* $\dot{x}_0$. Then, substituting $t = 0$ and $x = x_0$ in Eq. (12.2), we obtain $C_1 = x_0$. Likewise, substituting $t = 0$ and $\dot{x} = \dot{x}_0$ in the first time derivative of Eq. (12.2), we find $C_2 = \dot{x}_0/p$. With these values of the constants C_1 and C_2, Eq. (12.2) becomes

$$x = x_0 \cos pt + \frac{\dot{x}_0}{p} \sin pt \tag{12.4a}$$

It is seen that this expression for vibrations consists of two parts; one, depending on initial displacement, is proportional to $\cos pt$, and the other, depending on initial velocity, is proportional to $\sin pt$.

Sometimes it is advantageous to represent the solution (12.4a) in another form by means of rotating vectors. Referring to Fig. 12.3, let $\overline{OB}$ be a vector of length x_0 which rotates in the counterclockwise direction about the origin O with constant angular velocity p. Counting time from the instant $t = 0$ when

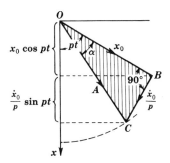

FIG. 12.3

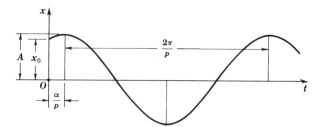

FIG. 12.4

this vector coincides with the x axis, we see that at any time t it will make with the x axis an angle pt, and its projection on the x axis represents the first term in Eq. (12.4a).   Now, at right angles to the vector $\overline{OB}$, let us construct a second vector $\overline{BC}$ of length $\dot{x}_0/p$.   Then its projection on the x axis represents the second term in Eq. (12.4a), and we see that the projection on the x axis of the resultant vector $\overline{OC}$, of length A, represents the complete solution given by Eq. (12.4a).   Denoting the angle between $\overline{OB}$ and $\overline{OC}$ by α, we may now write expression (12.4a) in the form

$$x = A \cos (pt - \alpha) \tag{12.4b}$$

where, by reference to Fig. 12.3,

$$A = \sqrt{x_0{}^2 + \left(\frac{\dot{x}_0}{p}\right)^2} \tag{e}$$

$$\alpha = \tan^{-1} \frac{\dot{x}_0}{px_0} \tag{f}$$

The quantity A, representing the maximum displacement of the vibrating weight, is called the *amplitude of vibration;* it is readily calculated from Eq. (e) when x_0 and $\dot{x}_0$ are given.   The quantity α, defined by Eq. (f), is called the *phase angle.*   We see from Fig. 12.3 that α/p represents the time that elapses after the initial moment $t = 0$ until the vibrating weight reaches the first extreme position.   This *time lag* is also shown in Fig. 12.4, which represents Eq. (12.4b) in graphic form.

Natural frequencies of vibrating systems can often be calculated by using the law of conservation of energy, provided damping is negligible.   Consider, for example, the system shown in Fig. 12.2.   Neglecting the mass of the spring and considering only the mass of the suspended body, the kinetic energy of the system during vibration is

$$T = \frac{W}{g} \frac{\dot{x}^2}{2} \tag{g}$$

The potential energy of the system in this case consists of two parts: (1) the strain energy of deformation in the spring and (2) the potential energy of the weight W by virtue of its position. Considering the strain energy first, the tension in the spring for any displacement x from the equilibrium position is $k(\delta_{st} + x)$, and the corresponding strain energy is $k(\delta_{st} + x)^2/2$. For the position of equilibrium ($x = 0$), this energy becomes $k\delta_{st}^2/2$. Hence, the energy stored in the spring during the displacement x is

$$\frac{k(\delta_{st} + x)^2}{2} - \frac{k\delta_{st}^2}{2} = k\delta_{st}x + \frac{kx^2}{2} = Wx + \frac{kx^2}{2}$$

The potential energy due to position of the weight W diminishes during the displacement x by the amount Wx. Hence, the total change in the potential energy of the system during the displacement x is

$$V = Wx + \frac{kx^2}{2} - Wx = \frac{kx^2}{2} \tag{h}$$

It will be noted that this is simply the strain energy in the initially unstressed spring extended by the amount x.

Having expressions (g) and (h) and neglecting damping, we see that the equation of conservation of energy for the vibrating system becomes

$$\frac{W}{g}\frac{\dot{x}^2}{2} + \frac{kx^2}{2} = \text{const} \tag{i}$$

The magnitude of the constant on the right-hand side of this equation is determined by the initial conditions of motion. Assuming that, for $t = 0$, $x = x_0$ and $\dot{x} = 0$, the initial total energy of the system is $kx_0^2/2$, and Eq. (i) becomes

$$\frac{W}{g}\frac{\dot{x}^2}{2} + \frac{kx^2}{2} = \frac{kx_0^2}{2} \tag{j}$$

When, during vibration, the displacement x becomes equal to x_0, the velocity $\dot{x}$ becomes equal to zero, and the energy of the system consists of potential energy only. When x becomes equal to zero, i.e., when the vibrating body passes through its middle position, the velocity $\dot{x}$ has its maximum value, and we obtain from Eq. (j)

$$\frac{W}{g}\frac{\dot{x}_{\max}^2}{2} = \frac{kx_0^2}{2} \tag{12.5}$$

Thus, the maximum kinetic energy of the system in its middle position is equal to the maximum potential energy in an extreme position.

In all cases where it can be assumed that the vibration of a system is a simple harmonic motion, Eq. (12.5) can be used to calculate the frequency. We simply assume that the motion is represented by the equations

$$x = x_0 \cos pt \qquad \dot{x} = -x_0 p \sin pt$$

Then we see that for such simple harmonic motion

$$\dot{x}_{max} = px_0 \tag{k}$$

Substituting this relationship into Eq. (12.5), we find

$$p^2 = \frac{kg}{W}$$

which coincides with Eq. (c) obtained previously. Several examples of this method of frequency calculation will be shown in the next article.

PROBLEMS

1   A weight $W = 500$ lb is dropped through a height $h = 1$ in. onto the middle of a simply supported steel beam having a span $l = 8$ ft and a cross-sectional moment of inertia $I = 12$ in.^{4} Neglecting the mass of the beam, calculate the maximum deflection of the beam and the period τ of the ensuing free vibrations.
       Ans. $\delta_{max} = 0.252$ in., $\tau = 0.0511$ sec.

2   An elevator cage of weight $W = 10$ kips is supported by a flexible twisted steel cable the upper end of which is unwinding from a rotating drum. As the cage is being lowered with uniform velocity $v_0 = 3$ ft/sec, the drum suddenly stops when the length of unwound cable is $l = 50$ ft. What will be the maximum tensile stress induced in the cable if its cross-sectional area is $A = 2$ in.^{2} and its modulus of elasticity is $E = 20(10^6)$ psi?
       Ans. $\sigma_{max} = 29,300$ psi.

3   Calculate the natural period of free lateral vibration of the portal frame shown in Fig. 12.1c if $W = 2$ kips and the length of each vertical column is $l = 10$ ft. Each column is a channel section having a cross-sectional area $A = 4$ in.^{2}, least radius of gyration $r = 0.60$ in., and $E = 30(10^6)$ psi. The columns are built in both top and bottom. The cross beam is completely rigid.
       Ans. $\tau = 0.583$ sec.

12.2 RAYLEIGH'S METHOD

In discussing free vibrations in the preceding article, we simplified the problem by neglecting the mass of the spring in comparison with the mass of the suspended body. In order to determine the effect of such simplification on the frequency of vibration and to calculate a closer approximation, a method developed by Lord Rayleigh[1] will now be discussed. In applying this method some assumption regarding the configuration of the vibrating system has to be

[1] See his book "Theory of Sound," 2d ed., vol. 1, pp. 111, 287, 1894.

made.   The frequency of vibration will then be found from Eq. (12.5) of the preceding article.

As a simple example of the application of Rayleigh's method, we take again the case represented in Fig. 12.2.   Assuming that the mass of the spring is small in comparison with the mass of the vibrating body W, the *mode of vibration* will not be substantially affected by the mass of the supporting spring, and, with sufficient accuracy, it can be assumed that the displacement of any element of the spring at a distance c from the fixed end is the same as in the case of a massless spring, i.e., proportional to the distance c from the fixed end equal to

$$\frac{c}{l} x \qquad\qquad (a)$$

where l is the natural length of the spring.

If the displacements are not affected by the mass of the spring, the expression for the potential energy of the system will be the same as shown by the right side of Eq. (12.5), and only the kinetic energy of the system has to be reconsidered.   Let w denote the weight of the spring per unit length.   Then the mass of an element of length dc will be $w\,dc/g$, and the corresponding kinetic energy of the element, if we use expression (a), becomes

$$\frac{w}{2g} \left(\frac{\dot{x}c}{l} \right)^2 dc \qquad\qquad (b)$$

The total kinetic energy of the spring then becomes

$$\frac{w}{2g} \int_0^l \left(\frac{\dot{x}c}{l} \right)^2 dc = \frac{\dot{x}^2}{2g} \frac{wl}{3} \qquad\qquad (c)$$

This kinetic energy must be added to that of the load W, so that the energy equation becomes

$$\frac{\dot{x}^2}{2g} \left(W + \frac{wl}{3} \right) + \frac{kx^2}{2} = \frac{kx_0^2}{2} \qquad\qquad (d)$$

Comparing this with Eq. (j) of the preceding article, it can be concluded that, in order to estimate the effect of the mass of the spring on the frequency of free vibrations of the system in Fig. 12.2, it is only necessary to add one-third of the weight of the spring to the weight W of the suspended load.

This conclusion, obtained on the assumption that the weight of the spring is very small in comparison with that of the load, can be used with sufficient accuracy even in cases where the weight of the spring is of the same order as W.   Comparison with the rigorous solution shows that in the case $wl = 0.5W$, the error of the approximate solution is about $\frac{1}{2}$ percent, and for $wl = W$, the error is about $\frac{3}{4}$ percent.

As a second example, let us consider the case of vibration of a beam of

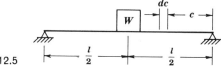

FIG. 12.5

uniform cross section loaded at the middle (Fig. 12.5). If the weight wl of the beam is small in comparison with the load W, it can be assumed with sufficient accuracy that the deflection curve of the beam during vibration has the same shape as the static deflection curve. Then, denoting by x the displacement of the load W during vibration, the displacement of any element wdc of the beam, at a distance c from the support, will be

$$x \frac{3cl^2 - 4c^3}{l^3} \tag{e}$$

and the kinetic energy of the entire beam will be

$$2 \int_0^{l/2} \frac{w}{2g} \left(\dot{x} \frac{3cl^2 - 4c^3}{l^3} \right)^2 dc = \frac{17}{35} wl \frac{\dot{x}^2}{2g} \tag{f}$$

This kinetic energy of the vibrating beam must be added to the kinetic energy $W\dot{x}^2/2g$ of the load concentrated at the middle in order to estimate the influence of the weight of the beam on the period of vibration; i.e., the period of vibration will be the same as for a massless beam carrying at the middle the load

$$W + \tfrac{17}{35}wl$$

Expression (f), developed on the assumption that the weight of the beam is small in comparison with that of the load W, can be used in all practical cases, even in the extreme case of an unloaded beam, where $W = 0$. In such a case, if the assumption is made that $\tfrac{17}{35}wl$ is concentrated at the middle of the beam, the accuracy of the approximate method is sufficiently good for all practical applications. The deflection of the beam under the action of the load $\tfrac{17}{35}wl$ applied at the middle is

$$\delta_{st} = \frac{17}{35} wl \frac{l^3}{48EI}$$

Substituting this into Eq. (12.3a), the period of natural vibration is

$$\tau = 2\pi \sqrt{\frac{\delta_{st}}{g}} = 0.632 \sqrt{\frac{wl^4}{EIg}}$$

The exact solution for this case is

$$\tau = \frac{2}{\pi} \sqrt{\frac{wl^4}{EIg}} = 0.637 \sqrt{\frac{wl^4}{EIg}}$$

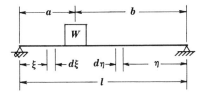

FIG. 12.6

It is seen that for this extreme case the error of the approximate solution is less than 1 percent.

The same method can be applied also in a more general case where the load W is not placed at the middle of the beam (Fig. 12.6). The statical deflection under the load in this case is

$$\delta_{st} = \frac{Wa^2b^2}{3lEI} \tag{g}$$

and the spring constant is

$$k = \frac{3lEI}{a^2b^2} \tag{h}$$

If we neglect the mass of the beam, the period of vibration, from Eq. (12.3a), will be

$$\tau = 2\pi \sqrt{\frac{\delta_{st}}{g}} = 2\pi \sqrt{\frac{Wa^2b^2}{3glEI}} \tag{i}$$

To take the mass of the beam into account, we use the expressions

$$x_1 = \frac{Wb\xi}{6lEI}[a(l + b) - \xi^2] \qquad x_2 = \frac{Wa\eta}{6lEI}[b(l + a) - \eta^2] \tag{j}$$

for the static deflections of the two portions of the beam. Then, denoting by $\dot{x}_{max}$ the maximum velocity of the load W, the velocities for the two portions of the beam will be

$$(\dot{x}_1)_{max} = \dot{x}_{max} \frac{x_1}{\delta_{st}} \qquad (\dot{x}_2)_{max} = \dot{x}_{max} \frac{x_2}{\delta_{st}}$$

and the corresponding kinetic energy is

$$\frac{w\dot{x}_{max}^2}{2g}\left[\int_0^a \left(\frac{x_1}{\delta_{st}}\right)^2 d\xi + \int_0^b \left(\frac{x_2}{\delta_{st}}\right)^2 d\eta\right] = \frac{w\dot{x}_{max}^2}{2g}(\alpha a + \beta b) \tag{k}$$

where
$$\alpha = \frac{1}{3}\frac{l^2}{b^2} + \frac{23}{105}\frac{a^2}{b^2} - \frac{8}{15}\frac{al}{b^2}$$

$$\beta = \frac{1}{12}\frac{(l + a)^2}{a^2} + \frac{1}{28}\frac{b^2}{a^2} - \frac{1}{10}\frac{b(l + a)}{a^2}$$

To take care of the mass of the beam in calculating the period of vibration, we have only to add the kinetic energy [Eq. (k)] of the beam to the kinetic energy $W(\dot{x})^2_{\max}/2g$ of the weight W. Then, instead of Eq. (i), we obtain

$$\tau = 2\pi \sqrt{\frac{(W + \alpha wa + \beta wb)a^2b^2}{3glEI}} \qquad (l)$$

In the case of a cantilever beam with a weight W at the free end (Fig. 12.7), the same method can be used in calculating the period of vibration. Assuming that during vibration the shape of the deflection curve of the beam is the same as the one produced by a load statically applied at the end and denoting by x the vertical displacement of the load W, we see that the kinetic energy of the cantilever of uniform cross section will be

$$\int_0^l \frac{w\dot{x}^2}{2g}\left(\frac{3c^2l - c^3}{2l^3}\right)^2 dc = \frac{33}{140}\, wl\, \frac{\dot{x}^2}{2g} \qquad (m)$$

Thus, the period of vibration will be the same as for a massless cantilever carrying, at the end, a weight

$$W + \tfrac{33}{140}wl$$

This result was obtained on the assumption that the weight wl of the beam is small in comparison with W, but it also is accurate enough for cases where wl is not small. Applying the result (m) to the extreme case where $W = 0$, we obtain

$$\delta_{st} = \frac{33}{140}\frac{wll^3}{3EI}$$

and the corresponding period of vibration is

$$\tau = 2\pi \sqrt{\frac{\delta_{st}}{g}} = \frac{2\pi}{3.567}\sqrt{\frac{wl^4}{EIg}}$$

The exact solution for the same case is

$$\tau = \frac{2\pi}{3.515}\sqrt{\frac{wl^4}{EIg}}$$

It is seen that the error of the approximate solution is about $1\tfrac{1}{2}$ percent.

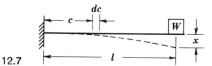

FIG. 12.7

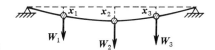

FIG. 12.8

Similar approximate solutions can be made also in the case of a portal frame like that in Fig. 12.1c, provided the compressive forces in the columns are small in comparison with the Euler loads.

The described approximate method of frequency calculation can be used also in the case of a beam supporting several loads W_1, W_2, W_3. If x_1, x_2, x_3 are statical deflections under the loads, the potential energy of deformation stored in the beam is

$$V = \tfrac{1}{2}(W_1 x_1 + W_2 x_2 + W_3 x_3) \qquad (n)$$

In calculating the frequency of the lowest mode of vibration, the static deflection curve, shown in Fig. 12.8, can be taken as an approximation for the extreme configuration of the system during vibration. Then, assuming simple harmonic motion, we see that the displacements of the loads W_1, W_2, W_3 during vibration will be

$$x_1 \cos pt \qquad x_2 \cos pt \qquad x_3 \cos pt \qquad (o)$$

The kinetic energy of the system becomes a maximum at the moment when the beam, during vibration, passes through its middle position. It will be noted, from expressions (o), that the numerical values of the load velocities corresponding to this position are px_1, px_2, px_3, and the kinetic energy of the system becomes

$$T = \frac{p^2}{2g}\,(W_1 x_1{}^2 + W_2 x_2{}^2 + W_3 x_3{}^2) \qquad (p)$$

Equating expressions (n) and (p) in accordance with Eq. (12.5), we obtain

$$p^2 = g\,\frac{W_1 x_1 + W_2 x_2 + W_3 x_3}{W_1 x_1{}^2 + W_2 x_2{}^2 + W_3 x_3{}^2}$$

and the period of vibration is

$$\tau = \frac{2\pi}{p} = 2\pi\,\sqrt{\frac{W_1 x_1{}^2 + W_2 x_2{}^2 + W_3 x_3{}^2}{g(W_1 x_1 + W_2 x_2 + W_3 x_3)}} \qquad (12.6)$$

It is seen that for calculating τ, the statical deflections x_1, x_2, x_3 of the beam alone are necessary. These quantities can easily be calculated by the usual methods. If the beam has a variable cross section, a graphical method of getting the deflections can be used to advantage. The effect of the weight of the beam itself also can be taken into account if desired. It is only necessary, for this purpose, to divide the beam into several parts, the weights of which, applied at their respective centers of gravity, must be considered as concentrated loads.

PROBLEMS

1   Referring to the portal frame in Fig. 12.1c, what portion of the total weight wl of each vertical column should be added to the weight W of the rigid beam in order to correct for the mass effect of the columns on the period of free lateral vibration of the frame? Neglect the effect of axial compression in the columns on their flexural rigidities, and assume built-in ends.

      Ans. $13wl/35$.

2   A thin circular disk having mass moment of inertia I_0 with respect to a diameter is rigidly attached to one end of a shaft of length l and weight wl, as shown in Fig. 12.9. The shaft is supported in bearings A and B, which are loose enough to allow the shaft to bend as shown. For small amplitudes of rotational oscillations of the disk about its horizontal diameter, the period of oscillation, neglecting the mass of the shaft, is $\tau = 2\pi \sqrt{I_0/k}$, where $k = 3EI/l$, EI being the flexural rigidity of the shaft. To correct this period for the mass effect of the shaft, we should use, instead of the moment of inertia I_0, the increased moment of inertia $I_0 + \alpha wl^3/g$. Calculate, by Rayleigh's method, the proper value of the factor α.

      Ans. $\alpha = \frac{2}{105}$.

3   Neglecting the weight of the cantilever I beam shown in Fig. 12.10, and using Rayleigh's method, Eq. (12.6), calculate the approximate period τ of the fundamental mode of free vibration of the system. The following numerical data are given: $W = 1,000$ lb, $I = 15$ in.⁴, $E = 30(10^6)$ psi.

      Ans. $\tau = 0.27$ sec.

4   Using Rayleigh's method, calculate the approximate period of the fundamental mode of free vibration of the beam carrying two weights W as shown in Fig. 12.11. Neglect the distributed mass of the beam and assume $W = 1,000$ lb, $E = 30(10^6)$ psi, $I = 15$ in.⁴

      Ans. $\tau = 0.248$ sec.

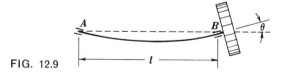

FIG. 12.9

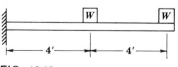

FIG. 12.10

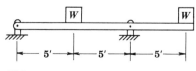

FIG. 12.11

12.3 FORCED VIBRATIONS: STEADY STATE

In preceding articles, it was assumed that vibrations were produced by impart-
ing to the suspended mass some initial displacement or initial velocity.   Such
vibrations are called *free vibrations*.   Because of various kinds of damping such
as friction, air resistance, and imperfect elasticity of the spring, free vibrations
are gradually damped out and soon disappear.   We shall now consider another
kind of vibrations produced by the action of an externally applied *disturbing
force*; these are called *forced vibrations*.   In practice, periodic disturbing forces
produced by some unbalance of rotating machines are especially important.
In Fig. 12.12a, such a disturbing force is represented by the centrifugal force of
an unbalanced rotor.   Denoting by P_0 the magnitude of this force and measuring the angle of rotation ωt as shown in the figure, we obtain vertical and
horizontal components of the disturbing force equal to $P_0 \sin \omega t$ and $P_0 \cos \omega t$,
respectively.   If the frame of the machine is rigidly attached to the foundation
(Fig. 12.12a), it will have no motion and the total centrifugal force will be
transmitted to the foundation.   To diminish this transmitted force, a spring
mounting as shown in Fig. 12.12b is sometimes used.   Assuming that there
are rollers to prevent lateral movement of the frame W, we obtain a system
similar to that previously considered in Fig. 12.2.   To determine the pulsating
vertical force transmitted through the springs to the foundation, vertical vibrations of the frame under the action of the disturbing force $P_0 \sin \omega t$ must be
considered.   The required differential equation of motion will be obtained if,
to the previously considered forces [see Eq. (*b*), page 564], the vertical disturbing force will be added.   Thus,

$$\frac{W}{g}\ddot{x} = W - (W + kx) + P_0 \sin \omega t \tag{a}$$

and with the notations

$$q_0 = \frac{P_0 g}{W} \qquad p^2 = \frac{kg}{W} \tag{b}$$

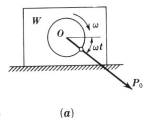

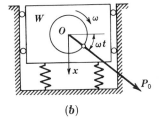

FIG. 12.12   (*a*)   (*b*)

the equation of motion (a) becomes

$$\ddot{x} + p^2 x = q_0 \sin \omega t \tag{12.7}$$

A particular solution of this equation is obtained by assuming

$$x = A \sin \omega t$$

where A is a constant. Substituting this into Eq. (12.7), we find

$$A = \frac{q_0}{p^2 - \omega^2}$$

and the required particular solution becomes

$$x = \frac{q_0}{p^2 - \omega^2} \sin \omega t \tag{12.8a}$$

Adding to this the expression (12.2), representing free vibrations, we obtain the complete solution of Eq. (12.7):

$$x = C_1 \cos pt + C_2 \sin pt + \frac{q_0}{p^2 - \omega^2} \sin \omega t \tag{12.9}$$

It is seen that this solution consists of two parts: The first two terms represent free vibrations, already discussed in Art. 12.1, and the last term, depending on the disturbing force, represents forced vibrations. It is seen that the latter vibrations have the same period $\tau_1 = 2\pi/\omega$ that the disturbing force has. Considering only these forced vibrations and using notations (b) for q_0 and p^2, Eq. (12.8a) takes the form

$$x = \frac{P_0}{k} \frac{1}{1 - \omega^2/p^2} \sin \omega t \tag{12.8b}$$

In this expression, $(P_0/k) \sin \omega t$ represents the displacement that the disturbing force would produce if acting statically, and the factor $1/(1 - \omega^2/p^2)$ accounts for the dynamic nature of this force. The absolute value of this factor is called the *magnification factor*. It depends only on the ratio ω/p, which is obtained by dividing the frequency of the disturbing force, called the *impressed frequency*, by the *natural frequency* of the system. In Fig. 12.13, values of this factor, denoted by β, are plotted against values of the ratio ω/p. It is seen that for small values of ω/p, that is, when the impressed frequency ω is small compared with the natural frequency p, the magnification factor β is approximately unity, and dynamic displacements are about the same as they would be in the case of a purely statical action of the force $P_0 \sin \omega t$. As the ratio ω/p approaches unity, the magnification factor and the amplitude of forced vibrations rapidly increase and become infinite for $\omega = p$, that is, for the case when

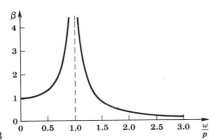

FIG. 12.13

the impressed frequency coincides with the natural frequency of the system. This condition is called *resonance*. The infinite value of the magnification factor at resonance indicates that the amplitude of vibration increases indefinitely if there is no damping. In practice, we always have some damping, and this keeps the amplitude finite at resonance, although it may become dangerously large.

When the frequency of the disturbing force increases beyond the condition of resonance, the magnification factor again becomes finite, and its absolute value diminishes as ω/p increases so that it approaches zero as shown in Fig. 12.13. This means that a high-frequency pulsating force produces forced vibrations of very small amplitude, and in many cases the body W may be considered as remaining immovable in space. The practical significance of this situation will be discussed later.

Forced vibrations of a system like that in Fig. 12.12b can be produced not only by a periodic force but also by a periodic movement of the foundation. Consider, for example, the spring-mass system shown in Fig. 12.2, page 564, and assume that the upper end of the spring supporting the weight W performs a simple harmonic motion

$$\xi = a \sin \omega t \tag{c}$$

in the vertical direction. Then, measuring displacement x of the suspended weight W from its equilibrium position, when $\xi = 0$, the elongation of the spring at any instant t will be $x - \xi + \delta_{st}$, and the corresponding tension in the spring is $k(x - \xi) + W$. Thus, the equation of motion of the suspended weight becomes

$$\frac{W}{g}\ddot{x} = W - k(x - \xi) - W = -k(x - \xi) \tag{d}$$

Substituting for ξ its expression (c) and using the notations

$$q_0 = \frac{akg}{W} \qquad p^2 = \frac{kg}{W} \tag{e}$$

Eq. (d) becomes

$$\ddot{x} + p^2 x = q_0 \sin \omega t$$

which is identical with Eq. (12.7). Thus, it may be concluded that giving the upper end of the spring a *ground motion* $a \sin \omega t$ is equivalent to applying directly to the suspended weight W a disturbing force $ak \sin \omega t$. All previous conclusions regarding the solution of Eq. (12.7) hold also in this case, and we again obtain steady-state forced vibrations defined by the equation

$$x = a \, \frac{1}{1 - \omega^2/p^2} \, \sin \omega t \tag{12.8c}$$

This coincides with Eq. (12.8b) for $ak = P_0$.

As a first application of the foregoing theory, let us consider a device, called an *oscillator*, which is used for experimentally determining the natural frequency of vibration of various engineering structures[1] (Fig. 12.14). This device consists of two identical disks rotating in opposite directions with constant angular velocities ω as shown in the figure. The bearings of the disks are housed in a rigid frame which is attached to the structure, the vibrations of which are to be studied. By attaching to the disks unbalanced weights as shown, we see that the centrifugal forces P produced during rotation of the disks give a resultant pulsating force $2P \sin \omega t$ acting along the axis of symmetry mn. This produces forced vibrations of the structure which can be recorded by proper instruments. By slowly changing the speed of the disks, we can establish the number of revolutions per second at which the amplitude of forced vibrations of the structure becomes a maximum. Assuming that this occurs at resonance, the natural frequency of free vibration of the structure is then equal to the observed number of revolutions per second of the disks. Such oscillators have been very useful in determining the natural frequencies of large structures such as bridges, office buildings, and missile launching stands.

As a second example, let us consider an instrument for measuring the amplitude of vertical vibrations. It consists of a weight W suspended inside a box on rather flexible springs, as shown in Fig. 12.15. If the points of suspension A are immovable and free vertical vibration of the weight W is produced, the equation of motion (12.1) can be applied. Assume now that the box con-

[1] Such an oscillator is described in a paper by W. Späth, *Z. Ver. Deut. Ing.*, vol. 73, p. 963, 1929.

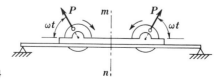

FIG. 12.14

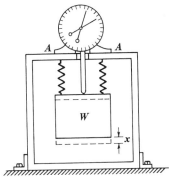

FIG. 12.15

taining the suspended weight is attached to a foundation performing small vertical vibrations. In such a case, the upper ends A of the springs move with the foundation, and forced vibrations of the weight W will be produced. Let us assume that vertical vibration of the box is represented by Eq. (c). Then we have forced vibrations of W as represented by Eq. (12.8c), and it is seen that when ω is small compared with p, the displacement x is approximately equal to ξ, and the suspended weight W performs practically the same motion as the box.

Consider now the case when ω is very large compared with p, that is, the frequency of vibration of the box is high in comparison with the natural frequency of the suspended weight W. Then, the amplitude of forced vibration, Eq. (12.8c), becomes very small, and the weight W can be regarded as immovable in space. The box simply moves up and down around it. Taking, for instance, $\omega = 10p$, we find that the amplitude of forced vibrations is only $a/99$. Thus, in such a case, vibrations of the box are scarcely transmitted to the weight W at all. This fact is utilized in various instruments for measuring and recording the amplitude of vibrations. If a dial is attached to the top of the box as shown in Fig. 12.15 with its plunger in contact with the upper face of the weight W, then, during vibration, the hand of the dial moving back and forth will record the double amplitude of relative motion of W with respect to the box. From Eq. (12.8c), this amplitude is equal to the maximum value of the expression

$$x - \xi = a \sin \omega t \left(\frac{1}{1 - \omega^2/p^2} - 1 \right)$$

from which

$$(x - \xi)_{max} = a \frac{\omega^2/p^2}{1 - \omega^2/p^2} \tag{12.10}$$

When p is small in comparison with ω, the numerical value of this expression is very close to the amplitude a of the vibrating body to which the instrument

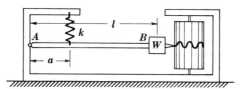

FIG. 12.16

is attached. Such an instrument is very accurate for measuring amplitudes of high-frequency vibrations and has proved very useful in power plants for studying vibrations of turbogenerators. The springs of the instrument are usually so chosen that the natural frequency is about 200 cycles/min. Then if a turbogenerator runs at 1,800 rpm, we get the amplitude of forced vibration with good accuracy.

To get a complete record of the vibrations in Fig. 12.15, a cylindrical drum rotating with constant speed about its vertical axis can be placed inside the box. Then a pencil attached to the weight W and pressing against the drum will produce a complete record of the relative motion, Eq. (12.10), between the box and the weight W. Introducing horizontal springs in addition to the vertical springs, we see that the same instrument can be used to measure horizontal vibrations.

For recording vibrations of low frequencies such as we encounter in large heavy structures, the instrument shown in Fig. 12.15 is not practical since, to attain the required very low natural frequency for the instrument, extremely flexible springs must be used, and the static deflection becomes excessive. This difficulty is overcome by using an instrument like that shown in Fig. 12.16. In such an instrument, we have

$$\delta_{st} = \frac{W}{k}\left(\frac{l}{a}\right)^2 \tag{f}$$

so that the natural frequency is

$$f = \frac{1}{2\pi}\sqrt{\frac{g}{\delta_{st}}} = \frac{1}{2\pi}\frac{a}{l}\sqrt{\frac{kg}{W}} \tag{g}$$

By adjusting the ratio a/l, this frequency can be made as small as desired.

PROBLEMS

1 A large generator having total weight $W = 20$ kips is mounted at the middle of two simply supported parallel I beams, each of which is a standard 23-lb 8-in. rolled-steel section with a clear span of 12 ft. The generator runs at 600 rpm and is out of balance to the extent of 5 lb at a radius of 10 in. What will be the amplitude of steady-state forced vibrations? Neglect the mass effect of the I beams.

   Ans. $x_{max} = 0.0036$ in.

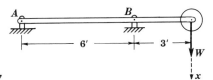

FIG. 12.17

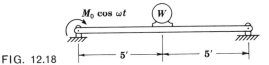

FIG. 12.18

2 The dial gauge of the vibrograph shown in Fig. 12.15 registers a relative amplitude of ± 0.08 in. during vibration of the foundation to which it is attached. Assuming that vertical motion of the foundation is simple harmonic and has a frequency of 1,200 cycles/min, what is its true amplitude a? The static deflection of the suspended weight W is $\delta_{st} = 1.00$ in.

  Ans. $a = 0.078$ in.

3 A steel beam having flexural rigidity $EI = 30 \times 4(10^6)$ lb-in.^{2} is supported as shown in Fig. 12.17 and carries a weight $W = 600$ lb at its free end. Compute the amplitude of steady-state forced vibrations of the weight W if the support A performs small vertical vibrations defined by the expression $x_A = a \sin \omega t$, where $a = 0.12$ in. and $\omega = 30$ sec^{-1}. The support B does not move, and the mass of the beam can be neglected.

  Ans. $x_{\max} = 0.131$ in.

4 The simply supported beam in Fig. 12.18 consists of two 6- $\times$ 2-in. 13-lb steel channel sections set back to back and supporting at mid-span a weight $W = 12$ kips. Compute the amplitude of steady-state forced vibrations of W if a pulsating external moment $M_0 \cos \omega t$ acts on the left end of the beam as shown. Assume that $\omega = 0.9p$, where $p = \sqrt{g/\delta_{st}}$, and $M_0 = 1,000$ in.-lb.

  Ans. $x_{\max} = 0.00457$ in.

12.4 GENERAL CASE OF A DISTURBING FORCE

In the preceding article, only the steady-state forced vibrations of a spring-suspended mass produced by a periodic disturbing force $P_0 \sin \omega t$ were considered. Very often, especially in structural dynamics, we may have to deal with a disturbing force $Q(t)$ that is not periodic. In such a case there will be no steady-state forced vibrations, and we need to know the complete response of the system which will consist of a mixture of both free and forced vibrations caused by the disturbing force. A method of obtaining a solution of the differential equation in such cases will now be considered.[1]

[1] This method was introduced by G. G. Stokes in a paper on diffraction. See "Collected Papers," vol. 2, p. 243. It was also widely used by Lord Rayleigh in his book "Theory of Sound," p. 74.

To explain the method, let us consider the system shown in Fig. 12.19*a* consisting of a spring-supported weight W constrained to move vertically and acted upon by a disturbing force $Q(t)$. The magnitude of this disturbing force per unit of mass, denoted by $q(t)$, is represented as a function of time by the ordinates of the curve *mn* in Fig. 12.19*b*. Assuming that at the initial moment $t = 0$, the weight W is at rest in its equilibrium position ($x_0 = 0$, $\dot{x}_0 = 0$), it is required to find the displacement of the body at any time $t = t_1$. To calculate this displacement, we imagine that the continuous action of the force q is represented by a series of impulses $q\,dt$ one of which is represented in Fig. 12.19*b* by the shaded strip. As a result of this one impulse occurring at the instant t, the body obtains an increment of velocity

$$d\dot{x} = q\,dt \tag{a}$$

which states that the change in momentum per unit mass is equal to the corresponding impulse. Now considering this increment of velocity as an initial velocity imparted to the body at the instant t, it follows from the solution for free vibrations represented by Eq. (12.4*a*), page 565, that the displacement of the body at some later time t_1 will be

$$dx = \frac{d\dot{x}}{p}\sin p(t_1 - t) = \frac{q\,dt}{p}\sin(pt_1 - pt) \tag{b}$$

if no further impulses are considered. To obtain the displacement x of the body at time t_1 due to the continuous action of the disturbing force from $t = 0$ to $t = t_1$, it is only necessary to sum up expressions (*b*) over this time interval. This gives

$$x = \frac{1}{p}\int_0^{t_1} q\sin(pt_1 - pt)\,dt \tag{12.11}$$

This expression includes both free and forced vibrations produced by the disturbing force, and it is especially useful in studying the motion of a system due to some kind of transient disturbance such as a wind gust or bomb blast. It can be used even in cases where the variation of q with time cannot be expressed analytically but is only represented in graphical form. It is only necessary in

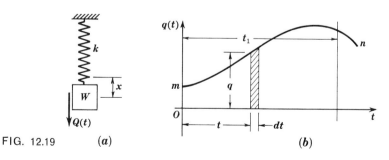

FIG. 12.19   (*a*)   (*b*)

such cases to evaluate the integral (12.11) by some numerical method of quadrature such as Simpson's rule.

If the weight W has some initial displacement x_0 and some initial velocity $\dot{x}_0$ at time $t = 0$, the solution for x at time $t = t_1$ becomes

$$x = x_0 \cos pt_1 + \frac{\dot{x}_0}{p} \sin pt_1 + \frac{1}{p} \int_0^{t_1} q \sin (pt_1 - pt)\, dt \quad (12.11a)$$

as is readily seen by referring again to the solution (12.4a), page 565.

As an example of the application of Eq. (12.11), let us again consider the case of a periodic disturbing force $Q_0 \sin \omega t$ and assume $x_0 = \dot{x}_0 = 0$. Substituting $q = q_0 \sin \omega t$, where $q_0 = Q_0 g/W$, into Eq. (12.11) and observing that

$$\sin \omega t \sin (pt_1 - pt) = \tfrac{1}{2}[\cos (\omega t + pt - pt_1)$$
$$- \cos (\omega t - pt + pt_1)]$$

we obtain, after integration,

$$x = \frac{q_0}{p^2 - \omega^2} \left(\sin \omega t_1 - \frac{\omega}{p} \sin pt_1 \right) \quad (12.12)$$

The first term in this result represents forced vibrations discussed in the preceding article [see Eq. (12.8a)], and the second term represents free vibrations. If the assumed initial conditions ($x_0 = 0$, $\dot{x}_0 = 0$, when $t = 0$) are substituted into the general solution (12.9) on page 576, we find

$$C_1 = 0 \quad \text{and} \quad C_2 = -\frac{\omega}{p} \frac{q_0}{p^2 - \omega^2}$$

and the solution (12.9) becomes identical with the solution (12.12).

Let us now consider the application of Eq. (12.11) in the case of an elastic structure subjected to a *blast pulse* as shown in Fig. 12.20. The pulse is assumed to begin with an initial value Q_0 and diminish uniformly with time until it vanishes at time $t = T$ (Fig. 12.20b). Thus, as a function of time

$$Q(t) = Q_0 \left(1 - \frac{t}{T} \right) \quad (c)$$

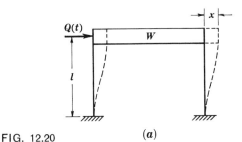

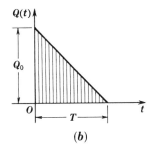

FIG. 12.20   (a)   (b)

or, if we consider the force q per unit of mass of the vibrating structure, we have

$$q(t) = \frac{Q_0 g}{W}\left(1 - \frac{t}{T}\right) = q_0\left(1 - \frac{t}{T}\right) \qquad (d)$$

The natural period of the structure in free lateral vibration may be calculated from Eq. (12.3a) on page 565. Assuming that the columns are built in top and bottom and that the horizontal beam of weight W is completely rigid, the lateral deflection of the top of the frame under the action of a horizontal force P would be $\delta = Pl^3/24EI$, and we see that the spring constant is $k = 24EI/l^3$. Thus, from Eq. (12.3a), the period is

$$\tau = \frac{2\pi}{p} = 2\pi\sqrt{\frac{W}{kg}} = 2\pi\sqrt{\frac{Wl^3}{24EIg}} \qquad (e)$$

From Eq. (12.11), we now have for the displacement of top beam of the frame at any time $t = t_1$

$$x = \frac{q_0}{p}\int_0^{t_1}\left(1 - \frac{t}{T}\right)\sin\,(pt_1 - pt)\,dt \qquad (f)$$

This expression, of course, holds only for $0 < t_1 < T$. For larger values of t_1, the blast pulse has vanished and we have to consider only free vibrations of the structure corresponding to the displacement and velocity imparted to it by the pulse.

Performing the integration indicated in Eq. (f), we obtain

$$x = \frac{q_0}{p^2}\left(1 - \frac{t_1}{T} - \cos\,pt_1 + \frac{\tau}{2\pi T}\sin\,pt_1\right) \qquad (g)$$

Noting from Eqs. (d) and (e) that $q_0/p^2 = Q_0/k$, Eq. (g) may be written

$$x = \frac{Q_0}{k}\left(1 - \frac{t_1}{T} - \cos\,pt_1 + \frac{\tau}{2\pi T}\sin\,pt_1\right) \qquad (12.13a)$$

and the corresponding velocity is, by differentiation,

$$\dot{x} = \frac{Q_0}{k}\left[p\sin\,pt_1 + \frac{1}{T}\,(\cos\,pt_1 - 1)\right] \qquad (12.13b)$$

Equations (12.13) represent the complete solution to the problem.

To get the time t_1 at which the displacement x becomes a maximum, we set the velocity $\dot{x}$ equal to zero and obtain

$$\tan\frac{\pi t_1}{\tau} = \frac{2\pi T}{\tau} \qquad (h)$$

If the duration T of the pulse is large compared with the natural period τ of the

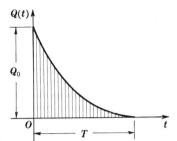

FIG. 12.21

structure, $\tan(\pi t_1/\tau)$ is a large number, and the angle $\pi t_1/\tau$ approaches $\pi/2$. Thus, the time t_1 at which the deflection of the frame becomes a maximum will be $t_1 \approx \tau/2$. Substituting this value of t_1 into Eq. (12.13a), we find

$$x_{max} = \frac{Q_0}{k}\left(2 - \frac{\tau}{2T}\right) \tag{i}$$

From this we see that when the ratio τ/T is small, the maximum displacement of the frame is approximately twice the static displacement Q_0/k.

If the duration T of the pulse is small compared with the period τ of the system, the velocity remains positive during the time $t = 0$ to $t = T$, and from Eq. (12.13b), we obtain

$$\dot{x}_T = \frac{1}{2}\frac{Q_0}{k}\frac{1}{T}\left(\frac{2\pi T}{\tau}\right)^2 = \frac{Q_0 g}{W}\frac{T}{2} \tag{j}$$

The corresponding value of the displacement from Eq. (12.13a) is

$$x_T = \frac{Q_0 g}{W}\frac{T^2}{3} \tag{k}$$

Having these values of displacement and velocity at time $t = T$ and using them as initial displacement and initial velocity in Eq. (12.4a), we obtain the displacement-time equation for the ensuing free vibrations of the system.

If the structure in Fig. 12.20a is subjected to a blast pulse of parabolic form as shown in Fig. 12.21, we have for the force per unit mass

$$q(t) = \frac{Q_0 g}{W}\left(1 - \frac{t}{T}\right)^2 = q_0\left(1 - \frac{t}{T}\right)^2 \tag{l}$$

instead of expression (d). In such case, Eq. (12.11) becomes, for $0 < t_1 < T$,

$$x = \frac{q_0}{p}\int_0^{t_1}\left(1 - \frac{t}{T}\right)^2 \sin\left(pt_1 - pt\right)\, dt$$

which, after integration, gives

$$x = \frac{q_0}{p^2}\left[(1 - \cos pt_1)\left(1 - \frac{2}{p^2 T^2}\right) + \frac{2}{pT}\sin pt_1 - \frac{2t_1}{T} + \frac{t_1^2}{T^2}\right]$$

Noting that $q_0/p^2 = Q_0/k$ while $p = 2\pi/\tau$, this can be reexpressed in the form

$$x = \frac{Q_0}{k}\left[\left(1 - \cos\frac{2\pi t_1}{\tau}\right)\left(1 - \frac{1}{2\pi^2}\frac{\tau^2}{T^2}\right) + \frac{\tau}{\pi T}\sin\frac{2\pi t_1}{\tau}\right.$$
$$\left. - 2\frac{t_1}{T} + \frac{t_1^2}{T^2}\right] \quad (12.14)$$

We see again that if τ is small compared with T, the maximum dynamic displacement approaches the value $2Q_0/k$ when $t_1 \approx \tau/2$.

While the triangular and parabolic pulses shown in Figs. 12.20b and 12.21 may be considered as rough approximations to a real blast pulse, the actual variation of force with time is more closely represented by the diagram shown in Fig. 12.22. Such a blast pulse is characterized by a very rapid rise in magnitude to a maximum value Q_{max} at time $t = t_a$ followed by a more gradual exponential decay. This variation of force with time can be very realistically expressed by the equation[1]

$$Q(t) = Cte^{-at} \quad (m)$$

where C and a are constants that can be chosen so as to give the desired strength Q_{max} of the blast at the desired time t_a. Setting the time derivative of expression (m) equal to zero, we obtain

$$C(1 - at)e^{-at} = 0$$

from which we see that Q_{max} occurs at time $t_a = 1/a$. Substituting this value of t into Eq. (m), we then find $Q_{max} = C/ae$. Thus, when Q_{max} and t_a are specified, the constants C and a can be determined.

[1] See L. S. Jacobsen and R. S. Ayre, "Engineering Vibrations," p. 154, McGraw-Hill Book Company, New York, 1958.

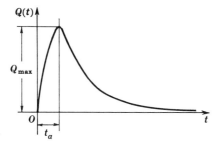

FIG. 12.22

Introducing the notation

$$c = \frac{Cg}{W}$$

the expression for the blast force per unit mass of the structure becomes

$$q(t) = cte^{-at} \tag{n}$$

Then, assuming that the structure is at rest in its equilibrium position at time $t = 0$, Eq. (12.11a) becomes

$$x = \frac{c}{p} \int_0^{t_1} te^{-at} \sin (pt_1 - pt) \, dt \tag{o}$$

Noting that

$$\sin (pt_1 - pt) = \sin pt_1 \cos pt - \cos pt_1 \sin pt$$

expression (o) can be integrated by parts, and we obtain finally for the dynamic displacement of the structure

$$x = \frac{ct_1 e^{-at_1}}{a^2 + p^2} + \frac{2ac}{(a^2 + p^2)^2} (e^{-at_1} - \cos pt_1) + \frac{c(a^2 - p^2)}{p(a^2 + p^2)^2} \sin pt_1$$

$$\tag{12.15}$$

A good approximation to the maximum value of this displacement can be obtained by evaluating x for $t_1 = \tau/2$.

Equation (12.11) is also useful in finding the response of a structure to a series of impulses. Assume, for example, that the weight W in Fig. 12.19a receives at the instants $t = t'$, $t = t''$, . . . increments of velocity $\Delta \dot{x}_1$, $\Delta \dot{x}_2$, ... Then at time $t = t_1$, the displacement will be

$$x = \frac{1}{p} [\Delta \dot{x}_1 \sin (pt_1 - pt') + \Delta \dot{x}_2 \sin (pt_1 - pt'') + \cdots] \tag{p}$$

If t', t'', . . . are multiples of $\tau = 2\pi/p$, the amplitude of vibration will grow with time.

PROBLEMS

1   Using Eq. (12.11), develop a displacement-time equation for the response of the system in Fig. 12.19a to a disturbing force $Q(t) = Wbt/g$, where b is a constant. Assume that $x_0 = 0$ and $\dot{x}_0 = 0$ when $t = 0$.
    Ans. $x = bt/p^2 - (b/p^3) \sin pt$.
2   An elevator cage of weight W is supported by a flexible steel cable which is unwinding from a circular drum of radius r so that the cage is being lowered with constant speed v_0. At a certain instant $t = 0$ a brake is applied to the rotating drum so that it begins to slow down with constant angular deceleration $\alpha = a/r$. If the

length of unwound cable at this instant, $t = 0$, is l and $AE/l = k$, what is the displacement x of the cage thereafter from its equilibrium position at $t = 0$?

Ans. $x = v_0 t - \frac{1}{2} a t^2 + (a/p^2)(1 - \cos pt)$, where $0 < t < v_0/a$.

3 After the drum comes to rest in the preceding problem, the cage will have some ensuing free vibrations as a mass suspended on the vertical elastic cable now fixed at its upper end. What will be the amplitude A of these residual free vibrations?

Ans. $A = (\sqrt{2}\, a/p^2) \sqrt{1 - \cos (pv_0/a)}$.

4 For the frame structure shown in Fig. 12.20a, the following numerical data are given: $W = 10$ kips, $k = 24EI/l^3 = 100$ kips/in. The structure is subjected to a horizontally acting blast pulse like that shown in Fig. 12.22 for which $Q_{max} = 100$ kips and $t_a = 1/a = 0.10$ sec. Calculate, from Eq. (12.15), the approximate value of x_{max}.

Ans. $x_{max} \approx 2.54$ in.

5 Using Eq. (12.11), calculate the complete response of the spring-supported weight W in Fig. 12.19a to a disturbing force $Q(t) = Q_0 \cos \omega t$, if $Q_0 g/W = q_0$ and $kg/W = p^2$. Assume $x = 0$, $\dot{x} = 0$, when $t = 0$.

Ans. $x = \dfrac{q_0}{p^2 - \omega^2} (\cos \omega t - \cos pt)$.

12.5 NUMERICAL INTEGRATION

In the preceding article, the spring force was assumed to be proportional to deflection, and on the basis of this assumption, the general solution (12.11) was obtained. Sometimes elastic forces follow a more complicated nonlinear law, in which case a rigorous solution of the differential equation of motion becomes difficult, and recourse must be had to some approximate method. One such procedure, applicable in these cases, consists in using numerical step-by-step integration. To explain this procedure, let us consider the case of free vibrations without damping where the differential equation of motion will have the form

$$\ddot{x} = f(x) \qquad (a)$$

If the initial conditions, i.e., the values of displacement x and velocity $\dot{x}$ at $t = 0$, are given, the change in x and $\dot{x}$ with time can be calculated by using step-by-step integration. By substituting the value of $(x)_{t=0}$ into Eq. (a), we can calculate the value of $(\ddot{x})_{t=0}$. Then, knowing the initial acceleration, the velocity and displacement at the instant $t = t_1$, chosen very close to the time $t = 0$, can be calculated on the assumption that the acceleration remains constant during this short time interval. If we denote by Δt the small interval of time between $t = 0$ and $t = t_1$, the approximate values of $(\dot{x})_{t=t_1}$ and $(x)_{t=t_1}$ will be obtained from the following equations:

$$\dot{x}_1 = \dot{x}_0 + \ddot{x}_0\, \Delta t \qquad x_1 = x_0 + \tfrac{1}{2}(\dot{x}_0 + \dot{x}_1)\, \Delta t \qquad (12.16a)$$

Next, substituting the value of x_1 into Eq. (a), we shall obtain the value of $\ddot{x}_1$. Then, by using this latter value, still better approximations for $\dot{x}_1$ and x_1 can be calculated from the equations

$$\dot{x}_1 = \dot{x}_0 + \tfrac{1}{2}(\ddot{x}_0 + \ddot{x}_1)\,\Delta t \qquad x_1 = x_0 + \tfrac{1}{2}(\dot{x}_0 + \dot{x}_1)\,\Delta t \qquad (12.16b)$$

A second approximation for $\ddot{x}_1$ will now be obtained by substituting this second approximation for x_1 into Eq. (a).

Taking a second step and using the obtained values of x_1, $\dot{x}_1$, $\ddot{x}_1$, the magnitudes of x_2, $\dot{x}_2$, $\ddot{x}_2$ for the time $t = t_2 = 2\,\Delta t$ can be calculated in exactly the same manner as explained above, and so on. By taking the time interval Δt sufficiently small and making the calculations for every value of t twice, in order to get the second approximation, this method of numerical integration can usually be used with sufficient accuracy for practical applications, especially if we are only interested in the motion for a comparatively short period of time.

To illustrate the procedure and to give some idea of the accuracy that can be obtained with it, we consider the case of simple harmonic vibration, for which the equation of motion is

$$\ddot{x} = -p^2 x \tag{b}$$

Assuming that when $t = 0$, $x = x_0$, $\dot{x} = 0$, the exact solution of this equation is

$$x = x_0 \cos pt \qquad \dot{x} = -px_0 \sin pt \tag{c}$$

The results of the numerical integration, carried out as explained above, are given in Table 12.1 below. In this case, the time intervals were taken to be $\Delta t = 1/4p$. Since the period of vibration in this case is $\tau = 2\pi/p$, it is seen that the chosen interval Δt is approximately equal to one-sixth of a quarter period $\tau/4$. The first line of the table expresses the assumed initial conditions. Starting now with the first step, we obtain the first approximation for $\dot{x}_1$ and x_1 at the time $t = \Delta t = 1/4p$ by using Eqs. (12.16a). The results so obtained are shown in the second line of the table. To get better approximations for $\dot{x}_1$ and x_1, the calculations are now repeated, using Eqs. (12.16b). These results appear in the third line of the table. Proceeding in this manner, the complete table was calculated. In the last two columns, the corresponding values of $\cos pt$ and $\sin pt$ are shown. In this case they are proportional to the exact solution (c), so that the accuracy of the numerical integration can be seen directly from the table. We see that the velocities obtained from the numerical integration have a very high accuracy. The error in the displacements, however, is seen to be growing with time, and in the last line of the table it amounts to about 1 percent of the initial displacement x_0. These results were obtained by taking only six intervals Δt in a quarter period. By increasing the number of intervals, the accuracy can be improved, but at the same time, the amount of labor in making the calculations becomes greater.

TABLE 12.1   NUMERICAL INTEGRATION

t	x	$\dot{x}$	$\ddot{x}$	$\cos pt$	$\sin pt$
0	x_0	0	$-p^2x_0$	1.0000	0.0000
Δt	$0.9687x_0$	$-0.2500px_0$	$-0.9687p^2x_0$		
Δt	$0.9692x_0$	$-0.2461px_0$	$-0.9692p^2x_0$	0.9689	0.2474
$2\,\Delta t$	$0.8774x_0$	$-0.4884px_0$	$-0.8774p^2x_0$		
$2\,\Delta t$	$0.8788x_0$	$-0.4769px_0$	$-0.8788p^2x_0$	0.8776	0.4794
$3\,\Delta t$	$0.7321x_0$	$-0.6966px_0$	$-0.7321p^2x_0$		
$3\,\Delta t$	$0.7344x_0$	$-0.6783px_0$	$-0.7344p^2x_0$	0.7317	0.6816
$4\,\Delta t$	$0.5419x_0$	$-0.8619px_0$	$-0.5419p^2x_0$		
$4\,\Delta t$	$0.5449x_0$	$-0.8378px_0$	$-0.5449p^2x_0$	0.5403	0.8415
$5\,\Delta t$	$0.3184x_0$	$-0.9740px_0$	$-0.3184p^2x_0$		
$5\,\Delta t$	$0.3220x_0$	$-0.9457px_0$	$-0.3220p^2x_0$	0.3153	0.9490
$6\,\Delta t$	$0.0755x_0$	$-1.0262px_0$	$-0.0755p^2x_0$		
$6\,\Delta t$	$0.0794x_0$	$-0.9954px_0$	$-0.0794p^2x_0$	0.0707	0.9975
$7\,\Delta t$	$-0.1719x_0$	$-1.0153px_0$	$-0.1719p^2x_0$		
$7\,\Delta t$	$-0.1680x_0$	$-0.9838px_0$	$-0.1680p^2x_0$	-0.1792	0.9840

By using the data from Table 12.1, the period of free vibration also can be determined. It is seen from the values of x that for $t = 6\,\Delta t$, the displacement-time curve has a positive ordinate $+0.0794x_0$, while for $t = 7\,\Delta t$, the ordinate is negative and equal to $-0.1680x_0$. The point of zero displacement determines the time required to make a quarter cycle of vibration. Using linear interpolation, this time will be found from the equation

$$\frac{\tau}{4} = 6\,\Delta t + \Delta t\,\frac{0.0794}{0.0794 + 0.1680} = 6.32\,\Delta t = \frac{6.32}{4p} = \frac{1.58}{p}$$

The exact value of the quarter period is $\tau/4 = 1.57/p$. Hence, the above-calculated approximate value may be considered satisfactory.

The described method of numerical integration can be used also in those cases where the elastic spring force is not proportional to x but is represented by a more general function of x; see Eq. (a). As an example, let us consider free vibrations of the system shown in Fig. 12.23a, consisting of a particle of mass m attached to the mid-point of a tightly stretched wire of length $2l$. When the particle has a small displacement x from its middle position, the tension in each branch of the wire will be

$$S = S_0 + \frac{AE}{l}\,(\sqrt{l^2 + x^2} - l) \tag{d}$$

where S_0 is the initial tension when $x = 0$. Expanding the radical in Eq. (d) by the binomial theorem and keeping only the first two terms of this expansion

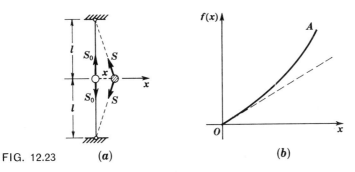

FIG. 12.23   (a)   (b)

on the assumption that $x \ll l$, we obtain

$$S \approx S_0 + \frac{AE}{2l^2} x^2 \tag{d'}$$

If S_0 is large, the second term in Eq. (d') can be neglected, and we have $S \approx S_0$ provided the ratio x/l is extremely small. This means that for very small amplitudes of free vibration the equation of motion becomes

$$m\ddot{x} = -\frac{2S_0}{l} x$$

or with the notations

$$k_0 = \frac{2S_0}{l} \qquad p_0^2 = \frac{k_0}{m} \tag{e}$$

$$\ddot{x} + p_0^2 x = 0 \tag{f}$$

which represents simple harmonic vibrations with the period

$$\tau_0 = \frac{2\pi}{p_0} \tag{g}$$

If the second term in Eq. (d') is not neglected, the equation of motion becomes

$$m\ddot{x} = -\frac{2S_0}{l} x - \frac{AE}{l^3} x^3$$

or using notations (e), together with the additional notations

$$k_1 = \frac{AE}{l^3} \qquad \beta = \frac{k_1}{k_0} \tag{h}$$

we obtain the equation of motion in the form

$$\ddot{x} = -p_0^2(x + \beta x^3) \tag{i}$$

We see that the restoring force $f(x)$ per unit mass of the particle in this case is a cubic parabola as shown in Fig. 12.23b. For very small values of x, the curve OA coincides very closely with its initial tangent, and we have practically a linear restoring force. This leads to simple harmonic vibrations having the period τ_0 given by Eq. (g). For somewhat larger values of x, the curve OA in Fig. 12.23b deviates noticeably from its initial tangent, and we must use the equation of motion (i) instead of (f). This Eq. (i) no longer represents simple harmonic motion, and we shall find that the period τ depends on the amplitude, becoming shorter and shorter for larger and larger amplitudes.

To carry out a step-by-step numerical integration of Eq. (i), we assume the following numerical data: $mg = 1$ lb, $k_0 = 2$ lb/in., $k_1 = 4$ lb/in.^{3}, and, as initial conditions at $t = 0$, $x_0 = 1$ in., $\dot{x}_0 = 0$. Then, $\beta = k_1/k_0 = 2$ in.$^{-2}$, and Eq. (i) takes the form

$$\ddot{x} = -p_0^2(x + 2x^3) \tag{i'}$$

In this case it is more convenient to work with the quantities x, $\dot{x}/p_0$, $\ddot{x}/p_0^2$, and then replace the time steps Δt in Eqs. (12.16) by $\Delta(p_0 t)$. Then, for numerical calculation, Eqs. (12.16a), for the first approximation, are written in the form

$$\frac{\dot{x}_1}{p_0} = \frac{\dot{x}_0}{p_0} + \frac{\ddot{x}_0}{p_0^2}\,\Delta(p_0 t) \qquad x_1 = x_0 + \frac{1}{2}\left(\frac{\dot{x}_0}{p_0} + \frac{\dot{x}_1}{p_0}\right)\Delta(p_0 t) \tag{12.17a}$$

and Eqs. (12.16b), for the second approximations, in the form

$$\frac{\dot{x}_1}{p_0} = \frac{\dot{x}_0}{p_0} + \frac{1}{2}\left(\frac{\ddot{x}_0}{p_0^2} + \frac{\ddot{x}_1}{p_0^2}\right)\Delta(p_0 t)$$

$$x_1 = x_0 + \frac{1}{2}\left(\frac{\dot{x}_0}{p_0} + \frac{\dot{x}_1}{p_0}\right)\Delta(p_0 t) \tag{12.17b}$$

For the length of the steps $\Delta(p_0 t)$, we divide the basic period τ_0, as given by Eq. (g), roughly into 40 parts, i.e., about ten steps in the quarter period $\tau_0/4$. This gives $\Delta(p_0 t) = p_0\tau_0/40 = 2\pi/40 = 0.157$; thus, in round numbers, $\Delta(p_0 t) = 0.15$ will be used. In choosing this time step, it should be realized that for amplitude $x_0 = 1$ in., the period τ will be considerably less than τ_0, and so we are probably dividing the true quarter period $\tau/4$ into only seven or eight parts. This means that we can expect about the same degree of accuracy from the numerical integration in this case that we had in the preceding example.

On the basis of the chosen interval $\Delta(p_0 t) = 0.15$ and Eq. (i'), the numerical calculations made from Eqs. (12.17) are shown in Table 12.2. After seven steps, each repeated once, we find that the displacement x becomes negative, indicating that we have completed a little more than a quarter cycle of vibration. Using a linear interpolation between the last two values $x = 0.153$ and $x = -0.059$, we find that $x = 0$ when $p_0 t = 1.01$. Hence, the complete

TABLE 12.2

$p_0 t$	x	$\dfrac{\dot{x}}{p_0}$	x^3	$\dfrac{\ddot{x}}{p_0^2}$	$\dfrac{\ddot{x}_0 + \ddot{x}_1}{2p_0^2}\Delta(p_0 t)$	$\dfrac{\dot{x}_0 + \dot{x}_1}{2p_0}\Delta(p_0 t)$
0	1.000	0	1.000	−3.000	−0.450	
0.15	0.966	−0.450	0.902	−2.770	−0.433	−0.034
0.15	0.968	−0.433	0.907	−2.782	−0.433	−0.032
0.30	0.871	−0.866	0.661	−2.193	−0.370	−0.097
0.30	0.875	−0.803	0.670	−2.215	−0.374	−0.093
0.45	0.727	−1.177	0.384	−1.495	−0.278	−0.148
0.45	0.734	−1.081	0.395	−1.524	−0.280	−0.141
0.60	0.551	−1.361	0.167	−0.885	−0.181	−0.183
0.60	0.558	−1.262	0.174	−0.906	−0.182	−0.176
0.75	0.355	−1.444	0.045	−0.445	−0.101	−0.203
0.75	0.361	−1.363	0.047	−0.455	−0.102	−0.197
0.90	0.149	−1.465	0.003	−0.155	−0.045	−0.212
0.90	0.153	−1.408	0.004	−0.161	−0.046	−0.208
1.05	−0.062	−1.454	0.000	−0.062	−0.016	−0.215
1.05	−0.059	−1.424				−0.212

period corresponds to $p_0\tau = 4(1.01) = 4.04$, and with $p_0 = \sqrt{k_0/m} = \sqrt{2g}$ $= \sqrt{772} = 27.8$ sec^{-1}, we find

$$\tau = \frac{4.04}{27.8} = 0.1452 \text{ sec}$$

The exact value of τ in this case can be calculated from an elliptic integral and is $\tau_{ex} = 0.1447$ sec. We see that the error in the period from the results of the numerical integration is about 0.3 percent.

For very small amplitudes of vibration of the nonlinear system shown in Fig. 12.23a, the period calculated from Eq. (g) is

$$\tau_0 = \frac{2\pi}{p_0} = \frac{6.28}{27.8} = 0.266 \text{ sec}$$

Comparing this with the above calculated period for an amplitude of 1 in., we see that the nonlinear effect on the period is quite significant.

If necessary, the accuracy of numerical integration can be further improved by using, instead of simple equations like (12.16) or (12.17), more elaborate expressions[1] for calculating consecutive values of x and $\dot{x}$. Recourse to such methods should be had if the motion during a long interval of time is to be studied.

[1] See H. von Sanden, "Practical Mathematical Analysis," E. P. Dutton & Co., Inc., New York, 1926.

12.6 GRAPHICAL INTEGRATION

In many practical cases of structural dynamics, the disturbing force, as a function of time, may be given in the form of a curve, as shown in Fig. 12.24, which cannot be expressed analytically. In such cases, an approximate solution for the response of the system to the disturbing force can be obtained by a method of graphical integration.[1]   To accomplish this, we replace the given $Q(t)$, represented by the smooth curve *abcde* in Fig. 12.24, by a *step function* having constant ordinates $Q_1, Q_2, Q_3, \ldots$ over equal intervals of time Δt as shown.   Then beginning at $t = 0$ and knowing the initial displacement x_0 and the initial velocity $\dot{x}_0$, we calculate the motion of the mass produced by the constant force Q_1 acting for the first time interval Δt and find the displacement x_1 and the velocity $\dot{x}_1$ at the end of this interval, i.e., at time $t = \Delta t$.   Then with x_1 and $\dot{x}_1$ as new initial displacement and new initial velocity, we again calculate the motion of the system under the action of the constant force Q_2, suddenly applied at time $t = \Delta t$, and find the displacement x_2 and the velocity $\dot{x}_2$ at the end of the second interval, i.e., at time $t = 2\,\Delta t$, etc.   In this way, the complete motion of the system under the influence of the step function can be determined.

We see that in order to carry out the procedure outlined above, it is first necessary to study the response of the system to the action of a suddenly applied constant force Q_i.   To do this, we consider the system in Fig. 12.25a and assume that $Q(t) = Q_i = \text{const.}$ Then the equation of motion becomes

$$m\ddot{x} = -kx + Q_i$$

or with the notations

$$p^2 = \frac{k}{m} \qquad \delta_i = \frac{Q_i}{k} \qquad\qquad (a)$$

[1] The method to be described is due to J. Laméon; see *Rev. Universelle Mines*, vol. 11, 1935.

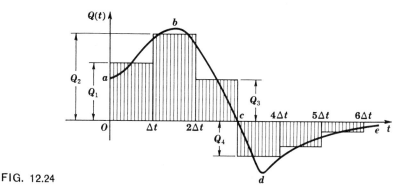

FIG. 12.24

we obtain

$$\ddot{x} + p^2 x = p^2 \delta_i \qquad (b)$$

The solution of this differential equation is

$$x = C_1 \cos pt + C_2 \sin pt + \delta_i \qquad (c)$$

which can easily be verified by substituting back into Eq. (b). Differentiating Eq. (c) once with respect to time, we obtain

$$\dot{x} = -pC_1 \sin pt + pC_2 \cos pt \qquad (d)$$

Now, assuming initial conditions of motion $x = x_0$, $\dot{x} = \dot{x}_0$, when $t = 0$, we find, for the constants of integration,

$$C_1 = x_0 - \delta_i \qquad C_2 = \frac{\dot{x}_0}{p}$$

Using these values, we find, with some rearrangement of terms, that Eqs. (c) and (d) become

$$x - \delta_i = (x_0 - \delta_i) \cos pt + \frac{\dot{x}_0}{p} \sin pt$$

$$\frac{\dot{x}}{p} = -(x_0 - \delta_i) \sin pt + \frac{\dot{x}_0}{p} \cos pt \qquad (e)$$

Squaring and adding Eqs. (e), we obtain

$$(x - \delta_i)^2 + \left(\frac{\dot{x}}{p}\right)^2 = (x_0 - \delta_i)^2 + \left(\frac{\dot{x}_0}{p}\right)^2 \qquad (f)$$

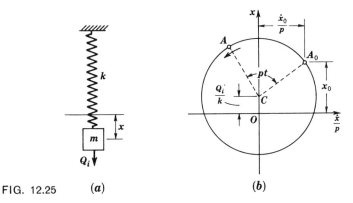

FIG. 12.25 (a) (b)

This expression will be recognized as the equation of a circle of radius

$$R = \sqrt{(x_0 - \delta_i)^2 + \left(\frac{\dot{x}_0}{p}\right)^2}$$

which has its center at the point $(\delta_i, 0)$ in the coordinate plane x versus $\dot{x}/p$. This plane is usually called the *phase plane* and the circle is called the *phase-plane trajectory*. Thus, we may conclude that the motion produced by a suddenly applied constant force Q_i is a simple harmonic vibration centered about a new equilibrium position $x = \delta_i = Q_i/k$ instead of $x = 0$. For assumed values of Q_i/k, x_0, and $\dot{x}_0$, the phase-plane circle is shown in Fig. 12.25b. To visualize the motion from its representation in the phase plane, we need only to imagine that a point A, starting from A_0 at time $t = 0$, moves in the counterclockwise direction around the circle with constant angular velocity p. Then at any instant t, defined in Fig. 12.25b by the angle pt, the displacement x and the velocity $\dot{x}$ are given by the coordinates of the moving point A.

Having this graphical phase-plane representation of the motion produced by a suddenly applied constant force, we may now return to the step function shown in Fig. 12.24 and see how to trace out a phase-plane trajectory representing the response of a spring-supported mass to a series of constant-force impulses. Referring to Fig. 12.26a, we let the point A_0, with coordinates x_0 and $\dot{x}_0/p$, represent the initial state of motion in the phase plane at time $t = 0$. Then with C_1, having the coordinates $(Q_1/k, 0)$, as a center, we construct the circular arc A_0A_1 with a central angle $p\,\Delta t$, as shown. Point A_1, obtained in this way, represents the displacement x_1 and the velocity $\dot{x}_1$ of the disturbed mass at the end of the first time interval, i.e., at time $t = \Delta t$. Now with C_2, having the coordinates $(Q_2/k, 0)$, as a new center, we construct the circular arc A_1A_2 with central angle $p\,\Delta t$ as before and obtain the point A_2, defining the displacement x_2 and velocity $\dot{x}_2$ at the end of the second interval,

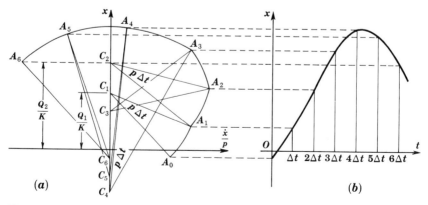

(a)   (b)

FIG. 12.26

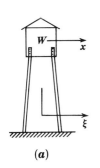

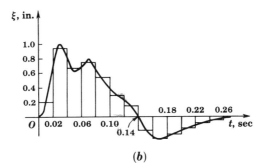

(a)

(b)

FIG. 12.27

i.e., at time $t = 2\ \Delta t$. Proceeding in this way, the construction in Fig. 12.26a has been carried out to time $t = 6\ \Delta t$ on the basis of the step function in Fig. 12.24.

Having completed the construction in Fig. 12.26a, the points $A_0, A_1, A_2, \ldots$ can be readily projected onto a displacement-time plane and the curve $x = f(t)$ constructed as shown in Fig. 12.26b.

The described graphical procedure will give good accuracy if reasonable care is taken in choosing the step curve to approximate the given disturbing force $Q(t)$. In general, this should be done in such a way that the area under each step is the same as that under the corresponding portion of the given smooth curve representing $Q(t)$. In choosing the time interval Δt, we must be guided not only by variations in the given $Q(t)$ curve but also by the natural period $\tau = 2\pi/p$ of the spring-suspended mass. In general, Δt must be a small fraction of this period. If the disturbing force exhibits rapid variations over part of its duration and is fairly constant over another part, it may be expedient to vary the time intervals Δt accordingly. There is no fundamental reason for the time intervals to be equal.

As an example of the application of the above-described method of graphical integration, let us consider the case of a water tank, shown in Fig. 12.27a, the base of which is subjected to a horizontal ground motion $\xi = q(t)$ as represented graphically by the smooth curve in Fig. 12.27b. The weight of the tank is W, and the flexural rigidity of the columns is such that the natural period of free lateral vibration of the tank is $\tau = 0.48$ sec. Considering this period together with the fluctuations in the given ground motion, we conclude that $\Delta t = 0.02$ sec will be a satisfactory time interval for the problem, and we make the step function as shown in Fig. 12.27b accordingly. Since $p = 2\pi/\tau$, the angular steps in the phase plane will be

$$p\ \Delta t = \frac{2\pi}{\tau}\ \Delta t = 2\pi\ \frac{0.02}{0.48} = \frac{\pi}{12} = 15°$$

Denoting by x the lateral displacement of the tank and by ξ the displacement of the ground, the equation of motion becomes

$$\frac{W}{g}\ddot{x} = -k(x - \xi)$$

or with the notation $kg/W = p^2$,

$$\ddot{x} + p^2 x = p^2 \xi \tag{g}$$

Comparing this equation with Eq. (b), we see that, in this case, the ground displacement ξ corresponds exactly to the quantity $\delta_i = Q_i/k$ in the case of a disturbing force. Hence, we may proceed with the phase-plane constructions as already explained above. These constructions made on the basis of the approximate step curve in Fig. $12.27b$ are shown in Fig. $12.28a$, and the corresponding displacement-time curve is shown in Fig. $12.28b$. It was assumed in making the constructions that the initial conditions of motion of the tank were $x_0 = 0$ and $\dot{x}_0 = 0$ at $t = 0$. We note that the tank attains, within the duration of the disturbance, a maximum absolute displacement $x = 0.85$ in. at $t = 0.17$ sec and is left with an ensuing free vibration having the amplitude $A = 0.925$ in., which is the length of the radius vector $\overline{OA}_{13}$ of the last point A_{13} of the phase-plane trajectory (see Fig. $12.28a$). However, comparison of the displacement-time curve $x = f(t)$ with the ground-motion curve $\xi = q(t)$, also shown in Fig. $12.28b$, shows that the maximum relative displacement between the tank and the ground is $(x - \xi)_{max} \approx 1.13$ in. and that this occurs at $t = 0.16$ sec. Naturally, this maximum relative displacement represents the critical point of the response, since it will determine the maximum bending stresses induced in the columns.

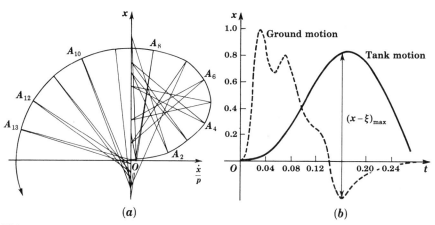

(a) (b)

FIG. 12.28

As a second example, let us consider the simple portal frame shown in Fig. 12.29a which is subjected to a horizontally acting rectangular blast pulse of strength $Q_0 = 1,492$ lb and duration $t_1 = 0.2$ sec as shown in Fig. 12.29b. Each of the two side columns is a steel channel section built in at both ends and having cross-sectional moment of inertia $I = 1.54$ in.[4] Hence, the lateral deflection δ under the action of a horizontal force P acting as shown in Fig. 12.29c is

$$\delta = \frac{Pl^3}{24EI} \tag{h}$$

and the spring constant for the structure becomes

$$k = \frac{24EI}{l^3} = 373 \text{ lb/in.}$$

Then $p = \sqrt{kg/W} = \sqrt{373 \times \frac{386}{2400}} = 7.75 \text{ sec}^{-1}$, and $\tau = 2\pi/p = 0.813$ sec.

Noting that the bending moments at a, b, c, d in Fig. 12.29c have the magnitude $M = Pl/4$, Eq. (h) can be expressed also in the form

$$\delta = \frac{Ml^2}{6EI} \tag{h'}$$

Then, if the yield stress for the steel is such that the plastic moment for the channel section is $M_p = 40,000$ in.-lb, we find from Eq. (h') that

$$\delta_p = \frac{M_p l^2}{6EI} = 3 \text{ in.}$$

i.e., when the displacement x of the disturbed structure attains the value δ_p, the columns begin to behave plastically and offer no further increase in resistance to lateral displacement.

Let us assume now that at $t = 0$ the frame stands vertically in its equilibrium position, that is, $x_0 = 0$ and $\dot{x}_0 = 0$. Then, so long as the columns remain

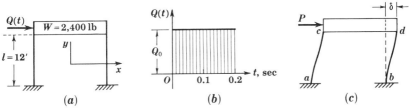

FIG. 12.29

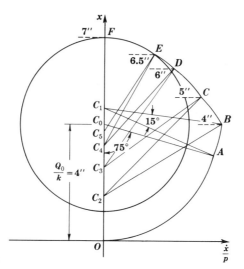

FIG. 12.30

elastic, i.e., up to the displacement $x = \delta_p = 3$ in., the equation of motion is

$$\ddot{x} + p^2 x = p^2 \frac{Q_0}{k} \tag{i}$$

where $Q_0/k = 1{,}492 \div 373 = 4$ in. Hence, with C_0 having the coordinates $(4, 0)$ in the phase plane (Fig. 12.30) as a center, we construct the arc OA of such length that point A has the ordinate $x = \delta_p = 3$ in. as shown. The corresponding subtended angle is $pt = 75° = 5\pi/12$, and with $p = 7.75$ sec^{-1}, this corresponds to $t = 0.167$ sec. Hence, at this instant the structure begins to behave plastically, and the disturbing force Q_0 has another 0.033 sec to act, which corresponds to an angle $p\,\Delta t = 15°$ in the phase plane. For this remaining time that the disturbing force has to act, that is, for $0.167 < t < 0.200$, the equation of motion will be

$$\frac{W}{g}\ddot{x} = -k\delta_p + Q_0$$

which can be written in the equivalent form

$$\ddot{x} + p^2 x = p^2 \left(\frac{Q_0}{k} - \delta_p + x \right) = p^2 \delta_i \tag{j}$$

where δ_i determines the position on the x axis in Fig. 12.30 of the center C_i for each arc of the phase-plane trajectory. In our example, we have $Q_0/k = 4$ in. and $\delta_p = 3$ in., so that $\delta_i = 1 + x$. Noting that we begin with $x = 3$ in. and that a step $p\,\Delta t = 15°$ will carry us to $x \approx 4$ in., we take, for the average value of δ_i during the interval, $(\delta_i)_{av} = (4 + 5)/2 = 4.5$ in. and obtain the center C_1 as shown. In this example, we have reached, at point B, the limit of validity of Eq. (j), since the disturbing force vanishes at $pt = \pi/2 = 90°$, and only one step is required.

After the disappearance of the disturbing force and until the structure comes to a stop, the equation of motion will be

$$\frac{W}{g}\ddot{x} = -k\delta_p$$

which, for the purpose of phase-plane representation, can be written in the equivalent form

$$\ddot{x} + p^2x = p^2(x - \delta_p) = p^2\delta_i \tag{k}$$

Succeeding centers C_2, C_3, C_4, . . . are now determined from the expression

$$\delta_i = x - \delta_p = x - 3$$

Since these values of δ_i again depend upon the displacement x, the average value of δ_i for each step should be used in locating the center C_i for that step. For example, to make the arc BC, we decide in advance to go from $x = 4$ in. at point B to $x = 5$ in. at point C. Then for this step $(\delta_i)_{av} = (1 + 2)/2 = 1.5$ in., and we choose the center C_2 accordingly. Proceeding in this way, the constructions in Fig. 12.30 have been continued until the trajectory $BCDEF$ intersects the x axis at F, indicating that the frame has come to a stop, $\dot{x} = 0$. The ensuing free vibrations of the structure are represented in the phase plane by the circle centered again at C_0 and having the radius $x_F - \delta_0 = 7 - 4 = 3$ in. This indicates that, as a result of the blast pulse, the structure suffered some permanent damage and vibrates about a new distorted equilibrium configuration that is displaced 4 in. to the right of the original vertical equilibrium configuration. This example illustrates how the phase-plane construction may be used to follow out the response of a structure to a given disturbing force in both elastic and plastic phases of its behavior.[1]

12.7 STATICAL AND DYNAMIC STRESSES IN RAILS

Let us assume that a rail can be considered as a long bar continuously supported by an elastic foundation. Then, considering the simplest case of a single load P (Fig. 12.31) and denoting by k the modulus of the foundation, i.e., the load per unit length of rail required to produce a deflection of the foundation equal

---

[1] Such extended applications of the graphical phase-plane method have been developed by L. S. Jacobsen. See his paper On a General Method of Solving Second Order Ordinary Differential Equations by Phase-plane Displacements, *J. Appl. Mech.*, December, 1952.

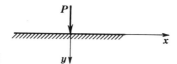

FIG. 12.31

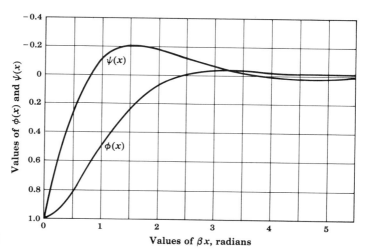

FIG. 12.32

to unity, the differential equation of the deflection curve is

$$EI \frac{d^4y}{dx^4} = -ky \qquad (a)$$

Using the notation

$$\beta = \sqrt[4]{\frac{k}{4EI}} \qquad (b)$$

we write the solution of Eq. (a) in the form[1]

$$y = \frac{\beta P}{2k} e^{-\beta x}(\cos \beta x + \sin \beta x) = \frac{\beta P}{2k} \phi(x) \qquad (c)$$

The corresponding deflection curve is shown by the curve $\phi(x)$ in Fig. 12.32. The maximum deflection takes place under the load, and substituting $x = 0$ in Eq. (c), we obtain

$$y_{x=0} = \frac{\beta P}{2k} \qquad (d)$$

[1] For the derivation of this solution see S. Timoshenko, "Strength of Materials," 3d ed., vol. II, p. 2, D. Van Nostrand Company, Inc., Princeton, N.J., 1956.

This expression can be used to calculate the modulus k of the foundation, provided the deflection of the rail under known load has been measured. The maximum deflection depends on the constants β and k. It increases with decrease of the foundation modulus k and of the flexural rigidity EI of the rail. For a 130-lb rail ($I = 72.8$ in.^{4}) and good track conditions, we may take $k \approx 1,500$ psi and $\beta \approx 0.020$ in.$^{-1}$ For calculating bending stresses, we use, for bending moment, the expression

$$M = -EI \frac{d^2y}{dx^2} = \frac{P}{4\beta} e^{-\beta x}(\cos \beta x - \sin \beta x) = \frac{P}{4\beta} \psi(x) \tag{e}$$

The function $\psi(x)$ is also represented graphically in Fig. 12.32. It is seen that the maximum bending moment occurs under the load and has the value

$$M_{max} = \frac{P}{4\beta} \tag{f}$$

For maximum stress in the rail, we then have

$$\sigma_{max} = \frac{M_{max}}{Z} = \frac{P}{4\beta Z} = \frac{P}{4Z} \sqrt[4]{\frac{4EI}{k}} \tag{g}$$

where Z denotes the section modulus of the rail.

In order to compare the stresses in rails, which have geometrically similar cross sections, Eq. (g) can be put in the following form:

$$\sigma_{max} = \frac{P}{A} \frac{A \sqrt[4]{I}}{4Z} \sqrt[4]{\frac{4E}{k}} \tag{h}$$

in which A denotes the cross-sectional area of the rail. Since the second factor in this expression remains constant for geometrically similar cross sections and since the third factor does not depend on the dimensions of the rail, the maximum stress is inversely proportional to the area of the cross section, i.e., inversely proportional to the weight of the rail per unit length.

An approximate value of the maximum pressure R on a tie is obtained by multiplying the maximum deflection, Eq. (d), by the tie spacing l and by the foundation modulus k. Thus,

$$R = \frac{\beta P}{2k} kl = \frac{P\beta l}{2} = \frac{Pl}{2} \sqrt[4]{\frac{k}{4EI}} \tag{i}$$

It may be seen from this that the pressure on the tie depends principally on the tie spacing l. It should also be noted that the modulus k of the foundation appears in both Eqs. (g) and (i) as a fourth root. Hence, an error in the determination of k will introduce only a much smaller error in the magnitudes of σ_{max} and R.

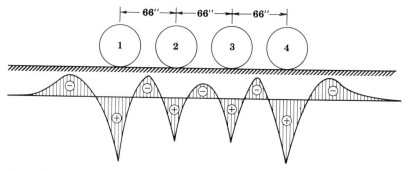

FIG. 12.33

When several loads are acting on the rail, as in the case of a set of locomotive wheels, the bending moments and stresses in the rail can be obtained by superposition. In Fig. 12.33, for example, the result of such superposition for the bending moments produced by four equal and equally spaced wheel loads is shown.

The above analysis was made on the basis of several simplifying assumptions which are only an approximation. Nevertheless, the results obtained have proved very useful especially as a guide to experimental investigations of stresses in rails.[1]

The dynamic deflection of rails and the dynamic stresses under the action of the moving wheels of a locomotive may become much larger than those calculated on the basis of static formulas. There are various causes which may produce such an increase in deflection and stress, the principal ones being:

> *1* Different kinds of irregularities in the shape of the wheel or rail, such as flat spots on the rim of the wheel, low spots on the rail, and discontinuities at the rail joints
> *2* Variation in the forces acting on the rail caused by variable spring forces on the wheel, the vertical component of the centrifugal force of a counterweight, and the vertical component of the forces in the connecting rods

In discussing dynamic stresses produced in a rail by the effect of a low spot (Fig. 12.34), let η be the variable depth of the low spot, a given function of x measured along the rail. Let W/g denote the unsprung mass per wheel, $2k/\beta$ the vertical load required to produce a rail deflection equal to unity [see Eq. (d)], and y the additional deflection of the rail under the wheel due to the dynamic effect of the low spot. Then the vertical displacement of the wheel

[1] See the paper by S. Timoshenko and B. F. Langer, *Trans. ASME*, vol. 54, p. 277, 1932.

due to both the dynamic deflection of the rail and the low spot is $y + \eta$, and the differential equation of motion of the wheel in the vertical direction is

$$\frac{W}{g}\frac{d^2(y + \eta)}{dt^2} + \frac{2ky}{\beta} = 0 \tag{12.18a}$$

Denoting by v the uniform locomotive speed, we obtain

$$\frac{d\eta}{dt} = \frac{d\eta}{dx}\frac{dx}{dt} = \frac{d\eta}{dx}v \qquad \frac{d^2\eta}{dt^2} = \frac{d^2\eta}{dx^2}v^2$$

and Eq. (12.18a) can be put in the following form:

$$\frac{W}{g}\frac{d^2y}{dt^2} + \frac{2ky}{\beta} = -\frac{W}{g}v^2\frac{d^2\eta}{dx^2} \tag{12.18b}$$

If the shape of the low spot and the speed v are known, the right-hand member of Eq. (12.18b) can easily be expressed as a function of time, and we arrive at the equation of forced vibration as discussed in Art. 12.4, the solution of which can be easily obtained in each particular case.

As an example, let us consider the case of a low spot as shown in Fig. 12.34, the shape of which is given by the equation

$$\eta = \frac{\lambda}{2}\left(1 - \cos\frac{2\pi x}{l}\right) \tag{j}$$

in which l is the length of the low spot and λ the depth at the middle of its length. Then the right-hand member of Eq. (12.18b) becomes

$$-\frac{W}{g}v^2\frac{\lambda}{2}\frac{4\pi^2}{l^2}\cos\frac{2\pi x}{l}$$

Measuring time from the instant when the point of contact of the wheel coincides with the beginning of the low spot, as in Fig. 12.34, we have $x = vt$, and Eq. (12.18b) becomes

$$\frac{W}{g}\frac{d^2y}{dt^2} + \frac{2ky}{\beta} = -\frac{W}{g}v^2\frac{\lambda}{2}\frac{4\pi^2}{l^2}\cos\frac{2\pi vt}{l}$$

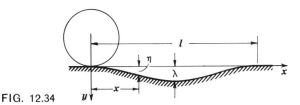

FIG. 12.34

or, using the notation

$$\frac{2kg}{\beta W} = p^2$$

we obtain

$$\frac{d^2y}{dt^2} + p^2y = -\frac{2\lambda\pi^2v^2}{l^2}\cos\frac{2\pi vt}{l}$$

To solve this differential equation, we use the method described in Art. 12.4. Then proceeding as indicated by Eq. (12.11), we obtain

$$y = -\frac{2\lambda\pi^2v^2}{pl^2}\int_0^{t_1}\cos\frac{2\pi vt}{l}\sin p(t_1 - t)\,dt \qquad (k)$$

Performing the indicated integration and denoting by $\tau = 2\pi/p$ the period of free vibration of the wheel on the rail and by $\tau_1 = l/v$ the time it takes the wheel to pass over the low spot, we obtain

$$y = \frac{\lambda}{2(1 - \tau_1^2/\tau^2)}\left(\cos\frac{2\pi t_1}{\tau_1} - \cos\frac{2\pi t_1}{\tau}\right) \qquad (12.19)$$

From this expression the additional dynamic deflection at any instant $t_1 \leq \tau_1$ can be calculated. It is seen that the deflection produced by the low spot is proportional to its depth λ and depends also on the ratio τ_1/τ. For various values of this ratio, the dynamic deflections are represented by curves in Fig. 12.35. The abscissas give the position of the wheel along the low spot, and the ordinates give the additional deflection expressed in terms of λ. As soon as the wheel enters the low spot, the pressure on the rail, and consequently the deflection of the rail, begins to diminish (y is negative) while the wheel begins to accelerate in a downward direction. Then follows a retardation of this movement with corresponding increases in pressure and in deflection. From the figure we see that for $\tau_1 < \tau$ the maximum pressure occurs when the wheel is approaching the far end of the low spot. The ratios of this maximum dynamic deflection to the depth λ of the low spot, calculated from Eq. (12.19), are as follows:

$\dfrac{\tau_1}{\tau}$	2	$\frac{3}{2}$	1	$\frac{4}{5}$	$\frac{2}{3}$	$\frac{3}{5}$	$\frac{1}{2}$
y_{max}/λ	0.33	0.65	1.21	1.41	1.47	1.45	1.33

It is seen that the maximum value of this ratio is about equal to 1.5 which occurs when the locomotive speed is such that $\tau_1/\tau \approx \frac{2}{3}$, that is, when the time required for the wheel to cross the low spot is equal to two-thirds of the period

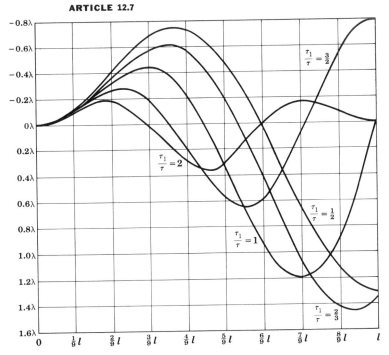

FIG. 12.35

of natural vibration of the wheel on the rail. It can be concluded that the additional dynamic pressure due to the low spot is about equal to the force which produces a static deflection of the rail equal to 1.5λ. Similar results can be obtained for low spots having other shapes. Calculations of this kind show that the ratio y_{max}/λ does not depend substantially on the shape of the low spot provided it is represented by a continuous smooth curve. The calculation made above can be applied also to the case of a flat spot on the rim of the wheel, because such a flat spot produces exactly the same vertical movements of the wheel as a low spot of the same shape on the rail.

In considering the additional wheel pressure of a locomotive due to the centrifugal force Q of a counterweight, we can use the theory of forced vibrations as discussed in Art. 12.3 and multiply this force by a magnification factor. Then the additional pressure on the rail, produced by the counterweight, is $Q/(1 - \tau^2/\tau_2^2)$, where τ denotes the period of natural vibration of the wheel on the rail, and τ_2 the time of one revolution of the wheel. In this calculation, the mass of the rail is neglected, which is justified, because the time τ_2 is large in comparison with the period of natural vibration τ_3 of the rail. The lowest type of rail vibration is an oscillation of the rail in the vertical direction as a rigid body. To get the period τ_3 of this vibration, we use the known equation

$$\tau_3 = 2\pi \sqrt{\frac{\delta_{st}}{g}}$$

in which δ_{st} is the statical deflection of the rail due to its own weight.   Taking, for example, a 130-lb rail and assuming $k = 1,500$ psi, we obtain $\tau_3 = 0.0157$ sec, which is small in comparison with the time τ_2 of one revolution of the wheel.

12.8 LATERAL VIBRATIONS OF PRISMATIC BEAMS

The differential equation for the static deflection curve of an elastic prismatic beam is[1]

$$EI\frac{d^4y}{dx^4} = q$$

where q denotes the intensity of the distributed load and EI is the flexural rigidity of the beam.   To adapt this equation to the case of free lateral vibrations of a beam, we have only to use D'Alembert's principle and replace the intensity q of lateral load by the inertia force per unit length of the beam. The equation then becomes

$$EI\frac{\partial^4y}{\partial x^4} = -\frac{w}{g}\frac{\partial^2y}{\partial t^2} \tag{12.20}$$

where w/g is the mass per unit length of the beam.   The solution of Eq. (12.20) is especially simple in the case of a beam with simply supported ends as shown in Fig. 12.36.   In such a case, the vibrating beam has a sinusoidal shape, and we can satisfy Eq. (12.20) and also the conditions at the ends A and B by taking a solution in the form

$$y = \phi_i \sin\frac{i\pi x}{l} \tag{a}$$

where i denotes the number of half waves in which the vibrating beam is subdivided, and ϕ_i is a function of time.   Substituting expression (a) into Eq. (12.20), we obtain the equation

$$\ddot{\phi}_i + p_i^2\phi_i = 0 \tag{12.21}$$

in which we use the notation

$$p_i^2 = \frac{i^4\pi^4}{l^4}\frac{EIg}{w} \tag{12.22}$$

The differential equation (12.21) represents simple harmonic motion as discussed in Art. 12.1, and it has the frequency

$$f_i = \frac{p_i}{2\pi} = \frac{\pi i^2}{2l^2}\sqrt{\frac{EIg}{w}} \tag{12.22a}$$

[1] See "Strength of Materials," vol. I, p. 140.

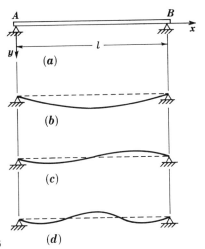

FIG. 12.36   (d)

Taking $i = 1, 2, 3, \ldots$, we obtain vibrations of the beam in the various modes shown in Fig. 12.36b, c, d, ... It is seen that the frequencies of vibration in the various modes are proportional to the square of the number i of half waves and inversely proportional to the square of the length l of the beam. For geometrically similar beams, the frequency of lateral vibration decreases in direct proportion to the increase in the linear dimensions.

To discuss forced vibrations of beams, we denote by $q(x, t)$ the intensity of some distributed disturbing force and add this to the inertia force on the right-hand side of Eq. (12.20) so that it becomes

$$EI \frac{\partial^4 y}{\partial x^4} = -\frac{w}{g}\frac{\partial^2 y}{\partial t^2} + q(x, t) \tag{12.23}$$

Taking the solution of this equation again in the form (a) and substituting back, we obtain

$$\ddot{\phi}_i \sin \frac{i\pi x}{l} + p_i^2 \phi_i \sin \frac{i\pi x}{l} = \frac{g}{w} q(x, t)$$

We now multiply both sides of this equation by $\sin (i\pi x/l)\ dx$ and integrate over the length l of the beam. In this way, we obtain

$$\ddot{\phi}_i + p_i^2 \phi_i = \frac{2g}{wl} \int_0^l q(x, t) \sin \frac{i\pi x}{l}\ dx \tag{12.24}$$

For any given distribution of the disturbing force $q(x, t)$, the integral on the right-hand side of Eq. (12.24) can be evaluated. Then using the general solutions (12.17) developed in Art. 12.5, we obtain the solution for ϕ_i.

As an example, let us consider the case of a beam acted upon by a stationary

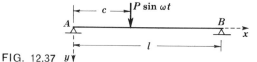

FIG. 12.37 u↓

pulsating force $P \sin \omega t$ as shown in Fig. 12.37. In this case the function $q(x, t)$ vanishes for all values of x except the point $x = c$, and we get

$$\int_0^l q(x, t) \sin \frac{i\pi x}{l} \, dx = P \sin \omega t \sin \frac{i\pi c}{l}$$

When this is substituted on the right-hand side of Eq. (12.24), it becomes

$$\ddot{\phi}_i + p_i{}^2 \phi_i = \frac{2gP}{wl} \sin \omega t \sin \frac{i\pi c}{l} \tag{b}$$

and then using Eqs. (12.17), we obtain the general solution

$$\phi_i = \frac{2gP}{p_i wl} \sin \frac{i\pi c}{l} \int_0^{t_1} \sin \omega t \sin (p_i t_1 - p_i t) \, dt \tag{c}$$

After integration, this becomes

$$\phi_i = \frac{2gP}{wl} \sin \frac{i\pi c}{l} \left(\frac{\sin \omega t}{p_i{}^2 - \omega^2} - \frac{\omega}{p_i} \frac{\sin p_i t}{p_i{}^2 - \omega^2} \right) \tag{d}$$

Substituting this expression for ϕ_i into Eq. (a), we get the ith mode of vibration of the beam. Taking $i = 1, 2, 3, \ldots$ and summing the corresponding modes of vibration, we get the complete solution for the response of the beam to the disturbing force $P \sin \omega t$. This is

$$y = \frac{2gP}{wl} \sum_{i=1}^{\infty} \frac{\sin (i\pi c/l) \sin (i\pi x/l)}{p_i{}^2 - \omega^2} \sin \omega t$$

$$- \frac{2gP}{wl} \sum_{i=1}^{\infty} \frac{\omega}{p_i} \frac{\sin (i\pi c/l) \sin (i\pi x/l)}{p_i{}^2 - \omega^2} \sin p_i t \tag{12.25}$$

The first series, proportional to $\sin \omega t$, represents forced vibrations having the same frequency $\omega/2\pi$ as the disturbing force itself. The second series, proportional to $\sin p_i t$, represents free vibrations having the frequencies as given by Eq. (12.22a). Owing to various kinds of damping which were omitted in the derivation, these free vibrations will gradually disappear and only the forced vibrations will remain.

We see that if ω is very close to any one of the natural frequencies p_i, then that term in the series becomes very large and we have a condition of resonance.

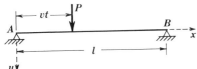

FIG. 12.38

To avoid the possibility of resonance completely, it is necessary that the frequency of the lowest mode of vibration ($i = 1$) be several times larger than the frequency of the disturbing force.

Take, as an example, the case in which the disturbing force acts at the middle of the beam ($c = l/2$). Then, introducing the notation $\omega^2/p_1^2 = \alpha^2$, we obtain from the first series in Eq. (12.25)

$$y = \frac{2Pl^3}{\pi^4 EI} \left[\frac{\sin(\pi x/l)}{1 - \alpha^2} - \frac{\sin(3\pi x/l)}{3^4 - \alpha^2} + \frac{\sin(5\pi x/l)}{5^4 - \alpha^2} - \cdots \right] \sin \omega t$$

For small values of α^2, that is, for $\omega \ll p_1$, the first term alone of this series represents the steady-state response with good accuracy, and we conclude that the ratio of dynamic to static deflection is $1/(1 - \alpha^2)$. If, for example, $\omega = p_1/4$, the dynamic deflection will be about 6 percent greater than the static deflection.

As a second example, let us consider the case shown in Fig. 12.38, where a constant force P moves along the beam with constant speed v. Measuring time from the instant when the force P is at A, its position will be defined by the distance vt as shown in the figure. Then, in such a case, the integral on the right-hand side of Eq. (12.24) is

$$\int_0^l q(x, t) \sin \frac{i\pi x}{l} \, dx = P \sin \frac{i\pi vt}{l}$$

and the equation for determining ϕ_i becomes

$$\ddot{\phi}_i + p_i^2 \phi_i = \frac{2gP}{wl} \sin \frac{i\pi vt}{l} \tag{e}$$

Comparing this with Eq. (b), we see that we have $i\pi v/l$ in place of ω, whereas the factor $\sin(i\pi c/l)$ vanishes. Introducing these changes into the general solution (12.25), we obtain the following solution for the case of a constant force P traveling at constant speed v along the beam:

$$y = \frac{2gP}{wl} \sum_{i=1}^{\infty} \frac{\sin(i\pi x/l) \sin(i\pi vt/l)}{p_i^2 - i^2\pi^2 v^2/l^2}$$

$$- \frac{2gP}{wl} \sum_{i=1}^{\infty} \frac{i\pi v}{p_i l} \frac{\sin(i\pi x/l) \sin p_i t}{p_i^2 - i^2\pi^2 v^2/l^2} \tag{12.26}$$

As before, the first series in this solution represents forced vibrations of the beam, whereas the second series represents free vibrations.

As a particular case of interest, let us assume that the time required for the force P to cross the span is just half the period τ of the first mode of free vibration, that is, $2l/v = \tau = 2\pi/p_1$. In such a case, $p_1^2 = \pi^2 v^2/l^2$, and we see that the first term in each series becomes infinite, but the difference is finite and can be expressed in the form[1]

$$ y \approx - \frac{Pgt}{wrv} \cos \frac{\pi vt}{l} \sin \frac{\pi x}{l} \tag{f} $$

This expression has its maximum value when $vt = l$, that is, just as the moving force P reaches the far end of the beam, when it has the value

$$ y_{\max} = \frac{Pgl}{w\pi v^2} \sin \frac{\pi x}{l} $$

or, observing that

$$ p_1^2 = \frac{\pi^4}{l^4} \frac{EIg}{w} = \frac{\pi^2 v^2}{l^2} $$

we obtain

$$ y_{\max} = \frac{Pl^3}{\pi^3 EI} \sin \frac{\pi x}{l} \tag{g} $$

This maximum dynamic deflection of the beam due to the traveling force is seen to be about 50 percent greater than the static deflection produced by the same force when applied at the middle of the span.

In the case of bridges, the time required for a moving load to cross the span is usually large in comparison with the period of the lowest mode of vibration. In such a case the ratio $\pi^2 v^2/l^2 p_1^2$ is small and will be denoted by α^2. Then, taking again only the first term in each of the series in expression (12.26) and assuming that in the most unfavorable case the forced and free vibrations may come into phase so that their amplitudes add together, we obtain, for the maximum deflection,

$$ y_{\max} = \frac{2gP}{wl} \left(\frac{1}{p_1^2 - \pi^2 v^2/l^2} + \frac{\pi v}{p_1 l} \frac{1}{p_1^2 - \pi^2 v^2/l^2} \right) $$

Introducing into this expression the factor α as defined above, it becomes

$$ y_{\max} = \frac{2Pl^3}{\pi^4 EI} \frac{1 + \alpha}{1 - \alpha^2} = \frac{2Pl^3}{\pi^4 EI} \frac{1}{1 - \alpha} \tag{12.27} $$

We see from this that for a slowly traveling force, the maximum dynamic

[1] See S. Timoshenko, "Vibration Problems in Engineering," 3d ed., pp. 47, 48, D. Van Nostrand Company, Inc., Princeton, N.J., 1955.

deflection of the beam is approximately in the ratio $1/(1 - \alpha)$ to the maximum static deflection produced by the same force.

As a final example, let us consider the case of a pulsating force moving along the beam with constant speed v.   Such a condition, for example, may occur in the case of an imperfectly balanced locomotive wheel moving across a bridge. In such a case the vertical component of the centrifugal force due to unbalance is $P \cos \omega t$, where ω is the angular velocity of the wheel.   Proceeding with this case in the same manner as in the preceding examples, we obtain for the dynamic deflection of the beam

$$
\begin{aligned}
y = \frac{Pl^3}{\pi^4 EI} \sum_{i=1}^{\infty} \sin \frac{i\pi x}{l} \Bigg\{ &\frac{\sin (i\pi v/l + \omega)t}{i^4 - (\beta + i\alpha)^2} - \frac{\sin (i\pi v/l - \omega)t}{i^4 - (\beta - i\alpha)^2} \\
&- \frac{\alpha}{i} \left[\frac{\sin p_i t}{-i^2\alpha^2 + (i^2 - \beta)^2} + \frac{\sin p_i t}{-i^2\alpha^2 + (i^2 + \beta)^2} \right] \Bigg\} \cdots \quad (12.28)
\end{aligned}
$$

where α is the ratio of the period τ of the lowest mode of vibration of the beam to twice the time $\tau_1 = l/v$ that it takes the moving force to cross the span, and $\beta = \tau/\tau_2$ is the ratio of the fundamental period of the beam to the period $\tau_2 = 2\pi/\omega$ of the pulsating force.

When the period τ_2 of the pulsating force is equal to the period τ of the beam in its lowest mode of vibration, $\beta = 1$, and we obtain a condition of resonance. The amplitude of the vibrations during motion of the pulsating force is gradually built up and attains its maximum at the time $t = l/v$, when the most important term of the series (12.28) may be reduced to the form

$$
\frac{1}{\alpha} \frac{2Pl^3}{\pi^4 EI} \sin \frac{\pi x}{l} \sin \omega t
$$

and the maximum deflection becomes

$$
y_{\max} = \frac{1}{\alpha} \frac{2Pl^3}{\pi^4 EI} = \frac{2\tau_1}{\tau} \frac{2Pl^3}{\pi^4 EI} \tag{12.29}
$$

This shows that the maximum dynamic deflection of the beam is approximately in the ratio $2\tau_1/\tau$ to the static deflection produced by the force P.   Since τ_1 is usually large in comparison with τ, we see that the value of $y_{\max}$ may become many times larger than the maximum static deflection.

12.9 VIBRATION OF BRIDGES

It is known that a rolling load produces in a bridge a greater deflection and greater stresses than the same load acting statically.   Such an impact effect of live loads on bridges is of great practical importance, and many engineers

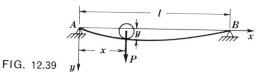

FIG. 12.39

have worked on the solution of this problem.[1]   There are various causes producing impact effect on bridges, of which the following will be discussed: (1) live-load effect of a smooth-running load, (2) impact effect of the counter-weights of locomotive driving wheels, and (3) impact effect due to irregularities of track and flat spots on wheels.

In discussing the live-load effect of a smooth-running mass, two extreme cases will be considered: (1) The mass of the moving load is large in comparison with the mass of the beam, girder, or rail bearer, and (2) the mass of the moving load is small in comparison with the mass of the bridge.   In the first case, the mass of the beam can be neglected.   Then, the deflection of the beam under the load for any position of this load will be proportional to the pressure R which the rolling load $P*$ produces on the beam (Fig. 12.39), and can be calculated from the known equation

$$y = \frac{Rx^2(l - x)^2}{3lEI} \qquad (a)$$

In order to obtain the pressure R on the beam, the inertia force $-(P/g)(d^2y/dt^2)$ should be added to the rolling load P.   Assuming that the load P moves along the beam with constant speed v, we obtain

$$\frac{dy}{dt} = v \frac{dy}{dx} \qquad \frac{d^2y}{dt^2} = v^2 \frac{d^2y}{dx^2}$$

and the pressure on the beam will be

$$R = P\left(1 - \frac{v^2}{g}\frac{d^2y}{dx^2}\right) \qquad (b)$$

Substituting this into Eq. (a), we obtain

$$y = P\left(1 - \frac{v^2}{g}\frac{d^2y}{dx^2}\right)\frac{x^2(l - x)^2}{3lEI} \qquad (12.30)$$

This equation determines the path of the point of contact of the rolling load with the beam.   An approximate solution[2] of Eq. (12.30) will be obtained by

[1] The early history of the subject is extensively discussed by Barré de Saint-Venant in his translation of A. Clebsch's book, "Theorie der Elastizität fester Körper," Paris, 1883.   See "note finale du paragraph 61," p. 597.

* P denotes the unsprung load, such as weight of locomotive drivers and their axles.   The force transmitted to the axle through the spring is considered as constant.

[2] Equation (12.30) and its approximate solution were established by R. Willis; see Appendix to the "Report of the Commissioners . . . to Inquire into the Application of Iron to Railway Structures," London, 1849.   This report was reprinted in P. Barlow, "Treatise on the Strength of Timber, Cast Iron and Malcabre Iron," London, 1851.

assuming that the path is the same as at zero speed and substituting

$$\frac{Px^2(l-x)^2}{3lEI}$$

for y on the right side of the equation. Then, it can be shown that y becomes a maximum when the load is at the middle of the span, and the maximum pressure is

$$R_{\max} = P\left(1 + \frac{v^2}{g}\frac{Pl}{3EI}\right)$$

The maximum deflection δ_d at the middle of the span increases in the same ratio as the pressure, so that

$$\delta_d = \delta_{st}\left(1 + \frac{v^2}{g}\frac{Pl}{3EI}\right) \qquad (12.31)$$

This approximate solution, as compared with the results of an exact solution[1] of Eq. (12.30), is accurate enough for practical applications. The additional term in the parentheses is usually small, and observing that the load P is the *unsprung weight* of the wheel and that the force transmitted to the axle through the spring remains practically constant, it can be concluded that the live-load effect of a smooth-running load is not of great practical importance in the case of short spans.

In the second case, when the mass of the load is small in comparison with the mass of the bridge, the moving load can be replaced, with sufficient accuracy, by a moving force,[2] and then the results given in the preceding article can be used. Assume, for example, that for three single-track railway bridges with spans of 60, 120, and 360 ft, the lowest frequencies of vibrations are as shown in the following table:

	l		
	60 ft	120 ft	360 ft
f, cps	9	5	2
$\dfrac{\tau}{2l/v}$	$\dfrac{1}{9}$	$\dfrac{1}{10}$	$\dfrac{1}{12}$

[1] The exact solution of Eq. (12.30) was obtained by G. G. Stokes; see his "Mathematical and Physical Papers," Cambridge, vol. 2, p. 179. The solution can be obtained also by numerical integration. Examples of such integration are given in a paper by E. Marquard, *Ingr.-Arch.*, vol. 23, p. 19, 1955.
[2] The case of a moving force together with a uniformly distributed moving load has been discussed by H. Steuding, *Ingr.-Arch.*, vol. 5, p. 275, 1934.

Then, taking the velocity $v = 120$ ft/sec, the ratio $\tau/(2l/v)$ of the period of the lowest type of vibration to twice the time l/v for the load to pass over the bridge will be as shown in the third line of the table. Considering the bridge as a beam of uniform cross section and using Eq. (12.27), it can be concluded that for a span of 60 ft, the increase in deflection due to the live-load effect is about 12 percent and will be even less for the longer spans. From these examples it can be concluded that the live-load effect of a smooth-running load is not an important factor.[1]

Much more serious effects may be produced by pulsating forces due to rotating counterweights of steam locomotives. The most unfavorable condition occurs in the case of resonance, when the number of revolutions per second of the driving wheels is equal to the frequency of natural vibration of the bridge. For shorter spans, the frequency of natural vibration is usually so high that the resonance condition is impossible at any practical velocity. But for larger spans, the resonance condition should be taken into consideration, and the impact effect should be calculated from Eq. (12.29) of the preceding article.

Let P_1 be the maximum resultant pressure on the rail due to the counterweights when the driving wheels are revolving once per second, and n the total number of revolutions of the driving wheels during passage along the bridge. Then, from Eq. (12.29) we obtain the following additional deflection due to the impact effect:

$$\delta_{\max} = \frac{2n}{\tau^2} \frac{2P_1 l^3}{\pi^4 EI} \tag{12.32}$$

In the case of shorter spans, when the frequency of natural vibration is considerably larger than the number of revolutions per second of the driving wheels, a satisfactory approximation will be obtained by using the first term of the series (12.28).

It should be noted that all our calculations were based on the assumption of a *pulsating force* moving along the bridge. In actual conditions we have *rolling masses* which will cause a variation in the natural frequency of the bridge in accordance with the varying position of the load. This variability of the natural frequency is very beneficial because the pulsating moving load will no longer be in resonance all the time during passage over the bridge, and its cumulative effect will not be as pronounced as implied by the above theory.

Irregularities such as low spots on the rails, rail joints, flat spots on the wheels may be responsible for considerable impact effect, which may become especially pronounced in the case of short-span bridges. These additional dynamic effects justify the high impact factors usually applied in the design of short-span bridges. By eliminating rail joints, the dynamic effect on short-

[1] See S. Timoshenko, Vibration of Bridges, presented at American Society of Mechanical Engineers, December, 1927.

span bridges and rail bearers can be substantially reduced and the strength conditions improved.

The theoretical solutions of the preceding article, which were used in the above discussion, indicate that the lowest mode of vibration usually has the greatest importance. This fact indicates that we can get a satisfactory approximation by considering only the first mode and treating a bridge as a system with one degree of freedom. Simplifying the problem in this way, we shall get for its solution an ordinary differential equation and can consider the mass of the bridge and the rolling masses simultaneously. The equation becomes a complicated one, but it can be treated by using step-by-step integration. This method is now widely used in Russia in the extensive theoretical and experimental investigations of bridge vibrations.[1]

12.10 STRUCTURES SUBJECTED TO EARTHQUAKES

In discussing the response of a structure to an earthquake disturbance, we begin with the case of a simple rectangular frame as shown in Fig. 12.40. Assuming that the horizontal beam AB is absolutely rigid and neglecting axial deformation of the vertical columns, we find that the spring constant k for the structure is

$$k = \frac{24EI}{h^3} = \frac{W}{g}\frac{4\pi^2}{\tau^2} \qquad (a)$$

where $\tau = 2\pi/p = 2\pi\sqrt{W/kg}$ is the period of free vibration (see page 565).

Denoting by u the absolute horizontal displacement of the ground, and by v the displacement of the top of the frame relative to the ground, the differential equation of motion for the structure becomes[2]

$$\frac{W}{g}\frac{d^2}{dt^2}(u + v) = -kv$$

[1] The description of the method and its application in various cases is given in the book by I. I. Kazey, "Dynamical Analysis of Railway Bridges," Moscow, 1960.
[2] The effect of damping is neglected in this discussion.

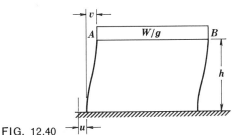

FIG. 12.40

With the notation $p^2 = kg/W$, this equation takes the form

$$\frac{d^2v}{dt^2} + p^2 v = -\frac{d^2u}{dt^2} \tag{b}$$

The complete solution of Eq. (b) is given by Eq. (12.11) of Art. 12.4, namely,

$$v = \frac{1}{p} \int_0^{t_1} \left(-\frac{d^2u}{dt^2} \right) \sin\,(pt_1 - pt)\,dt$$

or, with $\tau = 2\pi/p$,

$$v = \frac{\tau}{2\pi} \int_0^{t_1} \left(-\frac{d^2u}{dt^2} \right) \sin \frac{2\pi}{\tau}\,(t_1 - t)\,dt \tag{12.33}$$

The ground acceleration d^2u/dt^2 appearing under the integral sign in Eq. (12.33) is obtained directly from accelograph records taken during actual earthquakes. Using such an *accelogram*, the complete response $v = f(t_1)$ of the structure to the earthquake can be calculated from Eq. (12.33). This method of analysis of earthquake vibrations of a structure was first proposed by Biot.[1]

For practical applications, the horizontal shear force S induced in the frame during the disturbance is of particular interest. This shear force is $S = kv$, which, using expression (12.33) for v and notation (a) for k, becomes

$$S = \frac{W}{g}\frac{2\pi}{\tau} \int_0^{t_1} \left(-\frac{d^2u}{dt^2} \right) \sin \frac{2\pi}{\tau}\,(t_1 - t)\,dt = \frac{W}{g}\,a \tag{12.34}$$

where

$$a = \frac{2\pi}{\tau} \int_0^{t_1} \left(-\frac{d^2u}{dt^2} \right) \sin \frac{2\pi}{\tau}\,(t_1 - t)\,dt \tag{12.35}$$

is called the *effective acceleration*. During the earthquake, this effective acceleration varies in a complicated manner, but to obtain the largest shear force, we need only the maximum absolute value of a, which we denote by A. Then, the maximum shear force can be expressed as

$$S_{\text{max}} = \frac{W}{g}\,A \tag{12.36}$$

A study of expression (12.35) shows that this maximum shear force in the frame for a given earthquake depends on the natural period τ of lateral vibration of the frame. By changing the rigidity or mass of the structure, we change its natural period τ and therefore its response to the given earthquake, i.e., the value of A. Representing A as a function of τ, we obtain a so-called *acceler-*

---

[1] See M. A. Biot, *Proc. Natl. Acad. Sci.*, vol. 19, 1933; *Z. Angew. Math. Mech.*, vol. 14, 1934; A Mechanical Analyzer for the Prediction of Earthquake Stresses, *Bull. Seismol. Soc. Am.*, vol. 31, p. 151, 1941; and Analytical and Experimental Methods in Engineering Seismology, *Trans. ASCE*, vol. 108, p. 365, 1943.

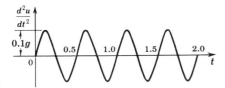

FIG. 12.41

ation spectrum. Having such a curve for a given earthquake, the maximum shearing force induced in a given structure is readily obtained from Eq. (12.36).

To actually obtain an acceleration spectrum for a given earthquake, defined by its accelogram d^2u/dt^2, requires laborious calculations. For each of a series of chosen values of τ, it is necessary to evaluate the effective acceleration a from Eq. (12.35) over the duration of the earthquake and then select its maximum absolute value. This procedure, repeated over a suitable range of values of τ, gives the values of A from which the acceleration spectrum can be plotted. Such calculations are usually made with the aid of a digital or analog computer. Biot, for example, used a simple torsional pendulum, the natural period of which could be suitably varied, to obtain acceleration spectra.[1]

It should be noted that in the derivation of Eq. (12.33) the effect of damping was neglected. Because of internal friction in the material and joints of a structure, the amplitude of vibration and consequently the induced stresses will be somewhat reduced. Thus, the shear force S, calculated from Eq. (12.36), must be considered only as an upper limit.

As an example of calculation of an acceleration spectrum, let us consider an artificial earthquake having a sinusoidal accelogram with period $2\pi/\omega = 0.5$ sec, amplitude $0.1g$, and duration of 2 sec, as shown in Fig. 12.41. In such a case,

$$\frac{d^2u}{dt^2} = 0.1g \sin \omega t$$

and expression (12.35) becomes

$$a = -0.1g \frac{2\pi}{\tau} \int_0^{t_1} \sin \omega t \sin \frac{2\pi}{\tau} (t_1 - t)\ dt \tag{c}$$

For the particular case where the natural period of the structure coincides with the period of the disturbance, that is, when $\tau = 2\pi/\omega$, this becomes

$$a = -0.1g \frac{2\pi}{\tau} \int_0^{t_1} \sin \frac{2\pi t}{\tau} \sin \frac{2\pi}{\tau} (t_1 - t)\ dt$$

which, after integration, gives

$$a = -0.1g \left(\frac{1}{2} \sin \frac{2\pi t_1}{\tau} - \frac{\pi t_1}{\tau} \cos \frac{2\pi t_1}{\tau} \right) \tag{d}$$

[1] For a description of this device see *ibid., Bull. Seismol. Soc. Am.* and *Trans. ASCE.*

Owing to the factor $\pi t_1/\tau$ in the second term of this expression, it is evident that the absolute maximum acceleration A occurs very nearly at $t_1 = 4\pi = 2.0$ sec, the full duration of the earthquake, for which value

$$|a_{max}| = A = 0.1g\ 4\pi = 1.26g$$

Other points on the acceleration spectrum for chosen values of τ can be calculated from Eq. (c), and the complete spectrum is shown by the dashed curve in Fig. 12.42.

Applying the artificial accelogram of Fig. 12.41 to the torsion pendulum, tuned to various periods τ, Biot obtained values of the absolute maximum acceleration A as shown by the small circles in Fig. 12.42. It is seen that these experimental points agree very closely with the theoretical curve. From this, it may be concluded that the experimental method of obtaining the acceleration spectrum is satisfactory for practical purposes.

In Fig. 12.43, we have an example of a real earthquake which occurred at Ferndale, Calif., on Feb. 6, 1937. The accelogram shown in Fig. 12.43a represents the horizontal ground motion in the northeast-southwest direction, and Fig. 12.43b shows the corresponding acceleration spectrum obtained from the mechanical analog. This spectrum shows a peak acceleration of $0.37g$ for a period $\tau = 0.315$ sec, whereas the maximum recorded ground acceleration was only $0.039g$. Thus, the maximum accelerations produced by the earthquake in buildings having the natural period $\tau = 0.315$ sec are about 9.5 times larger than the maximum ground acceleration itself.

The problem of stresses produced by earthquakes is most important in the case of tall buildings such as shown in Fig. 12.44a. Considering a simplified case in which all floors are identical, we can replace such a structure by a

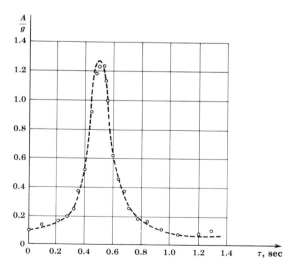

FIG. 12.42

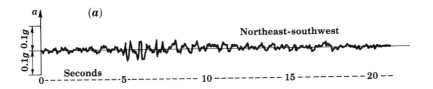

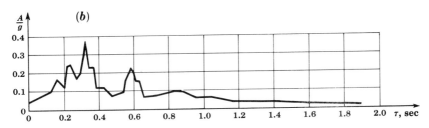

FIG. 12.43

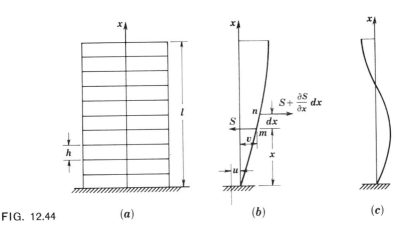

FIG. 12.44   (a)   (b)   (c)

hypothetical prismatic beam of homogeneous material that has elasticity only in shear as shown in Fig. 12.44b. Then, denoting by v the displacement at any cross section m, the shearing strain at that cross section will be $\partial v/\partial x$, and the corresponding shearing force will be

$$S = \mu \frac{\partial v}{\partial x} \qquad (e)$$

where, from Eq. (a),

$$\mu = kh = \frac{24EI}{h^2} \qquad (f)$$

Let us consider now the case of free vibrations of the beam, assuming that the foundation is immovable. Since the difference in shearing forces at the adjacent cross sections m and n in Fig. 12.44b must equilibrate the inertia force of the element mn of the beam, we obtain the equation of motion

$$\mu \frac{\partial^2 v}{\partial x^2} - \frac{w}{g} \frac{\partial^2 v}{\partial t^2} = 0 \tag{g}$$

where w denotes the weight per unit length of the hypothetical beam. Assuming that vibrations of the beam are harmonic and proportional to $\sin pt$, we try the solution of Eq. (g) in the form

$$v = X \sin pt \tag{h}$$

in which X is some function of x defining the shape of the beam during vibration. Substituting expression (h) into Eq. (g), we get

$$c^2 \frac{d^2 X}{dx^2} + p^2 X = 0 \tag{12.37}$$

in which

$$c^2 = \frac{\mu g}{w} \tag{i}$$

The general solution of Eq. (12.37) is

$$X = A \cos \frac{px}{c} + B \sin \frac{px}{c} \tag{12.38}$$

To determine the constants A and B, we consider the conditions at the two ends of the beam. At the ground ($x = 0$), the displacement v must vanish; hence, $A = 0$. At the free end of the beam ($x = l$), the shear strain $\partial v / \partial x$ must vanish. This requires that $\cos (pl/c) = 0$; hence, $pl/c = \pi/2, 3\pi/2, 5\pi/2,$ . . . , and $\tau = 2\pi/p = 4l/c, 4l/3c, 4l/5c,$ . . . . Thus, the assumed solution (h) takes the form

$$v = B_i \sin \frac{i\pi x}{2l} \sin \frac{i\pi ct}{2l} \tag{j}$$

where $i = 1, 3, 5,$ . . . . Taking $i = 1$, the first mode shape is seen to be a quarter sine wave as shown in Fig. 12.44b, and for $i = 3$ a three-quarter sine wave as shown in Fig. 12.44c. A general case of free vibration is obtained by superposition of all modes, and we get

$$v = \sum_{i=1,3,5} X_i \sin p_i t = \sum_{i=1,3,5} B_i \sin \frac{i\pi x}{2l} \sin \frac{i\pi ct}{2l} \tag{k}$$

Considering now the case of forced vibrations due to earthquake-induced ground motion u, the absolute displacement of a cross section m of the beam will be $u + v$, and instead of Eq. (g), we have the equation of motion

$$\mu \frac{\partial^2 v}{\partial x^2} - \frac{w}{g} \frac{\partial^2}{\partial t^2} (u + v) = 0$$

or, using notation (i),

$$c^2 \frac{\partial^2 v}{\partial x^2} - \frac{\partial^2 v}{\partial t^2} = \frac{\partial^2 u}{\partial t^2} \tag{l}$$

where $\partial^2 u/\partial t^2$ is the ground acceleration, given by an accelogram. In this case, we take a solution of Eq. (l) in the form

$$v_i = \phi_i(t) \sin \frac{i\pi x}{2l} \tag{m}$$

where ϕ_i is an undetermined function of time and $i = 1, 3, 5, \ldots$ When expression (m) is substituted into Eq. (l), we find that ϕ_i must satisfy the equation

$$\ddot{\phi}_i \sin \frac{i\pi x}{2l} + \frac{c^2 i^2 \pi^2}{4l^2} \phi_i \sin \frac{i\pi x}{2l} = -\frac{\partial^2 u}{\partial t^2}$$

Multiplying this equation through by $\sin (i\pi x/2l) \, dx$ and then integrating from $x = 0$ to $x = l$, we obtain

$$\ddot{\phi}_i + \frac{c^2 i^2 \pi^2}{4l^2} \phi_i = -\frac{4}{i\pi} \frac{\partial^2 u}{\partial t^2} \tag{12.39}$$

This has the same form as Eq. (b), and again we can use the solution (12.11) of Art. 12.4. Substituting the quantity $c^2 i^2 \pi^2/4l^2$ for p^2 and $-(4/i\pi) \, \partial^2 u/\partial t^2$ for q in that solution, we obtain

$$\phi_i = \frac{8l}{ci^2\pi^2} \int_0^{t_1} \left(-\frac{\partial^2 u}{\partial t^2} \right) \sin \frac{ci\pi}{2l} (t_1 - t) \, dt$$

Observing that $\tau_i = 4l/ic$, and returning to Eq. (m), we have

$$v_i = \frac{16l^2}{c^2 i^3 \pi^3} \frac{2\pi}{\tau_i} \int_0^{t_1} \left(-\frac{\partial^2 u}{\partial t^2} \right) \sin \frac{ci\pi}{2l} (t_1 - t) \, dt \sin \frac{i\pi x}{2l} \tag{n}$$

representing the ith mode of response of the hypothetical beam to the ground motion. The middle factor of this expression is the effective acceleration for the ith mode of vibration. Denoting its maximum absolute value by A_i and summing expression (n) for all modes, we obtain for the complete absolute maximum response

$$v = \frac{16l^2}{c^2 \pi^3} \sum_{i=1,3,5} \frac{A_i}{i^3} \sin \frac{i\pi x}{2l} \tag{o}$$

The corresponding shearing force at any cross section then becomes

$$S = \mu \frac{\partial v}{\partial x} = \frac{8\mu l}{c^2 \pi^2} \sum_{i=1,3,5} \frac{A_i}{i^2} \cos \frac{i\pi x}{2l}$$

The maximum value of this shearing force occurs at the built-in end ($x = 0$) and, with $\mu = wc^2/g$, becomes

$$S_{\max} = \frac{8wl}{\pi^2 g} \sum_{i=1,3,5} \frac{A_i}{i^2} \tag{12.40}$$

Taking the values of A_i, corresponding to the periods τ_i of the building in its various modes of free vibration, from a given acceleration spectrum, the corresponding absolute maximum shearing force can be calculated from Eq. (12.40). Comparing Eqs. (12.40) and (12.36), we see that for each mode of vibration of the building there appears the factor $8/i^2\pi^2$, indicating the portion of shearing force associated with that mode.

In a similar manner, earthquake-induced vibrations of the hypothetical beam in Fig. 12.44b can be investigated also in the case where the lower end of the beam is elastically attached to the ground. This case approximates the condition of a building in which the columns of the first floor are intentionally made more flexible than those above. Investigations have shown that such an increase in flexibility of the first floor may be of value in the case of buildings of comparatively small height having their lowest period in the range of 0.2 to 0.3 sec. For taller buildings having fundamental periods of 1.0 sec or more, such first-floor flexibility is not of much value.

Again, it must be repeated that damping due to internal friction in buildings and in their foundations was not taken into account in the above theory. Thus, the calculated $S_{\max}$ is only to be regarded as an upper limit to the maximum shear force.

Regarding practical application of the theoretical analysis of earthquake-induced vibrations of structures, the accepted point of view of engineers in earthquake areas is that the design should be such that the structure will survive the more frequent moderate ground motions without damage, but in the more rare event of a very strong earthquake, damage would be tolerated so long as it is not a hazard to life.[1] The above theory based on consideration of elastic deformations is applicable only in the case of moderate ground motion.

[1] See G. W. Housner, *Proc. ASCE, Eng. Mech. Div.*, 1955, pp. 109–129, and Blume, Newmark, and Corning, "Design of Multistory Reinforced Concrete Buildings for Earthquake Motions," Portland Cement Association, 1961. For a bibliography on the subject, see E. Rosenblueth, *Appl. Mech. Rev.*, vol. 14, pp. 923–926, 1961.

Name index

Subject index